C000228308

The Modern Railway

2014

The construction phase at Hitachi Rail Europe's new train manufacturing plant began at the end of 2013.

Looking to the future of rail

2013 was a year of celebrating the past and looking to the future. London Underground looked back over 150 years since the first underground railway ran between Paddington and Farringdon, revolutionising urban passenger transport and showcasing British engineering excellence. Looking to the future, the outlook for the rail industry remains positive with the industry challenged to provide additional capacity to support continued passenger growth, deliver existing capacity enhancing projects and maintain support for HS2.

Investment continued in 2013 and Crossrail, Thameslink and the Intercity Express Programme were among the rail projects that gained broad attention beyond the rail industry in 2013.

Tunnelling work for Crossrail progressed greatly in 2013. By the end of 2014, the vast majority of it will be completed, the concession for the operator will have been granted and a decision on the rolling stock supplier will have been made.

On the Thameslink project, the rolling stock contract reached financial close in 2013 and redevelopment of London Bridge, among the three busiest stations in Great Britain, has started.

The Intercity Express Programme reached a number of milestones in 2013. The additional order of 30 trains to replace the Intercity 225 trains currently running on the East Coast Main Line brought the total number of new trains for the two busy main lines to 122. Electrification of the Great Western Main Line started in the summer and made steady progress throughout the rest of the year. There is still a way to go to deliver this long overdue investment in the Great Western Main Line but the prize of delivering electrification on time and to budget is further electrification across the network.

The major projects I mentioned above will boost capacity on those routes, but technology such as ETCS and Traffic Management are further enablers to reduce train headways and optimise timetable planning in real time. Hitachi successfully completed testing of our trainborne ETCS system in 2013 and successfully demonstrated a working Traffic Management System (TMS) to Network Rail, controlling an accurate simulation of the highly complex Leeds Station area network. Both ETCS and TMS will take further significant steps forward in 2014 to improve capacity and reduce the operating cost of the railway.

Continuing with the investment theme, Secretaries of State Patrick McLoughlin and Vince Cable visited Newton Aycliffe in County Durham to celebrate the start of construction phase at Hitachi Rail Europe's new train manufacturing plant at the end of 2013. In 2014, the lead construction company Shepherd will make rapid progress on the site. By the end of the year, it is expected that the buildings will be ready for internal fit-out. Recruitment of a core team started in 2013 and by mid-2015, the employee numbers will rise to 730.

The topic of skills in the rail industry looms large in the minds of leaders in the rail sector. Initiatives like the National Skills Academy for Railway Engineering are a step in the right direction to bring young people into technical professions within rail. The national push for more apprenticeship schemes and academies to instil an early interest in technical jobs within school-aged children ensures that the problem is tackled from the roots up.

With the three major procurement projects mentioned above well under way, 2014 will also be a busy year for franchise competitions, and once they have been awarded, there might well be further opportunities for the rail industry and supply chain.

Overall, the topics of the capacity challenge, engaging the British rail supply chain and the skills gap will play a major role in 2014. How we tackle these will help support the long-term development and growth of the industry as a whole. If we can tie these topics in with a long-term vision for the industry, the rail industry will remain a good place to work and provide an attractive career path for generations to come. ■

Alistair Dormer
Executive Chairman and CEO,
Hitachi Rail Europe Ltd

CONTENTS

The Modern Railway

Editor:	Ken Cordner
Production Editor:	David Lane
Contributors:	Roger Ford
	Alan Williams
	John Glover
	Chris Shilling
	Ken Harris
	Tony Miles
	Chris Cheek
	Keith Fender
Advertisement Manager:	Chris Shilling
Advertising Production:	Cheryl Thornburn
Graphic Design:	Matt Chapman
	Matt Fuller
Managing Director and Publisher:	Adrian Cox
Commercial Director:	Ann Saundry
Project Manager:	David Lane
Executive Chairman:	Richard Cox

***The Modern Railway* is published by:**
Key Publishing Limited, PO Box 100,
Stamford, Lincs PE9 1XP

***The Modern Railway* is supported by:**

The Institution of Railway Operators

Railway Industry Association

RSA
Railway Study Association
Developing railway professionals

Printing:
Printed in England by Berforts Information Press Ltd, Southfield Road, Eynsham, Oxford, OX29 4JB

Purchasing additional copies of *The Modern Railway*:
Please contact our Kirsty Flatt on 01780 755 131
or by email at kirsty.flatt@keypublishing.com
Corporate and bulk purchase discounts are available on request.

Thank you!
We are very grateful to the many individuals from businesses in all sectors of the railway who have kindly provided help in compiling The Modern Railway. Information contained in The Modern Railway was believed correct at the time of going to press in November 2013. We would be glad to receive corrections and updates for the next edition.

Cover photos: Hitachi, Bombardier, Network Rail and Stewart Armstrong
ISBN 978-0-9462-1916-2

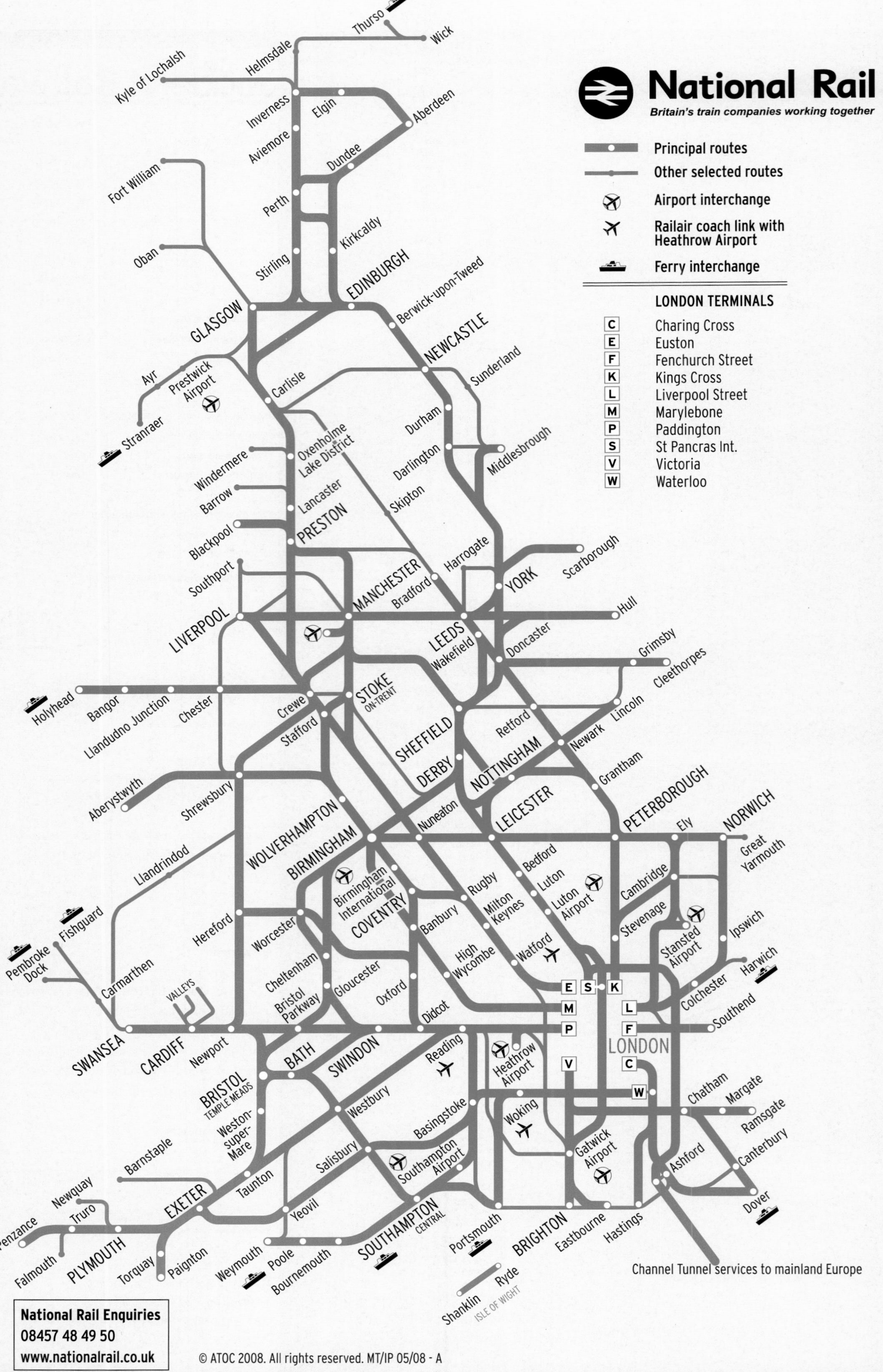
National Rail
Britain's train companies working together
Principal routes
Other selected routes
Airport interchange
Railair coach link with Heathrow Airport
Ferry interchange
LONDON TERMINALS
C Charing Cross
E Euston
F Fenchurch Street
K Kings Cross
L Liverpool Street
M Marylebone
P Paddington
S St Pancras Int.
V Victoria
W Waterloo
Thurso
Wick
Helmsdale
Kyle of Lochalsh
Inverness
Elgin
Aberdeen
Aviemore
Fort William
Dundee
Perth
Kirkcaldy
Oban
Stirling
EDINBURGH
GLASGOW
Berwick-upon-Tweed
NEWCASTLE
Ayr
Prestwick Airport
Sunderland
Carlisle
Stranraer
Durham
Oxenholme Lake District
Windermere
Middlesbrough
Darlington
Barrow
Lancaster
Skipton
PRESTON
Blackpool
Harrogate
Scarborough
Southport
MANCHESTER
Bradford
YORK
LIVERPOOL
Hull
LEEDS
Wakefield
Doncaster
Grimsby
Cleethorpes
Holyhead
Bangor
Llandudno Junction
Chester
Crewe
STOKE ON-TRENT
Stafford
SHEFFIELD
Retford
Lincoln
Newark
NOTTINGHAM
DERBY
Grantham
Aberystwyth
Shrewsbury
LEICESTER
PETERBOROUGH
Nuneaton
WOLVERHAMPTON
Ely
NORWICH
Great Yarmouth
BIRMINGHAM
Llandrindod
Birmingham International
Rugby
Bedford
Luton
Luton Airport
Cambridge
COVENTRY
Milton Keynes
Fishguard
Hereford
Worcester
Banbury
Stevenage
Stansted Airport
Ipswich
Pembroke Dock
Cheltenham
High Wycombe
Watford
Harwich
Carmarthen
Gloucester
Colchester
VALLEYS
Bristol Parkway
Oxford
Didcot
Southend
LONDON
SWANSEA
CARDIFF
Newport
BATH
SWINDON
Reading
Heathrow Airport
BRISTOL TEMPLE MEADS
Westbury
Chatham
Margate
Weston-super-Mare
Basingstoke
Woking
Ramsgate
Barnstaple
Salisbury
Gatwick Airport
Canterbury
Southampton Airport
Ashford
Taunton
Newquay
EXETER
Truro
Yeovil
SOUTHAMPTON CENTRAL
Dover
Penzance
Portsmouth
BRIGHTON
Eastbourne
Hastings
Falmouth
PLYMOUTH
Torquay
Paignton
Weymouth
Poole
Bournemouth
Channel Tunnel services to mainland Europe
Ryde
Shanklin
ISLE OF WIGHT
National Rail Enquiries
08457 48 49 50
www.nationalrail.co.uk
© ATOC 2008. All rights reserved. MT/IP 05/08 - A

SETTING THE AGENDA

IN ASSOCIATION WITH

HITACHI

Inspire the Next

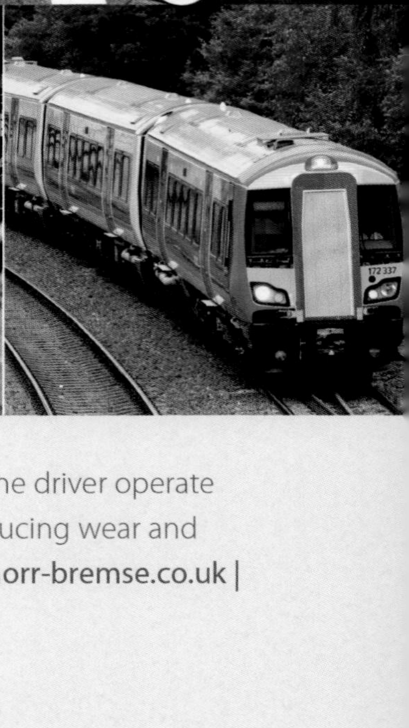

Unlocking rail innovation

As we move into 2014, great activity continues in the railway sector. The effects of the economic situation in recent years have clearly not affected railways as much as some other industry sectors, with most traffic levels remaining high. There is a widespread acceptance that investment in infrastructure is an effective means to get a nation's finances back on track after a recession, and that railways must be a key part of that infrastructure. Railway projects are going ahead in many parts of the world, both in developing nations and in more-established regions where addressing congestion and pollution is often a key factor.

Nonetheless, investment has to be cost effective, especially if we wish to see it sustained over the long term. The UK's railways have made great strides in reducing costs, but the settlement for the next 5-year financial control period makes it clear that substantial further gains have to be achieved.

One of the key mechanisms for this is through innovation, seeking better and more efficient ways of delivering both projects and day-to-day operations. The Railway Industry Association has developed the 'Unlocking Innovation Scheme', aimed precisely at encouraging innovation in both products and services, through addressing the barriers that hamper implementation and by learning from other industries.

This is one of a number of such initiatives organised by or with RSSB, the Transport Knowledge Transfer Network and the rail Enabling Innovation Team amongst others, all underpinned by support from the Department for Transport. Bringing together suppliers, academia and railway operators can produce effective solutions and achieve real benefits. Many of the companies listed in The Modern Railway are actively involved in these initiatives in one way or another, and a growing number are starting to reap the rewards.

Another area where the UK rail sector is well advanced compared to some other markets is in the move away from 'lowest first-cost' procurement. High-reliability, long-life, low-maintenance products can be much more cost-effective over their whole life cycle than cheaper alternatives. Real progress is being made in establishing and using metrics that can be applied during tender evaluation to take account of such factors, rather than the much narrower initial price comparisons used in the past.

Also important is the use of 'future-proofed' technologies and systems, that can continue to be developed and expanded as needs change, rather than having to face the unwelcome option of premature replacement. Thinking ahead to future needs is not always easy, but the costs of failing to do so can be considerable.

This is, of course, equally true of major projects. A lesser scheme may appear to meet the needs of today, but all too often proves to be inadequate even by the time it is completed, leading to vastly increased costs and disruption. Unnecessary delays in starting a project are also expensive. When a project is continually put off, the costs of eventual construction when it can be deferred no longer can be a multiple of the original costs.

This has certainly been demonstrated by London's Thameslink and Crossrail projects, finally well under way after decades of prevarication. We must not let the same thing happen to the new High Speed routes planned to bring much-needed capacity to the UK's rail network. If growth in rail traffic continues at anything like the current level, and with an increasing population all the signs are that it will, a new trunk rail route is the only realistic solution. We have a 'once-in-a-generation' chance to deliver it.

Jeremy Candfield
Director General,
Railway Industry Association

Work on London's Crossrail is well under way. Canary Wharf station is the furthest advanced, with fit-out of the 185-metre-long ticket hall nearing completion in autumn 2013, as platform construction began, 28 metres below the surface of North Dock. Crossrail

Rail Freight – the year ahead

The publication of the 2014 edition of The Modern Railway gives the opportunity to look forward across the coming year. 2013 was a year of some uncertainty, with the Office of Rail Regulator's periodic review of Network Rail, the Energy Bill and High Speed 2 - areas where we hope to see consolidation and progress in the months ahead.

The bulk sectors, such as coal and aggregates, have been perhaps most successful in recent months. Significant coal fired electricity generation over successive winters has been busy work for the rail freight operators and the ports. However, we have also seen the closure of some power stations, such as Didcot and Cockenzie, highlighting the longer term trend to reduce the use of coal.

Meanwhile, the Energy Bill has made progress in establishing the case for biomass based generation as a part substitute. Drax, the early adopters of this technology, have made a substantial investment in new rail wagons, alongside the planned investment at the power plant and ports, and we look forward to seeing more of these delivered over the coming year.

The move towards biomass, alongside the other commodity sectors moved particularly from the Northern ports, raises questions over how to optimise network use and performance. To that end, a study is being progressed under the Strategic Freight Network, to look at whether infrastructure interventions are likely to be necessary. This will of course need to be looked at along with the other priorities for freight funding, including upgrades to the route from Felixstowe to Nuneaton, as decisions are taken on how the welcome investment of £200m in England and Wales, and £30m in Scotland are best used.

In the early months of 2014 we expect to see a number of freight schemes reach completion, including the Ipswich Chord, and the complete gauge cleared route between Water Orton and Doncaster. It is worth remembering just how much of the network will have been cleared for high gauge freight in the last five years, leading to increased traffic levels and improved utilisation. With the new port at London Gateway set to open at the start of the year, we expect to see interesting developments in intermodal traffic, and the network enhancements such as these will ensure the operators are equipped to respond.

2014 will of course continue to be dominated by debate around HS2, with the Hybrid Bill expected to start its journey through Parliamentary process. HS2 is vital for the long term success of freight and the benefits that this will deliver need to be enshrined in the Bill. We are also pleased that discussions around the supply chain for the construction phase are starting now, opening up opportunities for rail freight to play its part in building the route.

We look forward to another busy and successful year for the rail freight sector, and to reading about it in the pages of Modern Railways each month.

Maggie Simpson
Executive Director
Rail Freight Group

In an area recently cleared for high gauge freight, and due to become part of the electrified north-south spine for rail freight, passenger and freight trains pass an electrification base at Fulscot, just east of Didcot on the Great Western main line, on 5 June 2013. DB Schenker's Class 66 No 66109 heads west past a First Great Western high-speed train. Keith Fender

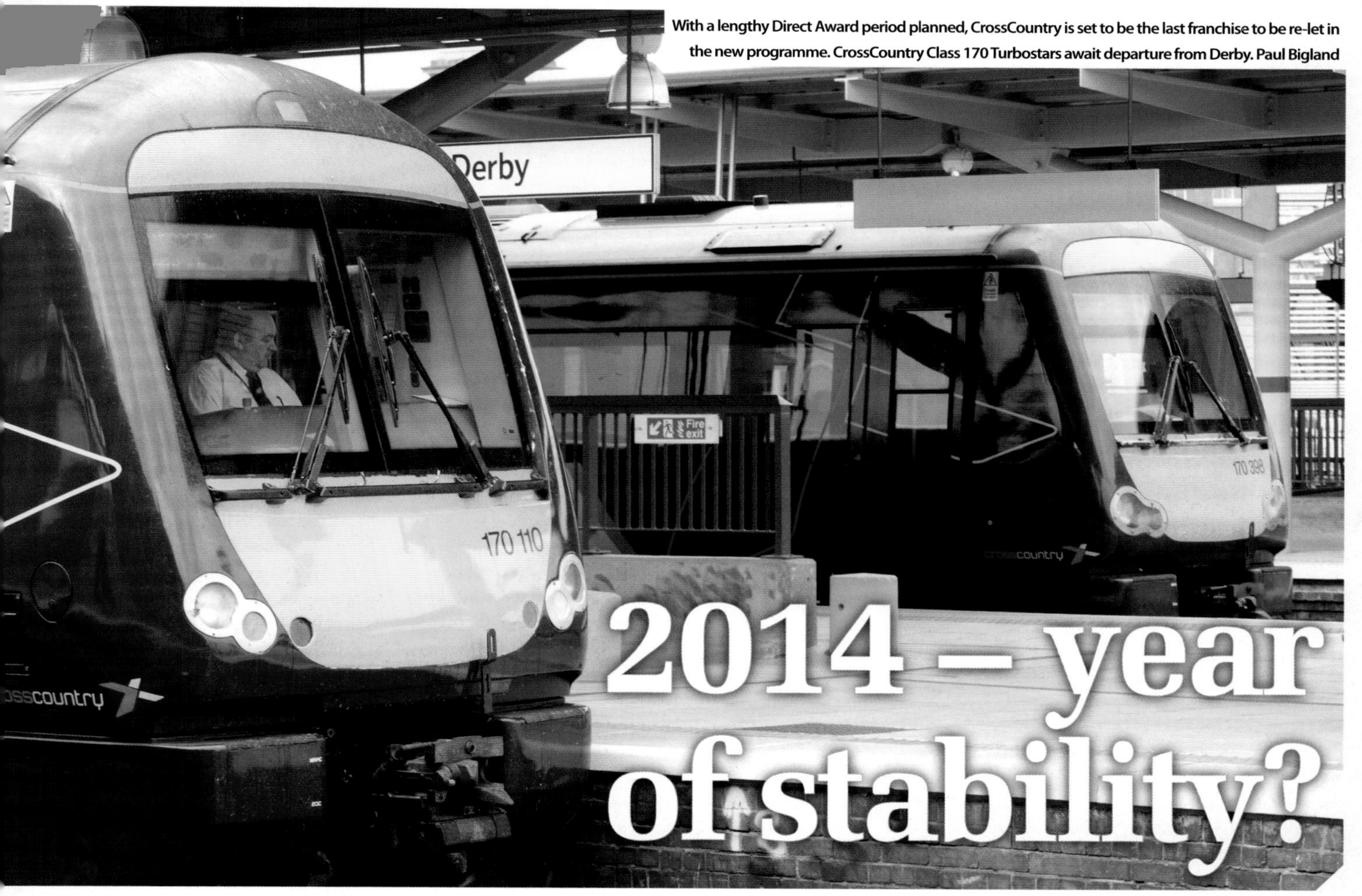

With a lengthy Direct Award period planned, CrossCountry is set to be the last franchise to be re-let in the new programme. CrossCountry Class 170 Turbostars await departure from Derby. Paul Bigland

2014 – year of stability?

ROGER FORD, INDUSTRY & TECHNOLOGY EDITOR OF MODERN RAILWAYS, SAYS THE RESPONSE TO THE COLLAPSE OF THE PASSENGER RAIL FRANCHISING PROGRAMME OFFERS A NEW CLIMATE OF STABILITY

Last year, The Modern Railway forecast that 2013 would be the 'Year of turmoil', after the collapse of the Intercity West Coast franchise competition had thrown the Department for Transport (DfT) into disarray. And so it turned out. But as the year progressed, it became clear that the enforced re-boot of passenger rail franchising had done more than restore order: it had created a framework for long-term stability in the industry.

For this we must thank Peter Wilkinson, Managing Partner of the First Class Partnerships consultancy. Mr Wilkinson was appointed the DfT's Interim Franchising Director on 28 January and by 26 March had produced a new rail franchise schedule (Fig 1).

Initially appointed for six months, in July 2013 Mr Wilkinson's term was extended to January 2015. This will maintain continuity of leadership of two high profile franchises – Thameslink, Southern & Great Northern, and InterCity East Coast - plus Essex Thameside, together with Direct Award contracts for four more franchises in what will be a critical year for the passenger railway.

In his review of franchising for the DfT following the West Coast collapse, Richard Brown had pointed to the lack of expertise in the DfT and the need to reduce the workload on bidders. He recommended that, ideally, the replacement franchise programme should be based on no more than three to four competitions running simultaneously.

Mr Wilkinson's new schedule converts the Brown recommendation into a staged programme, running through the five years of Control Period 5 (CP5) starting on 1 April 2014. Assuming that the programme can survive the political outcome of the May 2015 general election, it brings two benefits.

First, it gives the passenger rail industry a degree of certainty. But, more importantly (as has already been demonstrated by the Direct Award Franchise Agreement for First Great Western, signed in October 2013), while the new agreements are interim measure, the incumbent operators will be expected to continue developing the network pending the eventual replacement franchise.

Because they are new franchise agreements, as opposed to extensions to the previous contracts, DfT is using them to implement its aspirations for CP5. Even for existing franchisees, the prospect of a Direct Award several years in the future has considerable commercial benefit.

CONTINUITY

For a start, delaying franchise replacement means that a Train Operating Company's (TOC's) management is freed from the considerable distraction of supporting the owning Group's bidding team seeking to retain the franchise. But equally important is the benefit continuity of management brings to service upgrades and investment in rolling stock and stations.

With the allocation of funding for regional schemes being devolved to organisations such as Local Enterprise Partnerships, continuity of TOC management and philosophy is important to the fostering of local confidence: similarly with relationships with long term investors such as the Rolling Stock Companies.

A topical example is South West Trains, where the current franchise runs to February 2017. A Direct Award contract will extend this to April 2019. This means that the SWT/Network Rail Alliance can focus on the central task of providing the additional capacity into Waterloo funded under DfT's High Level Output Specification for CP5.

Only with one TOC does the schedule introduce a degree of

Network Rail proposed to spend around 25% of £12,388 million enhancement spending in Control Period 5 on Thameslink and Crossrail. Tunnelling machine Elizabeth breaks through into the Canary Wharf station box in May 2013 after a six-month drive from the Limmo site near Canning Town. Crossrail

uncertainty. First Great Western's Direct Award runs for 23 months from October 2013 although the Franchising Schedule shows the replacement franchise being let in July 2016, 10 months after the new agreement ends.

Compliance with European Procurement rules limited the agreement to under two years. DfT's announcement of the Award was ambiguous on the subject of the remaining 10 months, saying only, 'a further contract will be negotiated before a long-term franchise is let'. Given that by 2016 the Great Western Route Modernisation (GWRM) will be at its peak, with new trains being commissioned, electrified train services starting, and the resignalling with the European Train Control System (ETCS) at mid programme, the ambiguity may have been intentional.

A strong case can be made for delaying the replacement franchise to 2018 when the Route Modernisation should be nearing completion. This could be achieved by exchanging Great Western and SouthEastern in the schedule

DIRECT AWARDS

Four Direct Award franchise agreements with incumbent operators are due to be signed during 2014. These will provide a better indication of how DfT and the Train Operators intend to exploit the continuity provided by the new schedule. First Great Western's Direct Award includes the operator taking revenue risk which should encourage Virgin West Coast.

Currently on a management contract, with a fee of 1% of revenue, Virgin is known to be looking to revert to taking revenue risk and developing services. In its abortive bid for the replacement franchise Virgin was proposing the augmentation of the Class 390 Pendolino fleet with a build of six-car trains to exploit the electrification programme in North West England. With both SWT and Great Western, DfT has shown willingness to support the procurement of new trains and the Virgin Direct Award, to be signed in November, could continue this policy.

While staggering franchise replacement has reduced the bidding workload, negotiating the Direct Award Agreements is more demanding that a simple extension to existing terms. And the longer the extension, the more complicated the Direct Award.

From this point of view the SouthEastern Direct Award, running for just over four years, will effectively set the policy for services in Kent for almost all of CP5. As noted above, this timescale would be more suited to Great Western, with SouthEastern taking the July 2016 replacement 'slot'.

INVESTMENT

In previous years, the changeover from one Control Period to the next has seen a dip in expenditure on renewals and enhancements. This appears to have been avoided, with the end of CP4 seeing work on the major projects undiminished, and even accelerating in some cases.

Signalling contracts, long the canary in the mine for railway investment, have also avoided the previous dip, with orders reported by the UK majors both for the mega-projects and renewals. And, as reported in the Signalling and Control section of The Modern Railway, new business is coming on stream in the form of the roll-out of ETCS and a new generation of Rail Operating Centres.

This year will also see Network Rail's new £140 million electrification factory train start work on the Great Western main line. Investment on this scale indicates the importance of the Government's commitment to a rolling programme of electrification.

More correctly known as the High Output Plant System (HOPS), the 23-vehicle train is made up of several special-purpose self-contained consists. In the 1980s, electrification of the East Coast main line went on with trains running past work sites. However, the installation techniques used then could not be used today. HOPS is designed to work with adjacent lines open under current Health & Safety requirements and will operate six nights a week from its Swindon base.

Each consist within the train is self powered, capable of running sat up to 60 mph. The consists are a piling rig; an excavation and concrete batching plant; a structure consist which will erect the masts, portals and twin track cantilevers; the ancillary conductor installation consist; and, to complete the job, the contact and catenary consist, which will string up the remaining wires, under tension. A separate unit will handle non-standard tasks such as catenary wires under low bridges, neutral sections, and also record contact wire height and stagger and similar data.

Each consist within the train is 'top and tailed' with a powered Multi-Purpose Vehicle with driving cab. On arrival at the work site, the individual consists will then separate and proceed to its section of track.

Thus the piling consist will be able to install 30 bases in a shift, typically one tension length of catenary. The following structure consist will be able to install 30 masts in shift, and so on.

BACKLOG

Working at night with adjacent lines open is vital when Network Rail is under pressure to minimise disruption, while carrying out

TABLE 1 - DIRECT AWARDS DUE IN 2014

FRANCHISE	NEW DIRECT AWARD AGREEMENT	REPLACEMENT FRANCHISE	LENGTH
Northern	1 April 2014	1 February 2016	22 months
South Eastern	1 April 2014	1 June 2018	50 months
Greater Anglia	1 July 2014	1 October 2016	27 months
Virgin West Coast	1 November 2014	1 April 2017	29 months

Source: DfT

enhancements and renewals. But in the first two years of CP4, Network Rail deferred some £1 billion of renewals to the remaining years of the Control Period. In its 2013 annual assessment of Network Rail's efficiency, ORR estimated the backlog of outstanding renewals at the start of CP5 will be just under £400 million.

On the southern section of the West Coast main line, the renewals position is complicated by the fact that - to cut the soaring cost of the Route Modernisation initiated by Railtrack - the upgrade was de-scoped. This has had an increasingly severe impact on reliability.

But catching up on the deferred work will come at a heavy price, starting in 2014. Watford Junction will close for a total of 36 days between May 2014 and April 2015.

Work will include resignalling, to transfer control to the Rugby Rail Operating Centre, plus the renewal of over nine miles of track, as well as the crossovers at both ends of Watford station, which date from the 1966 electrification. Including overhead-line electrification upgrades to improve reliability, and raising the line speed through Watford Junction from 80 to 125 mph, Network Rail estimates the cost at £81 million.

In 2014 there will be three total closures of Watford Junction in May, August and December. Describing the works as 'absolutely essential to maintain the punctuality that passengers and freight customers rightly expect', Network Rail Route Managing Director, London North Western, Dyan Crowther said that the alternative would have required 54 complete weekend closures.

PERFORMANCE

While the Regulatory Determinations for each Control Period are essentially about Network Rail's income, the Office of Rail Regulation also sets the performance that money is intended to buy. As the end of CP4 approached, Network Rail was facing severe regulatory pressure over poor performance levels.

Already under an enforcement order over Long Distance performance Network Rail was told by the Office of Rail Regulation in August 2013 that in 2012-13 the company had been in breach of its network licence, having failed to meet performance Targets for the Long Distance and London & South East passenger sectors. The enforcement order will see Network Rail fined £1.5 million for each tenth of a percentage point the Long-Distance Public Performance Measure (PPM) of punctuality falls below the 90% target for the end of CP4. At the time of writing, the fine was predicted to be around £70 million.

DETERMINATION

One major uncertainty remained as The Modern Railway went to press. Following publication by ORR of its Draft Determination for CP5, Network Rail assessed the Regulator's proposals with the operational and financial aspirations of its own Strategic Business Plan (SBP) published earlier in the Periodic Review process. Network Rail's assessment concluded that 13 out of 22 of ORR's requirements were 'unrealistic'. The remaining nine were considered 'optimistic'.

Given that the Periodic Review is a negotiating exercise, with Network Rail trying to get as much income as possible, and ORR trying to drive down the cost of the railway to taxpayer, confrontation is inevitable. Network Rail's Chief Executive, Sir David Higgins, described the Draft Determination as 'unbalanced and therefore unrealistic'.

This is not simply posturing. Network Rail has the option to reject the Final Determination and refer it to the Competition Commission. In 2000 Railtrack decided to challenge, but backed down after a few days. In 2008 Network Rail described the challenge in that Review's Draft Determination as 'simply too great'. Responding with a Final Determination, which closed some of the funding gap, ORR found it necessary to warn of the potentially damaging consequences of the threatened Competition Commission referral.

CONCESSIONS

Operationally, this time round Network Rail was concerned that the improvement in PPM demanded was not realistic. The assumed spending on track and signalling renewals was too low by £365 million and by £316 million for Information Technology. Forecast property income was too high by £251 million. Network Rail was also unhappy about ORR's assumptions on the cost of financing.

In the Final Determination in October 2013, ORR softened its approach to these issues, but only slightly. This included two concessions on PPM.

First, because the PPM at the end of CP4 was likely to be lower than expected, ORR lowered its requirements for the first three

FIGURE 1: THE DFT'S FRANCHISE EXTENSION PLAN

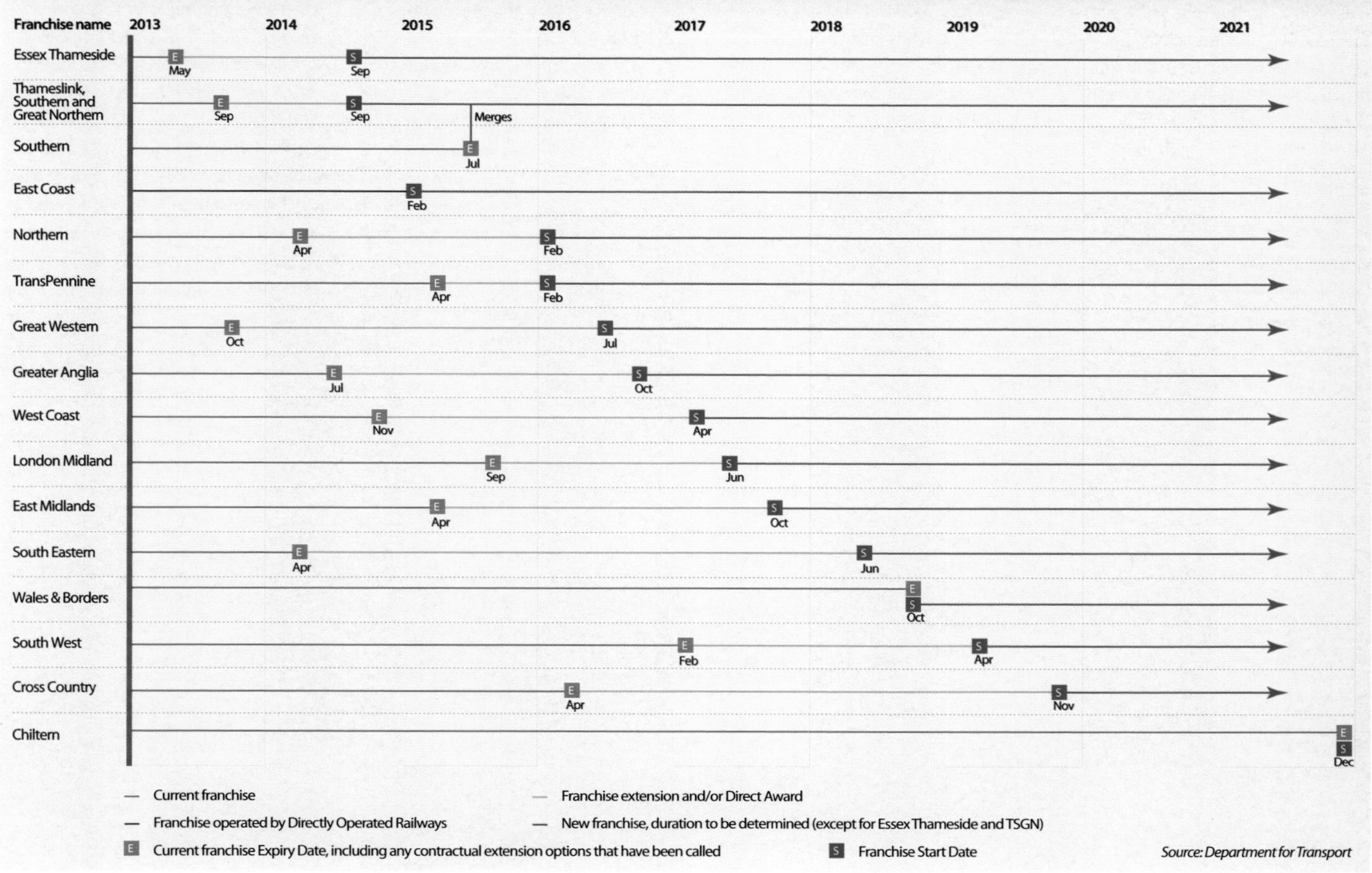

Timeline: 2013 2014 2015 2016 2017 2018 2019 2020 2021

Franchise name	E (Current franchise Expiry Date)	S (Franchise Start Date)
Essex Thameside	May	Sep
Thameslink, Southern and Great Northern	Sep	Sep (Merges)
Southern	Jul	
East Coast		Feb
Northern	Apr	Feb
TransPennine	Apr	Feb
Great Western	Oct	Jul
Greater Anglia	Jul	Oct
West Coast	Nov	Apr
London Midland	Sep	Jun
East Midlands	Apr	Oct
South Eastern	Apr	Jun
Wales & Borders	Oct	Oct
South West	Feb	Apr
Cross Country	Apr	Nov
Chiltern	Dec	Dec

— Current franchise
— Franchise operated by Directly Operated Railways
E Current franchise Expiry Date, including any contractual extension options that have been called
— Franchise extension and/or Direct Award
— New franchise, duration to be determined (except for Essex Thameside and TSGN)
S Franchise Start Date

Source: Department for Transport

TABLE 2 - SUMMARY OF CP5 'EFFICIENT EXPENDITURE' ASSUMPTIONS, £M (2012-13 PRICES)

	PR08	CP4	SBP	DD	FD*	FD
Support	4,113	2,740	2,232	2,093	2,119	2,119
Operations		2,239	2,027	1,968	1,968	1,968
Traction electricity, industry costs and rates	2,175	2,349	3,701	3,114	3,056	3,056
Maintenance	6,126	5,553	4,669	4,645	4,645	5,166
Schedule 4	870	875	712	1,131	1,058	1,058
Total operating expenditure	13,284	13,756	13,341	12,950	12,846	13,367
Renewals	13,141	12,686	14,365	12,681	12,822	12,107
Enhancements	9,296	11,294	12,388	12,239	12,625	12,818
Total capital expenditure	22,437	23,980	26,754	24,920	25,447	24,925
Total expenditure	35,721	37,735	40,095	37,869	38,293	38,293

Table shows the offer in the Office of Rail Regulation's draft and final determinations (DD and FD) compared with Control Period 4 (CP4), and the Strategic Business Plan (SBP) for CP5. 'PR08' shows figures determined for CP4 in the 2008 Periodic Review but later revised.

** This comparability adjustment to the FD column allows for changes to the classification of reactive maintenance and ETCS cab fitment to make the Final Determination figures comparable with those in the SBP column.*

years of CP5, while still demanding 92.5% for England & Wales by 2019. ORR had also required all individual TOCs to achieve a PPM of 90%. Following approaches from Network Rail, Virgin and East Coast, the target for Long Distance services, including First Great Western, is now 88%.

Expenditure for track, signalling and IT was increased by £191 million. ORR says that Network Rail did not make a strong case in seeking another £759 million.

Similarly, ORR accepted that that its property income forecast was £92m too high, but not by the £251m the company claimed. And on financing costs, Network Rail received about half of the £689m it wanted.

Network Rail had until 7 February 2014 to respond in detail and accept or reject the Determination. Table 2 shows the offer in the draft and final determinations compared with Control Period 4, and the Strategic Business Plan.

A point to note in the table is the two columns for the Final Determination. This is because in the SBP, Network Rail changed its definition of maintenance to include what it called 'reactive maintenance', such as civils and buildings inspections and examinations costs, some of which were treated as renewals in CP4. This clearly increases maintenance expenditures and reduces renewals spend compared to the SBP while leaving the grand total the same.

On enhancement, in the SBP, Network Rail was proposing to spend £12,388 million in CP5, compared to £11,294 million in CP4. Of this total, around 30% was for the rolling programme of electrification, 25% was split between Thameslink and Crossrail. A further 10% was allocated to other specific programmes such as the Strategic Freight Network.

ORR cut this spend to around £11.6 billion after reviewing each of the projects, but then added back some extra costs that were not included in the SBP, such as disruption compensation to train operators, giving the final total of £12.2 billion.

Further complicating this latest Periodic Review has been the number of major enhancement projects announced by Government – such as electrification schemes - which have yet to be costed accurately. Total value of these schemes is around £7 billion.

Because they are at an early stage of development, costs are uncertain and writing these into the Final Determination would mean adding a large 'risk premium'. To avoid this distortion, ORR has made a provisional cost assessment which will be finalised between now and 2015 as project plans become more mature.

This pragmatic approach to a fast development industry suggests that, provided Network Rail does not challenge the Final Determination, 2014 may indeed be the year of stability. ■

ORR amended its requirements for Public Performance Measure punctuality in the October 2013 determination. Following approaches from Network Rail, Virgin and East Coast, the target for Long Distance services was set at 88%. A Class 221 Virgin Voyager is seen in wintry conditions on a Birmingham-Scotland service. Virgin Trains

Across the Industry

DEPARTMENT FOR TRANSPORT

The Department for Transport (DfT) is the government body responsible for rail transport. Its main areas of responsibilities are in setting the strategic direction of the rail industry in England & Wales, funding investment in infrastructure through Network Rail, awarding and managing the passenger rail franchises, and the regulation of rail fares.

The failed attempt to let the West Coast main line franchise in 2012 involved both Virgin Trains as the incumbent and First Group as the prospective operator. Subsequently, a report by former Eurostar chairman Richard Brown endorsed the principle of franchising as an appropriate means of securing passenger rail services. The DfT was restructured to ensure that financial and other risks would be managed effectively in future. To ease pressures all round, it is intended that there will be three or four franchise renewals each year and a Franchise Advisory Panel has been created.

Franchise conditions vary, but in general invitations to bidders specify frequency levels and carrying capacity to be provided, punctuality and reliability standards, and the control of some fares levels.

The train operating companies (TOCs) also commit themselves to financial regimes. Typically, these require less subsidy as time progresses, or payment of an increased premium. They may also undertake specific enhancements.

The Department works with local and regional bodies, the rail industry and Passenger Transport Executives for major urban areas. Transport Scotland and to some extent the Welsh Assembly Government have devolved rail responsibilities.

The McNulty Value for Money study of 2011 put forward recommendations focused on cost reduction, new efficiencies, and methods of implementation. It estimated that annual savings of between £700m and £1bn could be made by 2019. These continue to be progressed, together with industry reform.

Present priorities include continuing to develop and lead the preparations for a high speed rail network, expanding capacity of the rail network generally, and maintaining a high standard of safety and security.

The DfT also sponsors Directly Operated Railways (whose subsidiary operates the East Coast train service) and the British Transport Police.

The five-year High Level Output Statement (HLOS) for the period 2014-19 (Control Period 5) specified what the government wants to buy from the railway in terms of safety, performance and capacity. This was accompanied by a Statement of Funds Available (SoFA) and a long term rail strategy.

DIRECTOR GENERAL, RAIL GROUP Clare Moriarty

TRANSPORT SCOTLAND

Transport Scotland is an agency of the Scottish Government, whose purpose is to increase sustainable economic growth through the development of national transport projects and policies. It is accountable to Parliament and the public through Scottish Ministers.

The Glasgow area is the largest commuter operation outside London and its users account for about 60% of railway passengers in Scotland.

The Rail Directorate is responsible for securing, monitoring and managing the ScotRail franchise; long term strategic decisions about future investment; and funding and specification of where resources are targeted by Network Rail on track maintenance and investment in Scotland. Safety and the licensing of railway operators remain reserved for Westminster.

The Scottish High Level Output Statement (HLOS) runs concurrently with that for England & Wales for 2014-19. Aims include hourly services between Aberdeen and Inverness, taking around two hours, and development of the Highland main line to provide an hourly service between Inverness and Perth. Network Rail is expected to electrify further parts of the network at a rate of 100 single track

First TransPennine Express's Class 185 No 185117 and Northern's Class 158 No 158851 pass at Colton South Junction near York. These two train operating companies could be merged under proposals under discussion with Passenger Transport Executives and other stakeholders. Brian Morrison

km per annum when Edinburgh-Glasgow Improvement Programme electrification is finished. There are funding schemes for stations, freight, network improvements and level crossings, while passenger and train handling capacity at the main Edinburgh and Glasgow stations is clearly a concern.

The HLOS includes this statement from ministers: 'It is our ambition that Scotland's railways are a source of pride, with an international reputation for efficiency and service, supporting sustainable economic growth to make Scotland a better place to live and a more competitive place to do business'.

Transport Scotland also co-ordinates the National Transport Strategy and is responsible for the national concessionary travel scheme.

DIRECTOR OF RAIL
Aidan Grisewood

TRANSPORT WALES

The Transport (Wales) Act 2006 conferred a general duty on the Welsh Assembly Government to promote and encourage integrated transport in Wales. Full responsibility for the Wales & Borders rail franchise became the Assembly's responsibility on 1 April 2006. The Assembly Government can specify services and regulate fares, and is responsible for the franchise's financial performance and for enhancements.

The Assembly is able to develop and fund infrastructure enhancement schemes, develop new passenger rail services, and invest in improving the journey experience for rail users.

Revenue support is given to rail links such as Cardiff-Holyhead which bring together south and north Wales, and capital spending is allocated.

£62million was allocated in autumn 2013 for new capital projects in south Wales, including rail improvements, and to progress future 'Metro' transport priorities including Newport-Ebbw Vale trains, and light rail and tram-train options, such as links with Cardiff Bay.

DIRECTOR, DEPARTMENT FOR TRANSPORT Frances Duffy

PASSENGER TRANSPORT EXECUTIVES

There are six Passenger Transport Executives (PTEs) covering the former Metropolitan Counties of West Midlands (Centro), Greater Manchester, Merseyside (Merseytravel), South Yorkshire, West Yorkshire (Metro) and Tyne & Wear (Nexus).

These are statutory bodies, responsible for setting out policy and expenditure plans for public transport. They are funded by a combination of local council tax and grants from national government. They are responsible to Integrated Transport Authorities (ITAs), made up of elected representatives of the local councils.

In Greater Manchester, a Combined Authority (Transport for Greater Manchester) takes on the functions of the ITA. Others are set to be created elsewhere.

ITAs are responsible for setting out transport policy and public transport expenditure plans in their regions, to be implemented by the PTEs. The PTEs manage and plan local rail services, in conjunction with the DfT. They have the power to secure additional passenger rail services in their areas, contracting with the local franchised TOC and funded by themselves.

PTEs invest in local networks, including new stations. They also develop and promote new schemes, notably light rail. They are neither bus nor rail operators themselves.

Merseytravel itself lets and manages the concession (not franchise) for Merseyrail Electrics.

The Northern and TransPennine franchises, providing local rail services in all PTE areas other than Centro, are to be re-let in 2014/15. The PTEs have long argued for a bigger say in the planning and development of their local railways. The devolution of powers to local and accountable bodies under the Localism Act 2012 could allow a greater integration of rail with other modes and, crucially, unlock the opportunity for more investment by PTEs and others.

PTEG, the Passenger Transport Executive Group, is a non-statutory body bringing together and promoting PTE and related interests.

Outside PTE areas, for large local authority transport projects in England to be funded from 2015 onwards, 39 new Local Transport Bodies are to take charge of the funding provided by the DfT - but seem set to be relatively short-lived, with their functions incorporated into Local Enterprise Partnerships.

City Deals negotiated with government give new powers to cities throughout England to raise funds and decide what to spend them on, including on transport infrastructure. Councils are able to keep income from growth in local business rates, among other funding streams. A Greater Bristol Metro, improving and extending local rail services, is one prominent proposal.

EUROPEAN UNION (EU)

The common European transport policy has the objective of promoting the efficiency and competitiveness of railways through gradual liberalisation. The aims of the Railway Packages that followed were to open up the trans-European rail freight market for international services, provide a legally and technically integrated European railway, revitalise international rail passenger services by extending competition, improving interoperability of the systems, and growing the rail freight market; as well as providing standards and authorisation for rolling stock, workforce skills, independent management of infrastructure, and liberalisation of domestic passenger services.

HOUSE OF COMMONS TRANSPORT COMMITTEE

The Transport Committee is appointed by the House of Commons to examine the expenditure, administration and policy of the Department for Transport and its associated public bodies.

During the course of a year, the Committee will consider around 20 topics on which they will call formally for written evidence from interested parties. Formal reports are made to the House, which are published together with a verbatim report of the evidence sessions and the main written submissions.

CHAIR Louise Ellman

NETWORK RAIL

Network Rail (NR) is the national railway infrastructure manager.

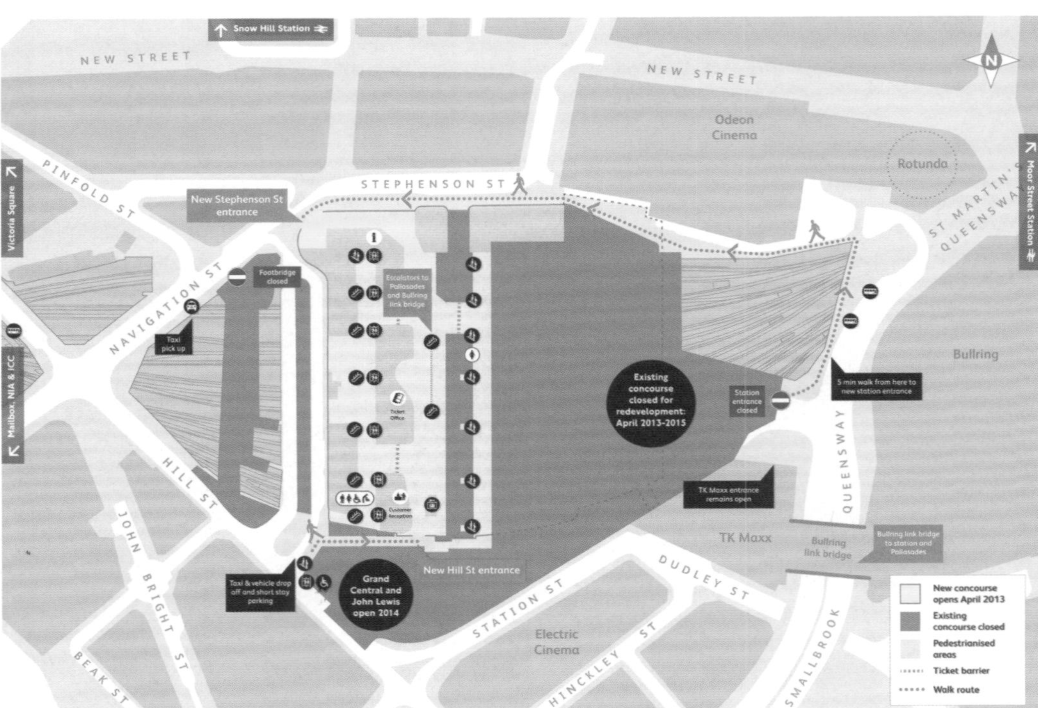

More than three years in the making, the first half of the new concourse at Birmingham New Street station opened to passengers in April 2013, marking the completion of the first phase of the project to transform the station. The Network Rail and Mace delivery team then turned their attention to redeveloping the old station concourse and the remainder of the Pallasades shopping centre. Network Rail

A £44m transformation of Manchester Victoria began in April 2013, with work getting under way on a spectacular new station roof. The new roof is part of a scheme intended to bring the station up to 21st century standards and turn it into a major regional interchange, allowing for electrification, and other improvements to services included in the Northern Hub rail capacity expansion scheme. Network Rail

Formed in October 2002, the company owns, operates, maintains and develops the railway infrastructure in Great Britain. This consists of the track, signals, bridges, viaducts, tunnels, level crossings and electrification systems, of which it is the monopoly owner. It also owns and operates 17 large stations (18 from 2015 when Reading is added). With minor exceptions, the others are owned by Network Rail, but day-to-day operations are by the franchised train operating company which has the most train calls there.

The task is the delivery of a safe, reliable and efficient railway network. Network Rail is a company limited by guarantee, operating as a commercial business, but with members in place of shareholders. It aims to make surpluses from its operations, but its profits are re-invested in the infrastructure. The members do not have any financial or economic interest in the company.

Network Rail Ltd is licenced by the Secretary of State for Transport. The company is accountable to its train and freight operator customers through their access contracts and to the Office of Rail Regulation (ORR).

Decentralising the organisation has led to the appointment of ten Route Managing Directors. Network Rail is also developing the practice of alliancing, forming closer bonds with its operator customers through joint management teams, but with each company retaining its own legal identity and obligations. A 'deep' Alliance of Network Rail Wessex and South West Trains takes the concept further.

The Long Term Planning Process is how Network Rail works with its stakeholders to predict future demand for rail services over the next 30 years, agree priority uses for the capacity available and assess value for money options for investment. Four market studies covering the various business sectors were published in 2013.

CHAIRMAN Richard Parry-Jones
CHIEF EXECUTIVE Sir David Higgins (Mark Carne from April 2014)

OFFICE OF RAIL REGULATION

The Office of Rail Regulation (ORR) is both an economic and safety regulator.

The principal economic regulatory functions are to regulate Network Rail's stewardship of the national rail network, to license operators of railway assets, and to approve track, station and light maintenance depot access arrangements.

Passenger train operating companies (TOCs) are granted franchises by the DfT and apply to ORR for licences to operate. ORR also licenses freight train operators. TOCs and Network Rail undertake track and station access agreements and these require ORR approval. ORR also regulates High Speed 1.

The High Level Output Statements and Statements of Funds Available produced by Westminster and the Scottish Government are considered by the ORR in the five-yearly Periodic Reviews of the railway industry. In October 2013 ORR published its final determination for Control Period 5.

This sets the outputs, incentives and financial framework for Network Rail for the five years 2014-19, identifying the scope for further efficiency gains and performance improvements. Network Rail's Delivery Plan is to be published in March 2014.

The ORR has concurrent jurisdiction with the Office of Fair Trading to investigate potential breaches of the Competition Act 1998 in relation to railways.

The ORR is the independent health and safety regulator for the railway industry, covering the safety of the travelling public and industry workers. HM Railway Inspectorate (HMRI) is part of ORR and its inspectors and policy advisors develop and deliver the safety strategy. ORR is the enforcing authority of the Health & Safety at Work Act 1974 and various railway specific legislation.

ORR is led by a Board appointed by the Secretary of State for Transport.

CHAIR Anna Walker
CHIEF EXECUTIVE Richard Price

RAIL DELIVERY GROUP

Network Rail, train operating companies and freight operating companies announced in October 2013 an agreement for the Rail Delivery Group (RDG) to assume responsibility for policy formulation and communications on behalf of the rail industry.

To advance this objective, the Association of Train Operating Companies (ATOC) will combine its communications and policy functions with complementary resources from Network Rail and support from other RDG members, to operate in future for the RDG as a whole. Michael Roberts, ATOC's

An East Midlands Trains Class 153 train negotiates Alsager level crossing. The report of the Law Commission and the Scottish Law Commission in September 2013 recommends reform of the law aimed at improving the safety regime for level crossings. East Midlands Trains

chief executive, became the director general of the RDG.

The creation of an expanded executive team was intended to strengthen the RDG's capabilities to develop policies which benefit rail users and taxpayers, and enable it to provide the railway with a unified voice.

The combination of resources from ATOC and Network Rail was also intended to signal the RDG's intent to work increasingly in partnership and with common purpose, mirroring developments elsewhere in the industry.

The RDG was created following the McNulty report of May 2011 on rail value for money. The purpose was to lead a substantial programme of change, focused particularly on cost reduction, changing the industry culture, encouraging more integrated whole-system approaches where necessary, and improving the speed and effectiveness of cross-industry bodies.

In 2013 the structure of the RDG was formalised to ensure, according to the Office of Rail Regulation, that it continued to receive the full commitment of key people and organisations from across the railway industry. This was achieved through the incorporation of a new membership condition into the licences of Network Rail and passenger and freight operators.

ATOC's business services teams continue to run National Rail Enquiries, Rail Settlement Plan, Rail Staff Travel, and Commercial, Operations and Engineering schemes. The governance arrangements and bodies for these remain unchanged: ATOC's Board's new main focus shifted from policy to ensuring a co-ordinated approach to business service provision.

ATOC was set up after privatisation in 1993, to bring together all train companies to preserve and enhance the benefits for passengers of Britain's national rail network.

The Rail Settlement Plan provides a central clearing house for the train operators, allowing passengers to buy tickets to travel on any part of the rail network, from any station.

National Rail Enquiries is a customer service operation providing information on train times, fares, reservations and service disruption across the country.

ATOC's Commercial activities cover discounted and promotional railcards for groups including young people, families, senior citizens and people with disabilities.

RAIL FREIGHT GROUP

The Rail Freight Group is the leading representative body for rail freight in the UK, with a membership which includes some of the biggest names in logistics along with many smaller companies, all of whom contribute to the success of rail freight. Its members include ports, terminal operators, property developers, equipment suppliers and support services.

Since 1991, the RFG has been working to increase the amount of goods conveyed by rail. It seeks to achieve this in three ways: by campaigning for a policy environment that supports rail freight; promoting the rail freight sector, and supporting members as they grow their businesses.

Chairman: Lord Berkeley

EXECUTIVE DIRECTOR

Maggie Simpson

FREIGHT ON RAIL

Freight on Rail, a partnership between the rail trade unions, the rail freight industry and Campaign for Better Transport, works to promote the economic, social and environmental benefits of rail freight, both nationally and locally. It advocates policy changes that support the shift to rail and provides information and help on freight related issues.

HIGH SPEED 1

HS1 Ltd is the long term concession holder of HS1, the 109km high speed rail line connecting London St Pancras International with the Eurotunnel boundary. The concession to operate, maintain and renew the railway was awarded to Borealis Infrastructure and the Ontario Teachers' Pension Plan by the UK Government in 2010. The concession continues until 31 December 2040, when asset ownership reverts to the government. The concession may then be relet.

Delivery of operations and maintenance responsibilities is achieved principally through contracts with Network Rail (High Speed) Ltd. HS1 Ltd is policed by the Office of Rail Regulation.

Four stations are served along the route. St Pancras International has 9 high-speed train platforms, 6 for international and 3 for domestic. Stratford International has 4 high-speed platforms, 2 for international (as yet unused for that purpose) and 2 for domestic. Ebbsfleet International has 6 high-speed platforms, 2 for international and 4 for domestic. Ashford International has 4 high-speed platforms, 2 for international services and the others shared with the classic railway which has a further 2 platforms.

Present operators are Eurostar for international services under an open access agreement and Southeastern TOC for domestic operations as part of its franchise agreement. Vehicle operating on HS1 must be specifically authorised so to do, and their compatibility with the route (including signalling systems) demonstrated.

Ashford Area Signalling Centre is the location of the traffic, signalling and electrical controls and the communications centre for HS1.

HS1 Ltd has the rights to sell access to track and stations on a commercial basis. As the 2013 New Operator Guide puts it: 'HS1 has spare capacity to accommodate new international or domestic service and we are keen to work with and support new operators...'

The first revenue earning freight train was run by DB Schenker in 2011. All such movements are at night as conventional freight trains are limited to 140km/h. There are possibilities for using high-speed freight trains during normal service hours at up to 300km/h.

BRITISH TRANSPORT POLICE

British Transport Police (BTP) is the specialised police service for Britain's railways. BTP provides a service to rail operators, staff and passengers throughout Britain, as well as London Underground, the Docklands Light Railway, Glasgow Subway, Midland Metro, London Tramlink, and London's Emirates Air Line cable car.

BTP is divided into seven geographical areas. There are over

2,800 Police Officers and 1,450 support staff.

Four strategic objectives are set by its Police Authority: keeping the railway running, making the railway safer and more secure, delivering value for money, and promoting confidence in use of the railway.

National targets for 2013/14 are: reducing police-related disruption by at least 3% from 2012/13; non-suspicious and unexplained fatalities to be cleared within an average of 90 minutes; reduce overall notifiable crime by at least 3% from 2012/13; maintain or increase detection rates for notifiable offences; increase percentage of budget spent on frontline resources to at least 58% (previously 57%); increase staff availability through reduced sickness rates and temporary duty restrictions; greater visibility of officers during the small hours.

CHIEF CONSTABLE Andy Trotter

RAILWAY INDUSTRY ASSOCIATION

The Railway Industry Association (RIA) is the representative body for UK-based suppliers of equipment and services to the world-wide rail industry. It has around 170 member companies across the whole range of railway supply. RIA is an active member of UNIFE, the trade association for the European railway supply industry, and of the Confederation of British Industry.

RIA members represent the greater part of the UK railway supply industry. This includes the manufacture, leasing, component supply, maintenance and refurbishment of rolling stock, the design, manufacture, installation, maintenance and component supply of infrastructure, and specialist expertise in consultancy, training, project management and safety.

DIRECTOR GENERAL
Jeremy Candfield

RSSB

RSSB is a not-for-profit company owned by the major industry stakeholders. Its primary purpose is to help the rail industry to improve continuously the level of safety where reasonably practicable; to drive out unnecessary cost; and to improve business performance.

RSSB's core activities concern standards, risk modelling and safety intelligence data, research and network-wide initiatives.

This includes the development of the industry's Safety Risk Model (identifying all significant risks), a Precursor Indicator Model (risk from train accidents) and the SPAD ranking methodology (risk from passing signals at danger).

RSSB manages the industry's research and development programme (funded by the Department for Transport). Other activities are funded by member levies.

Five separate committees manage interfaces between vehicles and, respectively, Structures, Track, Train Energy, Train Control & Communications, and Other Vehicles.

Safe operation is supported by the Railway Group Standards (RGS), which are managed by RSSB on behalf of the industry. These define mandatory engineering and operational matters and include the national Rule Book.

(RSSB is registered as the Rail Safety & Standards Board though it does not use the full name as its status and activities have changed with time.)

CHIEF EXECUTIVE Len Porter (from 2014, Chris Fenton)

TECHNICAL STRATEGY LEADERSHIP GROUP

The Technical Strategy Leadership Group (TSLG) is a cross-industry RSSB-facilitated expert body with representatives from Network Rail, train and freight operating companies, rolling stock leasing companies, suppliers, Transport Scotland, Crossrail, High Speed 2, and RSSB - as well as from groups with access to expertise such as chairs of the systems interface committees, the university sector through Rail Research UK Association (RRUKA), other industry organisations such as RDG/ATOC and Railway Industry Association, and government and the regulator through DfT and ORR.

The Rail Technical Strategy (RTS 2012) was launched by TSLG and the RDG in December 2012. It sets out to outline industry's long term vision of the GB railway as a system and supports industry's planning processes. It aims to inform policy makers and funders about the potential benefits of new techniques and technologies and provide suppliers with guidance on the future technical direction.

Hosted by RSSB, the Enabling Innovation team forms part of the delivery of 'Future Railway' activities, on behalf of the TSLG. The team has been set up by the rail industry to accelerate the uptake of innovation, offering support to practical cross-industry demonstrator projects, and seeking out innovative ideas and proposals from across the industry. Its approach is to: understand the challenges that industry faces; connect potential innovators with these challenges; and, where necessary with potential funding. The team reports to TSLG, and is supported by the RDG, RSSB and the DfT.

LAW COMMISSIONS

Level crossings, of which there are around 8,000 in Britain, present the largest single risk of a catastrophic train accident. The report of the Law Commission and the Scottish Law Commission in September 2013 recommends reform of the law aimed at improving the safety regime for level crossings by bringing it into line with that of the railway generally, while making such special provision as is necessary; as well as providing a new procedure to allow for the compulsory closure of level crossings, and clarifying the law relating to rights of way across railways.

RAIL ACCIDENT INVESTIGATION BRANCH

The Rail Accident Investigation Branch (RAIB) is the UK's statutory but independent body for investigating accidents and incidents occurring on railways and tramways. It is part of the DfT but functionally independent, and the Chief Inspector reports directly to the Secretary of State.

The RAIB's determines the causes and circumstances of accidents; its reports are available on the web. These contain safety recommendations, aimed at reducing the likelihood of similar events in the future and mitigating their consequences.

The RAIB is not a prosecuting body and it does not apportion blame or liability. It investigates any serious railway accident, meaning those involving a derailment or collision which has an obvious impact on railway safety regulation or the management of safety. It includes those that result in the death of at least one person, that cause serious injuries to five or more persons, or that cause extensive damage to rolling stock, the infrastructure or the environment.

The RAIB may also investigate other accidents or incidents on

A programme of rail replacement, falling due on Sheffield Supertram after nearly 20 years of service, will include all areas where the new tram-trains will operate, and will now use a new rail profile which has a wider and deeper groove, compatible with tram-trains. Stagecoach Supertram/PTEG

The National Rail Passenger Survey of passengers' overall satisfaction, and satisfaction with 30 specific aspects of service, is produced by Passenger Focus twice a year, and is widely consulted by rail policymakers. Passengers await their train in the East Midlands Trains part of London St Pancras station. Tony Miles

railway property where it believes there may be significant safety lessons.

CHIEF INSPECTOR Carolyn Griffiths

PASSENGER FOCUS

Passenger Focus is the consumer watchdog for Britain's rail passengers and England's bus, coach and tram passengers (outside London). Using research findings from in particular the Rail Passenger Survey and the Bus Passenger Survey, Passenger Focus seeks to drive change that will make a difference for passengers.

Passenger Focus is structured as an executive non-departmental public body. It is sponsored by the Department for Transport. The Scottish Executive, the Welsh Assembly Government and the Greater London Authority are each able to appoint a Board member. The organisation's independence is guaranteed by Act of Parliament.

CHIEF EXECUTIVE Anthony Smith

THE ASSOCIATION OF COMMUNITY RAIL PARTNERSHIPS

The Association of Community Rail Partnerships (ACoRP) is a federation of over 50 community rail partnerships and rail promotion groups, focused on practical initiatives to advance the local railway. Improved station facilities, better train services and improved integration with other forms of transport are central to the work of ACoRP and its members.

The government's Community Rail Development Strategy provides a framework in meeting social, environmental and economic objectives.

GENERAL MANAGER Neil Buxton

DERBY & DERBYSHIRE RAIL FORUM

The Derby & Derbyshire Rail Forum (DDRF) dates from 1993 and represents over 100 businesses across the East Midlands. These employ over 25,000 people and contribute £2.6bn to the local economy. The area is thought to contain the largest cluster of rail companies in the world.

As well as providing a collective voice and promoting the area's rail industry, DDRF holds quarterly networking meetings and an annual conference. DDRF has dedicated local support from local authorities and industry groups.

THE INSTITUTION OF MECHANICAL ENGINEERS

The Railway Division of the Institution of Mechanical Engineers (IMechE) is one of eight divisions and was founded in 1969. Its scope covers research, design, development, procurement, manufacture, operation, maintenance and disposal of traction, rolling stock, fixed equipment and their components within rail, rapid transit and all forms of rail-borne guided surface transport.

CHIEF EXECUTIVE Stephen Tetlow

RAILWAY CIVIL ENGINEERS ASSOCIATION

The Railway Civil Engineers Association (RCEA) is an Associated Society of the Institution of Civil Engineers, whose members are

THE PRIVATISED RAIL INDUSTRY

Until 1994, the nationalised British Railways Board (BRB) operated what became known as the vertically integrated railway. The Board itself provided the infrastructure, owned the trains and operated the services.

Under the Railways Act 1993, these and other functions were separated. The ownership of the track went to a new company, Railtrack, subsequently privatised. All operators paid Railtrack access charges for the use of the track, signalling and electrification systems.

Passenger train operations were split into what initially were 26 separate franchises. They were the subject of competitive tendering, mostly for a seven year term. Franchise awards took into account the additional services and investment commitments of each bidder, and whether that company would require a subsidy or would pay a premium to the government over the franchise term.

The passenger stations were owned by Railtrack, but all except from the very largest were run by the train operating companies (TOCs).

The passenger rolling stock became the property of three rolling stock companies (ROSCOs), which then leased the stock to the TOCs. This surmounted the problem of relatively short franchise terms and asset lives of around 30 years.

The freight companies were also privatised, but they owned the locomotives and any wagons which were not privately owned by customers.

Franchising was carried out by the Office of Passenger Rail Franchising (OPRAF) and various aspects of the industry including licensing were carried out by the independent Rail Regulator plus the Health & Safety Executive.

The Association of Train Operating Companies (ATOC) was created to manage passenger railway affairs such as running the National Rail Enquiry Service (NRES), Railcard schemes, and settling accounts between companies.

The last franchises were let very shortly before the 1997 General Election, which brought a change of government from Conservative to Labour. Labour said it wished to improve overall direction and planning in the industry, and created the short-lived Strategic Rail Authority (SRA). But other problems afflicted the industry, in particular the inability of some franchisees to make the financial returns they had expected, plus the level and quality of maintenance and investment by Railtrack.

Rising traffic levels and the operation of many more trains led to performance problems. These became chronic following the Hatfield derailment of 2001, caused by poor track quality. The result, according to SRA chairman Sir Alastair Morton, was that 'the system suffered a collective nervous breakdown'. This led to huge political and media driven criticism, the downfall of Railtrack, and a strong move to centralisation.

Over time, many of the franchises, including the management buy-outs, were acquired by groups active in the bus industry. More recently, franchise ownership has extended to companies based in France, Germany, the Netherlands and Hong Kong.

The cost of the railway to the public purse rose fast, not least with the West Coast Route

involved in the development, design, construction or maintenance of railway infrastructure. It exists to foster continuing professional development and the exchange of knowledge and experience. Presentations, meetings and visits take place on current projects and issues.
CHAIRMAN Colin Evison

PERMANENT WAY INSTITUTION

The Permanent Way Institution (PWI) promotes and encourages the acquisition and exchange of technical and general knowledge about the design, construction and maintenance of every type of railed track.

The PWI holds local meetings in all its geographically-based Sections, as well as arranging technical conferences and visits. Its textbooks have been the industry standard works for over half a century and members receive a widely consulted Journal.
CHIEF EXECUTIVE OFFICER
David Packer

INSTITUTION OF RAILWAY SIGNAL ENGINEERS

The Institution of Railway Signal Engineers (IRSE) was formed in 1912. Its objective was and remains the advancement of the science and practice of railway signalling, telecommunications and related matters. The IRSE is an international organisation, active throughout the world. It is the professional institution for all those engaged or interested in signalling and aims to maintain high standards of knowledge and competence within the profession.
CHIEF EXECUTIVE & SECRETARY
Colin Porter

INSTITUTION OF RAILWAY OPERATORS

The Institution of Railway Operators (IRO) exists to advance and promote the safe and reliable operation of the railways by improving the technical and general skills, knowledge and competence of all those thus engaged.

At the heart of the IRO's educational provision is its Professional Development Programme, run in conjunction with Glasgow Caledonian University. This comprises the Certificate and Diploma of Higher Education in Railway Operational Management and the Degree in Railway Operational Management, all delivered through the combination of distance learning and direct tutorials.

Through its seven Area Councils, the IRO provides a full programme of local events and visits.
CHIEF EXECUTIVE Fiona Tordoff

INSTITUTION OF ENGINEERING AND TECHNOLOGY

The Railway Network of the Institution of Engineering and Technology (IET) covers the electrical engineering aspects of the promotion, construction, regulation, operation, safety and maintenance of railways, metros, tramways and guided transport systems.
CHIEF EXECUTIVE & SECRETARY
Nigel Fine

CHARTERED INSTITUTE OF LOGISTICS AND TRANSPORT (UK)

The Chartered Institute of Logistics and Transport (CILT UK) is the professional body for individuals and organisations involved in all aspects of transport and logistics. As it is not a lobbying organisation, it is able to provide a considered and objective response on matters of transport policy. Through a structure of forums and regional groups, it provides a network for professionals to debate issues and disseminate good practice. There is a very active Strategic Rail Policy Group and another on Light Rail & Tram.
CHIEF EXECUTIVE Steve Agg

YOUNG RAILWAY PROFESSIONALS

The Young Railway Professionals (YRP) was founded in 2009 to bring together young people from across the railway industry, starting with those in UK railway related Institutions.

At a time of industry growth, it is more important than ever

Construction of the 300 metre Todmorden west curve began in October 2013. The project, funded by Burnley Borough Council and Network Rail, with Regional Growth Fund funding, will enable improved, direct rail services giving faster journeys between Burnley and Manchester Victoria. Manchester Victoria-Rochdale services are initially to be extended to Todmorden, with services to Burnley and Blackburn to follow. Network Rail

Modernisation. When the Rail Regulator ruled in 2003 on the level of access charges needed to fund Railtrack's successor, Network Rail, this proved too much. This became a charge funded by government, since the TOCs were protected by an indemnity clause in their contracts.

The Railways Act 2005 abolished the SRA with most of its functions (including strategy, finance and the awarding of franchises) transferred to an enlarged Department for Transport. Safety policy, regulatory and enforcement functions are now the responsibility of the Office of Rail Regulation (ORR). Separately, the government set out what Network Rail was expected to deliver for the public money it receives in a High Level Output Statement (HLOS) plus a Statement of Funds Available (SoFA). The access charges review process was amended, and there was some transfer of powers and budgets to Scotland, Wales and London.

Political and public faith in the ability of the railway to contribute to capacity shortfalls in all modes, to regional economic growth, and the wellbeing of society in general, seems to be have been growing. It is now seen as a solution to problems which affect us all, rather than a problem in its own right. Thus large scale electrification across the system is now under way.

To what extent is more freedom for TOCs compatible with the aims of public funding and the protection of the interests of the travelling public?

Localism is a new name in the political game. Network Rail has pushed out more of its activities to their Route Directors, while further decentralisation of planning and perhaps some franchising is becoming more likely. Realignment of the Rail Delivery Group and Association of Train Operating Companies is intended to provide the railway with a unified voice, and signal the RDG's intent to work increasingly in partnership and with common purpose, mirroring developments elsewhere in the industry such as Network Rail/TOC alliances.

High Speed 2 is being pursued by the Coalition Government, albeit with considerable opposition in some quarters. Potentially, this leaves the existing network with greater capacity for the traffic which it can hardly accommodate at present, but completion of Phase 1 (London to Birmingham) will not be before 2026 and Phase 2 (extensions to Manchester and separately to Leeds) in 2032. In autumn 2013 the present Secretary of State, Patrick McLoughlin, reaffirmed the central part that HS2 has in the government's transport policy.

Meanwhile, as already discussed, franchising policy has suffered recent setbacks but continues.

Where does the commercial passenger revenue come from? With 49% of the national rail revenue of £7,229m in 2011/12, the dominance of the London & South East sector is only too clear, while Long Distance passengers accounted for 35% of the total revenue. The remaining 15% came from Regional passengers, which includes both urban services (principally but not exclusively in the PTEs) and rural operations. All sectors were showing strong annual growth rates.

that strong relationships across organisations are built and best practice shared, making the most of social media and tapping into the skills of rail's younger employees. The YRP organises networking events designed both to inspire and entertain.

The YRP also runs an ambassadors' programme, providing opportunities for its members to visit schools, colleges and universities to attract the next generation into a dynamic rail industry.

CHAIRMAN Paul Cooper

REF

The REF (Railway Engineers' Forum) is an informal liaison grouping of the rail interest sections of the eight professional institutions listed above. As a non-political body, the REF aims to provide a common view on railway topics and a co-ordinated response to requests for professional comments. The REF also organises multi-disciplinary conferences and produces a monthly resumé of professional meetings around Britain, which is available on its own website and also those of its constituent bodies.

CHAIRMAN Lawrie Quinn

RAILWAY STUDY ASSOCIATION

The Railway Study Association (RSA) provides a forum for the exchange of experience, knowledge and opinion on issues relating to all aspects of the railway industry, and the part played by railways in the total transport scene. RSA members have a wide range of backgrounds and expertise, embracing operations, engineering, business planning, project management, marketing and consultancy.

The Association's calendar of events including evening lectures in London, regional meetings in Birmingham, an Annual Dinner, a Presidential address and an overseas study tour. These provide opportunities for learning, professional development and networking.

The President for 2012-2014 is Richard Morris of Eurostar.

CHAIRMAN Jonathan Pugh

NATIONAL SKILLS ACADEMY FOR RAILWAY ENGINEERING (NSARE)

What skills will be required in future for those entering railway engineering as a profession? How will they be recruited? Will there be enough of them? When will they be needed and where? At what level of expertise and in which disciplines? Who will do the training and accreditation? How will this be funded? Are these general requirements for the industry as a whole, or for specific large scale projects such as HS2 or ETCS?

These questions and a host of others are the concern of NSARE, which has a strategic role in their solution and ensuring that the industry has the necessary capabilities overall. For the two broad categories of infrastructure and rolling stock, there will always be the need for maintenance, renewal and enhancement.

CHIEF EXECUTIVE Gil Howarth

RAIL RESEARCH UK ASSOCIATION

Rail Research UK Association (RRUK-A) is a partnership between the British rail industry and UK companies. It was set up in 2010 with the aims of supporting and facilitating railway research in academia; common understanding of research needs to support the rail network and its future development; identification of research, development and application opportunities in railway science and engineering; and provision of solutions to the rail industry.

It is funded by RSSB and Network Rail and managed by an executive committee.

RAILWAY RESEARCH IN BIRMINGHAM

The Birmingham Centre for Railway Research and Education brings together a multi-disciplinary team from across the University to tackle fundamental railway engineering problems. The team actively engage with industry, other Universities through RRUK-A, and international partners. Mission Statement: Providing fundamental scientific research, knowledge transfer and education to the international railway community.

INSTITUTE OF TRANSPORT STUDIES, UNIVERSITY OF LEEDS

The Institute of Transport Studies at Leeds is the largest of the UK academic groups involved in transport teaching and research. For more than two decades, a principal interest has been the economics of rail transport. Key research topics include demand forecasting and travel behaviour, infrastructure cost modeling, efficiency analysis and pricing, project appraisal methodology, off-track and on-track competition, and transport safety. Fostered by close links with British Rail, more recent projects have been undertaken a worldwide range of clients.

THE INSTITUTE OF RAILWAY RESEARCH (IRR)

Headed by Professor Simon Iwnicki, the IRR is based at the University of Huddersfield and is one of the partners in a Euro 15 million, four-year project funded by the European Union under its Seventh Framework Programme. Named CAPACITY4RAIL, the ambitious scheme aims to ensure that railways will continue to meet Europe's transport needs over the decades to come. Low maintenance infrastructure, more resilient and easily repairable points, and higher-speed freight vehicles are among the goals. This will build on the findings of previous projects that the IRR has been closely involved with, such as the EU-backed INNOTRACK, which has investigated many of the technical challenges posed by the European Commission's goal of doubling rail passenger traffic and tripling freight traffic by 2020.

The University of Huddersfield and RSSB signed a Memorandum of Understanding in 2013, agreeing to pool resources and talent for research into system and engineering risk modelling to support informed decision making and future risk prediction.

East Coast intercity services have been operated since November 2009 by a subsidiary of government-owned holding company Directly Operated Railways, but are planned to be returned to private sector ownership in February 2015. East Coast

FINANCE AND LEASING

IN ASSOCIATION WITH

angel Trains

Rail People
Real Expertise

As one of the UK's leading train leasing specialists, Angel Trains is passionate about financing and delivering high quality, modern assets to its customers and is committed to providing innovative funding solutions to modernise and improve the UK's train fleet.

Employing over 110 professional, technical and support staff at its headquarters in Victoria, London and at a second office in Derby, Angel Trains has invested £3.4 billion in new rolling stock and refurbishment programmes since 1994. This makes the company one of the largest private investors in the UK rail industry. Angel Trains is unique in leasing to all 19 franchised operators and open access operators in the UK.

Angel Trains owns and maintains over 4,500 rail vehicles in the UK, about 37% of the nation's rail stock. Angel Trains was created in 1994 as one of the three rolling stock companies in preparation for the privatisation of the UK rail industry.

In August 2008 Angel Trains was acquired by a consortium of global infrastructure and pension fund investors.

SKILLS FOR EACH STAGE OF ROLLING STOCK ASSET LIFE

SPECIFICATION

We have engineers who are able to write and evaluate technical and performance specifications of new rolling stock to ensure Angel Trains only invests in assets that will be desirable to lessees in the long-term (also maintenance).

PROCUREMENT

Our commercial and procurement experts use the specifications to negotiate formidable terms from manufacturers and maintainers (supplier development).

PROJECT MANAGEMENT

Our engineers and project managers take procurement contracts and ensure timely delivery of goods and services.

PERFORMANCE GROWTH

Our engineers and project managers work with suppliers to ensure that rolling stock is not only delivered but properly commissioned to ensure that performance grows to optimum levels and continues throughout its asset life.

FLEET MANAGEMENT

Our engineers ensure that a detailed understanding is retained in Angel Trains and all performance issues and changes of maintenance plans are accurately documented, so that assets can transfer from one lessee to another with comprehensive knowledge databases.

MAINTENANCE MANAGEMENT

Our engineers, contract managers and planners ensure that documentation is kept up to date throughout the asset life, that vehicle maintenance is carried out in a timely manner, and that maintenance is delivered to the right quality and safety levels.

REFURBISHMENTS & ENHANCEMENTS

Our team of experts ensure that any planned changes to rolling stock meet either customer or owner requirements and are carried out in a professional manner with a view to maximising asset value for the longer term

CONTINUOUS SERVICE OPERATION

Our engineers, with detailed knowledge of the assets, are able to consider future developments such as obsolescence, environmental performance, and other legislative changes.

DISPOSAL

Our procurement specialists deal with the responsible disposal of assets when the time comes.

WHAT WE DO

Angel Trains bridges the worlds of finance and operations. Angel Trains attracts the necessary finance to procure, refurbish and enhance rolling stock to meet the needs of the UK's Train Operating Companies (TOCs) and provide a long term, reliable and safe asset to users of the UK railways.

Angel Trains has a diversified fleet including high-speed passenger trains, regional and commuter passenger multiple units and freight locomotives.

We place great importance on long-term asset stewardship, in order that the value of the asset can be consistently delivered and optimised throughout its lifecycle.

RAIL PEOPLE, REAL EXPERTISE

We employ a strong and committed team with extensive rail experience and trusted relationships within the industry. Angel Trains has strength in depth in finance, engineering, commercial and customer service.

With assets in all stages of the lifecycle, the strength of our company lies not only in our commercial approach, but in our structured approach to the stewardship of our rolling stock from cradle to grave. Angel Trains works through the various stages in rolling stock asset life, and through its staff, provides the different skills needed throughout. The rolling stock asset life and the necessary skills that we provide are outlined in the panel.

DIVERSITY – WOMEN IN RAIL

Angel Trains is wholly committed to supporting the diversification of the rail industry's workforce and is particularly dedicated to encouraging more women to view the UK rail sector as a long-lasting career option. As such, Angel Trains is a proud sponsor of the Women in Rail group which was founded by Adeline Ginn, General Counsel at Angel Trains, following a discussion with her CEO, Malcolm Brown, to provide networking opportunities and support for all women in the rail industry, promote rail as an attractive career choice and develop strategies for engaging young people to consider a career in rail.

TOMORROW'S TRAIN, TODAY: THE CLASS 317 EXAMPLE

Angel Trains has been working hard over the last year to re-engineer and refurbish a Class 317 unit. The Class 317 will have a whole host of improvements including a completely new interior as well as major improvements to its traction system which will ensure a significant reduction in energy usage, maintenance and operating costs, as well as create a stepped change in reliability. The Class 317 trial unit, after its official unveiling in November, should be in service in 2014.

SENIOR PERSONNEL

ANGEL TRAINS

CHIEF EXECUTIVE OFFICER
Malcolm Brown

CHIEF OPERATING OFFICER
Kevin Tribley

CHIEF FINANCIAL OFFICER
Alan Lowe

TECHNICAL DIRECTOR
Mark Hicks

Class 442 train on Brighton main line.

Class 455 trains are to benefit from new three-phase AC solid-state traction equipment from Vossloh Kiepe. Porterbrook

porterbrook

As one of the three major Rolling Stock Companies (ROSCOs), Porterbrook has owned and leased rolling stock and related equipment for more than 19 years and has invested over £2.3 billion in new equipment for the UK rail industry.

In addition Porterbrook has invested £300 million on existing fleet refurbishment and reliability work, having participated in some of the UK's most successful rolling stock enhancement programmes.

2013 has seen the continued investment in both new and existing rolling stock. In regard to new rolling stock, Porterbrook with its customer, Southern, has started to take delivery of the 170 Class 377/6 and 377/7 vehicles being produced by Bombardier in their Derby facility. The vehicles will operate alongside the other 792 Electrostar vehicles Porterbrook already has on lease with Southern.

The acquisition of these new trains will mean that since privatisation Porterbrook has either delivered or has on order more than 2,000 passenger rolling stock vehicles, giving a portfolio of more than 4,000 passenger vehicles and over 2,000 locomotives and wagons in use with the majority of train operators on the UK rail network.

A wide range of development projects are also being undertaken on the existing Porterbrook fleets. Three of these are:

1. The South West Trains operated Class 455s are being augmented further by the introduction of a modern traction package. Porterbrook have commissioned Vossloh Kiepe to undertake the replacement of the existing DC control equipment and traction motors with modern AC equivalents. This will enable a range of benefits to be derived, with regenerative capability and extended maintenance periodicity.
2. The integration of the former Class 460 fleet with the Class 458 fleet has commenced. The project will deliver 36 five-car units when it is completed, supporting South West Trains in delivering their High Level Output Statement obligations while bringing some much needed additional capacity to some of the busiest routes in the UK.
3. There has been a significant increase in the application of Driver Advisory Systems (DAS) across the Porterbrook fleet. These modifications have been applied to all types of rolling stock and they are delivering significant energy savings to operators up and down the country.

PRM (Persons with Reduced Mobility) legislation has set an implementation date for all vehicles operating on the UK rail network to be made to be compliant by 31 December 2019 or risk withdrawal. In recognition of this Porterbrook has embarked upon a programme of work to make its fleet compliant with these requirements. Design work is being conducted on a wide range of the fleets that the company owns, while work has physically commenced on the Class 156 fleet operated by Abellio in the Greater Anglia franchise. This work is being coupled to Continued Service Operation (CSO) activities on the fleet and is leading to significant additional investment being made.

Porterbrook is also involved in a joint ROSCO project to reduce the diversity of wheelset components and develop recovery procedures to significantly reduce material wastage/scrap.

The company employs a team of 90 professional staff with expertise in areas of Finance, Engineering, and Asset Management. Their extensive experience and knowledge of the rail industry gives Porterbrook a strong base to deliver value for money for the services they offer.

2013 has seen Porterbrook achieve reaccreditation by the Institution of Mechanical Engineers for its graduate training scheme, an arrangement which is helping bring new professionals into the UK rail industry. The scheme provides a comprehensive industry based training programme giving a wider awareness of engineering management within the organisation.

Having achieved RISAS accreditation in 2012, Porterbrook is now planning for its re-accreditation audit in November 2013. RISAS (Railway Industry Supplier Approval Scheme) certification means that Porterbrook has proven its capabilities at the highest level, in the procurement of maintenance and other services needed to support its rolling stock.

Over the next few years further high levels of investment are required for the UK rail industry for new train projects and on-going vehicle enhancements. Porterbrook recognises that undertaking engineering improvement work and carrying out PRM compliance modification of existing stock will offer the industry substantial value for money benefits. In this context Porterbrook's aim in the coming years is to continue to develop its existing fleet and invest in new trains where the opportunity fits with its investment strategy - bearing out Porterbrook's commitment to the future of the UK rail industry. ■

An Eversholt-funded, Hitachi-built Class-395 'Olympic Javelin' calls at Stratford International to collect spectators during the London 2012 Games. Govia/Southeastern

Eversholt owns approximately a third of the total current British rail passenger fleet - some 3,500 vehicles - and more than 1,000 freight wagons and locomotives.

Eversholt Rail Group is owned by Eversholt Investment Group, a consortium consisting of investment funds managed by 3i Infrastructure plc, Morgan Stanley Infrastructure Partners, and STAR Capital Partners, which purchased the group from HSBC at the end of 2010. The transaction valued Eversholt's gross assets at approximately £2.1 billion.

In November 2013, Eversholt successfully completed new £600m senior debt financing, providing additional funding capacity for investment in rolling stock and allowing prepayment of existing bank facilities.

The Eversholt Rail Group brand replaced that of HSBC Rail in 2010, and the business separated its maintenance, asset management and advisory services into different legal entities. The name echoes that originally given to the business - Eversholt Leasing - when privatised.

DEMONSTRATORS

With the industry facing competing demands for better performance, increased passenger satisfaction and extra capacity on the one hand and reduced cost on the other, Eversholt has recently offered solutions to these challenges with both a Mk4 coach concept interior and a Class 321 demonstrator.

The full-scale concept interior mock-up of a Mk4 coach demonstrated how a new train feel can be achieved in existing rolling stock at a fraction of the cost of new trains, with interior refinements including four possible classes of travel – Standard, Business, First and Premium - and technology upgrades. The invaluable stakeholder feedback already gained will inform future enhancement plans for Mk4 and other fleets.

The 4-car Class 321 demonstrator electric multiple-unit has been upgraded at Wabtec in Doncaster in a £4.5m project to showcase how high-specification refurbishment of the existing fleet of Class 321 EMUs can compare favourably with the passenger experience and performance of new trains, at a significantly lower cost. Unveiled in November 2013, the demonstrator will operate in service on the Greater Anglia route for a year and Eversholt will be inviting feedback from passengers on the options being demonstrated - including both metro and suburban interior designs and revamped First class accommodation with new leather seats.

Eversholt is also developing a prototype traction system for the Class 321 fleet with Vossloh Kiepe to increase traction performance and energy efficiency to that of a new train.

DESIRO

For the new Siemens Desiro City trains for Thameslink, Eversholt has signed a long-term agreement to provide project and asset management services to the Cross London Trains, the consortium providing the new fleet. Services under the 22 year agreement will include project management during the build and delivery of the rolling stock, and then long-term asset management, including both technical and commercial support to Cross London Trains. Eversholt has more than 16 years' experience in procurement and through-life asset management of new rolling stock, and maintenance and enhancements of existing stock. The company believes the Cross London Trains agreement provides a significant opportunity to utilise its proven skills and expertise for the benefit of new entrants to the market.

The first upgraded Class 315 unit re-entered service on the Greater Anglia route in 2013 and work continues on the fleet at Bombardier Transportation, Ilford. Work includes fitment of an automated passenger information system, and installation of wheelchair bays.

Successful completion and delivery back to ScotRail of the Class 320 fleet was completed on 4 October 2013, following C6 heavy maintenance and enhancements, including compliance with the latest accessibility requirements. The first ScotRail Class 318 was delivered to Wabtec in Doncaster for refurbishment the next day. This is a 2.5 year programme and the £18m Eversholt Rail investment builds on the successful Class 320 programme. Work includes major overhaul and corrosion repairs, with new cab and saloon doors, plus full interior refurbishment, LED lighting installed throughout, upgrading of traction electronics, and accessibility modifications.

First Capital Connect's fleet of Class 365 trains is to be transformed with fresh interiors and enhanced accessibility features as part of an expected £31m investment which will also include heavy maintenance to ensure their continued reliability.

The most recent new fleet financed by Eversholt is the Class 380 electric multiple-units for ScotRail, valued at over £185m. Transport Scotland funded the contract with Siemens and Eversholt to provide 130 new vehicles - the first 'fly by wire' electric multiple-units in the country (using coded digital signals to control equipment).

The company is the funder (and project managed introduction) of the high profile Hitachi Class 395 trains for Southeastern high-speed services, under an investment programme worth some £260million. The trains' new depot at Ashford was developed by Eversholt in conjunction with its Depco partners.

Another successful role for Hitachi traction on the Southeastern network is fitment of the Eversholt-owned 'Networker' Class 465/0 and 465/1 electric multiple-unit fleets with a reliable new traction system designed, built and maintained by Hitachi.

Eversholt gained RISAS (Railway Industry Supplier Approval Scheme) certification in 2011.

SENIOR PERSONNEL

EVERSHOLT

CHIEF EXECUTIVE OFFICER Mary Kenny
CHIEF OPERATING OFFICER Andy Course
CHIEF FINANCIAL OFFICER Fred Maroudas
HEAD OF RELATIONSHIP DEVELOPMENT Steve Timothy
HEAD OF COMMERCIAL AND BUSINESS SERVICES Clive Thomas

MANAGED SERVICE SOLUTIONS
THALYS
eurostar
RMF
RMF is a leading provider of railway reservation based international settlement and clearing services, providing sophisticated revenue and cost allocation, including business critical management information.
Client base
>> Eurostar International Ltd
>> Thalys International Scrl
>> SNCF
>> Department for Transport
Key partners
>> Atos Origin
>> Resarail 2000 GEIE
>> Hinagge and Company
>> Davison & Shingleton
Times House, Bravingtons Walk, Regent Quarter, London N1 9AW
Telephone : + 44 (0) 20 7042 9961 | Fax : 44 (0) 20 7633 0224
Email : david.hiscock@rmf.co.uk | www.rmf.co.uk

TenBroeke Co

TenBroeke Co

A line-up of 'Pacer' DMUs stabled at Huddersfield on 22 September 2013 - from left, Angel Trains-owned Class 142s Nos 142091 and 142018, and Porterbrook Leasing Company-owned Class 144 No 144012. Paul Bigland

Britain's rolling stock - who owns it?

ROLLING STOCK ALLOCATION ON THE NATIONAL NETWORK

Three rolling stock leasing companies (ROSCOs) were established at railway privatisation in 1994 to take ownership of all passenger rolling stock owned by the nationalised British Rail, and were sold to the private sector, with their initial leases in place.

The aim was for each ROSCO to have a reasonably diversified portfolio, with comparable fleets allocated to each. Larger fleets of a single type were divided, and smaller fleets were allocated to a single ROSCO. This gave each a range of customers and gave most train operating companies (TOCs) a relationship with at least two ROSCOs.

Table 1 shows how different types of passenger rolling stock were allocated to the three ROSCOs. Approximately 38 per cent of passenger rolling stock was allocated to Eversholt, 32 per cent to Angel and 30 per cent to Porterbrook. By 2009, ex-British Rail rolling stock formed approximately 60 per cent of the passenger fleet, with the rest purchased since privatisation, and Angel had a 36 per cent share of the total rolling stock, Porterbrook 32 per cent and HSBC (now Eversholt) 29 per cent.

Details of passenger rolling stock ordered since privatisation are shown in the opening article in the Train Fleet Manufacture and Maintenance section of The Modern Railway.

OTHER OWNERS

Another substantial lessor of rolling stock to franchised TOCs is Voyager Leasing, with a 3 per cent share of rolling stock. It was established to lease a new fleet of 'Voyager' trains to Virgin CrossCountry Trains. While it is a subsidiary of the Royal Bank of Scotland Group (RBS), ownership of the trains is equally split between the Lloyds Banking group (previously Halifax Bank of Scotland) and RBS.

Voyager Leasing originated when NatWest bank was appointed to arrange funding for the new fleet of 78 Voyager trains. The operating lease was arranged by a NatWest subsidiary, Lombard Leasing Contracts Ltd, later renamed Voyager Leasing. When NatWest was acquired by RBS (at that time the parent of Angel Trains), in order to reduce RBS's exposure to Virgin Trains, the

TABLE 1 - ALLOCATION OF PASSENGER VEHICLES AT PRIVATISATION

ROSCO	DMU	EMU	HST VEHICLES*	TOTAL
Angel	1,039	2,010	531	3,580
HSBC	0	2,864	1,366	4,230
Porterbrook	681	1,699	948	3,328
Total	**1,720**	**6,573**	**2,845**	**11,138**

**Diesel High Speed Trains - power cars and coaches.*
Source - Competition Commission

Eversholt Rail Group-owned Class 185 Siemens built DMU No 185131 (right) waits to leave Huddersfield en route to Manchester Airport on 11 June 2013, while Angel Trains-owned Class 150 Sprinter No 150210 stands alongside on a service to Manchester Victoria. Paul Bigland

CrossCountry fleet was evenly split and half the vehicles were sold to Halifax. RBS and Halifax then entered into head lease arrangements with Voyager Leasing.

Voyager Leasing has not undertaken any other leasing business. Though it had the same parent company as Angel Trains - RBS - it remained largely separate. It contracted Angel Trains to provide technical and other support, but these arrangements ended in 2008 when Angel was sold to a consortium of investors. Part of the Voyager fleet is now leased by the new CrossCountry franchise, held by DB group company Arriva.

QW Rail Leasing, a joint venture between Sumitomo Mitsui Banking Corporation and National Australia Bank, leases Class 378 electric multiple-units to London Overground Rail Operations Limited (LOROL) for Transport for London's London Rail Concession.

Some relatively small quantities of passenger rolling stock are owned by franchised train operating companies, most notably First Group which owns 12 HST power cars and 42 trailer vehicles, while Arriva owns Mk3 vehicles used on Chiltern Railways' London-Birmingham and Arriva Trains Wales' north-south Wales services, with others in reserve.

Connex Leasing Limited purchased rolling stock for the Southeastern / SouthCentral franchises which its parent group originally won. These vehicles were subsequently purchased and leased by HSBC (now Eversholt). Wiltshire Leasing was a subsidiary of Great Western Holdings, set up to finance new Class 175s for its North Western franchise and new Class 180s for Great Western. These vehicles were subsequently purchased and leased by Angel.

Six Class 43 HST power cars and 24 trailers used by Grand Central were purchased in 2010 by Angel Trains from Sovereign Trains, a ROSCO within the same group as Grand Central.

Heathrow Express trains were purchased by the airports company BAA, including the five 5-car Class 360/2 electric multiple-units used for Heathrow Connect services. (In October 2012, the name BAA was dropped, and Heathrow airport operates as a standalone brand.)

FREIGHT LOCOS

The three main ROSCOs lease out large fleets of freight and general purpose locomotives, as shown in the tables. Other leasers are Beacon Rail and Macquarie European Rail.

Ex-British Rail freight locomotives were transferred to the ownership of English, Welsh & Scottish Railway (now DB Schenker) or to Freightliner at privatisation. Significant numbers of freight locomotives, mainly ex-Brtish Rail, are owned by freight operating companies including Colas Rail, Mendip Rail and Direct Rail Services. In 2011, Class 66 locomotives were purchased from Eversholt Rail Leasing by GB Railfreight (4 locos) and Colas (5 locos), with five more purchased from Porterbrook by GBRf. In 2013, GBRf/Eurotunnel purchased three Class 66s from the Netherlands.

Several specialist companies including Harry Needle Railroad Company and Nemesis Rail also maintain smaller fleets of locomotives which are hired to UK freight and passenger operators and to Network Rail for infrastructure duties.

Alpha Trains - formerly Angel Trains International - manages a fleet of approximately 400 locomotives and 240 passenger trains in continental Europe.

Class 317/5 No 317510 (left, owned by Angel Trains) and Class 315 No 315804 (owned by Eversholt Rail Group) receive attention inside Greater Anglia's Ilford depot on 22 April 2013.

CROSS LONDON TRAINS

Cross London Trains is a a consortium comprising Siemens Project Ventures GmbH, Innisfree Ltd and 3i Infrastructure Plc which is to finance and purchase Desiro City trains from Siemens for the Thameslink rail franchise.

Eversholt Rail is to provide project and asset management services to Cross London Trains, including project management during the build and delivery of the rolling stock, and then long-term asset management, including both technical and commercial support.

MACQUARIE EUROPEAN RAIL

In November 2012 Macquarie Group announced that Macquarie Bank Limited had established a new business, Macquarie European Rail, and agreed to acquire the European rolling stock leasing business from Lloyds Banking Group.

The business comprises three separate portfolios of rolling stock:

- the 30 four-car Class-379 EMUs operated by Greater Anglia;
- a UK rail freight portfolio - leasing 19 Class 70s to Freightliner, 26 Class-66s to Freightliner (some of them in Poland), and 14 Class-66s to Direct Rail Services.
- the former CB Rail business, with locomotives, passenger trains and wagons on operating lease to operators in Europe.

Lloyds was also part of the consortium that purchased Porterbrook Leasing in 2008 but it exited from the consortium in 2010.

Lloyds banking group remains the owner of DB Schenker's Class-92s and has an interest in Voyager Leasing.

BEACON RAIL

Beacon Rail Leasing Limited was established in January 2009 by BTMU Capital Corporation as a wholly-owned subsidiary, to be its business entity for freight rolling stock leasing in the European market. Beacon Rail is a UK company headquartered in London and with an additional office in Rotterdam.

In Britain, Beacon Rail leases ten low-emission Class 66s to Freightliner and five Class 66s to Direct Rail Services. Two Class 66s transferred from Germany were expected to enter service with GBRf in late 2013.

Beacon Rail has worked with Direct Rail Services on the development of Vossloh Eurolight diesel locomotives for the UK: 15 were ordered in January 2012 in a contract worth roughly Euro 50 million. In September 2013, an order for ten electric/diesel dual-mode Class 88 locomotives from Vossloh was announced by Beacon and DRS.

Beacon's first passenger trains were acquired in 2012 - twenty Class-313 dual-voltage electric multiple-units, retained by HSBC when it sold rolling stock company Eversholt Rail. The Southern train operating company leases 19 of the Class 313s, and Network Rail has leased the 20th as the resident test train for the Hertford North Integration Facility, the new test track for different manufacturers' European Train Control system equipment.

BTMU Capital Corporation is a wholly-owned subsidiary of The Bank of Tokyo-Mitsubishi UFJ Ltd.

ROLLING STOCK - SIMPLIFIED GUIDE TO CLASSES

Multiple units are self-propelled vehicles with their own driving cabs, usually comprised of one to five carriages. The main groups of ex- British Rail diesel multiple-unit (DMU) are:

- Class 142-144 'Pacers' - 4-wheeled bus-based trains.
- Class 150-159 'Sprinters'. Class 150 is the most basic, with Class 153 / 155 / 156 'Super Sprinters' for longer cross country services, and Class 158 / 159 Express units. Class 165 Networker Turbo and Class 166 Network Express fulfill similar roles.

Post privatisation, the main designs were Class 170-172 Turbostars (and similar Class 168) built by Bombardier Transportation, and less numerous Class 175 Coradia designed by Alstom. Class 180 is an Alstom design for express services, and Class 185 a Siemens design introduced for TransPennine Express. Class 220, 221 and 222 'Voyagers' and 'Meridians', built by Bombardier, also operate InterCity services.

Electric multiple-unit (EMU) Classes 313-315, 455, 456, 465, 466, 507 and 508 are ex-British Rail inner-suburban trains; Class 317-323, 365 and 442 are outer-suburban/long-distance types.

The main post-privatisation EMUs built by Alstom are Classes 334 and 458; by Bombardier, Classes 357, 375-379; and by Siemens, Classes 332, 333, 350, 380, 444 and 450.

The main electric locomotive designs are Class 91 built for East Coast high-speed services, designed for 140mph (225kph) running in semi-permanent 'InterCity225' (IC225) formations; and Classes 86 and 90, used for both passenger and freight work.

The West Coast main line's Pendolino electric tilting trains are known as Class 390 and the new Southeastern high-speed trains using High Speed 1 are Class 395.

The dominant freight diesel locomotive type is the Class 66 from General Motors / Electro-Motive Diesel, designed for 75mph freight work. The Class 67 is an express locomotive from the same stable, and Class 57 is a rebuilt ex-British Rail freight and passenger locomotive. Class 70 is the recent General Electric PowerHaul design operated by Freightliner.

Class 43 is the power car (locomotive) type used at both ends of diesel 'InterCity125' High Speed Trains: the ROSCOs also own substantial numbers of IC125 and IC225 passenger vehicles.

Class 67 locomotives which power Chiltern Railways' London-Birmingham 'Silver' trains are hired from sister company DB Schenker. No 67010 has arrived at London Marylebone on 5 August 2013, propelling a train from Birmingham. Paul Bigland

The ROSCO fleets

MULTIPLE-UNIT VEHICLES, HST POWER CARS, AND LOCOMOTIVES - LISTED BY ROLLING STOCK LEASING COMPANY AND TRAIN OPERATING COMPANY

porterbrook

Class	No of vehicles
ARRIVA TRAINS WALES	
Class 143	22
Class 150/2	72
Class 153	3
C2C RAIL	
Class 357	184
CHILTERN	
Class 168/0	20
Class 168/1	17
Class 168/2	21
CROSSCOUNTRY	
Class 170 (2 Car) 26	
Class 170 (3 Car) 48	
Class 43 HST Power Car	5
EAST COAST	
Class 43 HST power car	9
EAST MIDLANDS TRAINS	
Class 43 HST power car	24
Class 153	11
Class 156	22
Class 158	18
FIRST CAPITAL CONNECT	
Class 319/0	52
Class 319/2	28
Class 319/3	104
Class 319/4	160
Class 377	104*

**sub-leased from Southern*

Class	No of vehicles
FIRST GREAT WESTERN	
Class 43 HST Power Car	22
Class 57	4
Class 143	10
Class 150	34
Class 153	5
Class 158	43
FIRST SCOTRAIL	
Class 158	80
Class 170 (3 car)	150
FIRST TRANSPENNINE	
Class 170 (2 Car)	18
GREATER ANGLIA	
Class 153	5
Class 156	18
Class 170 (2 Car)	8
Class 170 (3 Car)	24
Class 90	15
LONDON MIDLAND	
Class 139	2
Class 153	8
Class 170 (2 car)	34
Class 170 (3 car)	18
Class 172 (2 car)	24
Class 172 (3 car)	45
Class 323	78
Class 350	148
NORTHERN	
Class 144	56
Class 150	22
Class 153	8
Class 155	14
Class 156	36
Class 158	24
Class 323	51
SOUTHERN	
Class 171 (2 car)	20
Class 171 (4 car)	24
Class 377	688*
Class 456	48
Class 73	1

** plus 170 vehicles being delivered*

Class	No of vehicles
SOUTH WEST TRAINS	
Class 158	22
Class 159	90
Class 455	364
Class 458	120
FREIGHTLINER	
Class 66	35
Class 86	10
Class 90	9
NETWORK RAIL	
Class 57	6
Class 43 HST Power Car	3
DIRECT RAIL SERVICES	
Class 57	14
GB RAILFREIGHT	
Class 66	9

EVERSHOLT RAIL GROUP

Class	No of vehicles
CHILTERN	
Class 168	9
EAST COAST	
Class 91	31

Porterbrook-owned Class 170/5 No 170523 heads a CrossCountry train at Gloucester, while a First Great Western high-speed train waits in the opposite platform. Paul Bigland

EAST MIDLANDS TRAINS	
Class 222	143

FIRST SCOTRAIL	
Class 170	27
Class 318	63
Class 320	66
Class 334	120
Class 380	130

FIRST TRANSPENNINE EXPRESS	
Class 185	153

FIRST CAPITAL CONNECT	
Class 313	132
Class 321	52
Class 365	160

GREATER ANGLIA	
Class 315	244
Class 321	376

LONDON MIDLAND	
Class 321	28

NORTHERN	
Class 158	20
Class 321	12
Class 322	20

SOUTHEASTERN	
Class 375	438
Class 376	180
Class 395	174
Class 465	388

SOUTHERN	
Class 455	184

FREIGHTLINER	
Class 66	56

GB RAILFREIGHT	
Class 66	27

angel Trains
Rail People
Real Expertise

ARRIVA TRAINS WALES	
Class 142	30
Class 153	5
Class 158	48
Class 175 (2-car)	22
Class 175 (3-car)	48

C2C RAIL	
Class 357/2	112

CHILTERN	
165/0 (2-car)	56
165/0 (3-car)	33
172	8

CROSSCOUNTRY	
Class 43 HST power car	5

EAST COAST	
Class 43 HST power car	22

EAST MIDLANDS TRAINS	
Class 153	6
Class 156	8
Class 158	32

FIRST CAPITAL CONNECT	
Class 317	48

FIRST GREAT WESTERN	
Class 150	46
Class 153	9
Class 165/1 (2-car)	40
Class 165/1 (3-car)	48
Class 166	63
Class 180	25
Class 43 HST power car	86

FIRST SCOTRAIL	
Class 156	96
Class 158	14
Class 314	48

FIRST TRANSPENNINE EXPRESS	
Class 350/4	40*

** delivery from 2013*

GRAND CENTRAL	
Class 180	25
Class 43 HST power car	6

GREATER ANGLIA	
Class 317/5	60
Class 317/6	96
Class 317/8	48
Class 360	84

HULL TRAINS	
Class 180	20

LONDON MIDLAND	
Class 150	6
Class 350/1	120
Class 350/4	40*

** delivery from 2014*

LONDON OVERGROUND	
Class 172	16

MERSEYRAIL	
Class 507	96
Class 508	81

NORTHERN	
Class 142	158
Class 150	94
Class 153	11
Class 156	56
Class 158	52
Class 333	64

SOUTHERN	
Class 442	120

SOUTH WEST TRAINS	
Class 444	225
Class 450	508

SOUTHEASTERN	
Class 465/2	64
Class 465/9	136
Class 466	86

VIRGIN TRAINS	
Class 390	574

DB SCHENKER	
Class 66	250
Class 67	30

TRAIN FLEET MAINTENANCE AND MANUFACTURE

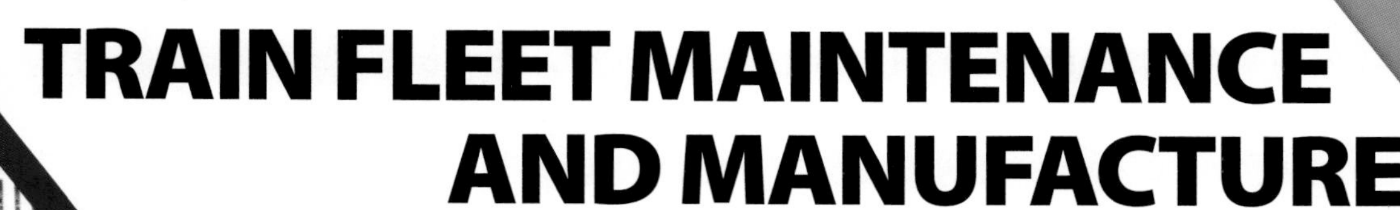

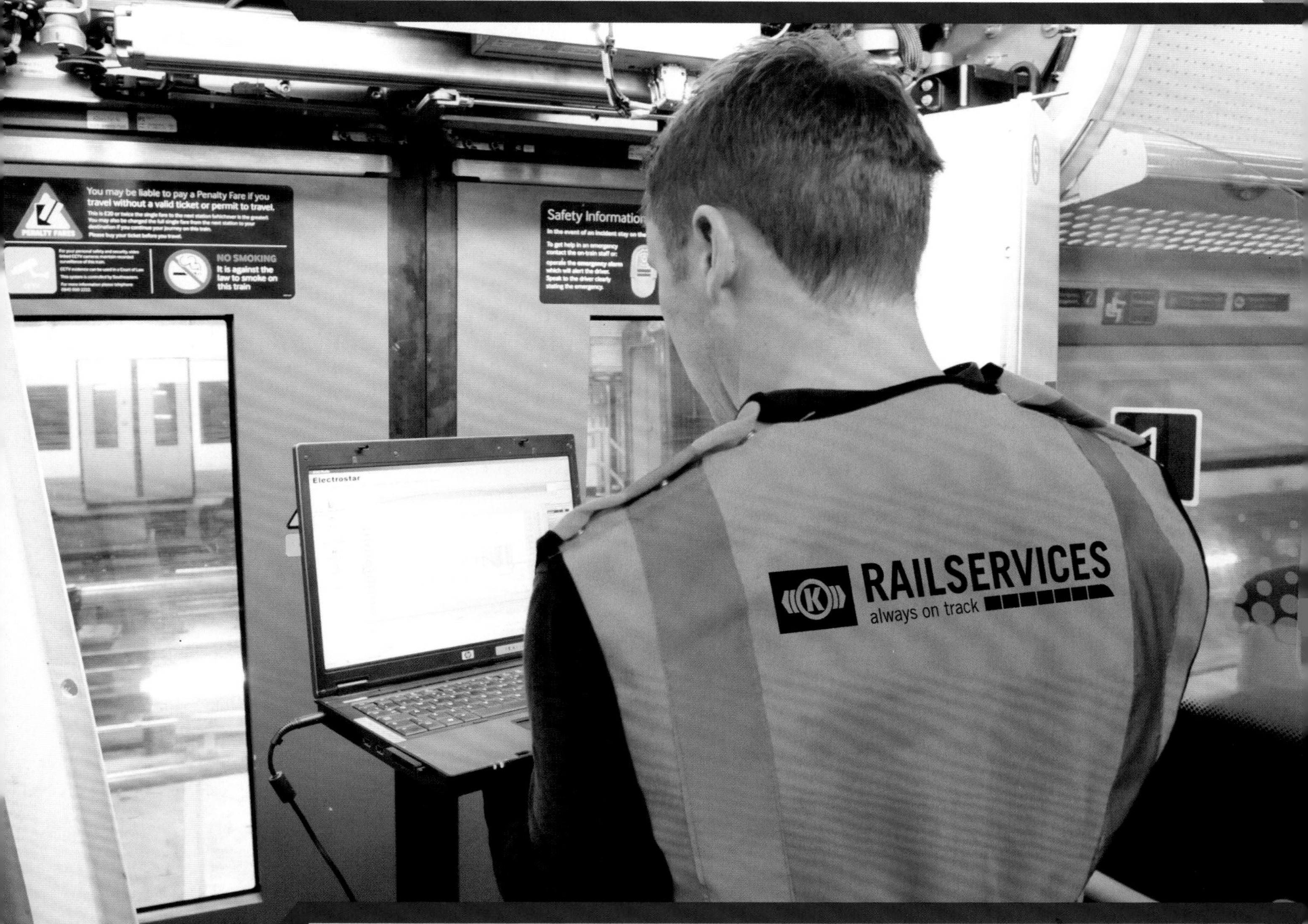

IN ASSOCIATION WITH

RAILSERVICES
always on track

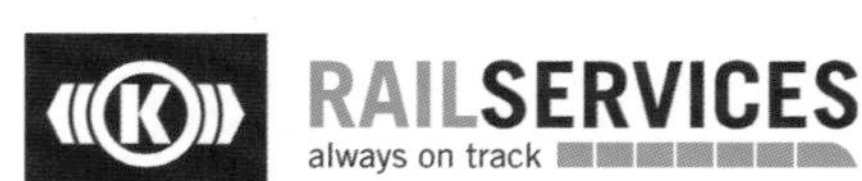

Knorr-Bremse RailServices

THE CAPACITY AND CAPABILITY TO DELIVER SOLUTIONS TO THE RAIL INDUSTRY

With the largest total facilities of their kind in the UK with a combined area of some 420,000 square metres, Knorr-Bremse RailServices has the capacity to deliver solutions to train operators who are based in the UK and Ireland.

The impressive RailServices facilities can undertake major 'whole train' and systems refurbishment projects which improves existing rail stock. Both Springburn and Wolverton facilities boast large and dedicated bogie shops, wheel overhaul shops and paint shops. The bogie shops include wash and strip facilities where all the bogie systems can be overhauled including the traction motors. The wheel shops have the capability to overhaul and carry out the heaviest of repairs on all wheel set types. The paint shops can handle the most challenging of refinish demands including repairs and they also include a complete vehicle re-livery service.

CAPABILITY

However, capacity and the sheer size of the RailServices facilities alone cannot deliver what customers need and RailServices possesses not only the capacity but also the capability to deliver support and solutions for customers. This capability is made possible by the two hundred plus highly skilled and experienced employees who work at the two RailServices sites; Springburn near Glasgow in the North and Wolverton near Milton Keynes in the South.

These employees are supported by the other four hundred plus Knorr-Bremse UK Rail Group employees who are based at Burton-upon-Trent in Staffordshire (the HVAC specialist facility) and at Melksham in Wiltshire (the UK headquarters and centre for original equipment brake control engineering, Knorr-Bremse Rail Group distribution and specialist platform screen system division, Westinghouse Platform Screen Doors).

RailServices can manage the entire assets of the operator against pre-agreed targets.

EXPERIENCE AND EXPERTISE

Located at the Wolverton and Springburn facilities are highly experienced and qualified staff, including engineers, project managers and planners who, between them, can offer customers their expertise and support to provide a range of major service types to keep train running safely and reliably.

The types of service offered by RailServices include; vehicle overhaul, refurbishment, upgrade, re-livery and incident repair (on all EMUs/DMUs, coaching stock and locomotive types). In addition there are a wide range of flexible service types available to customers which include; component repair and overhaul, wheel set refurbishment, bogie overhaul, gear box and transmission repair and overhaul, peripheral equipment repair and overhaul, rail plant and equipment repair and overhaul and supply chain support and management using the latest in logistics techniques.

The RailServices facilities can undertake major 'whole train' and systems refurbishment projects which improves existing rail stock.

In addition to the services offered 'in-house' at either of the RailServices UK sites in Springburn and Wolverton, services can be provided at Customers' own locations and facilities. These include a 24 hour, 364 day incident and rectification service. Following a request for assistance with incident or rectification RailServices will visit the customer's site within 24 hours of the call and have the ability to transport and deliver the vehicle to a location as required. RailServices can offer customers RAIB investigation quarantine berths if they are required.

Components can also be supplied to customers whether the components are, overhauled, especially manufactured or re-manufactured, or from the original systems manufacturer. The extensive Knorr-Bremse Rail Group portfolio of systems and products is, of course, also available from RailServices. Consumables and rotable product supply can also be managed on behalf of the customer by RailServices who can use the latest in logistics techniques to supply directly from their own extensive warehousing facilities. Parts supply can be from stock or against an agreed customer demand schedules and lead times through structured but flexible supply contracts. Customers' assets can be fully managed by RailServices to optimise in-service availability of trains.

FLEXIBILITY

In addition to offering capacity and capability RailServices considers flexibility to be at the core of its proposition. Individual services can be demanded from the huge range available and provided to customers as and when needed or RailServices can manage the entire assets of the operator against pre-agreed targets with all of the variety of choices in-between through the entire life cycle of the train. RailServices sees its role as one of working together with and supporting the customer to keep their trains in safe, reliable, available and importantly, in revenue earning service. It certainly has the capability and capacity to do just that.

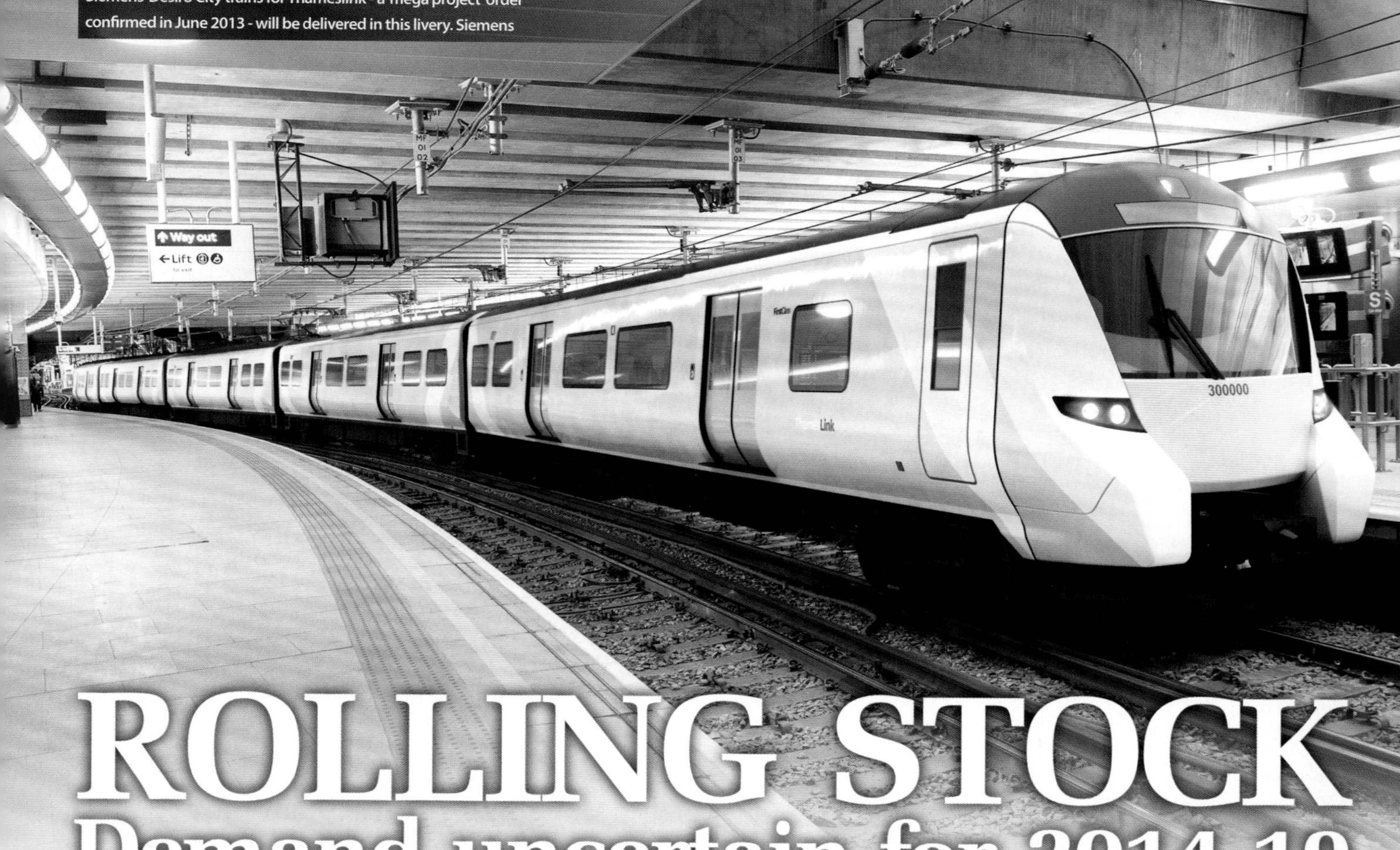

Siemens' Desiro City trains for Thameslink - a 'mega project' order confirmed in June 2013 - will be delivered in this livery. Siemens

ROLLING STOCK
Demand uncertain for 2014-19

ROGER FORD EXAMINES PROSPECTS FOR NEW TRAINS FOR BOTH 'MEGA PROJECTS' AND OTHER RAIL DEVELOPMENTS

The protracted procurement by the Department of Transport (DfT) of two major rolling stock programmes came to an end in 2013. Financial close was reached on both the Great Western tranche of the Intercity Express programme (IEP) and the Thameslink train service provision deal. In addition, the East Coast main line (ECML) IEP fleet orders were confirmed, with financial close due during 2014.

For Hitachi, who will assemble the electric and bi-mode Super Express Trains for IEP at its new plant at Newton Aycliffe, County Durham, the good news was that DfT had decided to add replacement of the East Coast InterCity 225 (IC225) electric high-speed train fleet to the IEP deal.

OPTIONS

This was a controversial decision, given that the InterCity East Coast franchise is due to be re-let in February 2015. Given DfT's new policy that train operating companies should be responsible for traction and rolling stock policy and procurement, there was pressure for the IC225 decision to be left to the new franchisee.

Two other solutions were being proposed for the future East Coast electric fleet. IC225 owners Eversholt had put forward a major re-engineering and upgrade programme, including the option to replace the Class 91 locomotive with the Bombardier Traxx. With a traction rating of 5.6 MW (7,500hp), the 125mph Traxx could have combined shorter journey times with improved reliability.

Following trial runs on the ECML with a Virgin Trains Class-390 Pendolino, Alstom was proposing its tilting train as the IC225 replacement. The unique combination of high power plus tilt offered the prospect of substantial journey time reductions – with Alstom arguing for 140mph running south of Doncaster.

In the event the Transport Secretary decided that replacing IC225 with an additional 30 nine-car electric Super Express Trains represented the best value for money.

LONDON

While working towards financial close on the contract, Siemens had already begun work on key components of its new Desiro City electric multiple-units (EMUs) for Thameslink, the bogie for example, and had begun construction of the two maintenance depots at its own risk. The total train service provision deal will provide 1,140 vehicles in 8-car and 12-car formations.

Manufacture of the Thameslink trains was delayed by around two years pending financial close. Combined with a heavy workload for other customers, the increased demand this would place on the company's resources saw Siemens decide to withdraw from the Crossrail train fleet competition, where it had been shortlisted with Bombardier, CAF of Spain, and Hitachi.

Bids for the 630 Crossrail vehicles are being evaluated and the winning supplier is expected to be announced in the second quarter of 2014. The contract marks a major change in government procurement policy for these mega rolling stock contracts, after the delays in finalising finance for the Thameslink fleet.

Instead of the Crossrail train builder being required to set up a consortium to finance the new rolling stock and new depot facilities, funding will be backed by a government guarantee.

Crossrail has become a 'must-win' contract for both Bombardier and Hitachi, although the Japanese company's order backlog was boosted by the IC225 replacement contract under the IEP deal. Bombardier's Derby plant, too, has a more secure future, having been made the group's centre of excellence for aluminium car bodies.

Recent design work has included

TABLE 1 - RECENT NEW TRAIN ORDERS AND PROSPECTS FOR CONTROL PERIOD 5 (APRIL 2014 TO MARCH 2019)

OPERATOR/ROUTE	MANUFACTURER	TYPE	CLASS NO	UNITS	FORMATION (VEHICLES)	VEHICLES (TOTAL)	STATUS	DELIVERY START	DELIVERY COMPLETE
MEGA PROJECTS									
Great Western	Hitachi	EMU	801	21	9	189	Ordered	May 2017	July 2018
Great Western	Hitachi	Bi-mode	800	36	5	180	Ordered		
East Coast	Hitachi	EMU	801	12	5	60	Financial close pending	Aug 2018	April 2019
East Coast	Hitachi	Bi-mode	800	13	9	117	Financial close pending		
East Coast	Hitachi	Bi-mode	800	10	5	50	Financial close pending		
East Coast (phase 2)	Hitachi	EMU	801	30	9	270	Financial close pending	2019	
Thameslink	Siemens	EMU	700	60	8	480	Ordered	2015	2018
Thameslink	Siemens	EMU	700	55	12	660	Ordered		
Crossrail	Shortlisted	EMU	345	63	10	630	Bidding	2017	2018
TOTAL 'MEGA PROJECTS'						**2366**			
OTHER PROJECTS									
Southern (for DfT)	Bombardier	EMU	387	29	4	116	Ordered	2015	2016
Southern (for DfT) Option	Bombardier	EMU				140	Option		
London Overground*	Bombardier	EMU	378			57	Ordered		Dec 2014
South West Trains		EMU		40	5	200	OJEU issued	2015	2016
Merseyrail		EMU		57	3	171	OJEU issued		2017
Great Western		EMU				150	Provisional		2016-17
ScotRail (EGIP)		EMU				400	Provisional		
TOTAL 'NON MEGA PROJECTS'						**1234**			

** To lengthen existing trains to 5 cars.*

the bodyshell for the Bombardier Twindexx double-deck EMU for Swiss Railways, and also for two monorail schemes for Sao Paulo in Brazil and Saudi Arabia.

Bombardier's contender for the Crossrail contract is its new Aventra EMU. As with the other European groups, Aventra is a modular platform which will be used as the basis for future EMU orders manufactured worldwide. Bombardier has invested around £20 million in Derby to support research and development of the new platform.

SPEED

Both Aventra and the latest Siemens Desiro EMU are 'platforms', that is, modular designs which can be configured for a range of duties. Significantly, both manufacturers are looking to increase the speed range of their new suburban EMUs.

On a mixed traffic railway, one way to improve capacity is to increase the speed of the slower trains. Siemens pioneered this approach for the congested southern end of the West Coast main line, by upgrading the Class 350/1 100mph Desiro EMUs operated by London Midland for 110mph running.

With the new generation Desiro, the 'City' variant is being supplied for Thameslink, but a high speed Desiro 'Express' will also be available. This is a 115mph train which exploits the new European Technical Specifications for Interoperability (TSIs), which now apply to new rolling stock ordered in the UK.

There are separate TSIs for Conventional and High Speed stock. The cross-over point at which the more demanding high speed crashworthiness come into force is 190km/h (118 mph). Siemens is arguing that a 115mph train would not only make better use of limited paths, but would also avoid the seating capacity lost in high-speed trains where the front third of the driving cars cannot be used for seating. On the Great Western main line, for example, the 115mph performance and high acceleration would allow the Desiro Express to run within the proposed IEP timetable.

Bombardier has similarly obtained acceptance for the latest Electrostar variant – the dual-voltage Class 387 - to run at 110mph. This is the fleet ordered by Southern on behalf of the Department for Transport to provide extra capacity for Thameslink in advance of the new fleet. Aventra variants will offer a nominal speed range from the 90mph 'Metro' to a 125mph high speed version.

PROSPECTS

While the new five-year rail industry funding period (Control Period 5) starting on 1 April 2014 includes delivery of firm orders for 2,400 new vehicles, the bulk of these are represented by the three government-procured mega-projects – IEP, Thameslink and Crossrail. DfT policy is that in future new train procurement will be the responsibility of the train operators, but the revised rail franchising schedule introduced following

The success of Transport for London's new London Overground services has led to an order in 2013 for a fifth carriage for all the Bombardier Class 378 electric multiple-units. Arriva/LOROL

the collapse of the Intercity West Coast franchise in October 2012 has introduced uncertainty.

Many existing franchises are to be awarded new direct award agreements during the next two years. These direct awards will vary in length, timed to ensure that no more than three replacement franchises are being let any time.

There have been fears that direct awards could see decisions on new rolling stock deferred to the subsequent replacement franchise. However, the direct award franchise agreement with First Great Western, signed in October 2013, included the requirement to progress new electric trains to replace existing diesel multiple-units on Paddington suburban services.

In addition, the invitation to tender for the replacement Essex Thameside franchise (currently held by c2c) includes provision for bidders to propose new or cascaded rolling stock. However, as Table 1 shows, firm prospects for new main-line rolling stock are slim.

TUBE

During 2014 London Underground is expected to revive procurement of replacement trains for the Piccadilly Line. After procurement was aborted in 2010, Alstom, Bombardier and Siemens were invited to develop proposals for a new deep-tube lightweight train code-named 'Evo' by LU.

Replacement of the Piccadilly Line 1973 stock would require just over 500 vehicles, assuming the same car length. These could be delivered by 2020 and be followed by further trains for the Bakerloo Line.

However, even adding the LU requirement to the possible orders in

TABLE 2 -PASSENGER TRAIN ORDERS 2007-13

OPERATOR / FINANCIER	CLASS	VEHICLES	MANUFACTURER	DELIVERED
London Midland / Porterbrook	350/2	148	Siemens	2009
Southern / Porterbrook	377/5	92	Bombardier	2009
Southeastern (HS1) / Eversholt	395	174	Hitachi	2009
London Overground / QW	378	228	Bombardier	2011
London Overground / Angel	172/0 DMU	16	Bombardier	2010
ScotRail / Eversholt	380	130	Siemens	2010
London Midland / Porterbrook	139*	2	Parry People Movers	2008
Virgin West Coast /Angel	390	106	Alstom	2012
Greater Anglia / Lloyds	379	120	Bombardier	2011
London Midland / Porterbrook	172/2 and /3 DMU	69	Bombardier	2011
Chiltern / Angel	172/1 DMU	8	Bombardier	2011
Southern / Porterbrook	377/6	130	Bombardier	2013
Southern / Porterbrook	377/7	40	Bombardier	2014
London Midland / Angel	350/3	40	Siemens	2014
TransPennine / Angel	350/4	40	Siemens	2014

** LPG/flywheel hybrid drive railcars.*

All are electric multiple-units except where shown (DMU - diesel multiple-unit)

Table 1 gives an average demand of under 300 vehicles a year in CP5. This should be compared with around 250 vehicles a year from a typical production line at Bombardier's Derby plant.

FREIGHT TRACTION

With the government backing a rolling programme of electrification, freight operators are revising long term traction programmes. While diesel traction, dominated by the ubiquitous General Motors Class 66, will remain the mainstay of the freight hauliers, the first contracts have been placed for electric locomotives.

A second diesel challenger has emerged for the 3,300hp (2,460kW) Class 66. Freightliner was the first to seek more power and performance, acquiring 20 Class-70 Powerhaul diesel-electrics from General Electric in 2007. More technically-advanced than the venerable GM design, the Class 70's 3,690hp allows longer trains to be hauled at up to 75mph.

In January 2012 Direct Rail Services ordered fifteen 3,750hp (2,800kW) Vossloh Eurolight diesel-electric locomotives. Designated Class 68, this is a mixed traffic design with a top speed of 100mph.

Now DRS has returned to Vossloh as launch customer for the company's new 25kV AC electro-diesel locomotive. Rated at 4MW (5,350hp), the 25kV Class 88 incorporates a 940hp (700kW) Caterpillar diesel engine. Maximum speed under electric power will be 100mph and the locomotive is designed to supply up to 500kW of 'hotel' power for passenger trains.

While the Bombardier Traxx UK proposal also includes an auxiliary diesel engine for 'last mile' operation into non electrified sidings, DRS emphasises that the Class 88 is expected to run under its own power on non- electrified routes. However, its primary role will be to replace Class 92 electric locomotives on intermodal flows on the West Coast main line.

An East Coast Class 91 locomotive, which powers the operator's InterCity 225 trains, is serviced at Bounds Green, north London. These trains are to be replaced by a further build of 30 nine-car Hitachi Super Express trains. East Coast

TABLE 3: PASSENGER TRAIN ORDERS FROM PRIVATISATION (1994) TO 2007

ORIGINAL CUSTOMER	MANUFACTURER	TYPE	NO OFVEHICLES	DELIVERY	FUNDER
Anglia Railways	Bombardier	Class 170 DMUs	32	2000	P
Arriva Tr Nthn	Siemens/CAF	16x4-car Class 333 EMUs	64	2000-04	A
c2c	Bombardier	74x4-car Electrostar EMUs	296	1999-2001	P,A
Central Trains[a]	Bombardier	23x2-car, 10x3-car Class 170 DMUs	76	2000-04	P
Central/Silverlink	Siemens	30x4-car Class 350/1 (West Coast route)	120	2004-05	A
Chiltern Railways	Bombardier	Class 168 DMUs	67	1998-2005	P, H
Connex (Southeastern)	Bombardier	Electrostar EMUs	618	2000-05	H
Connex / Southern	Bombardier	28x3-car, 154x4-car Electrostar EMUs	700	2002-05	P
First N Western	Alstom	16x3-car, 11x2-car Class 175 DMUs	70	2000	A
Gatwick Express	Alstom	8x8-car Juniper EMUs	64	1999	P
First Great Eastern	Siemens	21x4-car Desiro EMUs	84	2002	A
First Great Western	Alstom	14x5-car Class 180 DMUs	70	2000-01	A
Heathrow Connect	Siemens	5x5-car Class 360/2 EMUs	25	2005-06	T
Heathrow Express	CAF/Siemens	9x4-car, 5x5-car EMUs	61	1998-2002	T
Hull Trains	Bombardier	4x3-car Class 170 DMUs	12	2004	P
Hull Trains	Bombardier	4x4-car Class 222 DMUs	28	2005	H
Midland Mainline	Bombardier	17x2-car, 10x1-car Class 170 DMUs		2000-04	P
Midland Mainline	Bombardier	16x4-car, 7x9-car Class 222 DEMUs	127	2004-05	H
ScotRail	Alstom	40x3-car Class 334 Juniper EMUs	120	1999-2000	H
ScotRail	Bombardier	55x3-carClass 170 Turbostar DMUs	165	1999-2005	P, H
Southern	Bombardier	Class 170 DMUs	42	2003-04	P
South West Trains	Siemens	127 x 4-car Class 450 Desiro EMUs	508	2002-07	A
South West Trains	Bombardier	9x2-car Class 170 DMUs	18	2000-02	A
South West Trains	Siemens	45x5-car Class 444 Desiro EMUs	225	2002-05	A
TransPennine	Siemens	51x3-car Class 185 Desiro DMUs	153	2005-06	H
Virgin CrossCountry	Bombardier	40x5-car, 4x4-car tilting DEMUs	216	2001-03	V
Virgin CrossCountry	Bombardier	34x4-car non-tilting DEMUs	136	2000-02	V
Virgin West Coast	Alstom	53x9-car Pendolino trains	477	2001-05	A

[a] Plus 1x2-car and 2x3-car originally ordered by Porterbrook for spot hire
V Halifax Bank of Scotland and Royal Bank of Scotland.
T Owned by Heathrow Express.
A Angel Trains
P Porterbrook
H HSBC Rail (Eversholt)

The iconic Class 395 'Javelin' trains are maintained at the state-of-the-art Hitachi Rail Europe depot in Ashford, Kent.

Hitachi - full steam ahead

Hitachi Rail Europe is set to grow considerably over the next five years. The success of the Class 395 'Javelin' during the Olympics and in regular passenger service has brought the train builder and maintainer to the attention of the general public. With overall passenger satisfaction of the High Speed service at an outstanding 92% in the Spring 2013 Passenger Focus survey, it is no surprise that passenger numbers have been continuously rising since the introduction of the service. The iconic trains are maintained at the state-of-the-art Hitachi Rail Europe depot in Ashford, Kent, by a 100-strong, highly dedicated team.

Given the on-time delivery and successful track record of the Class 395 in service, expectations are high for the delivery of the Class 800/801 train as part of the Intercity Express Programme (IEP). Since July 2012 when Agility Trains, of which Hitachi Rail Europe is the main shareholder, was awarded the main contract to finance, design, manufacture, maintain and deliver the Class 800 series trains into daily passenger service for the IEP, a lot of work has gone into the programme.

The award of contract for an additional 30 trains for the East Coast Main Line in July 2013 was a further show of confidence in

the programme, bringing the total number of vehicles ordered to 866 (122 trains). Available in five-car and nine-car formations, the trains will be either fully electric (Class 801) or a bi-mode (Class 800) version, that includes a diesel generator in addition to electric propulsion. Financial close for the fleet of trains for the East Coast Main Line is expected in early 2014.

British design company DCA Design was picked to lead the interior design process for the trains, ensuring that the sound engineering basis of the trains is mirrored in the comfortable and high-quality interior. Input from a broad range of stakeholders and passenger groups has been taken on board and is reflected in a train mock-up used to ensure that the design was the best possible solution for all user groups. The design freeze for the interior is expected in early 2014, ready for pre-series production of the first four trains in Hitachi Rail's Japanese train factory in Kasado.

Throughout 2013, Hitachi Rail Europe engaged with its existing supplier base and was also in discussion with a broad range of potential new suppliers. A number of contracts were awarded to British-based suppliers. Gateshead-based Nomad will supply the On-Board Servers, Knorr-Bremse will supply brake systems from their base in Wiltshire, specialist glass maker Romag from County Durham will supply the side windows for the trains and Brecknell Willis are contracted to manufacture the pantographs for the Class 800 series trains.

In addition to this, Volker Fitzpatrick is busy with the refurbishment and new build of some of the depots required for the maintenance of the fleet of trains. Work in West London's North Pole depot is progressing well, and construction of the depot in Stoke Gifford in the Bristol area is underway as well. New builds in Swansea and Doncaster will commence in the course of 2014.

The Hitachi Rail Europe development that will have a long-lasting impact on the British rail industry, the plans for a train manufacturing facility in Newton Aycliffe, greatly moved forward. 2013 saw the award of contract to site developer Merchant Place Development, completion of the detailed design of the factory and the appointment of lead construction company Shepherd. Work on site will progress throughout 2014 with the buildings in place by the end of the year, ready for interior fit-out. Secretary of State for Business, Innovation and Skills, Dr Vince Cable, and Secretary of State for Transport, Patrick McLoughlin, were on site in November 2013 to celebrate the start of the construction phase that will create 150 mostly local jobs. Construction will continue during 2014 and the facility will open in mid-2015.

Even at this early stage, it is paramount for Hitachi Rail Europe to ensure that young people in the region are aware of the skills needed not only in the train building facility, but also in the maintenance depots. That is why engaging with local schools, setting up University Technical Colleges and putting in place apprenticeships and graduate schemes is so important.

Rolling stock manufacturing and maintenance are part of Hitachi Rail Europe's DNA, supplemented by signalling technology and Traffic Management Systems (TMS) that wed our company's engineering heritage to our IT know-how. Hitachi's TMS is the backbone to rail traffic control in some of Tokyo's busiest stations and the software controls up to 9,000 trains daily in the Japanese city's metropolitan area. In 2012, Network Rail picked Hitachi Rail Europe as one of three suppliers to provide a prototype Traffic Management System. The demonstration room was set up in early 2013 and in-depth testing allowed Network Rail to evaluate all three suppliers' technology. With a system proven in one of the busiest and most demanding rail markets, Hitachi Rail Europe has all confidence in a positive verdict by Network Rail.

Hitachi Rail has also developed its ETCS (European Train Control System) solution and agreed with Network Rail to trial the onboard equipment on the Cambrian Line in North Wales. As part of the project, a Class 97 locomotive was retro-fitted with the Hitachi onboard system and during testing on the line in summer 2013, the system was correctly identified on the Network Rail Signalling System and Control Centre in Wales without any system failures. The locomotive was driven under its own power with ETCS Level 2 via the GSM-R radio network in various operational modes such as 'Staff Responsible', 'On Sight', 'Shunting' and 'Full Supervision'. This proof of concept is evidence to the industry that Hitachi's technology has full interoperability and can communicate with other suppliers' systems.

2014 will bring a wealth of new opportunities, company growth and the chance to further showcase Hitachi's expertise beyond rolling stock and maintenance. ■

Expectations are high for the delivery of the Class 800/801 train as part of the Intercity Express Programme (IEP).

CAF wins new orders

CAF – Construcciones y Auxiliar de Ferrocarriles, S.A. – has constructed several fleets of electric multiple-units and diesel multiple-units for railway operators in the UK and Ireland and has delivered the Edinburgh tram fleet, its first light-rail project in the UK.

CAF has followed this by being selected as the supplier of 21 five-car Urbos trams for the Midland Metro in the West Midlands, in a deal worth in the region of £40 million.

The first new tram is scheduled to come into service – on the existing line – in February 2014. The city centre extension with the full new tram fleet is scheduled to be in service from March 2015. The five section air-conditioned trams have a passenger capacity of approximately 210, with two dedicated spaces for wheelchair users, and their features are fully compliant with the Disability Discrimination Act. Each section has passenger information and CCTV, and passenger assistance units at each door. The trams are similar to those commissioned in 2011 in Zaragoza: 30 metres long and 2.65 metres wide, with an aluminium body, 100% low floor access, and 70 km/h maximum speed.

Outside of light-rail, the company is demonstrating its intentions for the UK market by adapting its Civity platform specifically to the UK, and has become one of the pre-qualified bidders for the London Crossrail rolling stock procurement process.

CAF completed the delivery of 20 x 3 car diesel multiple-units to Translink, owner of Northern Ireland Railways, in July 2012 – under a new contract which includes maintenance by CAF Rail Services UK Ltd for a 15 year period. The new 100mph trains are arranged as 3 car units, like the Class 3000 series, but now with provision to increase the number of cars per unit in the future.

The Class 4000 is a development of the Class 3000 design, following a comprehensive review to produce a more environmentally-friendly train – adapting the traction system to meet new European emission regulations, cutting fuel consumption and maintenance costs.

Representing an investment of £105 million, the 20 Class-4000 trains replace 13 diesel-electric multiple-units and operate alongside the existing fleet of 23 Class 3000 trains delivered by CAF in 2005.

Additionally CAF has also supplied 29 x 4 car Class 2900 diesel multiple-units for Iarnród Éireann (IE – Irish Rail). The most recent order supplied to IE was for 67 125mph Mk4 intercity vehicles, capable of 10 car operation but currently formed up as 8 car sets, including driving cars.

CAF provided the 14 electric multiple-unit trains for Heathrow Express, in conjunction with Siemens, and 16 trains based on that design were also supplied for West Yorkshire.

As a result of its commitment to R&D, and long-standing experience, CAF has developed the OARIS solution, a family of very high-speed trains capable of reaching 350 km/h. Designed with exceedingly reliable in-house technology, this family of trains features the ultimate in design, accessibility, safety and comfort.

Its highlights are:

- Flexible interior layout, to vary the seating capacity and services according to requirements.
- Variable configuration, with 4, 6, and 8 car solutions.
- Multivoltage current collection (1.5 and 3 kV DC, 15 and 25 kV AC).

- Multi-signalling options.
- Cross-border interoperability.
- High reliability, and low operating and maintenance costs.
- Gauge change option: 1,435 - 1,668 mm.
- Complete user accessibility from different platform levels.

CAF's main objectives in this sector are new high speed train developments and technological solutions, and so it is running an R&D project called TENAV 350, where efforts are primarily focused on developing simulation techniques and innovative tests in the high speed field.

The company's products range from complete transportation systems for urban, suburban and long-distance routes and turnkey solutions, to custom-made parts and components. With several manufacturing plants in Spain, and others in North and South America, CAF has the capability and experience to manufacture using a variety of materials. CAF also offers maintenance, upgrading and overhaul of vehicles and components.

A snapshot of other recent orders includes: 14 x 6 car metro units for Metro Calcutta, with an option for a further 7 units; 35 x 8 car EMUs for CPTM in Sao Paulo, Brazil; 3 x 5 car trams for the city of Cagliari in Italy, with option for a further 6 trams; 12 x 7 car trams for the city of Freiburg in Germany; 20 x 4 driverless metro trains for Helsinki, Finland; and a turnkey project to build the first phase of the circular light metro line for the city of Kaoshiung in Taiwan.

Some of the company's other notable ongoing projects include the supply of suburban units for Belo Horizonte and Recife (in Brazil); Trieste (Italy); Montenegro; Auckland (New Zealand) and EuskoTrenbideak (Basque Railways); trains for Amtrak in the United States of America and for Saudi Arabia; LRVs for the cities of Birmingham, Sydney, Stockholm, Houston, Cincinnati, Debrecen, Besançon, Fribourg, Tallinn, Cuiaba, Granada, and Málaga; and metro units for the cities of Rome, Bucharest, Caracas, Sao Paulo, Helsinki and Santiago de Chile.

R&D plays a predominant role in CAF's activities. CAF is firmly committed to the achievement of a more sustainable world, as shown by the importance it attaches to the development of new technologies and expertise in order to offer efficient transport solutions.

CAF is therefore heading a number of research projects in order to develop a new generation of trains equipped with eco-friendly technologies - the energy technology project called SIENER stands out as an example.

The company employs about 7,400 employees worldwide.

LEFT AND ABOVE: The first new CAF Urbos tram for Midland Metro, unveiled at Wednesbury depot on 16 October 2013. John Whitehouse

GE POWERHAUL FOR EUROPE

GE Transportation's PowerHaul Series PH37ACai locomotive, unveiled at InnoTrans 2012 in Berlin, meets the latest interoperability requirements and has a full-width continental-gauge body, in contrast to Freightliner's UK-gauge version.

German open-access freight-hauler Heavy Haul Power International (HHPI) is the customer for the pilot batch of PowerHauls. Richard Painter, Group Chairman, 'HHPI is partnering with GE to produce a locomotive capable of operating more productive trains for bulk traffic than current technology. The focus is on "cost per tonne" which will be achieved by one train doing the job of three existing ones and therefore significantly benefiting the environment and the economy.'

The PH37ACai model, assembled by Turkish company Tülomsas, is equipped with GE's new Tempo ETCS solution, marking the first European Train Control System (ETCS) implementation on a PowerHaul Series locomotive. The system is part of Tempo Railway Solutions, a comprehensive onboard and wayside signalling portfolio designed around a common failsafe, scalable, hardware and software platform as well as an integrated suite of engineering tools.

Freightliner Group in the United Kingdom placed the largest locomotive order in its history with GE for 30 locomotives in 2007, partnering with GE on the new design configured to take into account current and future requirements for efficiency, emissions control and safety.

The 129-ton PowerHaul Series locomotive for Freightliner is designed to generate more horsepower and tractive effort while lowering fuel consumption and greenhouse gas emissions than locomotives currently in use. The locomotive features several leading technologies to achieve this performance including the new V16-cylinder, twin-turbo PowerHaul series engine – a product of Ecomagination, a GE-wide initiative to help meet customer demand for more energy-efficient products.

GE's unique AC individual-axle traction-control technology enables the PowerHaul Series to haul heavier loads by significantly reducing slippage on start-ups, inclines and sub-optimal track conditions. The PowerHaul Series also features dynamic braking in addition to air brakes to provide smoother handling when hauling heavier loads.

PowerHaul Series PH37ACai locomotive at InnoTrans 2012 in Berlin. GE

ELECTROSTAR trains are in operation on London Overground, carrying thousands of commuters around London daily.

Leader in rail manufacturing and servicing

Bombardier Transportation is a global leader in the rail equipment manufacturing and servicing industry. It has a workforce of over 3,200 people and a presence at 31 locations throughout the UK. Bombardier has built, or has on order, around 60 per cent of the UK's rolling stock and is contracted to service over 5,200 vehicles (a third of the current fleet) across the UK. Bombardier offers the broadest product portfolio in the rail industry and delivers innovative products and services that set new standards in sustainable mobility – conserve energy, protect the environment and help to improve total train performance for passengers and operators. Bombardier's global expertise ensures that the UK continues to benefit from the latest technology that the rail industry has to offer. Bombardier's rail transportation products are in operation in all major British regions, in the full range of rail services - intercity, urban and suburban, metros and light rail systems.

The award winning Bombardier *ELECTROSTAR* is the most successful post-privatisation EMU in the UK, with more than 2,000 vehicles entering service in the past decade. The proven *ELECTROSTAR* consistently excels in performance league tables, achieving some of the highest reliability figures in the country. *ELECTROSTAR* trains are in operation on Southeastern, Southern, First Capital Connect, London Eastern Railways, Essex Thameside and London Overground railways, where they help to bring thousands of commuters to, from and around London daily. In December 2011, Bombardier received a contract for the supply of 130 additional *ELECTROSTAR* trains for Southern to augment its existing fleet, with the new trains entering service in September 2013 - record time for a fleet of its size. In November 2012, an option for 40 additional new vehicles for Southern was exercised, and in July 2013 an order was placed for 116 *ELECTROSTARS* with a capability of 110mph operation. In May 2013, Bombardier also secured an order for the delivery of 57 new vehicles for London Overground.

The Gautrain Rapid Rail Link, a brand new complete rail system in South Africa also operates UK built *ELECTROSTAR* trains.

The CrossCountry and West Coast networks run Bombardier Voyager and Super Voyager diesel

electric multiple-units (DEMUs). Bombardier Meridian DEMUs are also in daily passenger service with UK operator East Midlands Trains, and Bombardier's *TURBOSTAR* diesel multiple-units are in service with many operators, helping to connect towns and cities across Britain.

The 'greener' next generation *TURBOSTARS* are lighter and offer reduced CO2 emissions, improved fuel consumption and are over 90 per cent recyclable.

Traffic congestion in Croydon has been significantly reduced through the use of Bombardier *FLEXITY* Swift light rail vehicles on Transport for London's Tramlink system, which are also supported by Bombardier's maintenance team, winners of an 'outstanding teamwork' award in 2012.

And linking the centre of London with the eastern Docklands area, the Docklands Light Railway is served by the first fully automated, driverless public transport system, operating 94 Bombardier-built vehicles proving enormously popular and reliable during the London Olympics 2012. Manchester's Metrolink System also benefits from a new fleet of Bombardier *FLEXITY* Swift trams - a further 20 were ordered in 2012, bringing the fleet size to 94.

The *FLEXITY* 2 trams, which have been in successful revenue service in Blackpool since April 2012, incorporate the 'best of the best', bringing the outstanding, proven features of Bombardier trams into one vehicle.

Bombardier provides a complete portfolio of services from technical support and material solutions to total train care packages that are tailored to the needs of any operator. In the UK, Bombardier has total fleet management responsibility for, among other fleets, the diesel-electric trains operated by Arriva CrossCountry and Virgin West Coast, maintained at a purpose-built facility, Central Rivers, and a number of overnight out-station depots. Bombardier fleets throughout the UK are supported by highly skilled maintenance teams and also by *ORBITA* a leading edge predictive maintenance capability which helps operators to increase fleet utilisation, improve reliability and availability, reduce in-service failures and improve the passenger's overall journey experience.

During the Olympics, Bombardier's maintenance teams supported 800 trains on 9 key routes into London, ensuring that fleets ensuring optimum reliability and availability to meet increased demand and attracting praise from visitors, train operators and the mayor of London. This, combined with Bombardier's contribution to the Victoria Line Upgrade, resulted in Bombardier receiving the award for 'Transport Supplier of the Year' at the 2013 National Transport Awards.

MAJOR LONDON UNDERGROUND CONTRACT

Bombardier is a participant in the renewal of the London Underground (LU) network, as the supplier of 191 *MOVIA* metro trains for the Sub Surface Lines (SSL) upgrade, currently being built at Bombardier's production site at Derby. LU's Victoria Line service has been provided entirely by new Bombardier *MOVIA* trains since July 2011 and Bombardier's system upgrade project for the line, which also includes replacement of the signalling system, was completed, on schedule in 2012.

Bombardier has also been awarded the major contract for the SSL automatic train control (ATC) signalling upgrade. The contract is valued at approximately £354million. Bombardier will provide the proven *CITYFLO* 650 ATC system, its innovative communication-based train control (CBTC) technology, similar to that running successfully on the Metro de Madrid in Spain.

The full scope of the contract is for the signalling renewal and provision of an ATC system for the four sub-surface lines (Metropolitan, District, Circle, Hammersmith & City) of the Underground network. Carrying 1.3million passengers a day, the lines comprise 40 per cent of the network and carry 25 per cent of the total ridership.

Bombardier will equip 310km of line (40km in tunnels), 113 stations, 191 trains, 49 engineering trains and six heritage trains by 2018, followed by a two-year warranty period.

Overall the upgrade will mean:

- 24 per cent more capacity on the District Line by providing space for an extra 10,000 passengers an hour.
- 27 per cent more capacity on the Metropolitan Line by providing space for an extra 9,500 passengers an hour.
- 65 per cent more capacity on the Circle and Hammersmith & City lines, delivered through new signalling, longer trains and recent improvements to service frequency. In total the upgrade will provide space for an extra 17,500 more passengers each hour. ■

MORE DRS ORDERS FOR VOSSLOH

Direct Rail Services announced in January 2012 an order for Vossloh España to supply 15 EuroLight Bo-Bo mixed traffic diesel-electric locomotives, with options for further orders.

The locomotives will have an axle load of 21.4 tonnes, and a 2,800 kW Caterpillar engine. The locomotives are being built at Vossloh's plant in Valencia, Spain.

The 'UKLight' design, developed in conjunction with Beacon Rail Leasing, is based on the EuroLight low-axleload freight and passenger locomotive design.

The locomotives will be fitted with AC traction equipment from ABB, will have a top speed of 100mph, and are designed for use on both intermodal and passenger trains. The locomotives are to meet Stage IIIA emission standards.

Vossloh España received a new order from Direct Rail Services, for ten Dual Mode locomotives, in September 2013. Delivery is to start in 2015. The locomotive has again been developed in partnership with Beacon Rail Leasing.

Key features of the Class 88 locomotive include 4MW ABB equipment delivering a continuous electric power rating on the 25kV electrified network, a 700kW diesel engine for work away from the electrified network (delivering 317KN of tractive effort in both modes), plus superior adhesion capacity. The Class 88 has a nominal 100mph top speed, 500KW train-heating rating and regenerative braking.

The Class 88 locomotive shares many parts with the Class 68, including the bodyshell, cabs (where the driver's environment has been developed together with union representatives), brake system, bogies, traction equipment and control software.

This new generation of dual-powered locomotives is designed for both heavy-haul freight and high-speed passenger services (with a self-rescue capability and flexibility to adapt to various passenger applications), while complying to Euro IIIB environmental targets.

Vossloh España is also to supply seven tram-trains to South Yorkshire Passenger Transport Executive, to operate between the centre of Sheffield and Rotherham Parkgate. The units will enter service in 2015 as part of the tram-train pilot project.

The Vossloh built tram-train vehicles, with modern traction systems from Vossloh Kiepe, will be compatible with operation on the existing Sheffield Supertram network as well the heavy rail route from Meadowhall to Rotherham Parkgate.

The project has a total budget of approximately £60 million and includes not only the seven tram-trains but also the electrification of a stretch of track between Rotherham Parkgate and Meadowhall in addition to the construction of a 400 metre line that will link the existing tramway to the heavy rail infrastructure.

Model of Vossloh Class 68 for Direct Rail Services. Keith Fender

Siemens seals Thameslink deal

Siemens' Desiro City has been selected for the Thameslink Programme. Siemens

The Department for Transport in June 2013 awarded a contract, worth about £1.6 billion, for 1,140 new Desiro City commuter rail carriages for the Thameslink route to Siemens plc and Cross London Trains (a consortium comprising Siemens Project Ventures GmbH, Innisfree Limited and 3i Infrastructure plc).

This is the largest contract awarded to Siemens plc, covering the capital cost of the trains and associated depot infrastructure. The consortium will be responsible for financing the deal, with Siemens also looking after the long-term maintenance of the trains. The order will boost Siemens' UK rail portfolio (including new Eurostar trains) to over 2,800 vehicles.

Siemens says it has invested around Euro 50 million to develop the Desiro City - the concept that has been selected for the Thameslink Programme - specifically for the UK. The second-generation, evolutionary Desiro City combines the latest technology with the proven Siemens Desiro, which travels more than 50 million miles nationwide each year.

The Desiro City will offer a much improved passenger travel experience and a step change in capacity and reliability, says Siemens, with a spacious and airy design that maximises capacity and significantly increases passenger comfort levels.

The Desiro City Thameslink fleet will be maintained at two new traincare depots at Three Bridges (Crawley) and Hornsey (Haringey). The trains are to be introduced into service from early 2016, with the full 24 trains per hour service coming into effect at the end of 2018. The fleet will consist of 60 eight-car and 55 twelve-car electric multiple-units.

Steve Scrimshaw, UK Managing Director at Siemens Rail Systems, said: 'The finalisation of the Thameslink contract reaffirms Siemens' commitment to ongoing development and continued innovation in the UK rail industry.

'The introduction of the new Desiro City will offer a much improved passenger travel experience and a step change in capacity and reliability. It's a technologically advanced train that has been designed with UK travellers in mind, incorporating proven technology and using the expertise, skills and feedback of highly experienced UK operators, train crew, cleaners and maintenance staff at every stage of the process.'

Established in the UK 170 years ago, Siemens has 13,520 UK employees. The company has sought to include locally sourced train components in the Desiro City design to further support the rail supply chain and offer additional employment opportunities. Siemens anticipates the creation of up to 2,000 jobs across the UK in component manufacturing and assembly, as well as in the construction of the new depots and subsequent train maintenance.

Siemens will be manufacturing hi-tech electrical components for the Desiro City train at its facility in Hebburn, South Tyneside – one of 13 manufacturing plants Siemens owns in the UK. This will help to develop a legacy of sustainable rail manufacturing skills in the North East. Further components sourced from the UK include, amongst others, train pantographs manufactured in Somerset; cab radios in Dorset; flooring in Hertfordshire; exterior lighting in the West Midlands; train protection and warning systems in Cheshire; and, CCTV in Tyne and Wear. The train bodyshells will be manufactured in Krefeld, Germany, with the trains tested to the latest standards at Siemens' test track in Wildenrath, Germany, minimising disruption to the UK network.

Siemens Rail Systems Division provides expertise and technology in the full range of rail vehicles – from heavy rail to metros to trams and light-rail vehicles. In the UK, the Division employs around 700 people and maintains over 350 Siemens passenger trains for First TransPennine Express, South West Trains, Heathrow Express, Greater Anglia, Northern Rail, London Midland and ScotRail.

Other current orders include ten 16-car Velaro high-speed trains for Eurostar, ten Class 350/3 Desiro EMUs for London Midland, and ten Class 350/4 Desiro EMUs for First TransPennine Express.

INSPIRO – THE NEW METRO FROM SIEMENS

Future developments for metro-style trains and stations were showcased in 'Going Underground: Our journey to the future', an exhibition presented by Siemens in conjunction with the London Transport Museum and media specialists CBS Outdoor from October 2013. The highlight was a full-scale mock-up of an Inspiro train, a new mass-transit metro concept, tailored for the London Underground deep-tube lines. Technologies to help travellers find their way more easily, electronic ticketing developments, passenger information systems and station management solutions were also on display.

The train interior aims to offer light and space, with LED lighting panels spanning the entire ceiling helping to maximise headroom. Open gangways allow users to move freely throughout the train, and light, bright colours on the floors, seats and grab handles are intended to accentuate a sense of openness. Practical air-conditioning technology for the small profile tube trains is being researched.

Siemens reckon the train is 30% more energy efficient and 20 % lighter than similar modern metro trains.

RAIL TRAINING ACADEMY

The go-ahead for a new rail training academy developed collaboratively by Siemens and NSARE (National Skills Academy for Railway Engineering) was given in September 2013. An innovative agreement between NSARE and the Department for Business, Innovation & Skills (BIS) with support from the Department for Transport (DfT) will provide half the funds required, with Siemens contributing the other 50 per cent.

The academy will specialise in traction and rolling stock skills, and will be located in a state-of-the-art facility at the site of Siemens' existing train depot and UK service headquarters in King's Heath, Northampton, creating around 100 jobs in its construction and subsequent operation. It is expected to open its doors to the first students in Spring 2015.

Currently some 13,500 people work in specialist traction and rolling stock roles across the UK. The new academy will focus on addressing the future skills shortage in this part of the UK rail sector – forecast to be around 4,500 people over the next five years - caused by a combination of factors, including: an ageing workforce; the technological advancement of rolling stock; and, investment and growth in the industry.

The Northampton training centre, which will offer 20,000 man days of training per year, will act as a national 'hub' with regional 'spokes' located at other train care facilities around the country. The 50/50 funding agreement will release 50% of the academy's training capacity to the wider UK industry, with the remainder used by Siemens' own rail sector employees.

The Inspiro London full-scale mock-up. Siemens

ELECTRO-MOTIVE DIESEL

GB Railfreight announced in September 2013 a deal with Electro-Motive Diesel Inc to purchase a further eight Class 66 locomotives. The new locomotives are due to be delivered by Chicago-based Electro-Motive in August 2014.

The order will expand GBRf's fleet to 58 Class-66 locomotives. GBRf says it will use the locomotives on biomass and infrastructure rail freight haulage.

A manufacture and supply agreement was signed by Paul Denton, senior vice president of international sales at Progress Rail, and John Smith, MD of GB Railfreight, at Rannoch station on the West Highland railway - taking a break from GBRf's service to Fort William.

Electro-Motive Diesel was acquired by Progress Rail Services, a wholly-owned subsidiary of Caterpillar Inc, in August 2010 from previous owners Greenbriar Equity Group and Berkshire Partners. EMD became a wholly-owned subsidiary of Progress Rail, creating a global locomotive manufacturing and rail services company.

Progress Rail Services is one of the largest providers of rail and transit products and services in North America, including: locomotive upgrade and repair; railcar remanufacturing; trackwork; rail welding; rail repair and replacement; signal design and installation; maintenance of way equipment; parts reclamation and recycling.

EMD's Class 66 locomotive has become the UK standard, and gained acceptance more widely in Europe, with DB Schenker company Euro Cargo Rail using its Class 66 locomotives for cross-border operations between France, Belgium and Germany. They are equipped with safety systems and radios for all three countries, with automatic switching when crossing borders.

UK company EMDL - a subsidiary of Electro-Motive Diesel - signed a 10-year contract with GBRf in 2012 to maintain its fleet of Class 66 locomotives – the company's first full-maintenance contract.

The company provides all post delivery services, including commissioning, locomotive modification and maintenance of EMD locomotives in Europe, Scandinavia and parts of the Middle East.

EMDL has invested in a new maintenance and warehouse facility, and a new 30 tonne wheel lathe, at its Doncaster base.

GBRf's Class 66 fleet is set to increase to 58 Class-66 locomotives. GBRf

New contracts for Alstom

Alstom Transport employs some 2,000 people in the UK at over 20 locations. Alstom has full service provision and technical support contracts with a number of train and metro operating companies, notably for the Alstom-designed and built Pendolino fleet for Virgin.

Alstom built much of the current fleet of trains running on the London Underground and today provides maintenance for the Northern Line fleet. From its Preston site, Alstom provides dual expertise as the company's UK supplier of spare parts and logistics and global centre of excellence for lifetime traction support. The site is the only traction systems engineering knowledge centre in the UK.

As well as maintaining and extending the life of many existing fleets on the UK rail network, Alstom led the move to high-speed rail in the UK, delivering the final 20km of track and overhead line for the final phase of High Speed 1.

NOTTINGHAM

Alstom officially unveiled in September 2013 the first of 22 Citadis trams ordered by Nottingham Express Transit (NET) for the tramway extension project. This is the first Alstom tram to be delivered to the UK.

The Citadis for Nottingham is 32 metres long and can carry up to 200 people. The trams are being built in Alstom's facility in Barcelona. After extensive testing, five will join the existing fleet on Line 1 in mid-2014.

As part of the Tramlink consortium, Alstom has also been awarded the contract to maintain the trams, including the 15 Bombardier trams already in service. Refurbishment worth over £300,000 has been carried out for the existing fleet.

Alstom is also building the two new lines, with associated overhead wires, track and signalling, with its consortium partner Taylor Woodrow.

Alstom's unique Appitrack machine was used for the first time in the UK on NET. Appitrack can lay the platform and insert the shoes for the rails with total accuracy, at rates averaging 150m a day. It holds the world record of 403m of single track laid in one day, in Orleans.

PENDOLINO

Alstom was awarded a contract worth over Euro 12 million by Virgin Trains in October 2013 to modernise its entire Pendolino fleet. The contract includes the refurbishment of the interiors, bar, kitchen facilities and toilets, over a period of eight months. The work is being undertaken at Oxley (Wolverhampton) and Longsight (Manchester) Traincare Centres.

The third heavy overhaul ('H3') of the Pendolino fleet was completed by Alstom in July 2013 - the end of a £60m process that saw 1.3 million parts changed on the trains, 936 bogies overhauled and 1,872 wheelsets delivered by suppliers.

28,000 components and parts were changed on each set, material spend totalled £43 million, mainly in the UK; 120 people were taken on and trained specifically for H3; and £3.7 million was spent on new and improved infrastructure, from lifting jacks to new workshops.

In addition to the overhaul work, the Longsight team extended 31 of the nine-car trains to 11 cars.

The first of 22 Citadis trams for the Nottingham Express Transit extension project is readied overnight for its unveiling in September 2013. Alstom

Alstom at Longsight also completed work in summer 2013 overhauling Northern Rail's 17-strong Class 323 fleet. After Longsight developed a specialist bogie workshop, Alstom is bringing bogie work on its Class 180 diesel multiple-units to the site.

UNDERGROUND

Starting in January 2013, the London Underground Northern Line mid-life project is a refurbishment of the Alstom-built fleet comprising upgrades to the interior and exterior of the 106 trains.

Alstom was awarded a contract by UK Power Networks Services in May 2013 to supply its innovative Harmonic and Energy Saving Optimiser (HESOP) energy recovery system for the Victoria Line. The contract, worth about Euro 1 million, is for a trial of inverting substation technology that will run until 2014. This will help make the Underground more energy efficient and will also help control tunnel temperatures.

HESOP works by converting and transferring any unused power, generated by the trains during braking, to accelerating trains elsewhere on the line or to the grid.

POWER

The ATC joint venture, consisting of Alstom, TSO and Costain, has been awarded the contract to fit out and commission the Crossrail tunnels under London fitting out the 21 km of twin tunnels with track and power equipment. The contract is worth over Euro 350 million.

Crossrail's contract for high voltage traction power supply, valued at about £15m, was awarded to the AC Joint Venture (Alstom and Costain). The contract covers the central tunnelled section. The non-traction high-voltage power supply contract (value about £25m) was also awarded to the AC Joint Venture.

ABC Electrification, the partnership of Alstom, Babcock and Costain, won its first contract in 2013, a £48m project for the third phase of the West Coast power supply upgrade.

Four new trams for Wimbledon branch

A Stadler Variobahn tram, in 'Love Croydon' livery, approaches East Croydon. John Glover

London Tramlink has ordered four new trams to deliver a 50 per cent increase in capacity on the Wimbledon to Croydon link, the busiest route on the network.

The new Stadler trams are part of the £30m Wimbledon Line Enhancement Programme and will complement the replacement of a single line section with double tracks and an additional tram platform at Wimbledon station.

Transport for London's Director of London Rail, Jonathan Fox, said: 'This increase from eight to 12 trams per hour with a 50 per cent rise in capacity on the Wimbledon branch will greatly improve tram frequency, reduce waiting times and increase reliability as well as making for a better passenger experience.

'As London's population grows this is an important expansion to the tram network, bringing more convenient and efficient tram connections and moving more people around the Capital to leisure, education and employment opportunities. At the same time, congestion on buses is relieved and car owners are encouraged to leave their vehicles at home, helping to reduce carbon emissions.'

The new service will provide improved access to central Croydon with 50,000 employees working within 750 metres walk of a tram stop.

An additional 25,000 people will now have a journey time of less than 60 minutes to central Croydon, giving Croydon's employers access to a larger labour market.

Since the London Tramlink system opened in 2000 it has experienced rapid growth in passenger numbers.

Nineteen million passengers were carried in the first year of operation and this has grown to 30.2 million passengers in 2012/13.

Expected population and employment growth indicate that by 2031, 38.8 million passengers are expected to be carried by London Tramlink (a 35 per cent increase).

The Stadler Variobahn trams are 32.37 metres long, are air-conditioned and are fully low-floor which provides good accessibility for passengers. Each tram is made up of five sections with wide gangways between each section giving them a more spacious interior. The bidirectional vehicles have 72 seats and standing room for 134 passengers, and can reach a maximum speed of 80 km/h.

The Wimbledon Line Enhancement Programme will improve journey times and reduce congestion on board trams and at Wimbledon station, is intended to make it easier to use Oyster touch in and touch out facilities and improve interchange between tram and National Rail services.

The first of the new vehicles is to be delivered during the summer of 2015 and the last is scheduled to arrive in 2016. The contract is worth £10.2m and the four new vehicles are being bought under an option in a contract which saw six new trams delivered in 2012.

Bochum, Nuremberg and Munich were some of the first cities to order Stadler's Variobahn in 2005. The manufacturer expanded the concept of the tram, adapting its fixtures and fittings to meet the needs of customers in the various towns and cities. In addition, the Berlin-based company developed a new design that received the iF design award from International Forum Design Hannover in 2006. While the existing modular construction was maintained, the bogies were fitted with transmission-free wheel hubs and external rotor motors, resulting in less wear and noise and improved sustainability. Passenger comfort was increased by the use of full air suspension, which also ensures a constant boarding height.

Stadler Rail Group has locations in Switzerland (Altenrhein, Bussnang and Winterthur), in Germany (Berlin-Pankow, Berlin-Hohenschönhausen, Berlin-Reinickendorf and Velten), in Poland (Siedlce), Hungary (Budapest, Pusztaszabolcs and Szolnok), the Czech Republic (Prague), Italy (Meran) and Algeria (Algiers). The group has a workforce of around 5,000 people. The best-known vehicle series from Stadler Rail Group are the articulated multiple-unit train GTW (563 trains sold), the Regio-Shuttle RS1 (497 trains sold), the FLIRT (910 trains sold) and the double-decker multiple-unit train KISS (170 trains sold) in the railway sector, and the Variobahn (320 vehicles sold) and the newly developed Tango (120 vehicles sold) in the tram sector. The Metro is another addition for the urban rail market (36 vehicles sold). Stadler Rail also manufactures passenger carriages and locomotives and is the world's leading manufacturer of rack-and-pinion rail vehicles.

Interior of London Tramlink Variobahn tram. John Glover

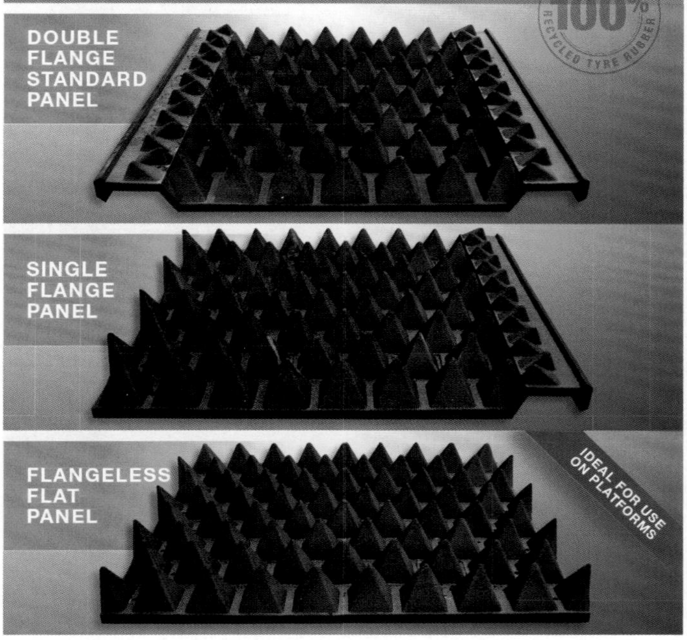

The Wabtec Group has the combined resources to provide an all-encompassing range of services to the UK rail industry. It is part of Wabtec Corporation, a worldwide leading supplier of value-added, technology-based products and services for rail, transit and other industries.

The group includes Wabtec Rail Limited, Wabtec Rail Scotland and Brush Traction, and now also LH Group, including the Hunslet Engine Company.

Based at Barton under Needwood in Staffordshire, LH is a leading supplier of multiple unit passenger rail products and services. A key part of the company's activities is the overhaul of rail vehicles, engines and transmission systems. Resources include a gear cutting and machining facility specialising in the manufacture of components, all types of gears, spiral bevels, castings, machining and reverse engineering. There is also a general fabrication facility offering a broad range of engineering capabilities.

The Hunslet Engine Company is renowned throughout the world as a designer and manufacturer of quality industrial shunting, tunnelling and specialised locomotives. With many operators finding the cost of new equipment to be prohibitive, the company also offers an extensive range of refurbishment, modernisation and repair services.

The acquisition of LH is complementary to Wabtec Group's activities as one of the UK's leading rail vehicle engineering companies. Through Wabtec Rail Limited's works at Doncaster and Wabtec Rail Scotland's works at Kilmarnock in Scotland, the Group undertakes the refurbishment and maintenance of railway rolling stock, locomotives, passenger trains and freight wagons. Brush Traction's facilities at Loughborough provide locomotive overhauls, services and aftermarket components, including traction motors, electrical control systems and wheelsets.

With these acquisitions, the Wabtec Group has the combined resources to provide an all-encompassing range of services to the UK rail industry.

Major refurbishment and overhaul contracts presently under way at Wabtec's works include creation of six additional Class 458 EMUs for Porterbrook, South West Trains and Alstom - reconfiguring the Class 458 fleet into 5-car units and incorporating equipment from the Class 460 fleet previously used on Gatwick Express.

One of the Greater Anglia fleet of Class 321 EMUs has been rebuilt by Wabtec at Doncaster, for Eversholt Rail Group, as a demonstrator for passengers to evaluate. The interiors have been revamped in two formats, suburban and metro.

Two cars have the new suburban-style interior, with air conditioning, double-glazed windows, energy-efficient LED lighting, redesigned seats, two wheelchair spaces and an accessible toilet. Two metro-style cars have air conditioning, new lights and windows, with slimline 2+2 seating, clear access and increased standing space.

Major coupler and brake interface modifications were completed on Network Rail's Class 57/3 locomotives at Wabtec's Brush Traction facility, to enable the haulage of virtually every electric multiple-unit class with full compliance to the Rule Book.

Other major contracts include the 'as new' refurbishment of the 90 Tyne & Wear Metrocars for DB Regio Tyne & Wear Ltd, and refurbishment of Mk3 vehicles for the new Chiltern Mainline services, fitting them with external sliding plug doors, with driving-van trailer vehicles also undergoing overhaul and modification.

New-look Tyne & Wear Metrocars in service. The 'as new' refurbishment of 90 Metrocars for DB Regio Tyne & Wear Ltd is being carried out by Wabtec. Nexus / PTEG

PASSENGER TRAIN OPERATORS

IN ASSOCIATION WITH

ESG

Designed to deliver

ESG delivers high profile projects

ESG has carried out substantial research, analysis and installation work on the Class 91 pantograph project. Brian Morrison

Derby based ESG and its sister company Railway Approvals Limited are two of the UK's leading railway consultancies specialising in Traction and Rolling Stock engineering. ESG prides itself on the high level of expertise and experience of its engineers, designers and project managers. Their commitment to team working and proactive customer focus have contributed massively to the continuing success of the business, which has doubled in size to over 80 engineers since 2011, and now provides services to the entire marketplace of train operators, leasing companies, overhaulers and original equipment manufacturers.

Since becoming part of DB Systemtechnik in 2011, ESG has actively engaged the skills and experience of its parent company to deliver a number of high profile projects. These include the extensive in-service testing of the revolutionary prototype duplex pantograph now installed on a Class 91 locomotive. The duplex pantograph eliminates a costly single-point failure on the loco; Eversholt Rail and East Coast engaged ESG as prototype installation designer and project manager. The project was completed in line with a demanding timescale as part of a collaboration that also included Brecknell-Willis and Wabtec.

The new design was developed following substantial research and analysis undertaken by ESG, underpinned by operating data including service impact, costs and consequences of failure of the overhead line equipment. The complexity of the installation meant the fitting of a prototype and in-service testing on a locomotive was necessary before fleet roll–out could be considered; it is hoped that this will follow in 2014 as part of the ongoing enhancement of the Class 91 fleet.

ESG and DB Systemtechnik are sharing knowledge across a range of smart solutions with both UK and European applications in mind. ESG has substantial experience in areas such as Remote Condition Monitoring, Wi-fi and Driver Advisory Systems; it is focused on offering cost-saving and efficiency-driven rolling stock solutions to UK operators, inputting to the latter's business cases where required.

Sister company Railway Approvals is committed to the evolution of homologation and audit processes to make them more efficient and fit-for-purpose, particularly to suit the European model - an area where rail has received recent criticism. ESG and Railway Approvals recognise the criticality of added value and eliminating unnecessary duplication. A core belief in team working underpins a focus on cost-effective, fast turn-round consultancy, ranging from discrete call-off tasks and audits to turnkey projects, complete design packages and approvals.

ESG's market-leading expertise in complex multi-discipline modification packages includes the accessibility requirements required to meet the PRM-TSI targeted compliance, so that existing trains can continue in service after 31 December 2019. It has already delivered a compliant Class 156 solution for the Greater Anglia fleet, and is now working on equivalent packages for Class 165, 166 and 365. ESG is also working with KBRS on revised interiors for Class 456. All designs and associated engineering work to ensure compliance with the relevant industry standards are undertaken by ESG and sister company Railway Approvals.

The breadth of expertise available to ESG and Railway Approvals has enabled them to provide a full suite of testing and homologation parameters to train manufacturers, de-risking the testing, delivery and commissioning phases for the introduction of new fleets.

These examples showcase ESG's ability to offer a whole life-cycle support package for rolling-stock. This is perfectly reflected in the work of ESG's Refranchising team, which provides independent, impartial and confidential consultancy across all aspects of the franchise lifecycle.

ESG has developed a strategic model which is a thorough and robust means of determining the optimum rolling stock solution for any franchise or concession. Whilst providing a structured and logical approach, the model has been designed with flexibility in mind and therefore is capable of meeting the requirements of different bid strategies.

Rolling stock strategy is crucial to the success of a franchise bid; ESG provides specialist support for leasing, new-train specification, maintenance and overhaul, utilisation, line-of-route, access agreements, fleet transition management and hand-back arrangements, to provide a few examples.

With electrification of the Midland main line now a reality, the spotlight is once more on Derby and its enviable rail industry culture. The industry has committed to the delivery of ambitious schemes throughout the UK, and ESG and Railway Approvals will embrace their growing role and responsibility in making these happen.

ESG is keenly aware of the challenge in recruiting the next generation of suitably qualified and enthusiastic rail professionals to take their place in this exciting journey. In support of this ESG is keen to nurture the talents of gifted young people looking for an exciting and challenging career in rolling stock engineering for the UK and world markets. ESG is proud of its strong links with Derby College, and is an enthusiastic and active supporter of the I-Rail, Young Railway Professionals and Women in Rail initiatives. ■

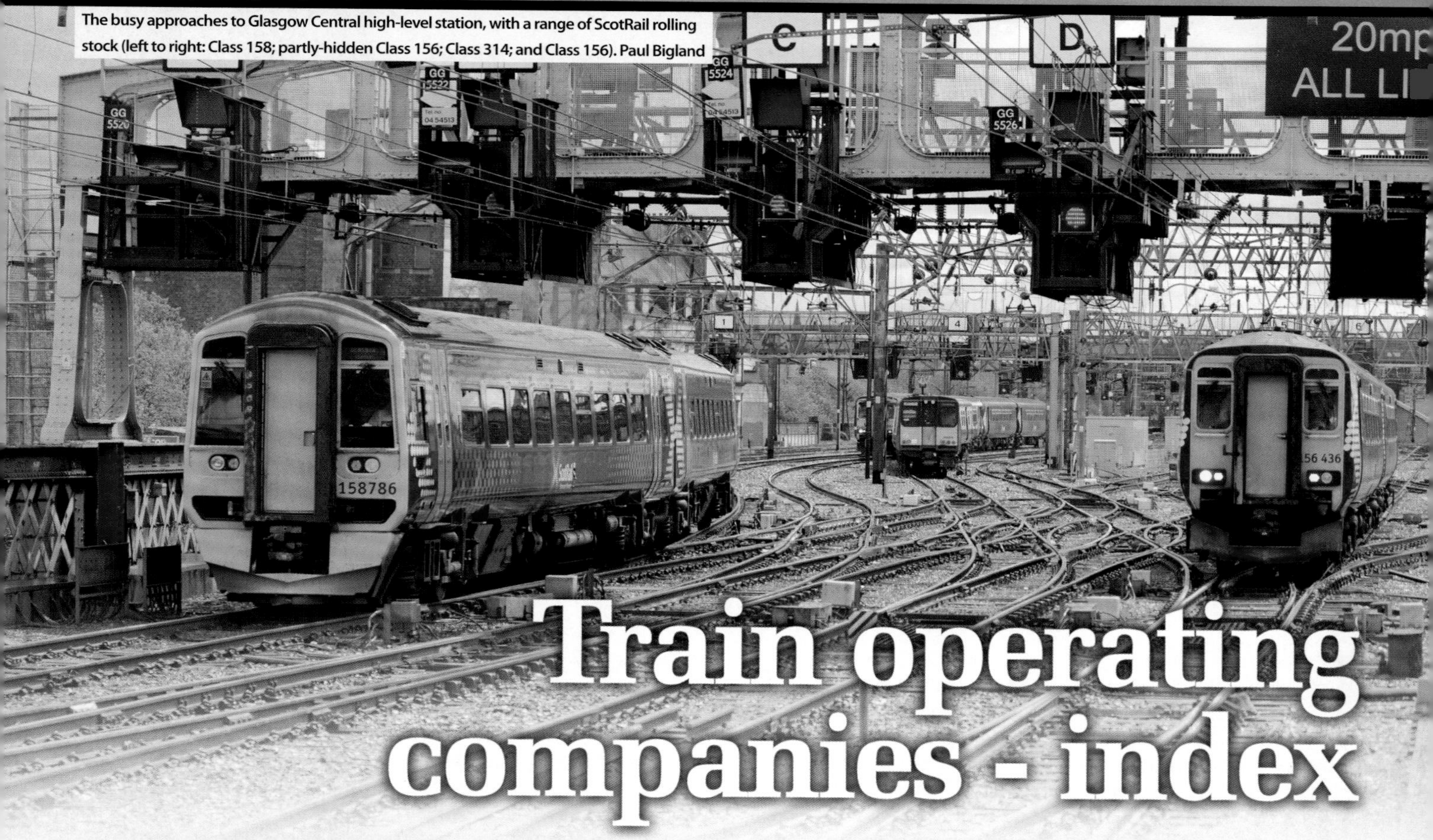

The busy approaches to Glasgow Central high-level station, with a range of ScotRail rolling stock (left to right: Class 158; partly-hidden Class 156; Class 314; and Class 156). Paul Bigland

Train operating companies - index

Notes:

** Not franchised by Department for Transport.*

(a) concession agreement with Merseytravel.

(b) concession agreement with Transport for London.

(c) Management of franchise devolved to the Welsh Government, but DfT is the procuring authority.

For more detailed refranchising timetable, see p13.

PASSENGER OPERATOR FINANCES

CHRIS CHEEK OF PASSENGER TRANSPORT SPECIALISTS TAS ANALYSES TRAIN OPERATING COMPANIES' FINANCIAL PERFORMANCE, AND FINDS PROFITS UNDER PRESSURE

Prior to the upturn during summer 2013, the news on the economic front for most of 2012/13 was grim, and this is reflected in a sharp slowdown in the growth of the market for rail services. Strip out the boost from the Olympics and Paralympics in summer 2012, and we could well have been looking at an annual fall. Indeed, there was a fall in demand for regional services during the year: it was only 1%, but it marks the first pause in growth in those markets for a decade.

Much of this could of course be accounted for by the economic situation, which continued to be grim during the year – particularly outside London and the South East. Growing resistance to above-inflation fare increases could also be a factor – though, in practice, the real problem is more likely to be the juxtaposition of these ticket price rises with falling household incomes: this is the first time for a generation that bus and rail travel costs have risen at a faster rate than the growth in average income – meaning that fares account for an increasing proportion of people's take home pay. The last time that happened was in the mid-1980s, and it tends to be resented.

The national patronage totals for the twelve months ended 31 March 2013 show the number of passenger journeys rising by 2.9% to 1,502 million. Passenger kilometres travelled rose by 1.8% to 57.9 billion, whilst passenger revenue was 6.6% higher at £7,707 million.

Nationally, a comparison in the compound annual growth rates either side of the financial crash in September 2008 is also interesting: in terms of passenger journeys, the growth in the five years leading up to the crash (2003-08) is 4.2%, against 4.1% in the five years since.

Looking at the individual sectors, passenger journeys on the London and South East routes grew at the fastest rate, winning another 39 million journeys – a rise of 3.9%, taking the total to 1,034 million. It is a sobering thought that this is higher than the total carried by the whole network as recently as a decade ago.

The longer distance operators won an extra 2.4 million passenger journeys, a rise of 1.9%, taking the total to 127.7 million. Outside the southeast, though, the regional, Scotland and Wales operators experienced a standstill in demand, leaving their total at 341 million journeys: however, passenger kilometres travelled fell by one per cent to 11.1 billion.

On the revenue front, all three sectors saw growth, as total railway revenue hit £7.7 billion – 6.6% up on the previous year. Commuter services gained 8%, regional routes 6.6% and InterCity services 4.7%. After taking inflation into account, revenue was ahead in real terms by around 5.0%.

This means that widespread predictions of financial problems amongst train operators have so far proved unfounded, though it is undoubtedly true that several operators continue to benefit from significant financial help from Government under the 'cap and collar' revenue sharing arrangements contained in franchise agreements.

However, train operating company (TOC) profits did fall in 2011/12, according to the latest research in the online Rail Industry Monitor publication from passenger transport specialists TAS. Overall, the figures show that operating profits fell by 15% during the year, marking the fourth fall in five years and wiping out the previous year's partial recovery in margins.

The analysis covers all the TOCs lodging accounts with financial year ends between 31 December 2011 and 30 June 2012. Across the franchised train operating companies as a whole, turnover was up by 7.1% at £9,438m, whilst operating profits totalled £233.5m (previous year: £274.7m on £8,816m), to give an operating margin of 2.5% (previous year: 3.1%).

Operating costs reached a total of £9,204m, 7.8% higher the 2010/11 total of £8,541m. The bulk of the increases were driven by increases in premium payments to Government.

The companies continued to be net earners of interest during the year – a figure that now includes pension scheme income. Proceeds earned rose sharply as investment returns improved. The total was just £60.4m, down from £45.2m a year earlier. Pre-tax profits were therefore just 8.1% lower at £294m (previous year: £319.8m). Pre-tax profit margins were 3.1% (previous year: 3.6%).

Total capital expenditure by the TOCs during the year rose by almost 9%, from the previous year's £143.3m to £155.9m. The value of net assets employed by the operators fell once again, by over 27% to £110.4m.

The analysis suggests that, as so often in the past, trends have not been uniform across the industry, with some sharp contrasts between sectors, and between different operators.

InterCity operators saw profits disappear completely, driven by the descent into the red at Cross Country, Greater Western and East Midlands. Total turnover amongst the companies rose by 8% to £3,383m, whilst operating costs rose by 10.2% to £3,416m. The resulting operating loss of £34m compared with the £31m profit achieved in 2010/11, and was achieved at a margin of just -1.0% (2008/09: +1.0%). Biggest gainer in all this was the Department for Transport, which extracted a whopping £497m in premium payments from these operators during the year.

By contrast, operators in London and the South East stayed in the black, albeit with slightly reduced profits. Again, the government was a big winner, extracting another £325m in premia from the sector as a whole: only Southeastern, Chiltern (just) and London Midland are now in receipt of subsidy from DfT, with London Overground getting its £26m subvention from Transport for London.

Total journeys on London and South East routes are now higher than the total carried by the whole GB rail network as recently as a decade ago. Commuters arrive at Chiltern Railways' London Marylebone terminus. Arriva

Turnover at these commuter companies rose by 7.6%, taking the total to £4,182m, whilst operating costs fell by 8% to £4,067m. The resulting operating profit of £115.2m compared with £120.8m in the previous year, at a margin of 2.8% (2010/11: 3.1%). Margins are well below the peak they hit before the recession – this was the 4.8% achieved in 2006/07.

The regional, Scotland and Wales franchises saw increases in profit levels. Turnover rose by 4.1% to £1,873m, whilst operating costs were 2.6% higher, totalling £1,721m. Operating profits were 24.2% up at £152.2m (last year £122.5m), at a margin of 8.1% (6.8%). As usually, this sector consumed the bulk of the subsidy paid to the train operators, soaking up £873m worth of taxpayer funding.

Individually, the most profitable TOC was once again TransPennine Express. The FirstGroup-Keolis joint venture saw its profits rise once more, reaching a 23.2% operating margin – the highest TAS has recorded for any TOC since privatisation began in the late 1990s. Next came National Express Group's surviving franchise, c2c Rail, on 11.5%, followed by the Merseyrail Electrics operation on 9.3%.

Overall, five of the 19 TOCs made an operating loss, up from three the previous year. Chiltern – now part of Arriva Trains - was the biggest loser on a 9.5% margin compared with a 3% profit the year before. Stagecoach Group's East Midlands Trains lost 9.0% (as in 2010/11), though it reports moving into profit in the second half of the year. A second Arriva business, Cross Country, came next on 7.7%, markedly worse than the 3.3% losses in 2010/11. Much smaller losses were incurred by First Great Western (0.9%, compared with a 1.7% profit in 2010/11) and Govia's London Midland company (0.7%, up from 0.9% the year before).

In the summaries below, figures are extracted from accounts lodged at Companies House. Practice concerning the declaration and calculation of different cost and revenue items varies between train operators. This occasionally makes interpretation and reconciliation difficult: major issues are noted in the brief commentaries.

LONG DISTANCE OPERATORS

CROSSCOUNTRY

Results at the company deteriorated sharply during the year, with operating and pre-tax losses more than doubled. Revenue fell during the year, largely as a result of a £40m cut in subsidy payments. Meanwhile, operating costs rose, albeit by much less than prevailing rates of inflation. This was the last year before the company qualified for revenue support from the Government.

PERIOD TO:	31/12/11	31/12/10
	£000	£000
Turnover	387,163	396,470
Operating Costs:	417,145	409,395
Operating Profit:	(29,982)	(12,925)
Operating Margin:	-7.7%	-3.3%
Turnover per Employee	£237,669	£246,714
Track Access	94,325	88,231
Rolling stock lease	48,507	45,373
Revenue Grant	3,641	43,268

FIRST GREAT WESTERN

The company recorded a small operating loss during the year, compared with the previous year's pre-exceptional profit. The result includes a premium payment to Government of £331m, less revenue support received of £205m.

Revenue growth well ahead of inflation was outstripped by rising operating costs, resulting in the operating loss. However, net interest receipts and tax refund meant that the company made a small operating profit.

PERIOD TO:	31/03/12	31/03/11
	£000	£000
Turnover	1,018,928	902,842
Operating Costs:	1,027,696	887,829
Operating Profit:	(8,768)	15,013
Operating Margin:	-0.9%	1.7%
Turnover per Employee	£210,175	£188,721
Track Access	135,893	132,317
Rolling stock lease	65,130	51,142
Revenue Grant	205,399	141,281

EAST COAST

The company improved its performance during this, the first full year of trading since taking over the East Coast franchise in November 2009.

On an estimated annualised basis, turnover was up by 4.8%

and costs by around 4.6%. The growth in passenger revenue was restricted to 2% during the year, as a consequence of ongoing economic uncertainties and the effects of poor weather.

PERIOD TO:	31/03/11	31/03/10
	£000	£000
Turnover	644,646	231,595
Operating Costs	640,087	230,292
Operating Profit	4,559	1,303
Operating Margin	0.7%	0.6%
Turnover per Employee	£236,567	£85,712
Track Access	43,524	16,087
Rolling stock lease	83,132	31,407

VIRGIN WEST COAST

Profits fell once again at the company that was at the heart of the furore over passenger franchising during the autumn of 2012. The company moved its financial year end to 31 March, resulting in an extended 56 week period, making comparisons difficult. On an estimated annualised basis, income was up by around 1.4% whilst operating costs rose by 3.8%, so producing the deterioration in margins and cash earnings.

PERIOD TO:	31/03/12	05/03/11
	£000	£000
Turnover	1,001,470	876,714
Operating Costs:	965,141	824,145
Operating Profit:	36,329	52,569
Operating Margin:	3.6%	6.0%
Turnover per Employee	£347,010	£301,069
Rolling stock lease	236,283	215,345
Revenue Grant	46,336	44,791

EAST MIDLANDS TRAINS

The company's performance deteriorated sharply during the year and substantial losses were once again recorded. A sharp increase in costs was driven by a sharp rise in the premium paid to Government. However, the margin was held, and the directors reported that the company moved into profit after November 2011 once government revenue support – worth some £36m - became available.

PERIOD TO:	30/04/12	30/04/11
	£000	£000
Turnover	378,523	310,180
Operating Costs:	412,566	338,023
Operating Profit:	(34,043)	(27,843)
Operating Margin:	-9.0%	-9.0%
Turnover per Employee	£186,373	£152,124
Track Access	71,225	69,294
Rolling stock lease	27,760	17,884
Revenue Grant	36,340	0

Adverse weather has plagued East Coast's train services repeatedly in recent years - this flooding was at Preston le Skerne, between Darlington and Durham, in November 2012. Network Rail

LONDON AND SOUTH EAST OPERATORS

FIRST CAPITAL CONNECT

The company continued to improve its financial performance after the losses incurred in 2010, though margins remained very tight indeed. Revenue was more than 10% up, but costs rose at a slightly lower rate.

PERIOD TO:	31/03/12	31/03/11
	£000	£000
Turnover	547,755	497,688
Operating Costs:	544,165	495,180
Operating Profit:	3,590	2,508
Operating Margin:	0.7%	0.5%
Turnover per Employee	£234,585	£219,536
Rolling stock lease	41,530	39,805
Track Access	65,380	62,222
Revenue Grant	33,300	29,500

LONDON MIDLAND

The company improved its performance during the year, recording reduced operating losses and a pre-tax profit in lieu of previous losses. This was achieved despite a cut in support from government of more than £15m during the year.

PERIOD TO:	30/06/12	02/07/11
	£000	£000
Turnover	333,327	325,385
Operating Costs:	335,742	328,405
Operating Profit:	(2,415)	(3,020)
Operating Margin:	-0.7%	-0.9%
Turnover per Employee	£143,799	£138,935
Track Access	75,299	73,559
Rolling stock lease	52,470	49,211
Revenue Grant	65,268	81,072

SOUTHERN

The company saw profits fall for the second successive year as revenue growth was outstripped by rising operating costs, primarily the premium payable to the Department for Transport.

PERIOD TO:	30/06/12	02/07/11
	£000	£000
Turnover	677,880	618,871
Operating Costs:	664,067	600,390
Operating Profit:	13,813	18,481
Operating Margin:	2.0%	3.0%
Turnover per Employee	£166,678	£153,224
Track Access	122,769	123,957
Rolling stock lease	109,481	113,555

SOUTHEASTERN

The company slipped back after the previous year's sharp profit increase.

Turnover growth was limited to a rise in line with inflation, but costs rose at a faster rate. The company reports continuing success with the high speed service, though, where increases in business offset falls elsewhere.

PERIOD TO:	30/06/12	02/07/11
	£000	£000
Turnover	750,802	728,675
Operating Costs:	733,799	706,893
Operating Profit:	17,003	21,782
Operating Margin:	2.3%	3.0%
Turnover per Employee	£199,469	£196,461
Rail contracts	404,279	383,186

NATIONAL EXPRESS EAST ANGLIA

The company saw profits rise sharply in what was the last full year of franchise operation, prior to the end of the contract on 4 February 2012 and the handover to Abellio, the Dutch state railway subsidiary.

Turnover was ahead at roughly double prevailing rates of inflation, outstripping the rise in operating costs.

PERIOD TO:	31/12/11	31/12/10
	£000	£000
Turnover	560,299	526,281
Operating Costs:	530,690	507,022
Operating Profit:	29,609	19,259
Operating Margin:	5.3%	3.7%
Turnover per Employee	£197,986	£185,965
Track Access	47,750	47,480
Rolling stock lease	129,590	107,025

C2C RAIL

The company saw profits increase by over 50% as strong passenger

While business travel on Eurostar has remained flat, increased passenger numbers are accounted for by continuing resilience in the leisure travel market. Eurostar

revenue growth outstripped rises in operating costs. The franchise was extended during the year with an expiry date of May 2013, but this has since been extended again until September 2014.

PERIOD TO:	31/12/11	31/12/10
	£000	£000
Turnover	127,827	116,095
Operating Costs:	113,135	106,392
Operating Profit:	14,692	9,703
Operating Margin:	11.5%	8.4%
Turnover per Employee	£231,571	£210,699
Rolling stock lease	22,696	22,034

CHILTERN

The company's financial position deteriorated sharply during the year, as the business recorded operating and pre-tax losses once more.

The company saw costs rise sharply as the new Project Evergreen timetable was introduced in September 2011, whilst revenue growth was impaired by the disruption caused by engineering works during the first part of the year needed to accommodate the new timetable.

Exceptional costs were also incurred, representing project costs for the delivery of Project Evergreen, £76.9m (previous year: £57.4m), less income received in respect of recharges to Network Rail £66.7m (previous year: £56.0m), less impairment of assets £34.7m (previous year: £18.6m).

PERIOD TO:	31/12/11	31/12/10
	£000	£000
Turnover	128,812	123,080
Operating Costs:	141,109	119,441
Operating Profit:	(12,297)	3,639
Operating Margin:	-9.5%	3.0%
Turnover per Employee	£167,724	£165,208
Rolling stock lease	17,970	14,922
Track Access	27,194	22,814

LONDON OVERGROUND

The company improved its results sharply during the year, as operating costs fell sharply following completion of the enhancement programme.

Growth in use of the services continued, as the final stage of the East London Line extension opened to Clapham Junction in December 2012, completing the 'Outer Circle' orbital surface railway round the capital.

PERIOD TO:	31/03/12	31/03/12
	£000	£000
Turnover	110,481	126,253
Operating Costs:	102,941	125,432
Operating Profit:	7,540	821
Operating Margin:	6.8%	0.7%
Turnover per Employee	£95,489	£111,827
Track Access	10,488	10,464
Rolling stock lease	2,091	2,102
Revenue Grant	86,473	80,866

SOUTH WESTERN

The company saw profits dip during the year, despite strong passenger revenue growth and £87m worth of revenue support from DfT. These offset the payment of a £228m premium as set down in the original franchise agreement. The figures vary from those shown in the statutory accounts: revenue support from the DfT is credited to the income account in this analysis, whereas the statutory accounts credit the amount received against operating costs. The different analysis is designed to make these accounts comparable with other TOCs.

PERIOD TO:	28/04/12	30/04/11
	£000	£000
Turnover	945,130	819,932
Operating Costs:	901,507	772,393
Operating Profit:	43,623	47,539
Operating Margin:	4.6%	5.8%
Turnover per Employee	£213,637	£188,360
Track Access	80,780	76,396
Rolling stock lease	105,309	103,422
Revenue Grant	87,133	68,321

REGIONAL, SCOTLAND AND WALES OPERATORS

ARRIVA TRAINS WALES

The company improved its performance during the year, with operating profits rising by one third, as above-inflation growth in revenue – including a small rise in subsidy payments – outstripped increases in costs.

PERIOD TO:	31/12/11	31/12/10
	£000	£000
Turnover	272,402	258,363
Operating Costs:	251,874	243,026
Operating Profit:	20,528	15,337
Operating Margin:	7.5%	5.9%
Turnover per Employee	£136,337	£128,603
Rolling stock lease	38,654	36,650
Track Access	48,740	47,884
Revenue Grant	141,022	136,901

FIRST SCOTRAIL

The company achieved a modest cash improvement in profitability during the year, as revenue and costs moved almost exactly in line with each other. Margins remained unchanged however.

Passenger revenue grew by 8.9% during the year, and was assisted by a grant from the Scottish Government which grew by 10.1%.

PERIOD TO:	31/03/12	31/03/11
	£000	£000
Turnover	613,686	563,294
Operating Costs:	596,259	547,647
Operating Profit:	17,427	15,647
Operating Margin:	2.8%	2.8%
Turnover per Employee	£137,321	£130,001
Rail contracts	231,514	200,175
Revenue Grant	297,536	270,029

FIRST TRANSPENNINE

The company improved its financial performance during the year, as revenue grew by over 6% whilst

InterCity operators have been struggling to maintain profitability with costs outpacing turnover. Passengers prepare to board an East Midlands Train at Derby. East Midlands Trains

operating costs were reduced slightly. Agreement was reached during the year for the franchise to be extended until 1 April 2015.

Turnover growth came from increased passenger revenue and other income, offset by a small £2.2m reduction in subsidy. Directors report that the extension agreement provides for lower subsidy payments from the government.

PERIOD TO:	31/03/12	31/03/11
	£000	£000
Turnover	284,941	268,329
Operating Costs:	218,943	219,978
Operating Profit:	65,998	48,351
Operating Margin:	23.2%	18.0%
Turnover per Employee	£279,903	£263,844
Track Access	75,630	77,397
Rolling stock lease	49,969	47,424
Revenue Grant	107,724	109,922

MERSEYRAIL ELECTRICS

Above-inflation revenue growth of 4.3% helped to deliver a modest increase in cash profits during the year, albeit at a slightly lower margin. Demand has fallen in both 2011/12 and 2012/13, though, and the company's reliance on public support has increased by over £5m in the last two financial years.

PERIOD TO:	07/01/12	08/01/11
	£000	£000
Turnover	131,649	126,264
Operating Costs:	119,403	114,352
Operating Profit:	12,246	11,912
Operating Margin:	9.3%	9.4%
Turnover per Employee	£108,175	£107,459
Track Access	10,847	10,613
Rolling stock lease	12,126	11,916

NORTHERN RAIL

The company improved its margin during the year, despite slightly reduced turnover and lower cash profits. Previously published results for 2010 were restated, following a decision to include revenue share payments to the DfT as an operating cost rather than netting them off revenue grant receipts. The effect was to increase revenue and operating costs by £15m (2011: £11.7m).

PERIOD TO:	08/01/11	09/01/10
	£000	£000
Turnover	571,930	614,694
Operating Costs:	540,658	582,746
Operating Profit:	31,272	31,948
Operating Margin:	5.5%	5.2%
Turnover per Employee	£119,801	£129,355
Track Access	125,258	166,971
Rolling stock lease	34,340	35,531
Revenue Grant	339,883	390,069

NON FRANCHISED OPERATORS

HULL TRAINS

The company returned to profitability during the year, as income grew but costs were reduced sharply. The directors report that they continued to experience problems with the Class 180 train sets which were fully refurbished during the year. However the business did carry more than 750,000 passengers during the year - a new record and virtually a tenfold increase compared with the company's first year total of 80,000 a decade earlier.

PERIOD TO:	31/03/11	31/03/10
	£000	£000
Turnover	21,743	21,160
Operating Costs:	20,008	23,034
Operating Profit:	1,735	(1,874)
Operating Margin:	8.0%	-8.9%
Turnover per Employee	£219,626	£218,144
Rolling stock lease	1,934	1,713

EUROSTAR

The accounts were drawn for the period to 31 August 2010 to reflect the major change in the nature and structure of the business which was completed at that date. Whereas the company previously only operated the UK share of the services, from 1 September 2010, Eurostar International Ltd owns and operates all the assets associated with the Eurostar train services, and is co-owned by London & Continental Railways, SNCF and SNCB. The company improved its performance during the year, recording reduced operating losses ahead of exceptional items.

PERIOD TO:	30/08/10	31/12/09
	£000	£000
Turnover	209,400	316,200
Operating Costs:	243,500	412,500
Operating Profit:	(34,100)	(96,300)
Operating Margin:	-16.3%	-30.5%
Turnover per Employee	£177,157	£243,418
Track Access	0	(6,000)

GRAND CENTRAL

The company achieved a further improvement in its results during the year, though it continued to make heavy losses. This was the first full year of operation of the full network of Bradford and Sunderland services. The company was purchased by Arriva in November 2011.

PERIOD TO:	31/03/11	31/12/09
	£000	£000
Turnover	18,959	11,580
Operating Costs:	25,762	18,006
Operating Profit:	(6,803)	(6,426)
Operating Margin:	-35.9%	-55.5%
Turnover per Employee	£151,673	£152,373
Rolling stock lease	5,236	1,185

PASSENGER OPERATOR ARTICLES

In the following pages, statistics for train operating companies (TOCs) are drawn from data published by the Office of Rail Regulation and Department for Transport (DfT).

Punctuality figures are the Public Performance Measure annual average - for long distance operators, the percentage of trains arriving within ten minutes of planned arrival time at final destination; and for London & South East operators and regional, Scotland and Wales operators, the percentage arriving within 5min of planned arrival time.

The subsidy figures include franchise payments and revenue support: negative values mean the DfT was receiving payments. Network grant figures are DfT estimates based on each TOC's share of track access charges. The grant is paid directly to Network Rail but is acknowledged by the DfT as a subsidy to TOCs, reducing the track access charges they pay.

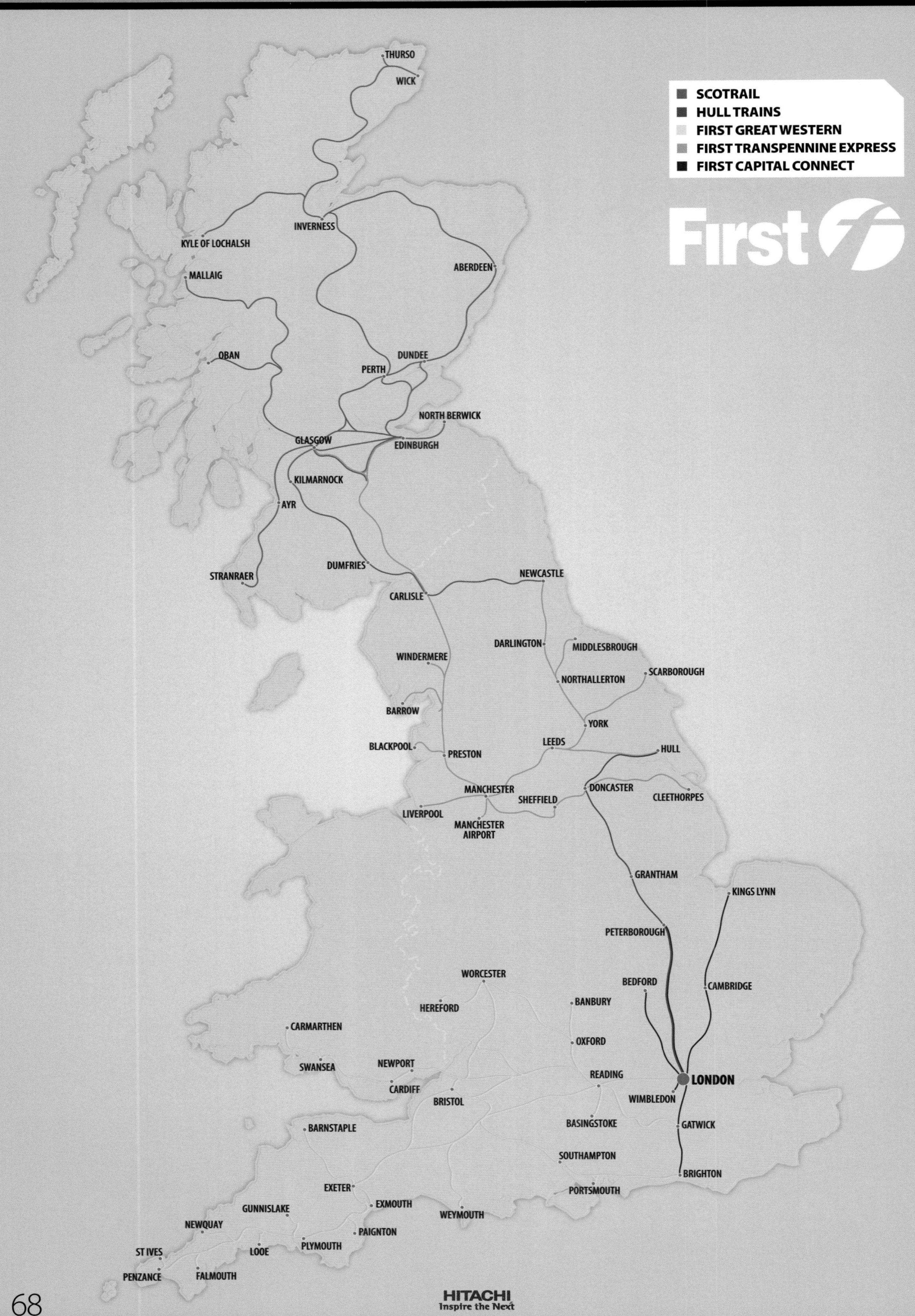
SCOTRAIL
HULL TRAINS
FIRST GREAT WESTERN
FIRST TRANSPENNINE EXPRESS
FIRST CAPITAL CONNECT
First
THURSO
WICK
INVERNESS
KYLE OF LOCHALSH
MALLAIG
ABERDEEN
OBAN
DUNDEE
PERTH
NORTH BERWICK
GLASGOW
EDINBURGH
KILMARNOCK
AYR
STRANRAER
DUMFRIES
NEWCASTLE
CARLISLE
DARLINGTON
MIDDLESBROUGH
WINDERMERE
NORTHALLERTON
SCARBOROUGH
BARROW
YORK
LEEDS
HULL
BLACKPOOL
PRESTON
MANCHESTER
DONCASTER
CLEETHORPES
SHEFFIELD
LIVERPOOL
MANCHESTER AIRPORT
GRANTHAM
KINGS LYNN
PETERBOROUGH
WORCESTER
BEDFORD
CAMBRIDGE
HEREFORD
BANBURY
CARMARTHEN
OXFORD
SWANSEA
NEWPORT
READING
LONDON
CARDIFF
BRISTOL
WIMBLEDON
BARNSTAPLE
BASINGSTOKE
GATWICK
SOUTHAMPTON
BRIGHTON
EXETER
PORTSMOUTH
EXMOUTH
GUNNISLAKE
WEYMOUTH
NEWQUAY
PAIGNTON
ST IVES
LOOE
PLYMOUTH
PENZANCE
FALMOUTH

FIRSTGROUP

FirstGroup is the largest rail operator in the UK, operating almost a quarter of the rail network. FirstGroup has a varied portfolio of long distance, regional and commuter rail companies and is the only operator of sleeper services. FirstGroup carried more than 310 million passengers in the year to 31 March 2013, an increase of 50m since 2006/07 when it commenced operating their current franchise mix.

First's UK Rail division has some 13,500 employees and around 2,800 rail vehicles. The division includes four franchises: First Capital Connect; First Great Western; First ScotRail; and First TransPennine Express. FirstGroup also operates First Hull Trains, the non-franchised open-access operator, in which it has an 80pc share, resulting from the purchase of GB Railways in 2003.

FirstGroup also operates the London Tramlink service on behalf of TfL which carried 29 million passengers in the last year; as well as operating passenger services in the Oresund region of Denmark in partnership with Danish State Railways. First's other major operations are in UK Bus and North America.

Revenue in UK Rail was £2,795.1m in 2012/13 (2011/12: £2,506.1m) and operating profit was £63.2m (2011/12: £110.5m) reflecting the reduction in profits at First TransPennine Express in the three year operating period at margins closer to the industry average. Like-for-like passenger revenue increased by 7.4pc, reflecting strong volume growth across all of its train companies.

FirstGroup has a strong track record of investment with nearly 750 new rolling stock vehicles introduced and punctuality and performance increasing across the franchises since they commenced operation.

FirstGroup's UK Rail Managing Director is Vernon Barker, appointed in September 2011, and previously Managing Director of First TransPennine Express which has seen growth since 2004 from 13m to 24m passengers per annum.

A First Great Western InterCity 125 train is headed by power car No 43124, powering away from Didcot towards London on 5 June 2013. Keith Fender

First Great Western

23 MONTH AWARD FROM OCTOBER 2013

Branded as First Great Western (FGW), the Greater Western franchise began operation on 1 April 2006, combining the previous Great Western intercity, Thames Valley, and West Country regional franchises.

In 2011 a contractual three-year extension to the franchise was not taken up by FirstGroup, and the Department for Transport (DfT) looked to develop plans for a longer term franchise to help deliver route electrification, Crossrail and introduction of Intercity Express Programme trains. But the DfT paused its franchising programme in October 2012, and a 28 week extension for FGW has been followed by a 23 month direct award agreement from 14 October 2013.

Investment over the course of the franchise on station facilities and maintenance, and customer information has totalled £85m, working with rail industry partners, the DfT and local authorities. The company has continued to work to improve performance and customer service, and, with Network Rail, to tackle infrastructure quality - and flood prevention after problems in 2012, the second wettest year on record. Public Performance Measure punctuality for the four-week period ending in mid-October 2013 was 89.3pc, with the annual average score standing at 88.8pc.

FGW successfully added 48 extra carriages to its fleet by 2012 as part of a third capacity deal with the DfT designed to reduce crowding on the most popular peak services. This delivered an additional 4,500 extra seats for customers on peak services into and out of London Paddington,

KEY STATISTICS

FIRST GREAT WESTERN

	2011-12	2012-13
Punctuality	90.6%	89.1%
Passenger journeys (millions)	95.6	97.3
Passenger km (millions)	5,840.4	5,867.8
Timetabled train km (millions)	42.7	42.8
Route km operated	1,997.2	1,997.2
Number of stations operated	210	209
Number of employees	4,874	5,156
Subsidy per passenger km (p)	-1.9	-2.9
Network grant / pass km (p)	5.5	5.7

as well as around 10pc more seats for customers using services to Reading, Bristol, Exeter and Plymouth.

Capacity solutions included conversion of 15 buffet cars to standard passenger vehicles. FGW re-introduced five Class 180 trains and acquired and re-engineered eight non-standard DMU vehicles.

This deal followed previous agreements with the DfT which enabled FGW to secure additional DMUs for Devon and Cornwall in 2008 and 2009; and for the Bristol area in 2011.

Working with Bristol City Council and the Severnside Community Rail Partnership FGW has worked to improve and promote services through Bristol. An additional evening return service for Avonmouth was introduced in September 2013.

A further £40m is being invested in improving stations throughout the network, and work has now started on a number of station upgrades, with several major car park enlargement schemes. The £800m redevelopment of Reading station has improved platform and track capacity.

Working with restaurateur Mitch Tonks, FGW launched a new, Southwest sourced menu in 2013 on its Pullman dining services, the UK's only remaining silver service on-train restaurant. Two additional Pullman services began in 2013 - breakfast from Penzance and lunch from Paddington.

Network Rail and FGW recently completed track re-doubling on the North Cotswolds line, and a similar scheme for Swindon-Kemble is due for completion in 2014.

FGW is working with the DfT to secure further service improvements in 2014-15, including a fleet of electric trains in the Thames Valley; a programme to increase standard class capacity on High Speed Trains; and extend Wi-Fi to more trains.

Provision of two additional sleeper vehicles, one sleeper and one seating carriage, will increase seasonal capacity. An additional six return services between Newton Abbot and Paignton will be introduced, and FGW will continue to support the Devon Metro and Tavistock proposals for more frequent services, and Cornwall Council's plans for a West Cornwall transport interchange.

An improvement in Standard-class capacity, particularly for Thames Valley commuters, was created in October 2013 with declassification of one First-class compartment on each of the 21 Class-166 trains.

FGW has seven train maintenance and servicing depots; Old Oak Common, London; Laira, Plymouth; St Philips Marsh, Bristol; Long Rock, Penzance; Landore, Swansea; Exeter; and Reading. A new depot at Reading, to replace the existing facility as a result of the infrastructure remodelling, opened in 2013.

The FGW diesel multiple-unit fleet consists has these 2-car units: Class 143 (8 units), Class 150/1 (15), Class 150/2 (19), Class 158 (2), Class 165/1 (20); and 3-car units: Class 150/0 (2), Class 158 (13), Class 165/1 (16), Class 166 (21); plus 14 Class-153 single-car units. There are five Class 180 trains (25 vehicles).

The HST fleet has 119 Class 43 power cars and 442 Mk3 coaches (12 of the power cars and 42 Mk3 vehicles are owned outright by FirstGroup).

There are 19 Mk3 Sleeper vehicles and four Class 57/6 locomotives mainly used on sleeper trains.

SENIOR PERSONNEL

FIRST GREAT WESTERN

MANAGING DIRECTOR Mark Hopwood (in photo)
ENGINEERING DIRECTOR Andrew Mellors
OPERATIONS DIRECTOR Ben Rule
PROJECTS AND PLANNING DIRECTOR Mike Hogg
BID DIRECTOR Matthew Golton
DIRECTOR OF COMMUNICATION Sue Evans
FINANCE DIRECTOR Ben Caswell
HEAD OF SALES & MARKETING Diane Burke
HEAD OF HR Sharon Johnston
HEAD OF SAFETY Paul Williams

First Capital Connect

The Thameslink/Great Northern franchise, operated by First Capital Connect (FCC) was awarded as a six year franchise from 1 April 2006, with a possible extension to nine years. In August 2011 The Department for Transport announced that FCC would be refranchised in 2012/13 to help delivery of the Thameslink route improvement programme, but then there was a 'pause' following the problems with Intercity West Coast refranchising. In March 2013 it was announced that a further award will extend the FCC franchise to September 2014: then a new seven-year franchise is due to begin, initially consisting of Thameslink/Great Northern plus some current Southeastern services, and later (in July 2015) adding the present Southern franchise.

FCC has meantime begun taking further steps to improve the punctuality and reliability of its services, with Network Rail given more opportunities in the evening and at weekends to maintain and upgrade the track, and appointment of a director to focus on improving the strategic approach of the company to improve service performance. A £350,000 programme to give all trains a 'deep clean' began in September 2013, with more cleaners employed on trains while in service.

FCC has two groups of routes. Thameslink runs from Brighton and Gatwick Airport through London to Luton and Bedford, with a south London loop line via Wimbledon and Sutton. Great Northern runs from London King's Cross and Moorgate to Welwyn, Hertford, Stevenage, Peterborough, Cambridge and King's Lynn. These include some of the busiest sections of the rail network.

The Thameslink and Great Northern routes will be linked at King's Cross using new infrastructure as part of the Thameslink Programme which will also provide major capacity improvements for the cross-London core of the Thameslink route.

The start of the programme saw significant changes to services during 2009, with the closure of the branch to Moorgate and bay platforms at Blackfriars. Through-running began of some Southeastern services to FCC stations north of London, in a joint operation.

Additional capacity was provided by transfer of the final eight Class 319 EMUs from Southern in March 2009, and delivery of 23 new Class 377/5 Electrostars on a long sub-lease

KEY STATISTICS

FIRST CAPITAL CONNECT

	2011-12	2012-13
Punctuality (0-5min)	90.0%	88.3%
Passenger journeys (millions)	99.7	106.3
Passenger km (millions)	3,456.1	3,637.6
Timetabled train km (millions)	24.5	24.8
Route km operated	500.9	500.9
Number of stations operated	78	78
Number of employees	2,374	2,459
Subsidy per passenger km (p)	-4.7	-5.1
Network grant / pass km (p)	3.3	3.3

First Capital Connect's Class 365 No 365515 at Ely on a service from King's Lynn to London King's Cross. Tony Miles

from Southern. From December 2011 FCC sub-leased a further three Electrostars from Southern to enable it to run 12-car trains on the Brighton line. Timetable changes have delivered a net gain since February 2009 of almost 5,000 seats per day in morning and evening peaks combined.

Thameslink Programme work is to see Thameslink trains diverted away from London Bridge, starting in December 2014. New Class 387 Electrostar trains ordered from Bombardier on behalf of the DfT by Southern (116 vehicles) are to be in service by May 2015, enabling Class 319 trains to be released for newly electrified routes elsewhere in the UK. The '387s' should later themselves be released by new Desiro City trains built by Siemens.

On the Great Northern route, 13 additional Class 321 and three Class 313 trains have added another 6,850 seats, delivering capacity improvements particularly on the Hertford Loop, as well as more 12-car trains to Cambridge.

FCC has made available a range of real time information tools for customers: using Twitter, email, SMS text, and its website. Over 40,000 people follow @firstcc on Twitter. FCC has launched a customer service apprenticeship scheme - the first of its type in the rail industry. It had a 76pc overall customer satisfaction rating in the spring 2013 National Passenger Survey.

FCC has been investing in station improvements in collaboration with DfT, NR and local authorities. St Albans station now has the most bike rack spaces of any station in the country. The company has achieved Secure Station status at all 74 of its managed stations and crime is down by 41.4pc since the start of the franchise.

First Capital Connect's train fleet comprises: Class 313 (44 trains); 317/1 (12), 319/0 (13); 319/2 (7); 319/3 (26); 319/4 (40); Class 321 (13 trains); 365 (40); Class 377/5 (23); 377/2 (3). All are 4-car units apart from Class 313 (3-car).

The Class 365s, serving the Great Northern route, are to be transformed with fresh interiors and enhanced accessibility features as part of a major investment by owners Eversholt Rail which will also include heavy maintenance.

FCC's main maintenance depot is at Hornsey on the Great Northern route, where heavy maintenance of all trains is carried out. The £13m maintenance depot at Bedford Cauldwell Walk was opened for servicing of trains which could not reach their depot south of the Thames when the Thameslink route was closed for rebuilding at St Pancras in 2004-05. It is now the main maintenance base for Class 319s. Cricklewood depot was reopened in 2006 for stabling, light maintenance and cleaning of Thameslink route trains.

SENIOR PERSONNEL

FIRST CAPITAL CONNECT

MANAGING DIRECTOR David Statham (in photo)
COMMERCIAL DIRECTOR Laura Dunley
ENGINEERING DIRECTOR Robin Kay
THAMESLINK PROGRAMME DIRECTOR Jonathan Bridgewood
OPERATIONS DIRECTOR Jackie Townsend
FINANCE DIRECTOR Chris Cornthwaite
CUSTOMER SERVICE DIRECTOR Keith Jipps

FRANCHISE EXTENDED TO MARCH 2015

ScotRail operates passenger services within Scotland, as well as cross-border Caledonian Sleeper services to London. In 2004, FirstGroup's present franchise began, and the Scottish Government took on full funding responsibility. In 2006 Transport Scotland assumed responsibility for the majority of rail powers in Scotland and also for infrastructure projects, working in conjunction with regional transport partnerships. In April 2008 the ScotRail franchise was extended by three years to November 2014, and in December 2012 by an additional 28 weeks (until 31 March 2015), to allow time to assess Westminster's franchising review.

The next ScotRail franchise will have a review in Year 5 to decide whether it will run for seven or 10 years. The sleeper service will have a separate 15-year franchise, with £100m jointly pledged by Westminster and Holyrood for modernisation of trains.

Network and train rebranding with the new Saltire livery continues, and will not change should new operators be chosen.

Improved customer service results are helping to drive increased passenger numbers. In the Spring 2013 National Passenger Survey, ScotRail ranked higher than the UK average in 30 of 36 categories.

ScotRail manages 346 stations but serves 363; its Public Performance Measure score for train punctuality stood at 91.8pc (annual average) in mid October 2013. Annual payments to FirstGroup vary with performance, monitored by a Service Quality Incentive Regime (SQUIRE) which focuses on 20 areas of station quality and 16 areas of train quality.

Transport Minister, Keith Brown, has capped peak fares increases in 2014 and 2015 to the Retail Price Index (RPI), with off-peak fares held after 2013 provided RPI remains below 3.5pc.

A revised Edinburgh Glasgow Improvements Programme (EGIP) will see platforms at Glasgow Queen Street extended for longer trains, with investment of £650million in the scheme. In 2013 Carillion started work on the £40m electrification of the 50km Cumbernauld-Glasgow Queen Street line, and this will be followed by the Glasgow Queen Street-Edinburgh line, with longer trains introduced to meet demand forecasts, and with journey time cut to 42min.

The Paisley Corridor Improvement (PCI) project has delivered higher-capacity infrastructure, and the £12m award-winning Paisley Canal route electrification took an innovative approach which saw the £28m cost estimate significantly reduced by use of neutral sections at locations with restricted clearances.

KEY STATISTICS

SCOTRAIL

	2011-12	2012-13
Punctuality (0-5min)	90.7%	93.0%
Passenger journeys (millions)	81.1	83.3
Passenger km (millions)	2,681.6	2,712.8
Timetabled train km (millions)	43.8	44.4
Route km operated	3,065.8	3,065.8
Number of stations operated	346	347
Number of employees	4,585	4,741
Subsidy per passenger km (p)	11.4	10.7

SENIOR PERSONNEL

SCOTRAIL

MANAGING DIRECTOR Steve Montgomery (in photo)
ACTING FINANCE DIRECTOR Billy Connelly
COMMERCIAL DIRECTOR Sean Duffy
OPERATIONS DIRECTOR Jacqueline Dey
ENGINEERING DIRECTOR Ken Docherty
HUMAN RESOURCES DIRECTOR Julie McComasky
CUSTOMER SERVICES DIRECTOR Jacqueline Taggart.
DIRECTOR OF BUSINESS PLANNING Jerry Farquharson
DIRECTOR OF FACILITIES & BUSINESS SERVICES Pat Callaghan

ScotRail has made significant investment to ensure the impact of disruption on passengers is minimised, and that reliable information is shared in an accessible and timely fashion. ScotRail has introduced Smartcard ticketing to its busiest routes during 2013.

ScotRail's pioneering alcohol ban which made it illegal to visibly carry or consume alcohol on ScotRail trains between 21.00 and 10.00 has been well received by passengers, and further customer focused plans include the installation of free wifi on all Class 170 and 380 trains, and 26 stations, in a £3.25m investment supported by the Scottish Government.

ScotRail is refining the successful Golflink concept for the 2014 Ryder Cup at Gleneagles, where rail access will play a key role for the huge crowds expected. In 2012 ScotRail began a £1million programme of improvements in passenger facilities at 19 stations in the run up to the 2014 Commonwealth Games.

First TransPennine Express

EXTENSION TO FEBRUARY 2016

First TransPennine Express (FTPE) is a joint operation by First Group (55pc share) and Keolis. French Railways (SNCF) is a major shareholder in Keolis, which operates trains, buses and metros across Europe and in other countries. Initially the franchise was awarded for eight years with an optional five-year extension: in August 2011 the Department for Transport (DfT) announced an extension, to April 2015 at the latest. Following the franchising review, in March 2013 the DfT scheduled an extension or new direct award, running to February 2016.

FTPE runs inter-city train services linking Liverpool and Manchester with Leeds, York and the Northeast, with Sheffield and Doncaster, and the Lake District. In 2006/07 it took over the Manchester Airport-Blackpool North and Manchester-Glasgow/ Edinburgh routes.

10 new 4-car Siemens Desiro electric multiple-units will all enter service by May 2014, providing 30pc more capacity and 25pc more luggage space across the FTPE fleet. They will take over most Glasgow/Edinburgh services, with 15 daily services each way, a 36pc increase in frequency, and giving an 82pc increase in capacity with the longer trains. (Sunday services will increase to 10 each way.)

Class 185 DMUs then released will provide an additional 21,000 seats a week between Manchester and Leeds. A new Liverpool-Newcastle service via Manchester Victoria will give significant journey time reductions - improvements supported by new traincrew depots at Liverpool and Preston.

In December 2014, electric trains will be able to run from Liverpool to Manchester via Newton le Willows; in December 2016 between Blackpool, Preston, Manchester and Stalybridge; and by December 2018 on to Huddersfield, Leeds, and York.

KEY STATISTICS

FIRST TRANSPENNINE EXPRESS

	2011-12	2012-13
Punctuality (0-10min)	93.3%	91.7%
Passenger journeys (millions)	24.8	24.9
Passenger km (millions)	1,575.8	1,603.9
Timetabled train km (millions)	17.4	17.4
Route km operated	1,250.5	1,250.5
Number of stations operated	30	30
Number of employees	1,030	1,126
Subsidy per passenger km (p)	5.0	2.6
Network grant / pass km (p)	7.5	7.6

Since the franchise began, passenger journeys have seen a 0.6pc year-on-year increase, with underlying income growth of 10pc (2.5pc ahead of industry average).

FTPE has been particularly successful in developing advance purchase ticket sales, with a 100pc increase between 2009/10 and 2012/13. Advance sales made up 11.5pc of revenue in 2009/10 and 17.6pc in 2012/13. Pioneering initiatives for the student market include a 50pc discount on FTPE advance fares for holders of the 16-25 Railcard.

FTPE recorded a PPM score of 87.8pc for punctuality in the four

In ScotRail 'Saltire' livery, Class 380 No 380006 departs from the Paisley Gilmour Street for Glasgow Central. The station was re-roofed in 2011 in a £9m project carried out by C Spencer Ltd for Network Rail. Tony Miles

From December 2012 the Glasgow-Ayr timetable was recast, following the Paisley Corridor improvement work, to provide two additional fast trains an hour. Highland main line timings have been accelerated following line-speed improvements. An extra early-morning train to Edinburgh and a Sunday service have been introduced on the Shotts route, with additional weekday trains between Edinburgh and Glasgow Central via Carstairs and Motherwell.

In 2014 ScotRail will introduce more frequent services between Glasgow and Ayr, improved services to Oban, additional Sunday services between Aberdeen and the central belt, as well as improved commuter services for Aberdeen.

ScotRail has also made significant infrastructure improvements for cycle users. In 2013 it spent £140,000 upgrading facilities at 20 stations.

The £4m current refurbishment and overhaul project for Class 334 trains was awarded to Railway Projects Limited, with much of the work sub-contracted to Kilmarnock-based Brodie Engineering, creating up to 20 new jobs.

The project to overhaul Class-320 EMUs to improve accessibility, managed by Eversholt, was completed in October 2013. Class 314 has been put through an £800,000 improvement programme, and work has begun to refurbish Class 318s.

Caledonian Sleeper services are hauled by locomotives hired from DBS (Class 90 electrics, usually carrying FirstGroup livery, for the main haul between London and Glasgow/Edinburgh, and Class 67 onwards to Aberdeen, Fort William and Inverness).

The ScotRail fleet has 2-car diesel multiple-units of Class 156 (48 trains) and Class 158 (48 trains). 3-car DMUs are of Class 170/3 (4 trains), and Class 170/4 (55). 3-car electric multiple-units are of Class 314 (16 trains), Class 318 (21), Class 320 (22), Class 334 (40). There are 22 three-car and 16 four-car Class 380 EMUs, delivered by Siemens from 2010.

First TransPennine Express Class 185 trains depart and arrive simultaneously at the west end of Leeds station, forming trains bound for Liverpool Lime Street (right) and Scarborough. Brian Morrison

weeks to mid October 2013, taking its annual average score to 90.5pc.

Following on from a £20m station improvement programme, additional funding from the DfT is providing accessibility improvements. All 30 FTPE-managed stations have been accredited as Secure Stations: a 9% drop in recorded crime at stations has been recorded.

In the Spring 2013 National Passenger Survey, FTPE scored 85pc for overall satisfaction. The company has invested heavily in staff training with 'Doing the Right Thing' and 'Your Customer Needs You' programmes proving particularly successful. The company has introduced a free customer mobile app and an innovative customer service facility on twitter. Staff are encouraged to involve themselves in community and charitable work and in 2012/13 FTPE raised almost £138,000 for good causes.

FTPE's Class 185 fleet continues to deliver effective fuel savings thanks to the 'Eco Drive' project, combining fuel saving technology with structured driving techniques. FTPE reports that from 1 April to 12 October 2013 it saved 1.98m litres of fuel, compared with estimated usage without the initiative. FTPE is certified to the ISO 14001 environmental performance standard.

The 10 additional 110mph Siemens Class 350/4 four-car 'Desiro' EMUs will join FTPE's existing fleet of 51 three-car, 100mph DMUs and 9 two-car Class 170 Turbostar sets. Effective management of the DMU fleet has enabled an uplift of 16pc in passenger miles to be delivered whilst using same level of fleet resource.

SENIOR PERSONNEL
FIRST TRANSPENNINE EXPRESS

MANAGING DIRECTOR Nick Donovan (in photo)
COMMERCIAL DIRECTOR Darren Higgins
ENGINEERING DIRECTOR Paul Staples
PROGRAMME DIRECTOR Chris Nutton
OPERATIONS DIRECTOR Paul Watson
FINANCE DIRECTOR Liz Collins
HEAD OF HR Sue Whaley

First Hull Trains

NON-FRANCHISED INTERCITY TRAIN COMPANY

First Hull Trains celebrated its 13th anniversary on 25 September 2013. In its first year, the company carried just 80,000 passengers between Hull and London on its three daily services. Today it runs 90 services per week and it carries around 750,000 passengers a year.

The non-franchised ('open access') intercity train company operating between Hull and London King's Cross had three trains a day at the outset: there are now seven return services on weekdays, and five on Saturday and Sunday.

First Hull Trains is 80pc owned by FirstGroup, following the buyout of its previous parent company, GB Railways. The original promoter of Hull Trains, Renaissance Trains, set up by two former British Rail managers, John Nelson and Michael Jones, owns the remaining 20pc.

In June 2002, the company was awarded 10-year rights by the Rail Regulator, and investment of some £36m saw a new fleet of 4-car Class 222 'Pioneer' trains come into use. These were released for use by East Midlands Trains, and in 2008 a new leasing deal with Angel Trains brought four 5-Car Class 180s in their place. The Class 180s offer valuable additional capacity (around half a million extra seats a year).

An application for rights to be extended until 2018 was made to the Office of Rail Regulation (ORR) in 2008, along with an application to introduce a new four-trains-per-day open-access service between Harrogate and King's Cross via York. ORR decided against the Harrogate service but granted firm rights for seven weekday and five weekend return services until December 2014 - later extended until the end of 2016 in exchange for a commitment on train refurbishment and car park improvement at Howden.

Class 180 No 180111 forms the 09.48 First Hull Trains service from London King's Cross to Hull, passing Offord Cluny, south of Huntingdon, on 13 July 2013. Ken Brunt

Sustained investment in the company's engineering capability following the completion of the £4.5m overhaul of the entire Class 180 fleet which delivered significant performance improvement. In late 2013, First Hull Trains was one of the most reliable long distance train operating companies, with record levels of punctuality and reliability alongside unprecedented miles per casualty (MPC) figures (15,000 MPC – a 500percent increase on when the company introduced the current trains in 2008).

A new commercial strategy, launched in 2012, has delivered a market share increase across First Hull Trains' route of 3pc. A commitment to client research, pro-active marketing, and the introduction of ticketing innovation has delivered particular success outside the Humber heartland with growth in Retford and Grantham of 4pc and 16pc respectively.

In June 2013, First Hull Trains was the highest ranking train operating company in the UK for customer service, as part of the National Passenger Survey - for two full consecutive years, the company has maintained an overall satisfaction rating of 95pc.

The company continues to pioneer client service and innovation, launching new M-ticketing technology, with 9pc of 'First Hull Trains only' advance tickets now issued via smartphones. A new website with greater functionality and real time train running information was launched in late 2012.

First Hull Trains is working with industry partners, regional politicians, financiers and business leaders to drive through ambitious electrification plans between Hull and Selby - 35 miles in total. Whilst still in the planning phase, First Hull Trains is spearheading the works in an attempt to secure longer access rights, to improve connectivity and to enhance reliability and punctuality.

KEY STATISTICS
FIRST HULL TRAINS

	2011-12	2012-13
Punctuality (0-10min):	81.8%	81.8%
Passenger journeys:	720,928	735,358
Timetabled train km (millions):	1.48	1.48
Route km operated:	329.0	329.0
Number of stations operated:	0	0
Staff employed:	105	106

SENIOR PERSONNEL
FIRST HULL TRAINS

MANAGING DIRECTOR Will Dunnett (in photo)
SERVICE DELIVERY DIRECTOR Keith Doughty
FINANCE MANAGER Glenn McLeish-Longthorn
HEAD OF ENGINEERING Jonathan Plowright
PERFORMANCE MANAGER Louise Mendham
ON BOARD STANDARDS MANAGER Paul Boulonois
HEAD OF HR Victoria Evans

GOVIA

Govia is a joint venture partnership between British company The Go-Ahead Group and Keolis. Go-Ahead, the 65pc majority partner, employs 23,000 people in UK rail and bus. More than one billion passenger journeys were made on Go-Ahead's bus and rail companies in 2012-13.

Keolis - in which French Railways (SNCF) is a major shareholder - operates trains, buses and metros across the world.

Rail has been a key element of Go-Ahead's transport strategy since privatisation and the businesses has continued to focus on strong commuter rail links into London. Today, Govia is responsible for nearly 30pc of national passenger rail journeys and is the UK's busiest rail operator.

Go-Ahead operated the Thames Trains franchise from 1996 to 2004 and Govia the Thameslink franchise from 1997 to 2006.

Govia took over the South Central franchise in 2001, later rebranding it as Southern. It retained the franchise in a new agreement from September 2009. In 2008, Gatwick Express became part of the franchise.

Govia was awarded the Integrated Kent franchise, now branded Southeastern, in 2006 and launched the UK's first domestic high speed service in 2009. In November 2007 Govia began operating the new West Midlands franchise under the name London Midland.

Govia was shortlisted in 2012 to bid for the Thameslink, Southern and Great Northern rail franchise, for which the invitation to tender was issued in September 2013.

SOUTHERN

5 YEAR 10 MONTH FRANCHISE FROM SEPTEMBER 2009

The South Central franchise, operated by Govia as 'Southern', is due to become part of the new Thameslink, Southern and Great Northern franchise in 2015.

The current franchise runs from 20 September 2009 to 25 July 2015: Govia also held the previous franchise, from 2003. Southern provides train services in South London and connects central London to the South Coast, East and West Sussex, Surrey and parts of Kent and Hampshire.

The franchise is meeting a commitment to deliver an additional 10pc capacity by December 2013, including extending eight-car trains to ten cars on key inner-suburban 'Metro' routes. In December 2011 Southern ordered 130 Electrostar vehicles, worth £200m, from Bombardier, to form 26 five-car sets. Porterbrook is providing capital funding. The first train went into service in September 2013.

An additional option for eight 5-car dual-voltage trains was exercised, and these will enter service in 2014, including on Croydon-Milton Keynes services, increasing capacity.

During 2014 Southern will be equipping its fleet with GSM-R cab radio, and a new Driver Advisory System will be fitted to the Class 171 diesel fleet: this continually calculates the correct speed in the prevailing circumstances for a specific route. The company's driver simulators have also been upgraded to enable training for energy efficient driving.

The flagship route of the franchise is the Brighton main line. Southern also operates Gatwick Express services, some of which are extended to Brighton in weekday peaks. In February 2014, opening of an additional platform at Gatwick Airport station will improve performance, as most Gatwick Express trains will no longer need to cross the slow lines at the airport station.

As part of the Thameslink Programme, Southern sub-leases 26 four-car dual-voltage Class-377 trains to First Capital Connect. Additional capacity at Southern was created through the reinstatement of five Class 442 trains from store, and transfer of 19 Class-313 units released by London Overground.

KEY STATISTICS
SOUTHERN

	2011-12	2012-13
Punctuality (0-5min)	90.0%	88.0%
Passenger journeys (millions)	174.1	171.4
Passenger km (millions)	4,395.4	4,386.0
Timetabled train km (millions)	38.0	37.8
Route km operated	666.3	666.3
Number of stations operated	158	156
Number of employees	4,104	3,979
Subsidy per passenger km (p)	-0.4	-4.9
Network grant / pass km (p)	4.3	4.5

A Southern Class 377 Electrostar approaches Clapham Junction. Porterbrook funds the entire Southern '377' fleet including recent orders for 170 vehicles. Porterbrook

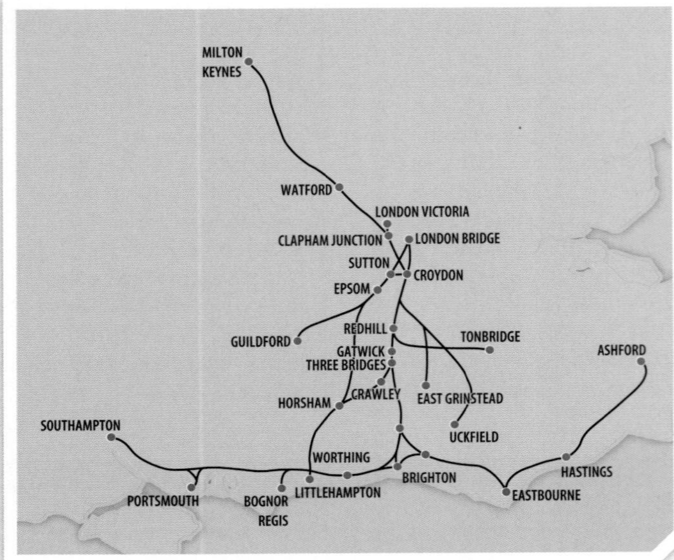

In July 2013, Southern - as delivery partner to the Department for Transport - ordered 116 new Class 377 vehicles, valued at about £180m, to help with Thameslink rolling stock transfers. The order has an option for 140 more vehicles. The new trains are to be used on the Thameslink route (releasing trains to newly electrified routes), and will themselves later move to other routes.

Southern is working through a £76m investment programme, including £23m of interior and reliability improvements to trains. All Class 377 trains now use regenerative braking, and the Class 377, 455 and 171 trains are currently being refurbished. Improved passenger access and integration at stations, security, easier ticket buying, enhanced revenue protection and an improved overall passenger experience are also moving ahead. The company has upgraded information screens and all stations have been deep cleaned and repainted. All Greater London stations have been staffed from the first to last service. Southern launched its online Passenger Panel in September 2010 and it now has over 5,000 members.

At Brighton, improvements valued at £5million have removed concourse clutter and opened up the view along the train shed. At East Croydon the new footbridge at the London end of the station will provide a new entrance, along with new retail units and lifts.

95% of passengers pass through stations that have secure station status (a Department for Transport accredited scheme). The company is working to create a sustainable rail network with passengers' needs at the centre of its business. It is committed to making rail travel more accessible, more affordable and environmentally efficient. Its new Smartcard system, 'the key', became available for use in London by some point-to-point season ticket holders in October 2013, the first time that a train company's ITSO smartcard had become live in London.

Revenue share has applied from the start of the franchise, and revenue support from 21 September 2013.

The cost base was significantly reduced following a change in the network access regime from April 2009, which cut Southern's access charges by almost £80m a year from the outset of the franchise. These changes were expected to result in a total premium over five years, ten months of £534m (net present value) to the DfT.

All Southern routes are electrified at 750V DC, except for Oxted-Uckfield and Ashford-Hastings, which are worked by Class 171 diesel units (six 4-car and ten 2- car).

Electric multiple-units are of: Class 313 (19 x 3-car); Class 377 (28 x 3-car, 154 x 4-car, plus additional deliveries from Sept 2013); Class 442 (24 x 5-car); Class 455 (46 x 4-car); Class 456 (24 x 2-car - to be transferred to South West Trains).

The main train depots are at Selhurst (also responsible for overhaul), Brighton, and Stewarts Lane, Battersea.

SENIOR PERSONNEL

SOUTHERN

MANAGING DIRECTOR Chris Burchell (in photo)
FINANCE AND CONTRACTS DIRECTOR Bob Mayne
FLEET DIRECTOR Gerry McFadden
SERVICE DELIVERY DIRECTOR James Burt
COMMERCIAL DIRECTOR Alex Foulds
PERFORMANCE DIRECTOR David Scorey
HUMAN RESOURCES DIRECTOR Matt Watson
HEAD OF SAFETY AND OPERATIONAL STANDARDS Colin Morris

southeastern.

FRANCHISE EXTENSION UNTIL JUNE 2018

The six-year Southeastern franchise from 1 April 2006 was extended until 12 October 2014: then, until June 2018, Southeastern is expected to move into a new direct award period, the longest extension granted to any operator.

The Southeastern franchise serves Kent, southeast London and part of East Sussex and includes domestic services on High Speed 1 (HS1 -the Channel Tunnel Rail Link). The automatic two-year extension from 31 March 2012 was granted when performance targets were met. Southeastern entered 80pc revenue support in April 2010, which the company says is a reflection of the recession.

Southeastern is committed to improving the number of trains arriving within 5min of schedule from 89.2pc in 2008 to 93.74pc in 2014. In October 2013 the score stood at 91.1pc, higher than the national average. In 2013, after a break of several years, the company re-launched an autumn timetable designed to improve performance during leaf fall.

The start of high-speed services in December 2009 saw a major recast of both main-line and inner-suburban (Metro) timetables, with a 5pc overall increase in peak capacity. The high-speed service has brought a dramatic reduction in journey times for many journeys, including: London to Ashford in 37min, Canterbury in 59min. The popularity of peak services has seen trains around 80pc full.

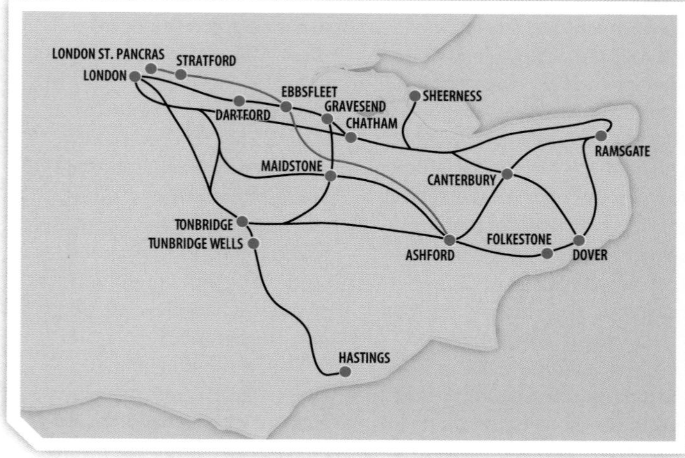

KEY STATISTICS
SOUTHEASTERN

	2011-12	2012-13
Punctuality (0-5min)	91.7%	91.1%
Passenger journeys (millions)	165.5	169.3
Passenger km (millions)	4,128.8	4,218.1
Timetabled train m (millions)	38.0	38.1
Route km operated	748.3	748.3
Number of stations operated	173	173
Number of employees	3,796	3,820
Subsidy per passenger km (p)	2.1	2.0
Network grant / pass km (p)	6.0	6.1

In May 2011, the high-speed service was extended to Maidstone West and in September 2011, funded by Kent County Council, to include Sandwich and Deal. The high-speed service has consistently been recognised in the National Passenger Survey as the best commuter service in the country, with 92pc overall satisfaction in Spring 2013. During 2013 Southeastern named 14 high-speed 'Javelin' trains in honour of Olympic and Paralympic medallists to commemorate the London 2012 Games.

In 2013 Southeastern retained its 5 star EFQM 'excellence model' accreditation, and built an award winning engineering 'wiki' - a virtual web-based manual to help its 800-strong maintenance team. It received a number of awards, including a Modern Railways' 2013 Railway Industry Innovation Award and a National Rail Award for the engineering 'wiki', plus recognition for London Cannon Street, London 2012 Games services, and City and Metro operations.

A Class 395 Southeastern high-speed train on HS1. Southeastern

Southeastern formed an alliance with Network Rail in 2012 and this has delivered upgrades to stations, weatherproofed the rail infrastructure and delivered the largest resignalling scheme in over 60 years. As a result, punctuality performance and emergency response times have improved. A trial with Network Rail on the Hastings line confined engineering maintenance works to Monday and Tuesday evening, improving passenger services on other evenings.

There are 95 secure station awards, and incidents of theft and assault have been at record lows. Three stations - Lewisham, Woolwich and Hither Green - became the UK's first CitySafe railway stations - places of refuge for young people in danger. Work at Dartford, Denmark Hill and Bromley South has improved accessibility and brought new and improved station facilities.

In partnership with local councils and the DfT, Southeastern has increased the number of available cycle spaces and the company has continued to work with Visit Kent to provide promotional deals to encourage tourism in support of the local economy.

Approximately 50pc of all employees now hold a National Vocational Qualification with the majority of these in customer services. Senior managers across the company have also taken Institute of Learning Management qualifications with an aim to improve the way the company manages and develops its staff. In 2012 Southeastern was recognised with Investors in People, Gold, joining the 3pc of UK organisations to reach this high standard. In 2013 the first ever intake of customer service apprentices completed training, earning an NVQs, and moved on to permanent positions.

Southeastern has improved communication with its customers, corresponding directly and instantly via Twitter, and an internal professional social networking site allows employees to connect, communicate and share information for customers' benefit.

A 'driving energy further' initiative has reduced carbon emissions by 42,000 tonnes of CO_2, saving around £6.2m. Southeastern was also the first train company to commit to '10:10' a carbon reduction commitment. 70pc of all waste is now recycled (up from only 10pc in 2006).

The distribution of train maintenance across the region, coupled with demanding targets, has seen significant improvements to 'miles-per-casualty' figures across the fleet, and work to develop managers' and employees' skills and changes to working practices has brought significant benefits.

Southeastern's all-electric train fleet is maintained at Slade Green (Dartford) and Ramsgate: 10 three-car and 102 four-car Class 375s; 36 five-car Class 376s; 147 four-car Class 465s; and 43 two-car Class 466s. Hitachi's depot at Ashford maintains the 29 Class-395 high-speed trains.

SENIOR PERSONNEL

SOUTHEASTERN

MANAGING DIRECTOR Charles Horton (in photo)
FINANCE DIRECTOR Wilma Allan
ENGINEERING DIRECTOR Wayne Jenner
HUMAN RESOURCES DIRECTOR Andy Bindon
PASSENGER SERVICES DIRECTOR Barbara Thomas
TRAIN SERVICES DIRECTOR Richard Dean

london midland

FRANCHISE EXTENSION TO JUNE 2017

The London Midland franchise began on 11 November 2007, combining the former Silverlink franchise's County routes and the major part of Central Trains. The franchise was due to expire in September 2015, but in March 2013, the Department for Transport (DfT) announced that it proposed a new award extending to June 2017.

The company has two brands, London Midland City (West Midlands conurbation and the wider region, with Centro's Network West Midlands brand prominent) and London Midland Express (longer distance routes connecting London, the Midlands and Northwest).

London Midland introduced a new timetable structure in 2008, with through services between Birmingham and London, and a new service between London Euston and Crewe via the Trent Valley and Stoke-on-Trent. This brought a significant improvement in service frequency to many stations.

Highlights of the franchise have included the introduction of 37 new four-car Siemens Class 350/2 Desiro electric trains and the replacement of most Class 150 Sprinters with new Class 172 Bombardier Turbostars. Three remaining Class 150s benefited during 2013 from a £72,000 programme of improvements, carried out by London Midland staff at Birmingham's Tyseley depot.

A joint initiative with Siemens upgraded the thirty Class 350/1 EMUs to run at 110mph, to cut journey times on the Trent Valley

Class 321/4 EMUs Nos 321413 and 321417 pass Headstone Lane on 14 August 2013, forming a northbound London Midland service. Brian Morrison

service and introduce additional services, following the ending of moderation of competition protection for the Intercity West Coast franchise in 2012. Phase two of the project will allow longer trains of 8 or 12-vehicles to run at 110mph in 2014.

Ten new four-car 110mph Class 350/3 Desiros will be delivered in 2014. Seven will be allocated to the West Coast main line, providing around 4,000 more peak-time seats per day in and out of Euston. The other three will release Class 323s to provide extra services on the Cross-City line through Birmingham, increasing frequency of services to Redditch from December 2014, using a new passing loop at Alvechurch.

During 2013 London Midland made a number of significant strategic and operational changes. A shortage of drivers, which led to a high level of cancellations in late 2012, led to an extensive review of business operations.

Driver recruitment is now ahead of the target agreed with the DfT, with 52 new drivers completing the 12-month training programme and deployed by autumn 2013.

A commitment to addressing passenger needs, raising punctuality, reducing cancellations and providing 'quality journeys for everyone' was at the very heart of the 'Strong Foundations' improvement programme implemented in March 2013.

Work has included building a greater level of resilience into timetables so LM is better prepared to address challenges such as major public events, where additional services are scheduled.

Public Performance Measure punctuality figures reflect progress, with the October 2013 score reaching 88.7pc. The moving annual average stood at 85.3pc, a positive shift following 18 four-week periods of decline. The number of cancellations caused by London Midland has also more than halved when compared to the worst performing period at the end of 2012.

London Midland has appointed four new heads of route to assume overall responsibility for the delivery of services on West Coast mainline, Snow Hill, Regional, and Cross City services. They will focus on train performance, customer service and passenger information, as well as working closely with Network Rail and other partners to improve the overall journey experience.

A review of the communications function as part of the wider business restructure recognised that a single co-ordinated and focused communications team was critical in laying strong foundations for the company. Heading up the team is Francis Thomas, who has returned to the railway after 20 years in other industries.

The National Station Improvement Programme (NSIP), funded by the Department for Transport, has already seen improvements at number of stations across the London Midland network. Phase three in 2014 will see the total price tag reach over £11m. This has been supported by contributions from Hertfordshire and Worcestershire county councils, Centro in the West Midlands and the Railway Heritage Trust.

A new partnership agreement between London Midland and Centro will see £10m of improvements to stations across the West Midlands in a continuation of a successful two year arrangement in 2011. Almost 50 commitments, under eight themes, include a smart-ticketing scheme, a business case for improvements on the Centro-funded Chase line, enhanced off-peak services to Stratford-upon-Avon, improved station facilities, and joint working to promote the proposed redevelopment of Wolverhampton station.

London Midland's diesel train fleet consists of: Class 172 Turbostars (12 two-car and 15 three-car), Class 170 Turbostars (17 two-car and six three-car), Class 150 Sprinters (3 two-car); Class 153 (8 single-car), Class 139 (2 single-car, LPG/flywheel-powered Parry People Movers).

The electric train fleet consists of 30 Class-350/1 and 37 Class-350/2 four-car Desiros (with 10 Class 350/3s due in 2014), and 7 four-car Class-321 and 26 three-car Class-323 units.

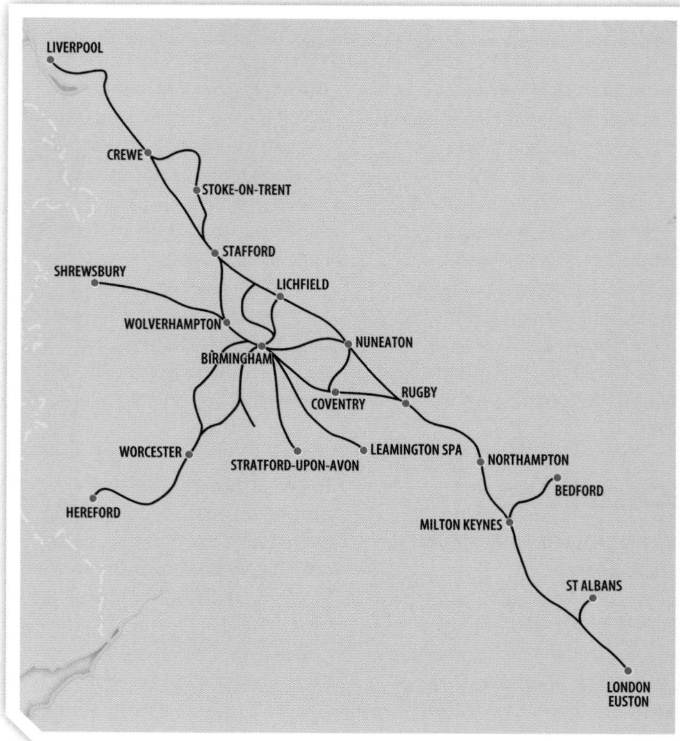

KEY STATISTICS
LONDON MIDLAND

	2011-12	2012-13
Punctuality (0-5min)	90.5%	86.0%
Passenger journeys (millions)	59.5	60.5
Passenger km (millions)	2,090.5	2,241.2
Timetabled train km (millions)	24.7	25.4
Route km operated	861.0	898.8
Number of stations operated	147	147
Number of employees	2,315	2,327
Subsidy per passenger km (p)	3.1	2.6
Network grant / pass km (p)	6.6	6.5

SENIOR PERSONNEL
LONDON MIDLAND

MANAGING DIRECTOR Patrick Verwer (in photo)
FINANCE & CONTRACTS DIRECTOR Wilma Allan
OPERATIONS DIRECTOR Tom Joyner
COMMERCIAL DIRECTOR Richard Brooks
ENGINEERING DIRECTOR Neil Bamford
HUMAN RESOURCES DIRECTOR Geraldine Goddard
HEAD OF TRAINCREW John Allen
HEAD OF CURRENT OPERATIONS Olly Glover

STAGECOACH GROUP

Holder of the South West Trains franchise since it was first awarded in 1996; Stagecoach Group has extensive bus, rail and light rail operations in the UK and North America, employing around 35,000 people, over 7,000 of them in UK Rail. Stagecoach is currently involved in running around 20pc of the passenger rail network. It was awarded the East Midlands rail franchise in 2007, and has a 49pc shareholding in Virgin Rail Group, which is expected to continue to operate the West Coast intercity rail franchise until 2017. Stagecoach Supertram holds a 27-year concession until 2024 for Sheffield's light rail network.

UK rail subsidiaries' revenue for the year to 30 April 2013 was up 5.3pc at £1,201.3m (2012: £1,140.7m). On a like-for-like basis, revenue, excluding tram operations, increased by 5.9pc. Operating profit was £49.9m (2012: £27.1m) and operating margin increased from 2.4 to 4.2pc. The share of profit, after tax, in Virgin Rail Group was £9.8m (2012: £15.9m).

East Midlands Trains was eligible for revenue support for the full year. This returned it to profitability, a results statement commented, with improved profitability of the UK Rail Division in the year to April 2013 largely due to that factor. Partly offsetting this was an increase in premium payments under franchise agreements.

The group was progressing its bid for the Thameslink franchise, and was also shortlisted for Transport for London's Docklands Light Railway franchise. Virgin Rail Group was also considering the opportunities in the InterCity East Coast franchise competition.

SOUTH WEST TRAINS

EXTENSION PLANNED UNTIL APRIL 2019

Stagecoach holds the passenger rail franchise, running from 4 February 2007, which combined the previous South West Trains (SWT) and Island Line (Isle of Wight) franchises. The DfT announced plans in 2013 for an extended award, by 26 months to April 2019.

A new alliance between SWT and Network Rail, from April 2012, sees a single management team responsible for one of the busiest, most intensely used and complex railways in Europe, setting out to improve performance by creating better working relationships. Teams are now co-located and putting an increased focus on even the smallest delays, with time taken to recover from incidents reduced by 11pc in a year.

The first of 36 newly created 5-car Class 458/5 sets arrived in late 2013, part of a programme to provide a 10-car railway on the lines from Hounslow, Weybridge and Windsor. Former Gatwick Express Class 460 vehicles are being used to extend the Class 458s, and 60 stations are having their platforms extended. SWT is to bring Platform 20 in the former Waterloo International Terminal into full use from Spring 2014.

The franchise extension should assist co-ordination with Network Rail's 2014-19 programmes in improving infrastructure and delivering additional capacity: growth of up to 51pc is forecast over the next 11 years. Two phases of work would deliver up to 35pc extra capacity by 2024 - proposals include procurement of extra trains, reopening remaining Waterloo International platforms,

KEY STATISTICS
SOUTH WEST TRAINS

	2011-12	2012-13
Punctuality (0-5min)	92.3%	91.4%
Passenger journeys (millions)	208.8	210.8
Passenger km (millions)	5,720.2	5,777.5
Timetabled train km (millions)	39.6	39.5
Route km operated	944.7	944.7
Number of stations operated	185	186
Number of employees	4,619	4,720
Subsidy per passenger km (p)	-4.0	-5.4
Network grant / pass km (p)	4.6	4.7

Siemens-built Class 444 trains at Bournemouth. Brian Morrison

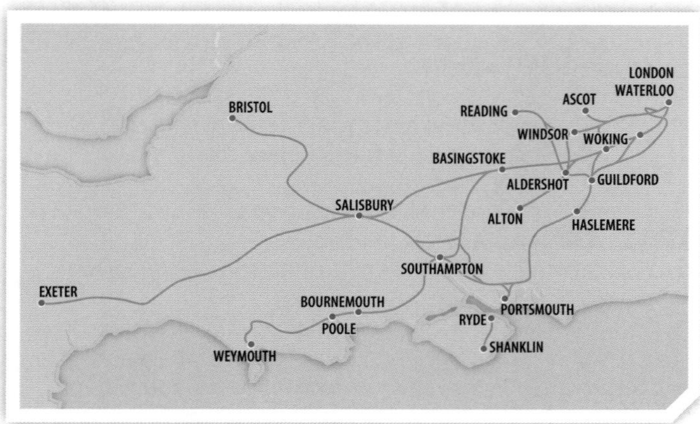

and resignalling, power supply improvements and further platform extensions. SWT has started procurement for more than 135 additional vehicles.

During 2013 the alliance has commissioned new signalling systems in the Farnham area and between Poole and Wool, valued at more than £50m. Work in the Clapham Junction area is also expected to help performance. Improved examination has helped improve reliability of critical sets of points by around 20pc over three years.

SWT has continued efforts to make stations more accessible and attractive, with a commitment to spend approximately £27m between 2012 and 2014. Another £20m station improvement scheme, part of the DfT's Access for All strategy, is under way.

At the busiest interchange station in Britain, Clapham Junction, extra dispatch staff are now in place to help ensure that trains keep moving quickly and safely, with a similar initiative at Earlsfield.

The company has introduced more robust contingency and on-call arrangements to provide assistance on trains and at stations during disruption, and strengthened arrangements in the integrated control centre at London Waterloo. In August 2013 the alliance launched its first passenger forum, when passengers were given the opportunity to talk to managers at Waterloo.

The company is also delivering improved environmental performance through initiatives including regenerative braking on Class 450 and 458 trains, metering of electricity use, intelligent lighting at stations, and increased waste recycling at depots and stations.

In many cases SWT is delivering 'best in class' levels of train reliability to underpin its performance. Work started in 2012 on the £23m overhaul of the Class 455 fleet at Bournemouth, with a new £3.2m state-of-the-art paint shop giving the opportunity to carry out all fleet painting and the majority of maintenance work in-house.

The electric multiple-unit fleet has 45 Class-444 five-car Siemens Desiro trains (designed for longer distance services), 127 Class 450 four-car Desiros, and 91 pre-privatisation Class 455 units (now being upgraded with new Vossloh Kiepe AC traction equipment to help improve reliability).

Completion of the Class 458 programme in 2014 will result in a fleet of 36 five-car Class 458/5 sets and further capacity is to be created with transfer of the 24 two-car Class 456 fleet as additional Class 377s are delivered to Southern. 30 three-car Class 159 and 11 two-car Class 158 diesel multiple-units are used on the non-electrified routes from Southampton and Basingstoke to Salisbury and beyond.

Main train depots are at Wimbledon, Salisbury and, for the Siemens-built Desiro units, Northam near Southampton, with upgraded facilities at Wimbledon and Farnham for additional vehicles being introduced.

SENIOR PERSONNEL

SOUTH WEST TRAINS

MANAGING DIRECTOR Tim Shoveller (in photo)
CUSTOMER SERVICE DIRECTOR Jake Kelly
INFRASTRUCTURE DIRECTOR Jim Morgan
COMMERCIAL DIRECTOR Sam McCarthy
OPERATIONS DIRECTOR Mark Steward
SAFETY AND ASSURANCE DIRECTOR Sharon Vye-Parminter
FLEET DIRECTOR Christian Roth
FINANCE DIRECTOR Andy West
HR DIRECTOR Kelly Barlow

EAST MIDLANDS TRAINS

EXTENSION PLANNED UNTIL 2017

The East Midlands franchise - combining the previous Midland main line intercity franchise with the eastern section of Central Trains - began operations on 11 November 2007 and was due to continue until 1 April 2015, subject to performance. In March 2013 the Department for Transport (DfT) announced an expected extended award until October 2017.

Passenger numbers have continued to increase through the recession, but revenue growth did not met expectations and East Midlands Trains (EMT) became eligible for revenue support from the DfT from November 2011.

In partnership with Network Rail, EMT has worked to deliver faster journeys, with Midland main line improvements for speeds of up to 125mph. From December 2013, EMT's average journey between Sheffield and London is reduced by 7min, between Nottingham and London by 5min (fastest Sheffield-London in 2hr, Nottingham-London in1hr 31min).

Leading a range of station improvements is the Nottingham Hub redevelopment scheme. During summer 2013 a new bay platform was created as the track layout was extensively remodelled. A new southern concourse will link the new tram bridge station, multi-storey car park and station.

Derby station's refurbished forecourt has transformed the gateway to the city in a £2.7m scheme. A £6m refurbishment at Leicester is creating an improved station, from entrance to ticket office, concourse, overbridge and platforms.

A further investment of £10m at stations across EMT's network will see new station footbridges, refurbishment of toilets and waiting rooms, and new car parks. The company is also rolling out improved cycle facilities, around £850,000 being spent at Sheffield to create a flagship cycle centre.

EMT's customer service team has been revamped following the launch of a new contact centre within EMT's control centre. EMT responds to questions via the phone, at station help-points or through Twitter and is working towards providing a 24hr service.

Smartcard technology has advanced across EMT's network with a scheme allowing monthly and annual season tickets to be stored electronically on a StagecoachSmart card.

EMT has continued to develop on-board service on its London trains, and in October 2013 began offering a complimentary breakfast for First Class customers on trains arriving in London before 10.00 on weekdays. All of EMT's long-distance trains now offer wi-fi, with a market-leading router aggregating signals from multiple 3G networks to provide an

KEY STATISTICS

EAST MIDLANDS TRAINS

	2011-12	2012-13
Punctuality	93.6%	92.5%
Passenger journeys (millions)	23.9	24.1
Passenger km (millions)	2,194.6	2,252.4
Timetabled train km (millions)	22.1	22.2
Route km operated	1,549.8	1,549.8
Number of stations operated	89	89
Number of employees	2,028	2,025
Subsidy per passenger km (p)	-1.8	0.1
Network grant / pass km (p)	8.5	8.6

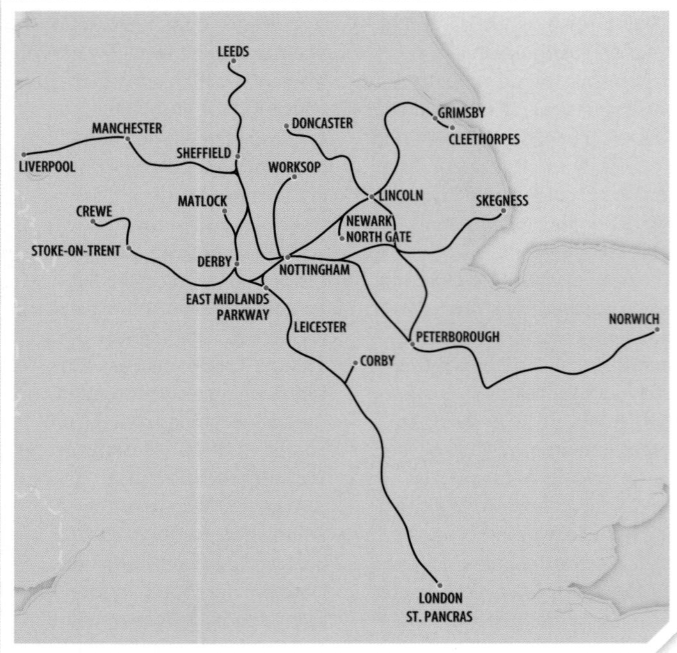

SENIOR PERSONNEL

EAST MIDLANDS TRAINS

MANAGING DIRECTOR David Horne (in photo)
SAFETY & OPERATIONS DIRECTOR Ian Smith
FLEET DIRECTOR Tim Sayer
FINANCE DIRECTOR Tim Gledhill
HR DIRECTOR Clare Burles
CUSTOMER SERVICE & COMMERCIAL DIRECTOR Neil Micklethwaite

enhanced service. EMT offers free WiFi at 30 stations in partnership with the Cloud.

The busy Liverpool-Norwich route saw a significant increase in capacity from December 2011 when four Class 156 sets transferred from Northern Rail enabled many services between Nottingham and Liverpool to be strengthened from 2-car to 4-car Class 158s.

A £22million depot refurbishment at Derby (Etches Park), designated EMT's centre of train maintenance operations, was completed in early 2010 after just 17 months, providing increased maintenance capacity. A £1m wheel lathe has been provided, whilst synchronised jacks are capable of lifting a full seven-car Meridian train.

EMT completed in 2012 a £30m programme to refurbish all 93 trains in its fleet, culminating with the Class 222 Meridian which received new leather seats in First Class and new seat covers and carpeting in Standard Class coaches. CCTV has been installed on all of EMT's trains, whilst the Energy Saving Mode on its Meridian trains allows some engines to be turned off when the trains are sitting in stations. The investment in the fleet modifications and depot improvements has paid off with fleet reliability having improved significantly.

East Midlands Trains' 11 HSTs are formed from a pool of 26 power cars with eight coaches per train. The Class-222 Meridian fleet was reorganised in 2008 to form six seven-car and 17 five-car sets, along with four additional 4-car Class 222s which transferred from Hull Trains. Regional and local services are operated by 17 Class-153, 15 Class-156 and 25 Class-158 DMUs. ■

An East Midlands Trains 'Meridian' at Leicester. EMT

Pendolino No 393131 negotiates the curve at Old Linslade on 20 July 2013 with the 09.35 Manchester Piccadilly to London Euston. Ken Brunt

SENIOR PERSONNEL
VIRGIN TRAINS

EXECUTIVE CHAIRMAN (JOINT) Patrick McCall
EXECUTIVE CHAIRMAN (JOINT) Martin Griffiths
LEAD EXECUTIVE Phil Whittingham
DIRECTOR OPERATIONS AND CUSTOMER SERVICE Phil Bearpark (in photo)
EXECUTIVE DIRECTOR, COMMERCIAL Graham Leech

WEST COAST INTERCITY

Virgin Rail Group (VRG) - a joint venture between Virgin Group (51pc) and Stagecoach Group (49pc) - runs the West Coast intercity franchise under the Virgin Trains banner, with main routes from London Euston to Glasgow, Liverpool, Manchester and Birmingham. Virgin also ran the CrossCountry franchise from 1997 until 2007. After a difficult period following the collapse of Railtrack, with a reduced scope for the West Coast Route Modernisation project, the original franchise terms were replaced by an interim agreement in 2002 and then by a new deal, agreed with the Department for Transport (DfT) in December 2006.

This franchise was extended from March 2012 to December 2012 as the DfT revisited terms for a new franchising exercise. Then a 'pause' was announced in October 2012 after the West Coast franchising process was challenged and cancelled. Virgin was awarded an interim extension to run for up to 23 months (until 9 November 2014), initially earning a fee equivalent to 1pc of revenue with the DfT taking revenue and cost risk.

Under the new programme announced in March 2013, the next long-term West Coast franchise is expected to start in April 2017, and discussions were under way about an interim arrangement.

Virgin's 'VHF' (Virgin High Frequency) timetable recast, introduced in 2008 after the West Coast Route Modernisation, sees nine Virgin trains departing from London every hour in the off-peak periods, and 11 in the peak. Virgin also runs the hourly Birmingham-Scotland service (taken over from the CrossCountry franchise in 2007) and London-Holyhead and Wrexham trains.

Following the 2012 contract extension, Virgin was asked by the Secretary of State to examine direct London services for Blackpool and Shrewsbury, but proposals for these to begin in late 2013 were rejected by the Office of Rail Regulation, pending further timetable work, after Network Rail raised concerns about pathing.

Demand projections led the DfT to sanction capacity increases in 2008, when train lessor Angel Trains signed contracts with Alstom for four new 11-car Pendolinos and two extra cars for 31 existing trains (106 additional vehicles in all), along with a 10-year maintenance regime, worth a total of £1.5bn. The project was completed in December 2012.

Virgin's train fleet now comprises 35 eleven-car and 21 nine-car Pendolino electric tilting trains, and 20 five-car Class-221 diesel Super Voyager units, supplemented by a 9-coach Mk3 loco-hauled rake. A refurbishment of the entire fleet started in 2013, including improved catering equipment in the Pendolino kitchens and shops.

Virgin has consistently delivered the best customer satisfaction score across all long-distance franchise operators. A rating of 92pc was achieved in the Autumn 2012 and Spring 2013 National Passenger Surveys. Over the 16 years of its franchise, passenger numbers have more than doubled, from 13m to 31m, and rail's share of the Manchester-London rail/air market has increased from 30pc to 88pc.

In October 2013 Virgin Trains announced that Tony Collins, Chief Executive Officer, and Chris Gibb, Chief Operating Officer, were to retire. Tony Collins remained as a consultant to Virgin, to support its franchise bid strategy, while Gibb, after 10 years with Virgin and over 30 years in the rail industry, joined Network Rail as a non-executive director. Phil Bearpark became Director, Operations and Customer Service and the safety system duty holder.

KEY STATISTICS
VIRGIN TRAINS

	2011-12	2012-13
Punctuality (0-10min)	85.9%	83.6%
Passenger journeys (millions)	30.2	30.4
Passenger km (millions)	5,923.0	5,958.4
Timetabled train km (millions)	35.9	35.8
Route km operated	1,190.9	1,190.9
Number of stations operated	17	17
Number of employees	3,104	2,914
Subsidy per passenger km (p)	-2.8	-1.6
Network grant / pass km (p)	5.0	5.2

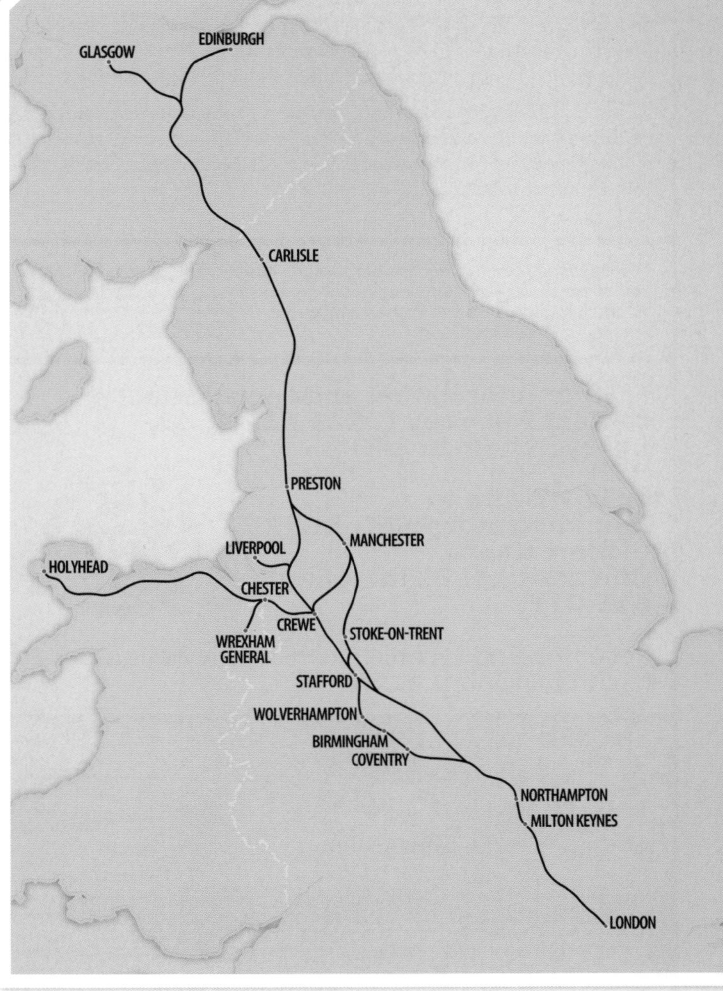

ARRIVA

Part of the German state rail group Deutsche Bahn since its acquisition of Arriva plc in August 2010, Arriva is responsible for regional passenger transport outside Germany. One of the largest providers of passenger transport in Europe, it has 55,900 employees operating in 15 countries, and had revenues of Euro 2billion in the first half of 2013.

Through three rail franchises, Arriva UK Trains operates about 10pc of the UK passenger network - CrossCountry and Arriva Trains Wales (Arriva plc held these two prior to the DB acquisition), and Chiltern Railways, which DB had run since acquiring its parent Laing Rail in 2008. Open Access train company Grand Central was acquired in November 2011.

The London Rail concession for London Overground was also involved in the Laing acquisition. Awarded in 2007 to London Overground Rail Operations Ltd (LOROL), this was a joint venture of Laing with Hong Kong's MTR. With a two-year extension confirmed in 2013, the concession is now set to expire in November 2016.

Arriva operates a seven-year Tyne & Wear Metro contract for Nexus, the Passenger Transport Executive. It covers the train service, fleet maintenance and modernisation, and day-to-day station management.

Arriva also owns rail maintenance business LNWR, based in Crewe and founded in 1996. Depots in Gateshead, Bristol, Cambridge and Eastleigh, transferred from Axiom Rail (part of sister company DB Schenker Rail UK), service CrossCountry trains on behalf of Bombardier.

Alliance Rail Holdings, acquired by DB in 2010, undertakes strategic development work for Grand Central as well as for its own proposed open access services. On the West Coast main line, these are London Euston to Bradford, Huddersfield and Leeds; also to Blackpool, Barrow and the Cumbrian Coast. On the East Coast route, the proposals are for services from London King's Cross to Micklefield, Leeds, Bradford and Ilkley; also to Scunthorpe, Grimsby and Cleethorpes. Other possible open access services are being evaluated.

Laing Rail/Chiltern in 2006 joined Renaissance Trains in the Wrexham, Shropshire & Marylebone Railway open-access venture. Later run by Chiltern alone, it closed in 2011 after a loss of £2.8m was made in 2010.

DB also plans to launch services through the Channel Tunnel, between London St Pancras and Brussels, Amsterdam (via Rotterdam), Cologne and Frankfurt.

DB Arriva was named an official bidder for the operations contract for London Crossrail in June 2013, and was also shortlisted by Transport Scotland in 2013 for the Caledonian Sleeper franchise.

Chiltern Railways

20 YEAR FRANCHISE FROM FEBRUARY 2002

Chiltern Railways' unique 20-year franchise, linked to delivery of investment, was awarded in 2002 by the former Strategic Rail Authority.

New London-Birmingham 'Mainline' services were introduced from 2011 as the first part of Chiltern's development package, 'Evergreen 3', with fast journeys to London Marylebone: currently 94min from Birmingham Moor Street, and 72min from Warwick Parkway. Over 50 miles of track were upgraded for 100mph, with key junctions improved. In the first year, Chiltern recorded a 33pc increase in West Midlands-London journeys.

A revised timetable from December 2012 gave 600 extra seats in the peaks, with a third locomotive-hauled 'Silver' train in service, and aimed to improve punctuality. In August 2013, Chiltern was top operator for 'right time' punctuality for the ninth consecutive four-week accounting period (87.5% of trains arriving within a minute of schedule, national average 67.6%).

Sunday afternoon frequency was increased from May 2013 between Aylesbury and London.

Free Wi-Fi and a new Business Zone, designed as a cost efficient alternative to First class, are offered on 'Silver' trains. The company has also restructured ticketing, and improved station facilities and parking capacity: a partnership with The Cloud for free WiFi in 24 stations was announced in 2013.

Transport & Works Act approval for Phase 2 of Evergreen 3 was confirmed in 2013 - this will provide a new Oxford-London Marylebone service via Bicester, with upgrading and partial doubling of the Oxford-Bicester line, a new link to the Chiltern line at Bicester, and a new multi-modal interchange, Oxford Parkway, north of the city.

A collaboration with Network Rail, announced in September 2013, will oversee the project, and

KEY STATISTICS
CHILTERN RAILWAYS

	2011-12	2012-13
Punctuality (0-5min)	93.0%	94.9%
Passenger journeys (millions)	19.7	21.4
Passenger km (millions)	1,000.9	1,132.5
Timetabled train km (millions)	10.3	10.7
Route km operated	341.2	341.2
Number of stations operated	30	32
Number of employees	750	778
Subsidy per passenger km (p)	0.6	0.6
Network grant / pass km (p)	7.7	6.9

Chiltern Railways Class 168 and 165 trains at the restored Birmingham Moor Street station. Tony Miles

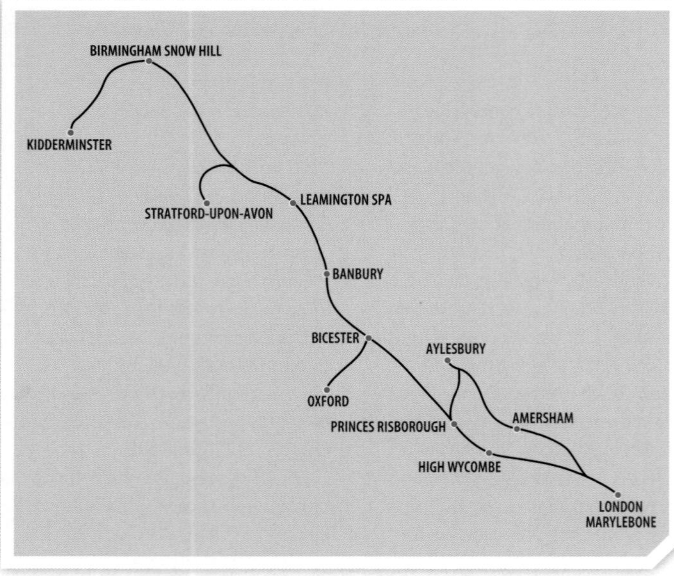

also the first phase of works on East West Rail (Oxford-Bicester-Bletchley-Bedford/Milton Keynes, with Chiltern services extended from Aylesbury to Bletchley and Milton Keynes).

Marylebone services are expected to begin in summer 2015 from Oxford Parkway (under 1hr to London), and reach Oxford in spring 2016.

Funding of about £259m for Evergreen 3, from Network Rail, is to be repaid by the train operator over 30 years. With this project, Chiltern says a total of £600m will have been invested since the start of its original franchise in 1996.

The £80m 'Evergreen 2', completed in 2006, was a Design, Build, Finance & Transfer project, improving station, signalling and line capacity for 20 trains per peak hour to use Marylebone. A new £20m Wembley train depot was completed in 2005. 'Evergreen 1' doubled single track between Aynho Junction and Princes Risborough.

Aylesbury Vale Parkway, 3km north of Aylesbury, designed to serve housing development and park-and-ride, opened in 2008, with a 20 year, £13m concession jointly funded by the Community Infrastructure Fund, Buckinghamshire County Council and John Laing. Chiltern and Laing were responsible for Warwick Parkway, the first non-Railtrack station delivered on the rail network, in 2000.

Chiltern Railways in July 2013 became the first operator to roll out 'App and Go' tickets, with mobile ticketing company Masabi. On-phone tickets can be scanned at barriers.

The 'Silver' trains of Mk3 coaches have undergone major refurbishment by Wabtec, including new power-operated bodyside doors, and controlled-emission toilets. The first Class 168 'Clubman' diesel multiple-unit refurbished by Wabtec in the same style, under a £5.3 million programme, was unveiled in September 2013: all will be updated by 2016. There are ten 4-car and nine 3-car Class 168s, used for longer-distance services.

Four new two-car Class 172 diesel multiple-units went into service in 2011. There are 28 two-car and 11 three-car Class 165 'Turbo' trains. Two refurbished Class-121 single-car diesels are used on Aylesbury-Princes Risborough shuttles. The main maintenance depot is at Aylesbury.

Chiltern leases six Class 67 locomotives from DB Schenker. Bids for alternative options were being compared against their continued use.

Novel vinyl images are appearing in train toilets as part of train refurbishments - the first depicting Compton Verney mansion.

SENIOR PERSONNEL

CHILTERN RAILWAYS

MANAGING DIRECTOR Rob Brighouse (in photo)
BUSINESS DEVELOPMENT DIRECTOR Graham Cross
CUSTOMER SERVICES DIRECTOR Jennifer Payne
ENGINEERING DIRECTOR Kate Marjoribanks
FINANCE DIRECTOR Duncan Rimmer
OPERATIONS AND SAFETY DIRECTOR Andrew Munden
COMMERCIAL DIRECTOR Thomas Ableman

15 YEAR FRANCHISE FROM DECEMBER 2003

Arriva Trains Wales/Trenau Arriva Cymru (ATW) includes national, regional and local routes within Wales; through services to Birmingham, Chester, Manchester and Cheltenham; and the 'Borders' route via Hereford and Shrewsbury.

The 15-year Wales & Borders franchise commenced on 7 December 2003, and in April 2006 the Welsh Government took responsibility for it, gaining powers to fund improvements.

While the franchise was let on assumptions of little growth, there has been 50pc growth in journeys since 2003. The business has invested more than £30m in train maintenance and improvements, station upgrades, improved ticketing, information and security, while government investment has included funding of additional trains and stations.

Electrification of the route between London and Swansea is set to take place by 2018, with the Valley Lines network around Cardiff to follow - current enhancements include the £220m Cardiff and valleys modernisation, allowing an extra four trains per hour through the Cardiff area, with additional platforms or new turnback facilities at Cardiff Central, Cardiff Queen Street, Barry, Tir-phil, Caerphilly and Pontypridd, and a new station at Energlyn near Caerphilly.

The doubling of five miles of single track between Swansea and Llanelli, aimed at improving reliability and capacity, was completed in 2013. In October 2013, the Welsh Governemnt confirmed a £4m project to double most of the Wrexham-Chester line, and other improvements, expected to reduce north-south journey times by 16min.

Capacity of 330,000 extra seats a year was added in May 2012. Services gaining included Shrewsbury-Birmingham, Birmingham-Aberystwyth, Chester-Llandudno Junction, and West Wales.

KEY STATISTICS

ARRIVA TRAINS WALES

	2011-12	2012-13
Punctuality (0-5min)	94.2%	93.3%
Passenger journeys (millions)	28.4	29.0
Passenger km (millions)	1,142	1,154
Timetabled train km (millions)	23.6	24.2
Route km operated	1,840.8	1,670.5
Number of stations operated	243	244
Number of employees	2,012	2.010
Subsidy per passenger km (p)	12.0	12.2

SENIOR PERSONNEL
ARRIVA TRAINS WALES

MANAGING DIRECTOR Ian Bullock (in photo)
OPERATIONS AND SAFETY DIRECTOR Mike Tapscott
CUSTOMER SERVICES DIRECTOR Lynne Milligan
COMMERCIAL DIRECTOR Mike Bagshaw
FINANCE DIRECTOR Rob Phillips
ENGINEERING DIRECTOR Matt Prosser
HUMAN RESOURCES DIRECTOR Sandie Mc Donnell

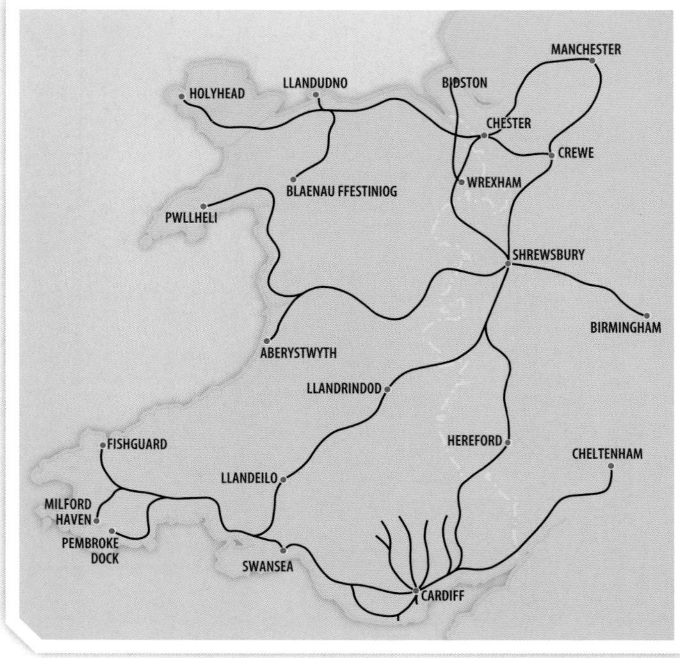

Another 125,000 seats a year were added from September 2012 on several commuter flows, and a revised north-south express service was introduced, linking Holyhead with Cardiff, via Wrexham. Mk3 vehicles were refurbished by Pullman Rail in Cardiff for the train, which is powered by a Class 67 locomotive, with a driving van trailer enabling reversal at Chester.

The Welsh Government provided £1.3m annually to provide five extra daily return trains for Fishguard, from 2011. A review will be carried out after the third year.

Previous timetable improvements included, in 2011, faster services between west and south Wales and Manchester.

As part of the National Stations Improvement Programme, major enhancements have been completed at Swansea and Chester, in addition to providing real time customer information screens and improved access for the disabled.

A new station at Ebbw Vale town, at the site of The Works, is to go ahead after the Welsh Government's May 2013 announcement of £11.5m funding. 1.3 miles of new track will run from Ebbw Vale Parkway.

£2.5m from the Department for Transport's New Station Fund will go to a new Pye Corner station, on the Ebbw Vale line. The Welsh Government will provide £1m.

Further improvement projects, including daytime hourly services between Aberystwyth and Shrewsbury, have been under consideration.

A complete upgrade of ATW's Class 158 fleet (carried out by LNWR) was completed in 2012, with the Welsh Government providing £7.5m. The Class 175 fleet has also recently been refurbished.

Apart from the Holyhead-Cardiff express, long-distance services use Class 158 diesel multiple-units (24 trains) and Class 175 'Coradias' (27 trains). A fleet of 30 Class-142/143 Pacer railbuses is mainly used in the Cardiff area. There are also 36 Class-150s and 8 single-car Class-153s in the fleet.

Most of the fleet is based at Cardiff Canton, with a £3million facility at Machynlleth servicing Class 158s, while Class 175s are maintained at manufacturer Alstom's Chester depot. Servicing is also undertaken at Holyhead.

No 150285 stands at Newport with Arriva Trains Wales' 10.45 Cheltenham Spa to Maesteg service on 23 July 2013. Stewart Armstrong

FRANCHISE EXTENSION TO NOVEMBER 2019 PLANNED

The CrossCountry (XC) network is the most extensive GB rail franchise, stretching from Aberdeen to Penzance (at 774 miles, the network's longest through journey), and from Stansted to Cardiff. Arriva's franchise started on 11 November 2007 and was due to run until 31 March 2016. Following the Department for Transport review of rail franchising, a 43-month extended contract was expected to be negotiated, running until November 2019.

There are regular half-hourly services on key route sections, including Birmingham to Bristol, Reading, Manchester, Sheffield and Leicester; hourly direct services between Bristol and Manchester; hourly through services for all destinations between Plymouth and Edinburgh (via Leeds), Southampton, Reading and Newcastle (via Doncaster), Bournemouth and Manchester, Cardiff and Nottingham, Birmingham and Stansted Airport. CrossCountry trains via Motherwell and Edinburgh connect Glasgow with Northeast England, Yorkshire, the Midlands and Southwest.

Work in conjunction with Nomad Digital to equip all High Speed Trains and Voyagers with wi-fi was completed in 2012.

CrossCountry has introduced a series of commercial innovations, including pioneering print-at-home rail e-tickets in the UK. Almost 20pc of all tickets bought online are now e-tickets. XC began a trial of sale of 'Advance' tickets on the day of travel in October 2013, an initiative from the DfT's fares and ticketing review.

CrossCountry's Train Tickets app, developed by Masabi, offers

KEY STATISTICS

CROSSCOUNTRY

	2011-12	2012-13
Punctuality (0-10min)	89.6%	86.9%
Passenger journeys (millions)	33.0	33.4
Passenger km (millions)	3,252.4	3,254.1
Timetabled train km (millions)	32.7	32.6
Route km operated	2,661.9	2,661.9
Number of stations operated	0	0
Number of employees	1,700	1,694
Subsidy per passenger km (p)	0.2	0.6
Network grant / pass km (p)	9.1	9.5

A CrossCountry high-speed train departs from Plymouth. Tony Miles

ABERDEEN
GLASGOW
EDINBURGH
NEWCASTLE
YORK
LEEDS
MANCHESTER
DONCASTER
SHEFFIELD
STOKE-ON-TRENT
NOTTINGHAM
STAFFORD
LEICESTER
PETERBOROUGH
BIRMINGHAM NEW STREET
COVENTRY
CAMBRIDGE
GLOUCESTER
STANSTED AIRPORT
READING
CARDIFF CENTRAL
BRISTOL TEMPLE MEADS
GUILDFORD
BOURNEMOUTH
PAIGNTON
PENZANCE

a one-stop shop to look up train times, check real-time running information, get prices and buy train tickets on smartphones. XC Advance tickets can be delivered to the app and displayed for inspection, while other tickets can be collected from a self service ticket machine at the station. The app is free to download and there is no booking fee.

Travellers can register for alerts as soon as advance purchase tickets become available for their journeys, and students can receive an extra 10pc discount on CrossCountry Advance tickets. Passengers can reserve a seat by mobile phone or online through CrossCountry's website up to 10min before train departure on all main routes.

At-seat catering is provided on most services, providing hot and cold refreshments appropriate to the time of day.

CrossCountry operates 34 Class-220 (4-car) and 23 Class-221 Voyager trains (22 x 5-car, 1 x 4-car); 29 Class-170 Turbostar diesel multiple-units (16 x 3-car, 13 x 2-car) and 5 HST sets, currently running in 7+2 configuration.

Since the beginning of the franchise CrossCountry has carried out £40m worth of improvements to its fleet. The Voyagers have been refurbished and reconfigured to provide additional seating and luggage space. Each four-car unit now has 202 seats, the five-car sets 264 seats. The Voyager fleet has won the coveted Modern Railways 'Golden Spanner' for the most reliable InterCity train for four consecutive years.

The five HSTs were fully refurbished by Wabtec at Doncaster, with a number of additional trailers converted from loco-hauled vehicles. MTU engines were fitted to the HST power cars. The HSTs offer either 457 or 462 seats and operate on the main Northeast-Southwest route, releasing Voyagers to strengthen services on other routes. The HST programme, along with the reconfiguration of the Voyagers, produced a 35% increase in capacity on principal routes in the evening peaks. HST sets are used on the busiest services between the Northeast and Plymouth.

The Class 170 Turbostars operate on Cardiff/Birmingham-Nottingham, Birmingham to Stansted Airport/Leicester routes. Various sub-classes inherited from a variety of operators are configured to a standard layout (120 seats in the two-car and 200 in three-car units) during a refurbishment by Transys Projects (now Vossloh Kiepe UK) with exterior repainting by Axiom Rail.

SENIOR PERSONNEL

CROSSCOUNTRY

MANAGING DIRECTOR Andy Cooper (in photo)
COMMERCIAL DIRECTOR David Watkin
FINANCE DIRECTOR Jonathan Roberts
CUSTOMER SERVICE DIRECTOR Jeremy Higgins
PRODUCTION DIRECTOR Will Rogers
HR DIRECTOR Maria Zywica
HEAD OF SAFETY Des Lowe

OPEN ACCESS COMPANY

Grand Central Railway became the second open-access train operator on the East Coast main line (ECML) when its Sunderland/Hartlepool to London service was launched in December 2007. A series of changes in ownership culminated in the company being acquired by Arriva in November 2011.

A successful application for a fourth path on weekdays and Saturdays enabled Grand Central (GC) to introduce an additional morning departure from Sunderland and mid-evening return service from King's Cross in 2009, both generating significant numbers of passengers. From December 2012 Grand Central introduced a fifth return service on this 'North Eastern' route. At the end of year 2012/13 GC's annual average punctuality score was 81.4pc. The company reports continued healthy growth in passenger numbers despite the economic situation.

GC has consistently scored well in the National Passenger Satisfaction survey, with the May 2013 result being 93pc.

Class 180 No 180101 passes Offord Cluny, south of Huntingdon, on 13 July 2013, forming the 06.43 Grand Central service from Sunderland to King's Cross. Ken Brunt

Access rights for three return services between Bradford Interchange and London King's Cross were granted in 2009, and this new 'West Riding' service started in May 2010, offering three direct services a day (calling at Halifax, Brighouse, Wakefield Kirkgate, Pontefract and Doncaster). GC was granted rights to run a fourth return path to Bradford from December 2013.

Access rights for GC's services were extended by two years to December 2016, after agreement on investment including part funding of improvements to stations GC serves, including additional car parking at Northallerton and Eaglescliffe and improved passenger information screens. Notable among these schemes is the transformation of Wakefield Kirkgate - a station previously dubbed by former Trasnport Secretary Lord Adonis as the worst medium sized station on the network. GC has introduced Station Ambassadors at Hartlepool and Eaglescliffe to improve passenger information and assistance when otherwise unstaffed on Sundays, and similar schemes are planned for the West Riding route. Independent retailer, Chester-le-Track, operates a ticket office at Eaglescliffe.

GC has invested over £40m in trains and people, as well as covering its start-up costs, completing a £400,000 programme of investment in stations by the end of 2013. It continues to develop further plans for station investment in conjunction with other industry partners.

In the summer 2013 Grand Central began consultation on extending its current Access Contract term beyond 2016, proposing a further programme of investment in its fleet and in stations.

GC leases five Class 180 trains from Angel Trains. All West Riding services are worked by these, with North Eastern services shared with three High-Speed Trains (HSTs). In 2010 the 21 HST vehicles (six Class 43 power cars and 15 Mk3 coaches) were sold by Sovereign Trains, a GC sister company, to Angel Trains, which invested in a substantial programme to improve performance and reliability, with installation of new MTU engines. In return GC agreed to lease the sets from Angel until at least December 2016.

The Class 180s have been refreshed with installation of Wi-Fi and at-seat power sockets. A programme of reliability modifications has been undertaken on all operators' '180s', and working with Angel Trains, First Hull Trains and First Great Western, Grand Central has entered into a unique technical support contract with Alstom, which covers all three Class 180 operators. This is delivering significant improvements in back office arrangements for maintenance, with remote conditioning monitoring equipment fitted to key systems.

Northern Rail maintains GC's trains at Heaton depot, Newcastle, and provides Riding Inspectors to check on the health of trains en route. Additionally, the two West Riding Class 180s are serviced overnight at Crofton depot, Wakefield, by Bombardier.

GC believes passengers should not be penalised for last minute decisions to travel, offering competitive and easy to understand fares with tickets that can be bought at the same price whether obtained online, on train or at a staffed station. The company has used a number of special price offers as part of a programme to encourage travellers to sample its services. It has also improved it advance purchase offer and its website. Seat reservations are free of charge for passengers to/from London.

With a total staff of 121, Grand Central has created more than 55 new jobs in Sunderland, 35 new jobs in Bradford and 20 in York - skilled, permanent positions, says GC, which make a real contribution to economic development in each city.

SENIOR PERSONNEL

GRAND CENTRAL

CHIEF OPERATING OFFICER, ARRIVA UK TRAINS Steve Murphy
MANAGING DIRECTOR Richard McClean (in photo)
OPERATIONS DIRECTOR Sean English
FLEET ENGINEER Dave Hatfield
CUSTOMER EXPERIENCE MANAGER Celia Knott

SERCO AND ABELLIO

A 50-50 partnership of Serco and Abellio (formerly NedRailways) holds the Northern Rail and Merseyrail franchises. Abellio alone has the Greater Anglia franchise.

Serco, an international service company, has operated, maintained and supported the Docklands Light Railway in London since 2006, securing an 18-month extension, valued at about £100m, until September 2014. It began operating and maintaining the new Dubai Metro in 2009, and in 2013 won a contract to operate the Dubai Tram for five years. Serco also has a renewed contract to provide a range of customer services for National Rail Enquiries. Serco Rail Technical Services offers services including vehicle testing and condition monitoring. Operations in transport and local authority direct services account for about 40pc of UK and Europe revenues.

Abellio, whose parent company is Netherlands Railways, is an international public transport company which delivers rail and bus services to over 650,000 passengers in the UK, Germany and the Czech Republic every day. Introducing a variety of innovative services, its stated philosophy is to improve the quality of life for passengers and the wider community, and help deliver the wider economic, environmental and social policies promoted by clients, working with government departments, passenger transport executives and councils in the design and implementation of new services.

FRANCHISE EXTENSION TO FEBRUARY 2016 PLANNED

The Department for Transport (DfT) in 2012 granted a continuation of Serco and Abellio's Northern Rail's franchise from 15 September 2013 until 1 April 2014, and in March 2013 the DfT announced a planned extension to February 2016, as part of its new franchising programme.

Northern runs local and regional train services for northwest and northeast England, Yorkshire, and Humberside, and previously secured a two-year extension in 2010, triggered by improved punctuality and reliability.

The DfT has been consulting on decentralisation and governance of future north of England franchises. Options included transfer of responsibility to a single franchising organisation; maintaining the status quo; or allocating control over groups of services to local bodies.

The new franchise end date in 2016 coincides with that planned for First TransPennine Express: combination of the franchises, possibly managed by a devolved Rail North group of metropolitan Passenger Transport Executives (PTEs) and other local authorities, is one option under consideration, with proposals presented by PTEs to the DfT in August 2013.

Since its franchise began in December 2004, Northern has provided a more punctual and reliable railway, increasing the number of trains arriving on time from 83.7pc, to 90.7pc for 2012-13; and it has attracted over 42pc growth in passenger demand. Against a 'no growth, no investment' franchise specification, it has attracted over £100m of external investment, and Serco and Abellio have invested £30m to deliver more trains, better stations and new services.

Research estimates that, each year, Northern services generate at least £690m of economic and other benefits for the economy, providing a 2:1 return on subsidy.

Northern secured 60 additional carriages up to 2011, as part of an agreement to meet the government's High Level Output Specification, adding 2.2

KEY STATISTICS
NORTHERN

	2011-12	2012-13
Punctuality (0-5min)	91.8 %	90.7
Passenger journeys (millions)	91.5	89.8
Passenger km (millions)	2,132.9	2,122.1
Timetabled train km (millions)	44.6	44.6
Route km operated	2,745.5	2,716.6
Number of stations operated	464	463
Number of employees	4,853	4,900
Subsidy per passenger km (p)	4.5	7.1
Network grant / pass km (p)	17.1	18.0

Northern Class 142 'Pacer' No 142064 at York. Brian Morrison

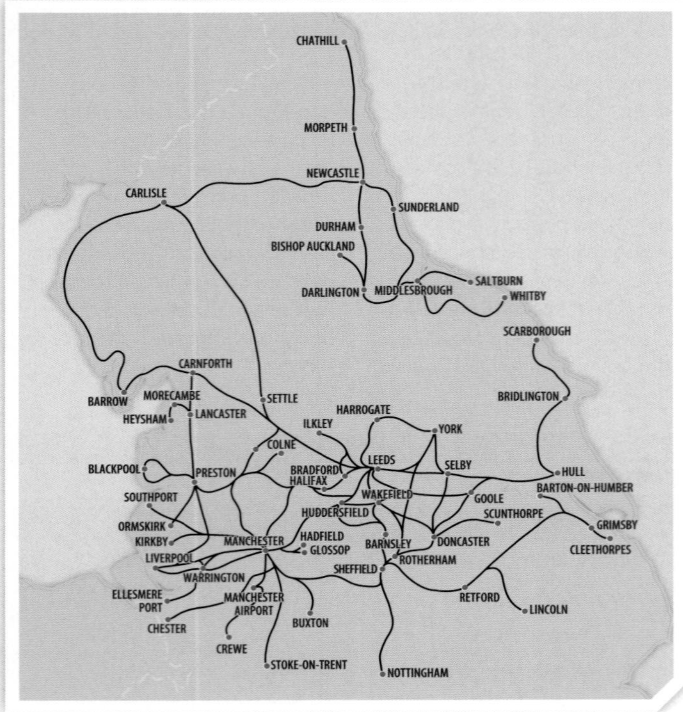

million additional peak seats for passengers per year.

Class 142 and Class 150 DMUs came from First Great Western and London Midland, and a small number of Class 156 and 180 trains left for other operators. Five 4-car Class 322 EMUs were transferred from ScotRail.

December 2011 saw an additional 8,550 seats every day on services into main urban destinations (Leeds, Liverpool, Manchester, Newcastle and Sheffield), with over 5,200 of these in peak hours.

Further EMUs will be added to Northern's fleet by 2019 as part of the Northwest electrification: some are likely to be based at the new Allerton depot. Operational since December 2011, it is initially home to Northern's fleet of additional '156' trains. The depot was made as 'green' as possible by, for example, using recycled concrete walkways; rain water harvesting and a train washer which recycles up to 80pc of water; and energy efficient lighting and radiant heaters. Delivered in partnership with Network Rail at a cost of £10.6m, time and cost savings were made by partially running design and construction work in parallel.

Northern Rail and Network Rail signed a framework agreement for an alliance in 2012. It focuses on seeking ways to improve industry efficiency and reduce costs to deliver improved facilities and services for passengers.

Northern supports 18 community rail partnerships on its routes, and a Community Ambassadors Scheme has been created to promote the use of local rail services with Black and Minority Ethnic (BME) and socially excluded groups.

Northern operates a diverse fleet of diesel multiple-units: 79 Class-142, and 13 two-car and 10 three-car Class 144 'Pacers'; 58 Class-150s; 7 Class-155s; 42 Class-156s; 37 two-car and 8 three-car Class-158s; and 18 single car Class-153s. There are eight Class-321/322 electric multiple-units and 16 Class-333s operated in West Yorkshire, with 17 Class-323s used mainly in Greater Manchester.

Almost 72pc of Northern's fleet has been refurbished, with train reliability improved by 60pc. A £600,000 refurbishment of the 29 Class-142 Pacer trains based at Newcastle got underway in 2013.

The main maintenance depots are at Newcastle (Heaton), Manchester (Newton Heath), Leeds (Neville Hill) and Liverpool (Allerton). Concentrating maintenance of each type of train at particular depots has helped to improve reliability. Alstom's West Coast Traincare maintains the Class 323s at Manchester. Alstom completed work in July 2013 on an overhaul of Northern's Class 323s, with more than 2,000 components exchanged.

Northern Rail won the 'Environment' title at Modern Railways' 2013 Rail Industry Innovation Awards for its commitment to conserving water at its train wash plants and f reducing water consumption at its four depots. Northern was the first rail operator in the country to measure its entire carbon footprint, reducing it by 23% since 2007.

SENIOR PERSONNEL
NORTHERN

MANAGING DIRECTOR Alex Hynes (in photo)
CHIEF OPERATING OFFICER Alan Chaplin
COMMERCIAL DIRECTOR Jonathan Stewart
ENGINEERING DIRECTOR Stuart Draper
PERFORMANCE AND PLANNING DIRECTOR Rob Warnes
SAFETY AND ASSURANCE DIRECTOR Gary Stewart
HR DIRECTOR Adrian Thompson
AREA DIRECTORS Lee Wasnidge, Richard Allan
FINANCE DIRECTOR Chris Harris
BUSINESS DEVELOPMENT Director Barry Graham

Merseyrail

25-YEAR CONCESSION FROM JULY 2003

The Merseyrail electric network is one of the most heavily used outside London, with almost 800 trains carrying 110,000 passengers per weekday, on 15min train frequencies, increasing to 5min on city centre sections. Nearly half of Merseyrail passengers are daily users.

Merseytravel, the Merseyside Public Transport Executive, manages the unique operating concession for this 75-mile, self-contained network of 750V DC, third-rail electrified railway. The 25-year contract, with a total value of £3.6bn, was awarded in 2003 to the Serco and Abellio joint venture 'Merseyrail Electrics 2002', subject to five-yearly reviews. Merseytravel livery is carried on trains and stations.

The Northern Line serves Southport, Ormskirk and Kirkby to Hunts Cross, and the Wirral Line serves West Kirby, New Brighton, Chester, Ellesmere Port and a central Liverpool loop line - 6.5 miles in tunnel with four underground stations in Liverpool and one in Birkenhead.

A £40m-plus overhaul for all five underground stations began with £20m of improvements completed in 2012 at Liverpool Central, the network's busiest station, and the underground station with the highest footfall outside London.

The funding package was shared between Network Rail, Merseytravel and the European Rail Development Fund. Work was completed in 2013 at James Street and Lime Street, and Network Rail also renewed 220 metres of slab track between Liverpool Central and James Street stations in summer 2013.

At Central, transformation of the concourse was carried out by Merseyrail and contractor Strategic Team Group, while Network Rail and contractor Morgan Sindall improved the platforms, escalators and passageways. The station has gained an additional lift, replacement escalators to the Northern Line; additional platform space; and improved toilets and waiting areas. A clear glazed roof and glass external walls allow natural lighting.

KEY STATISTICS
MERSEYRAIL

	2011-12	2012-13
Punctuality (0-5min)	95.2%	95.4%
Passenger journeys (millions)	43.5	41.7
Passenger km (millions)	634.3	611.7
Timetabled train km (millions)	6.4	6.4
Route km operated	120.7	120.7
Number of stations operated	66	66
Number of employees	1,220	1,267
Subsidy per passenger km (p)	11.8	12.3

Merseyrail Class 507 No 507020 at the recently refurbished Wirral Line platform at Liverpool Lime Street, on 7 October 2013. Tony Miles

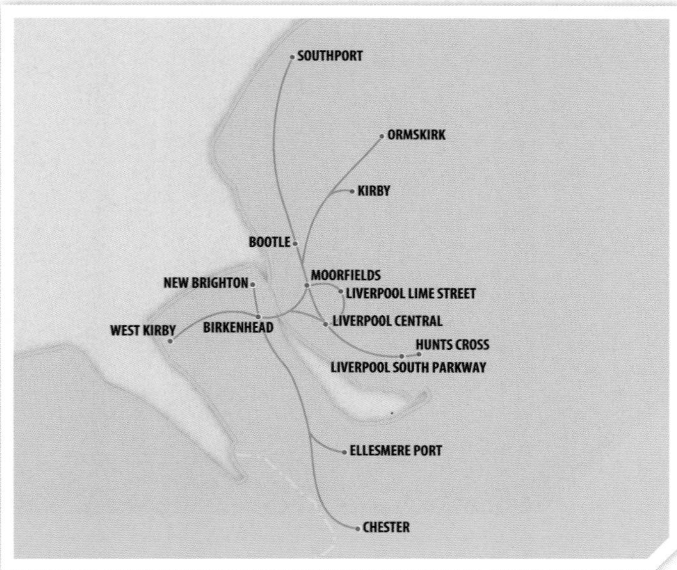

Merseytravel has begun work to procure a new train fleet by the time the current fleet of 59 Class 507 and Class 508 trains (built in 1978-79) come off-lease (now due in 2018, with a potential further extension to 2019). It has been building up a rolling stock reserve against the costs and financial risks associated with the project. Trains are maintained and stabled at Kirkdale and Birkenhead North depots.

A further external and internal refresh of the existing trains was announced in October 2013. In previous years, Merseytravel has invested more than £100m in Merseyrail, refurbished eight stations and built six new ones, with £32m invested in refurbishing rolling stock.

In the Spring 2013 National Passenger Survey, Merseyrail secured the joint highest score among train operating companies for overall satisfaction. The operator has excellent results for public performance measure punctuality (PPM), typically averaging over 95pc.

Electrification and integration into Merseyrail of the Bidston-Wrexham line is an ambition of Merseytravel, as are a number of new lines and stations, including an extension of electric trains east from Kirkby to Headbolt Lane.

Merseyrail in 2010 became the first 'fully secure' rail network in the UK with all 66 stations and 36 car parks accredited under the Secure Station and Safer Parking schemes by the British Transport Police. Merseyrail staff, police and partners such as byelaw enforcement officers work together to create a consistent high visibility presence to counter anti-social behaviour and ticketless travel. A penalty fare scheme covers all stations.

Liverpool South Parkway, a £32m new station, was opened in 2006 at the intersection of the Merseyrail electric and Liverpool-Crewe routes. It has a bus shuttle to Liverpool John Lennon Airport, acts as a hub for local bus routes, and offers park-and-ride.

Merseyrail has nine 'Mtogo' stores, combined retail outlet and ticket units tailored to suit both large and smaller stations. Mtogo is aimed at enhancing the customer experience and making passengers feel more secure, and a progressive revamp of the stores is underway.

Merseyrail collaborates with a wide variety of organisations on community initiatives, including community groups, schools and charities. In partnership with Merseytravel, it has set up 38 station adoption schemes, with more planned. The cycle centre at Southport station won in the station of the year category at the 2012 ATOC national cycle rail awards.

Merseyrail achieved NHS workplace wellbeing status in 2013 for promoting and improving workers' health, the first time the accolade has been given to a rail operator.

Work on phase two of Merseytravel's Birkenhead North station improvement scheme started in August 2013, to link the car park to the station via a new, fully accessible pedestrian bridge with lifts, giving step free access to both platforms.

Park and ride projects at both Birkenhead North and Bidston stations have been put in place by Merseytravel to meet the increasing demand for parking spaces with easy access to the rail network.

SENIOR PERSONNEL

MERSEYRAIL

MANAGING DIRECTOR Maarten Spaargaren (in photo)
DEPUTY MANAGING DIRECTOR Andy Heath
ENGINEERING DIRECTOR Mike Roe
FINANCE AND COMMERCIAL DIRECTOR Paul Bowen
SAFETY AND ASSURANCE DIRECTOR David Foster
CUSTOMER SERVICES DIRECTOR Kaj Mook

GreaterAnglia

EXTENSION PLANNED TO OCTOBER 2016

The Greater Anglia franchise was awarded to Abellio from 5 February 2012 for 29 months, a relatively short term, as the DfT prepared for revisions in franchising policy. In March 2013 the DfT announced plans to continue the franchise for another 27 months to October 2016, with a significantly longer franchise then planned. The previous franchise, National Express East Anglia, ran from April 2004.

The company has made consistent improvements in punctuality, working more closely with Network Rail through an alliance. Main line and Metro/Southend services reached the highest levels of performance for over 12 years, with the overall moving annual average Public Performance Measure score at 92.4pc in October 2013. The May 2013 four-week figure of 95.7pc was the highest since establishment of the Greater Anglia franchise structure in 2004. A revised approach to engineering work delivery has significantly reduced disruptions at weekends.

Greater Anglia has installed new ticket machines at key stations, introduced complimentary refreshments in First Class on London-Norwich and Stansted Express trains, and mobile ticketing. 1,600 frontline employees have been equipped with Blackberrys to improve communication, new information desks have been installed, and free Wi-Fi is now available at 100 stations. Colour-coded information on train loadings, so passengers can avoid heavily loaded trains if their journeys are less time-critical, has been introduced.

Greater Anglia was named Train Operator of the Year 2012 at the February 2013 Rail Business Awards. It received improved scores in both Autumn 2012 and Spring 2013 National Passenger Surveys and was the only operator to improve its rating in the Spring 2013 survey.

SENIOR PERSONNEL

GREATER ANGLIA

MD DESIGNATE Jamie Burles
OPERATIONS DIRECTOR Peter Lensik
CUSTOMER SERVICE DIRECTOR Andrew Goodrum
FINANCE DIRECTOR Adam Golton
ENGINEERING DIRECTOR Kate Marjoribanks
ASSET MANAGEMENT DIRECTOR Simone Bailey
HR AND SAFETY DIRECTOR Michelle Smart

Greater Anglia's No 90013 is prepared for departure on the 14.00 to London at Norwich on 27 June 2013. Tony Miles

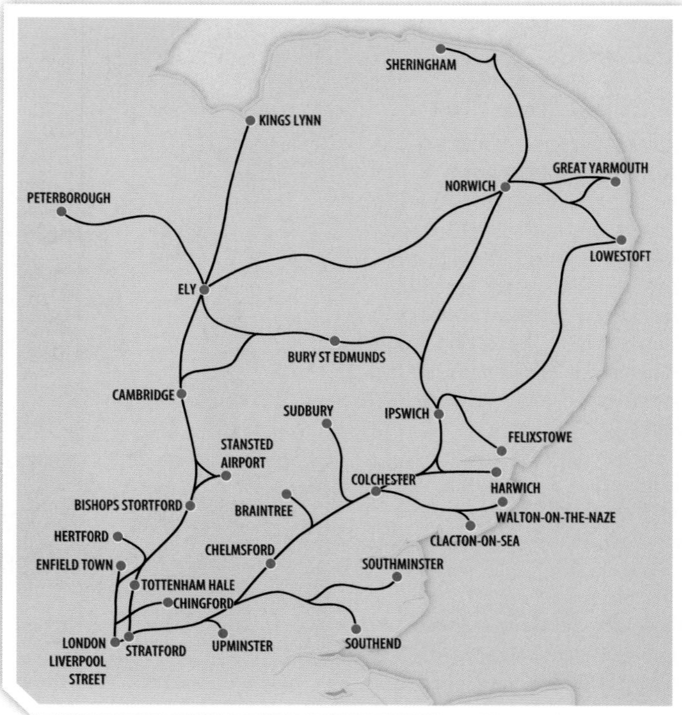

The company has played a pivotal role in developing an East Anglian Rail Prospectus, co-ordinating work with regional MPs, stakeholders and Network Rail in making the case for greater infrastructure investment.

Greater Anglia has continued to develop and promote rural 'community' railways and a new Hereward Community Rail Partnership was launched in October 2012 for services between Peterborough and Ely. Greater Anglia has doubled its financial contributions to CRPs and innovations such as 'Apps' for the Bittern and Wherry lines have been introduced.

From December 2013, Ipswich-Peterborough services will call at Manea, after journey time improvements enabled by additional platforms at Peterborough. An hourly Ipswich-Lowestoft service was introduced for 2013, following installation of a new passing loop at Beccles.

Station improvement schemes continue, with major schemes at Bishop's Stortford, Chelmsford and Cambridge, and a new transport interchange at Lowestoft in partnership with Suffolk County Council. A new 'Bike and Go' cycle-hire scheme has been implemented, a bus link at Saffron Walden was launched in September 2013, and an integrated bus link now runs from Halesworth to Southwold.

A renewed focus on marketing includes a partnership with Visit East Anglia to promote the many and varied regional attractions, and train travel, with '2 for 1' and other incentives. Greater Anglia is also extending advance fares to stations on the Clacton / Walton branch, and to Ely and Cambridge, to attract leisure and off-peak travellers.

The Class 153 fleet has been upgraded and a programme to improve and extensively refurbish the Class 156s is underway, including fitting accessible toilets. Information screens and wheelchair bays are being fitted to Class 315.

In April 2013 Porterbrook announced a £5m programme expanding overhaul of Mk3 coaches to include exterior improvements and work on electrical systems, air-conditioning and central door locking. Making the vehicles compliant with accessibility requirements was also being considered, which could see the fleet continue to operate beyond 2020.

Greater Anglia's main depots are at Ilford, Norwich and Clacton, with cleaning and stabling at other locations. The fleet of four-car electric multiple-units, based at Ilford, is made up of: 61 Class 315s, 51 Class 317s, 94 Class 321 s, 21 Class 360s, and 30 Class 379s.

The diesel fleet is made up of: five single-car Class 153s, nine Class 156s, four two-car Class 170s and eight three-car Class 170s. The locomotive-hauled fleet has 15 Class 90 locomotives and 15 Mk3 Driving Van Trailers along with 119 Mk3 coaches. Two Class 08 shunters are hired; and also Class 47 diesel locomotives for 'Thunderbird' rescue duties and to power the Norwich-Great Yarmouth legs of high season London-Great Yarmouth services, as well as additional trains for special events. ■

KEY STATISTICS

GREATER ANGLIA

	2011-12	2012-13
Punctuality	90.9%	92.3%
Passenger journeys (millions)	122.8	126.4
Passenger km (millions)	4,035.6	4,146.9
Timetabled train km (millions)	33.3	34.0
Route km operated	1,611.0	1,611.0
Number of stations operated	167	167
Number of employees	2,878	2,973
Subsidy per passenger km (p)	-2.6	-3.4
Network grant / pass km (p)	5.0	5.3

(Figures until 5 February 2012 for National Express East Anglia)

c2c

NEW FRANCHISE PLANNED FROM SEPTEMBER 2014

c2c's Class 357 Electrostars Nos 357024 and 357211 at London Fenchurch Street. Brian Morrison

The c2c franchise is the only one currently held by National Express, which became responsible for it in 2000, when it took over Prism Rail after financial problems at other Prism franchises. The London, Tilbury & Southend (LTS) route franchise had been awarded in May 1996 in a 15-year deal.

The company changed its name in 2002, and suggested 'c2c' could indicate 'coast to capital' or 'commitment to customers'.

Following the Department for Transport (DfT) review of rail franchising, a new short term contract was announced in May 2013. c2c will continue to operate the franchise until a new one begins - planned for September 2014, according to the invitation to tender issued in September 2013. Two station improvement projects were announced for the meantime, to create an extra exit/entrance for London Fenchurch Street station, on Coopers Row, to ease peak congestion; and to develop proposals for Stanford-le-Hope.

The c2c franchise was previously extended for two years, to 26 May 2013, as part of a previous round of DfT preparation for revisions in franchising policy.

Passenger demand broke records for c2c during the London 2012 Games, with 1.96m journeys during the 17 days of the games. c2c's timetable from December 2011 introduced 22 more weekday stops at West Ham in morning and evening peak periods, following upgrading of signalling equipment. From May 2013, c2c doubled the length of more than 50 off-peak trains each week, providing more than 14,000 extra seats.

c2c works in an alliance with Network Rail, building since 2012 on an established partnership, which included joint signalling and operating control based at Upminster. Better management of stations, better planning of engineering work, and further improvements to punctuality are key aspirations. c2c also set up a new security team in 2012 to tackle any anti social behaviour issues.

c2c holds the UK record for any four-week performance period, at 98.8pc by the Public Performance Measure, and also holds the record for punctuality on a moving annual average (97.5%).

The Spring 2013 results of the National Passenger Survey saw c2c top the national table for satisfaction with the overall service, punctuality, and with train upkeep. It was the leading London and Southeast commuter operator in 16 categories.

In August 2013, the DfT announced a £2.85 million trial of paperless ticketing on c2c. Systems at all c2c stations outside London will be upgraded for smartcard introduction in that area from January 2014, extending into the capital from April. In May 2013, c2c became the first train company in the Southeast to have automatic ticket barriers installed at every station.

c2c completed a £450,000 National Station Improvement Programme project at Basildon in August 2013, including one of its new passenger information display screens, designed to look like a giant smartphone.

All maintenance and servicing on the 74-strong fleet of four-car Class 357 Electrostar electric multiple-units are performed, in partnership with manufacturer Bombardier, at East Ham depot, along with some heavy maintenance: other heavy repairs including tyre turning, bogie overhauls, corrosion repairs, and painting are carried out at Bombardier's Ilford heavy maintenance depot. Stabling also takes place at Shoeburyness. The company switched its entire fleet to regenerative braking in 2007.

Train-washers at c2c depots have been upgraded by Garrandale to recycle water used to clean trains. This has reduced c2c's water consumption by 60pc and is one of several environmental initiatives.

Infrastructure works, including platform extensions, have been completed for 12-car trains. Driver-only operation (DOO) is used for trains of up to 8 cars: the invitation to tender for the new franchise envisages DOO of 12-car trains by 2024.

KEY STATISTICS

C2C

	2011-12	2012-13
Punctuality (0-5min)	96.8%	97.5%
Passenger journeys (millions)	36.4	37.4
Passenger km (millions)	988.8	1,008.6
Timetabled train km (millions)	6.5	6.5
Route km operated	115.5	115.5
Number of stations operated	25	25
Number of employees	779	702
Subsidy per passenger km (p)	-1.2	-1.7
Network grant / pass km (p)	4.3	4.4

SENIOR PERSONNEL

C2C

MANAGING DIRECTOR Julian Drury (in photo)
OPERATIONS DIRECTOR Kevin Frazer
FINANCE DIRECTOR Richard Bowley
ENGINEERING DIRECTOR Ben Ackroyd
HEAD OF RETAIL Hugh Jennings

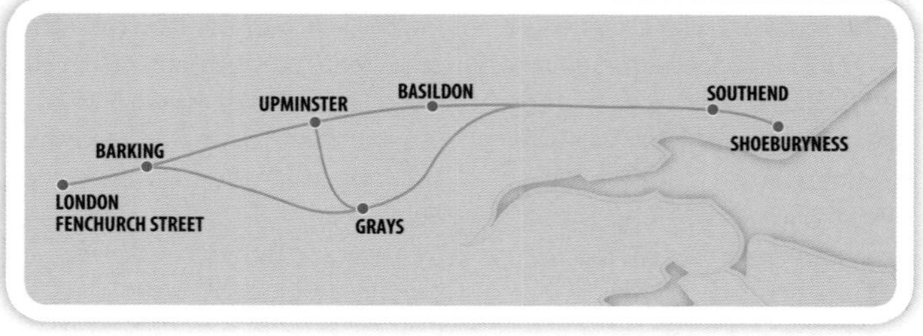

EAST COAST

NEW FRANCHISE PLANNED FROM 2015

East Coast's trains link London with Scotland, serving York, Newcastle, Edinburgh, Aberdeen, and also link London and Leeds, with less frequent services to Inverness, Hull, Lincoln, Harrogate, Skipton, Bradford and Glasgow.

A subsidiary of government-owned holding company Directly Operated Railways, East Coast Main Line Company Limited has operated intercity services since November 2009 when National Express's East Coast franchise was terminated: it was due to pay total premium payments of £1.4bn from December 2007 to March 2015, but revenue was undermined by the economic downturn.

In 2012-13, East Coast's turnover was £693.8m (2011/12: £665.9m), and operating expenditure was £690.0m (2011/12: £661.0m). DOR says this generated an operating profit, before Department of Transport (DfT) service payments and taxation, of £208.7m (2011/12: £195.7m), and an operating profit after DfT service payments but before taxation of £5.9m (2011/12: £7.1m).

Measured by average loads per train (of over 225 passengers), East Coast is Britain's busiest train operator, more than 36pc ahead of the next busiest. It achieved the best customer satisfaction result in the Passenger Focus autumn 2012 National Passenger Survey since rail privatisation.

In March 2013, the Secretary of State announced that East Coast was planned to be returned to private sector ownership in February 2015. Unlike previous franchise changes/ transfers, the East Coast company will be the subject of a business sale to a new private sector owner.

The current East Coast timetable provides 19 more services each weekday than prior to May 2011, and 3m extra seats per year. Highlights are the early morning 4hr 'Flying Scotsman' from Edinburgh to London, calling only at Newcastle, and a 2hr non-stop train from Leeds to London. One new daily Lincoln-London return train was introduced, instead of the two-hourly service previously proposed - a change estimated to save £9m a year, avoiding acquisition of additional trains. Most East Coast services on the Edinburgh-Glasgow section were replaced by CrossCountry trains.

A new First-class complimentary food and drinks offer saw some £10.2m invested in depots, trains and equipment. The company went from serving typically 100,000 meals a year to over a million. The new catering offer was projected to reduce losses by the previous operator of some £20m per year.

Following the changes, passenger numbers increased overall by 21pc in First Class in 2011-12. A new design cafe-bar is being introduced in 2013-14.

The best train punctuality on line since records in their current form began was achieved in summer 2012, but this deteriorated sharply during difficult winter weather and a number of significant failures of infrastructure assets.

Close working with Network Rail continues in an effort to improve punctuality and reliability. East Coast says that around two thirds of all delays are typically under the responsibility of Network Rail, and the vast majority of others have related to the train fleet. A comprehensive review of fleet engineering has led to significant overhaul of structure, people and processes, and has set an improving trend. A remote system that monitors the condition and functions of each train in service was introduced. A major £4.2m programme of air conditioning upgrading or replacement was also completed across the fleet.

The fleet consists of 31 Class-91 electric locomotives, powering 30 rakes of Mk4 coaches to make up InterCity225 trains; and 14 diesel HST sets. The DfT has announced the replacement of the entire fleet under the InterCity Express Programme.

The fleet operates from three depots: Bounds Green, London; Craigentinny, Edinburgh; and Clayhills, Aberdeen.

SENIOR PERSONNEL
EAST COAST

MANAGING DIRECTOR Karen Boswell (in photo)
OPERATIONS DIRECTOR Danny Williams
FINANCE DIRECTOR Tim Kavanagh
COMMERCIAL AND CUSTOMER SERVICE DIRECTOR Peter Williams
ENGINEERING DIRECTOR Jack Commandeur
BUSINESS PLANNING DIRECTOR Phil Cameron
PROPERTY AND PROJECTS DIRECTOR Tim Hedley-Jones

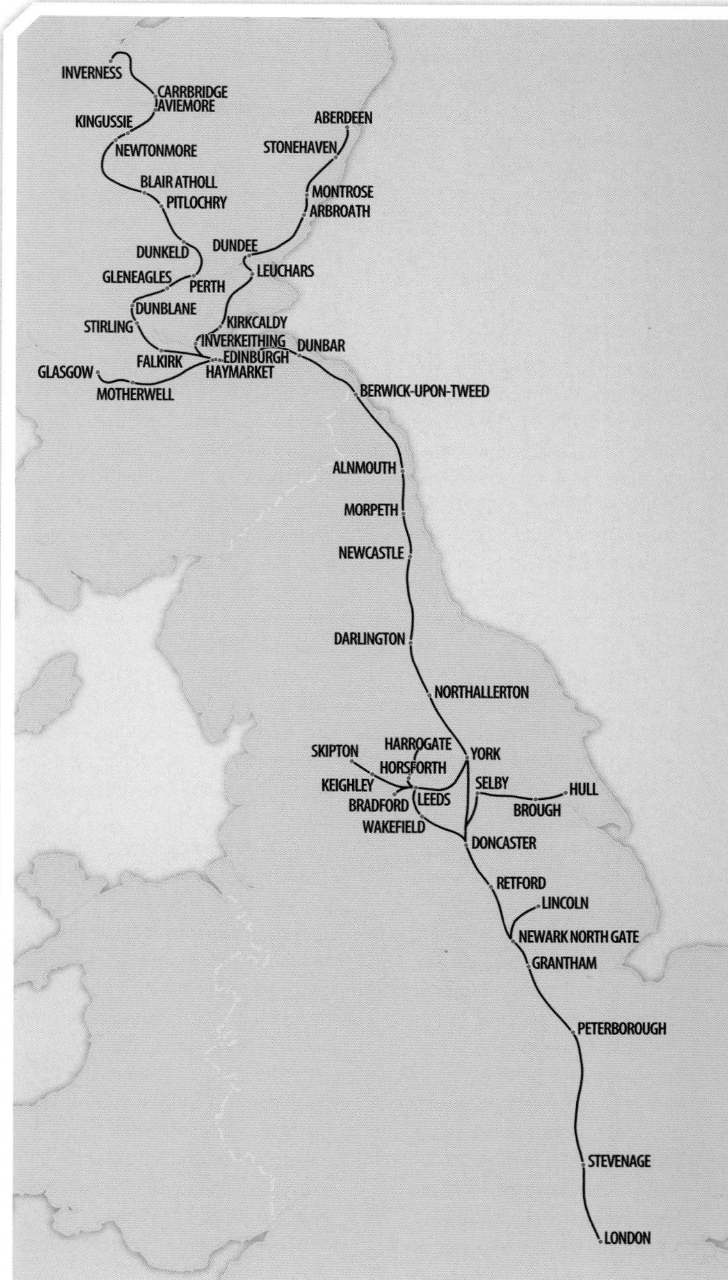

KEY STATISTICS
EAST COAST

	2011-12	2012-13
Punctuality (0-10min)	86.6%	83.9%
Passenger journeys (millions)	18.9	19.0
Passenger km (millions)	4,893.3	4,934.3
Timetabled train km (millions)	21.7	22.0
Route km operated	1,480.6	1,480.6
Number of stations operated	12	12
Number of employees	2,876	2,988
Subsidy per passenger km (p)	-3.8	-3.9
Network grant / pass km (p)	4.1	4.1

INTERNATIONAL INTER-CITY TRAINS

Since its launch in 1994, Eurostar's trains have carried more than 130m passengers on the high-speed service linking Britain with France and Belgium via the Channel Tunnel.

Eurostar was launched by the three countries' state railways, with the British interest sold to London & Continental Railways (LCR) when chosen as Channel Tunnel Rail Link developer by the government in 1996. As it prepared to sell the Channel Tunnel Rail Link (High Speed 1 - HS1), the government took control of LCR in 2009, and in 2010, a new standalone joint venture company, Eurostar International (EI), replaced the unincorporated joint venture of the three national companies. The UK has a 40pc shareholding, SNCF (French Railways) 55pc, and SNCB (Belgian Railways) 5pc.

Eurostar train at Paris Gare du Nord.

European Commission approval for EI was subject to conditions including access to stations, information systems and maintenance services for competitors.

Eurostar announced in 2010 that it was to buy a new fleet of 10 Siemens-Velaro-based 320km/hr trains (named 'e320'). A £700m rolling stock programme was also to cover overhaul and refurbishment of the existing 300km/hr trains, and rebranding. Nomad Digital is to supply onboard wi-fi on new and existing fleets. The same length as existing trains, the e320 will have about 150 more seats.

Eurostar links St Pancras International, Ebbsfleet International, and Ashford International in the UK with Paris, Brussels, Lille, Calais, Disneyland Resort Paris, Avignon and the French Alps. Trial direct services ran to Lyon and Provence in 2013, and in partnership with international operator TGV Lyria, a seasonal connection via Lille was introduced between London and Swiss ski resorts. Eurostar plans a fuller South of France service from 2015.

Eurostar in September 2013 announced an agreement with Netherlands Railways to launch direct, 4hr London-Amsterdam services from December 2016, using e320 trains, which will be interoperable and compatible with the Netherlands' high-speed infrastructure. Eurostar plans two services a day, calling at Antwerp, Rotterdam, and Schiphol Airport.

A joint venture of Keolis and Eurostar International in October 2013 announced plans to bid for the Inter-City East Coast passenger rail franchise. Eurostar would take a minority share.

In 2011, in its first full year of operation, Eurostar International delivered its first profit (£25.0m), and the 2012 operating profit was £52.3m, driven, said the company, by an increase in passengers (rising 2pc to 9.9m), combined with cost management. The number of international travellers originating outside the EU showed particularly strong growth, with volumes up 8pc year-on-year. Sales revenues in 2012 were broadly flat at £799m versus £803m in 2011 - but at constant (€1.15) exchange rates, increased by 5pc.

In the first six months of 2013, passenger numbers rose by 2pc year-on-year to 4.9 million. Sales revenues grew by 7pc in the first half of the year to £453m (from £425m in the same period of 2012).

Following major disruption to services during adverse winter weather in December 2009, new investment of £28m was committed, to improve resilience of trains, as well as passenger care, and communication systems inside and outside the Channel Tunnel.

The opening in 2007 of HS1, the new line from London to the Channel Tunnel, with its new London St Pancras terminal, saw journey times cut by about 20min. The London-Paris non-stop timing is now 2hr 16min. Record journey times were achieved on special runs before normal services began on HS1 in 2007: Paris-London, 2hr 3min, and Brussels-London, 1hr 43min.

New menus for Business Premier passengers were introduced in 2013 in partnership with Eurostar's new Culinary Director, Michelin-starred chef, Raymond Blanc. Eurostar and Waitrose announced in April 2013 that the supermarket company would supply refreshments to Eurostar's bar buffets, for passengers travelling in Standard class.

The flagship Business Premier class features a guaranteed boarding service; a mobile app for iPhone and Android users including mobile ticketing; on-board taxi bookings; and exclusive business traveller facilities at main stations. Standard Premier is a 'mid-class' designed for cost-conscious business travellers, and others who want extra space and service. Eurostar introduced a quiet coach facility in 2012.

Under its Tread Lightly environmental plan, Eurostar has set targets of reducing carbon dioxide emissions per traveller journey by 35pc, with a 25pc cut in wider Eurostar business emissions by 2015, alongside studies of Eurostar's direct and indirect carbon footprint, and new Sustainable Travel Awards to promote local initiatives in the UK, France and Belgium.

Eurostar operates a fleet of 28 trains - each 400 metres long, weighing 750 tonnes and carrying 750 passengers in 18 carriages. Three more trains are used only on French domestic services (as are most of a further seven, 14-car, trains built for aborted UK regional services).

SENIOR PERSONNEL

EUROSTAR

CHIEF EXECUTIVE OFFICER Nicolas Petrovic (in photo)
OPERATIONS DELIVERY DIRECTOR Frank Renault
DIRECTOR OF STATIONS Mikaël Lemarchand
CHIEF INFORMATION OFFICER Christophe Lemaire
COMMERCIAL DIRECTOR Nicholas Mercer
SERVICE AND PEOPLE DIRECTOR Marc Noaro
DIRECTOR OF REGULATORY AFFAIRS & COMPANY SECRETARY Gareth Williams
CHIEF FINANCIAL OFFICER James Cheesewright
DIRECTOR OF COMMUNICATIONS Mary Walsh

CROSS-CHANNEL AND RAIL FREIGHT GROUP

The 300 millionth passenger to use the Channel Tunnel since the start of commercial services in June 1994 was welcomed by Eurotunnel in October 2012.

The Channel Tunnel consists of twin railway tunnels and a service tunnel, and is operated by Eurotunnel under a 100-year concession signed in 1986 with the French and British governments. Terminals at Folkestone and Coquelles provide car, coach and lorry access to shuttle trains. International passenger and freight trains also run through the Tunnel.

15,982 vehicles travelled by shuttle (in both directions) on 17 August 2013, a new daily record.

For the first time in its history, in June 2013 Eurotunnel repaid a portion of debt capital. Its debt stood at Euro 3.9bn following repayment of Euro 30m. Group revenues for 2012 grew to Euro 993m, up by 14pc compared to 2011.

Eurotunnel's international rail freight subsidiary, Europorte, includes operations in France, and the British operator GBRf. It is responsible for UK-France freight haulage for operators other than DB Schenker (successor to British Rail's freight business).

Tests with new-generation Siemens Vectron and Alstom Prima II locomotives were conducted in 2012 and 2013 to check compatibility with Tunnel systems. Eurotunnel is pursuing application of European Interoperability Specifications, one aim being that rail freight services can run in the Tunnel without the specialised Class 92 locos.

Europorte owns 16 Class-92 locos (not all in use), equipped for North of London, Tunnel and North of France 25kV 50Hz pantograph supply; and for the UK 750V-DC third-rail network. Europorte has also encouraged the idea of a piggyback rail network to carry lorry trailers across Europe and into Britain.

Eurotunnel owns three ferries previously used by Sea France, purchased in 2012 for Euro 65m, with financial support from French local authorities, and leased to independent operator MyFerryLink. The UK Competition Commission decided in June 2013 to prohibit their operation: an appeal by Eurotunnel was to be heard in late 2013.

The basis of Channel Tunnel track access charges was challenged by the European Commission in June 2013: this was contested by Eurotunnel and the two governments.

Europorte revenues increased in 2012 to Euro 209m (a 28pc increase on 2011, like for like) - mostly generated by GBRf and Europorte France as a result of new contracts, full-year effect of 2011 contracts, and a small increase in volumes.

The number of through freight trains decreased by 3pc in 2012 and tonnage by 7pc, compared with 2011, attributed to the end of French Railways wagonload traffic and French rail infrastructure authority surcharges. The number of trains increased by 12pc in the first half of 2013, with increased steel traffic and some intermodal traffic resuming. Freight shuttle traffic experienced 16pc growth in 2012, increasing market share by 5 percentage points.

In May 2013, Eurotunnel launched ETICA (Eurotunnel Incentive for Capacity Additions), one-off financial support for operators launching intermodal rail freight services through the Tunnel.

A 2011 European Railway Agency report found passenger trains with distributed traction (rather than power cars at train ends) could be permitted in the Tunnel, as required by Eurostar and Deutsche Bahn plans for new international passenger services. In June 2013, the UK/France Intergovernmental Commission (the supervisory authority for safety and regulation) granted Deutsche Bahn a certificate to operate passenger services through the Tunnel.

Four SAFE fire-fighting points, installed in 2011, are designed to suppress fires on lorry shuttles, and hot-spot detectors are used on every lorry. The tunnel's radio system has been upgraded to digital GSM-R (Global System for Mobile Communications - Railways), with mobile phone capability, by Alcatel-Lucent.

Eurotunnel has nine passenger shuttles for cars and coaches (one was restored in 2012 after being out of use), and 15 lorry shuttles. Each 800-metre long shuttle has two locomotives.

Shuttle locos have three bogies, each with two motorised axles for good wheel/rail adhesion. There are 45 locos of 7MW rating, many uprated from 5.7MW, with 13 remaining at 5.7MW. There are also seven Krupp/MaK diesel auxiliary locos. Eurotunnel increased the top speed of its shuttles from 140km/h to 160km/h in 2012.

A 1,000MW electrical interconnector between Great Britain and France is under development by ElecLink, a Eurotunnel joint venture with STAR Capital.

SENIOR PERSONNEL

EUROTUNNEL

CHAIRMAN AND CHIEF EXECUTIVE Jacques Gounon (in photo)
CHAIRMAN OF EUROPORTE Pascal Sainson
DEPUTY CHIEF EXECUTIVE, CHANNEL TUNNEL Michel Boudoussier
DEPUTY CHIEF EXECUTIVE, CORPORATE Emmanuel Moulin
COMMERCIAL DIRECTOR Jo Willacy
BUSINESS SERVICES DIRECTOR Patrick Etienne

Eurotunnel Brush/ABB-built shuttle locomotives. No 9832 is a 7MW locomotive rebuilt from 5.7MW, No 5007 an original 5.7MW locomotive. Eurotunnel

The 13.40 Heathrow Express awaits departure from Paddington on 27 February 2013, formed by Class 332 No 332004 in Vodafone livery. Brian Morrison

15 YEARS OF AIR-RAIL LINK

Heathrow Express celebrated its 15th birthday in 2013, after transporting over 60 million passengers between Heathrow airport and London since 23 June 1998. With 150 train journeys a day, a total fleet mileage of 23,689,150 is estimated over the 15 years.

A fast and frequent service between Heathrow and London Paddington, Heathrow Express carries more than six million passengers a year. 150 trains each day depart every 15min each way, taking just 15min to/from Terminals 1-3.

Heathrow Express is a private train operating company and subsidiary of the airport owner: its infrastructure within the airport was built as part of a long-term strategy to increase public transport use for airport access.

Trains reach the airport on a dedicated line, tunnelling from near Hayes & Harlington on the Great Western main line, for about 3.5km to Heathrow Central (Terminals 1-3) and about 6.5km to Terminal 4 (both opened in 1998). A 1.8km extension to the new Terminal 5 opened in 2008.

Terminal 5 station has two platform spaces for western rail links: a proposed link via Staines was shelved in 2011 (though there is local authority enthusiasm for a revised version). Funding for a link towards Reading via the Great Western main line was pledged by government in the 2012 High Level Output Statement, subject to business case and agreements.

Terminals 1-3 and 5 are served direct by Heathrow Express. A regular shuttle service runs between Terminal 4 and Terminals 1-3.

Heathrow Express's Class 332 electric trains, the first Siemens train fleet in the UK, are owned (under a leaseback arrangement) by Heathrow, and were built by Siemens in partnership with CAF of Spain.

Heathrow Express launched new branding and a train refurbishment programme in 2012, a £16m project. The major refurbishment of rolling stock, with input from Siemens and Interfleet Technology, was completed by Railcare, Wolverton, in July 2013. Designs by the Tangerine agency aim to create an airliner ambience. In First Class, seats are all 1+1. Seats have new covers by Replin, upholstered by ProStyle.

LED lighting throughout improves energy efficiency and lighting intensifies when the train arrives in stations. New glazing (with additional windows to improve views), new bespoke Axminster carpets, and updated toilets are also part of the revamp. Over 1,300 new components were introduced from over 200 suppliers.

Internet access is available throughout the journey. Heathrow Express was the first UK train company to launch an app which allows users to buy a ticket and receive it on a phone. Print-at-home ticketing is also provided.

Fares (late 2013) for Express Class are £20 single, £34 return (£28/£52 First Class). Tickets can be purchased on-board trains, with a premium for Express Class. Flight information screens and self-service check-in machines for selected airlines are provided at Paddington. The identification of new passenger segments and price points has helped increase passenger volumes by 3% - promotional fares for two to four passengers travelling together, or adults with children, were introduced in late 2012.

Since April 2013, an online partnership with Aer Lingus has allowed customers to book train travel with flights - receiving both Heathrow Express and airline e-tickets.

The Heathrow Connect trains, aimed at providing access to the airport for London and Thames Valley residents and airport workers, run generally half-hourly between Paddington and Heathrow Terminals 1-3 (32min journey), calling at Ealing Broadway, West Ealing, Southall, Hanwell and Hayes & Harlington. Trains and on-board staff are supplied by Heathrow Express, and between Paddington and Hayes & Harlington, operation is by First Great Western. Introduced in 2005, it represented a £35m investment by Heathrow, in partnership with FirstGroup. Between Hayes & Harlington and Airport Junction, open-access rights apply. Heathrow Connect uses five 5-car Class 360/2 trains built by Siemens.

Heathrow Connect fares are aligned with price-sensitive and local markets. The London-Heathrow single (late 2013) is £9.50.

The 14 Class-332 Heathrow Express trains generally run in pairs, making up eight or nine-car trains. (Five additional carriages, valued at £6m, increased five trains to five-car length.) Distance travelled between major overhauls has been more than doubled from the originally expected 450,000 miles to one million miles.

Siemens carries out train maintenance, with reliability standards specified in the contract. The purpose-built depot is at Old Oak Common, near Paddington. The total value of the original train order, including a 10-year maintenance element, was about £70m. A new, 19-year maintenance contract valued at £70m was awarded in 2005, covering both Heathrow Connect and Heathrow Express.

In 2012, according to the airport company's accounts, rail income increased by 4.4% compared with 2011 to £116 million. Heathrow Express Public Performance Measure punctuality (moving annual average) at end of 2012-13 was 93.3%.

SENIOR PERSONNEL

HEATHROW EXPRESS

MANAGING DIRECTOR
Keith Greenfield (in photo)

OPERATIONS DIRECTOR
Keith Harding

HEAD OF COMMERCIAL
Joanne Gowing

HEAD OF ENGINEERING
Daniel Smith

FREIGHT AND HAULAGE

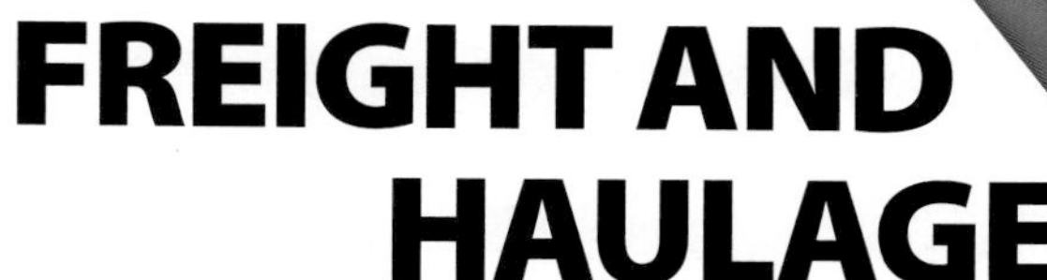

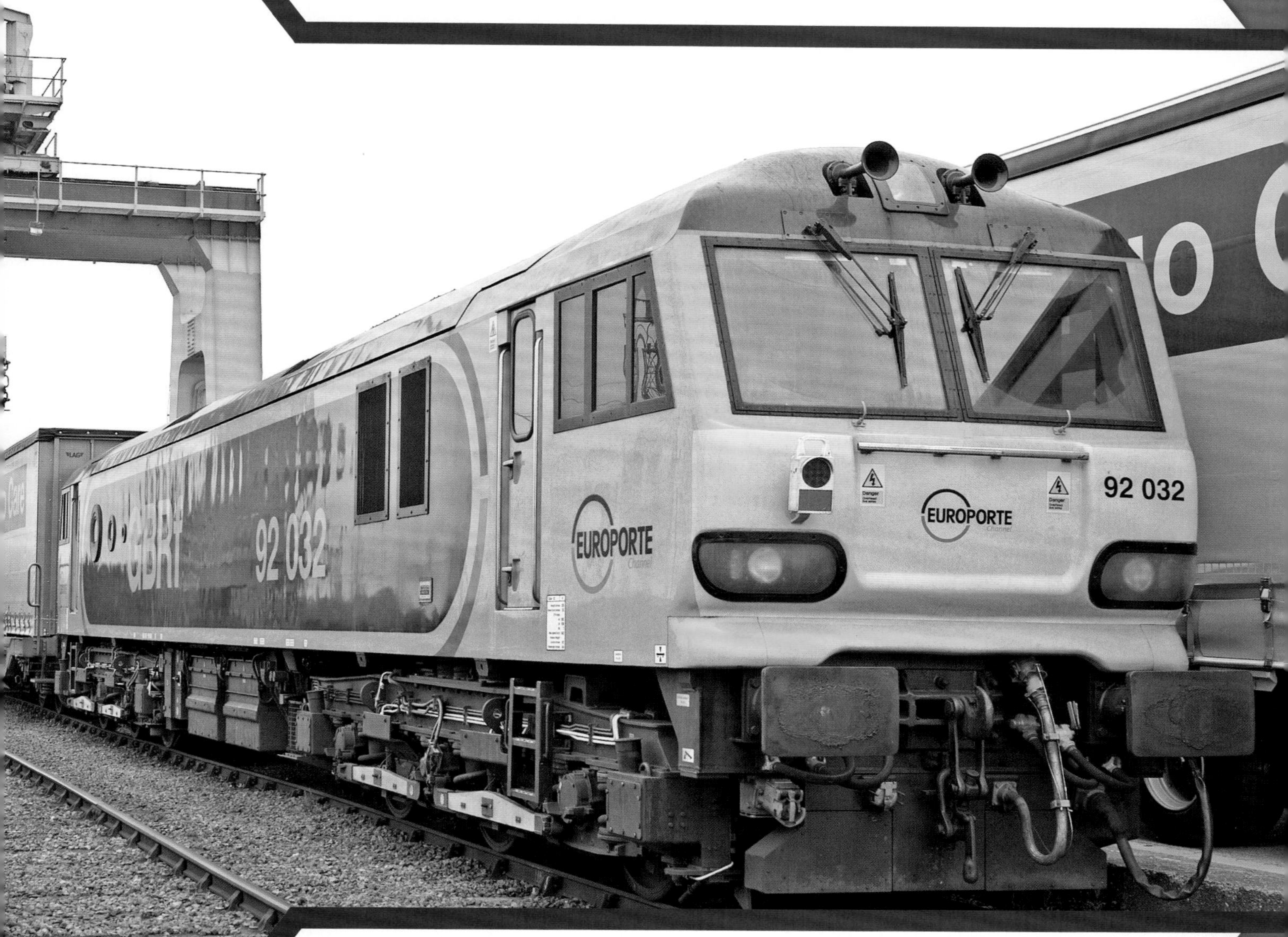

IN ASSOCIATION WITH

GB Railfreight
PART OF EUROPORTE

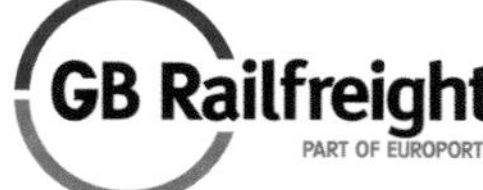

A GBRf intermodal service at Felixstowe. GBRf

The story of rail freight since privatisation is one of great success, and no company in the industry embodies that more than GB Railfreight (GBRf). The Freight Operating Company was set up in 1999 with two employees and zero contracts. Fourteen years later, and GBRf has just hired its 500th employee, reached a turnover in excess of £100 million, won contracts with major companies such as Greenergy, Crossrail and EDF Energy, and found a place for rail freight in new markets such as petroleum and biomass. The company is now part of the Eurotunnel subsidiary, Europorte, having been acquired from First Group in 2010.

The first contract GBRf won was with Railtrack in April 2000, with the first trains running the following year. Since then, the company has enjoyed significant successes. It entered the coal market and, within the space of a year, went from 0% to 12% of the market share. It currently holds 30%. It was also the first company to have regular contracts to transport biomass and continues to be the market leader in this area. It operates around 650 trains a week, cementing its position as the UK's third largest freight operator in terms of the number of trains run.

This success has not gone unnoticed. GBRf has won the acclaim of colleagues and competitors alike, with a raft of industry awards in the fourteen years since its founding. GBRf is a regular finalist and winner at Rail's National Rail Awards (NRA) as well as the Rail Business Awards. Notably, GBRf was awarded 'highly commended' in the NRA 2013 Freight & Logistics Achievement of the Year category, and in 2012 GBRf's Managing Director, John Smith, won the National Rail Award's Outstanding Personal Contribution for Senior Management. Speaking of the Award, John said: 'I think it is a reflection of the hard work we do. It reflects that we are personable. I look at other awards in other industries and it shows just how far we have grown in a short space of time.'

GB RAILFREIGHT'S SERVICES

Rail freight is integral to UK economic life. The industry carries goods worth over £30 billion and, without it, infrastructure projects such as Crossrail would jam Britain's roads, ports would become gridlocked and the energy industry would be unable to keep the lights on.

Rail freight, and more particularly GBRf, is integral to many of the UK's core industries, including power generation, construction and manufacturing. GBRf's specialist teams design transport answers for companies working in coal, biomass, infrastructure, petrochemical, construction, and intermodal amongst others.

The core of GBRf's locomotive fleet comprises 58 Class-66s. This number continues to grow at a rapid pace. Indeed, in 2013, GBRf made significant investment decisions. These include the purchase of eight locomotives from Electro-Motive Diesel in August 2013, the conversion of two further locomotives from Germany, and the purchase of three Dutch locomotives from Electro-Motive Diesel which were converted for UK use and given approval by the Office of Rail Regulation (ORR) in July 2013.

'Our customers tell us that they work with us because we get their traffic where they want, when they want, time after time at a cost effective price', says GBRf, and for those switching to GBRf, the company makes it seamless and trouble-free, placing great emphasis on professionalism, planning and clear communications.

GBRf's specialist teams use careful and flexible planning of people and rolling stock to respond to peaks and troughs of demand. This means that the company gets the best use for its customers from its fleet of wagons and locomotives.

GBRf also uses innovative solutions to provide the best service. The company introduced the Train Manager concept, a title that reflects the enhanced responsibility and status of its drivers in delivering a top class service for its customers. GBRf now has over 200 Train Managers, all of whom have progressed from ground staff.

COAL

In the coal haulage market, GBRf has built a share of around one-third of traffic, with British Energy, Drax Power and EDF Energy among its client list.

BIOMASS

Over the past number of years, GBRf has worked hard to investigate the potential for carrying biomass by rail. In 2010, GBRf put rail freight's marker on the industry's map, becoming the first UK rail freight operator to move renewable biomass material for Drax Power, operating four trains a day from the Port of Tyne to Drax power station near Selby using specially adapted HYA coal hoppers. The company also has a contract with E.ON's power station in Ironbridge. As part of this work, GBRf shifts 1.5 million tonnes of biomass per year between Liverpool Docks and the Ironbridge power station.

Over the past three years, GBRf has built up its Biomass specialist team and resources. Because of its diverse nature, there is more than one way to move biomass: hopper wagons, box wagons, containers or tanks. GBRf has all of these wagons and every day it delivers a variety of biomass from ports to power stations.

INTERMODAL

GBRf operations encompass a diverse mix that includes the provision of maritime container services linking Felixstowe with Doncaster, Selby and Birmingham Intermodal Freight

Terminal at Hams Hall. September 2011 saw the start of an additional service between Felixstowe and Manchester Trafford Park, contributing to the company's claim to operate almost 20% of trains out of Felixstowe. GBRf's strategic vision for the intermodal network is to expand to other ports including Tilbury and Southampton, as well as those in northwest and northeast England.

In 2011, GBRf and Europorte Channel commenced a contract with container shipper DFDS to operate a mixed goods intermodal service from Daventry through the Channel Tunnel to France and then on to Novarro in Northern Italy. A seasonal weekly train on behalf of Stobart Group carrying fruit and vegetables from Silla in Spain to Ripple Lane, east London, has also been operated.

INFRASTRUCTURE

From its inception, GBRf has been active in haulage of infrastructure trains out of Eastleigh, Hoo Junction and Whitemoor yards for Network Rail. It also continues to fulfil a ten-year £80 million contract awarded in 2006 to provide infrastructure haulage services for Metronet, now part of London Underground – much of it concentrated on a dedicated materials depot operated by the company at Wellingborough.

A small fleet of Class 73 electro-diesels is available for infrastructure duties on the third rail network. GBRf is also responsible for five Europorte Channel Class 92 dual-voltage electric locomotives in the UK – handling traffic through the Channel Tunnel and used on the Dollands Moor-Daventry DFDS service. 10 Class Di8 diesel locomotives acquired from Norwegian State Railways are used at Lackenby steelworks.

In 2013, GBRf signed a contract with Hitachi to provide train operations to facilitate the testing and commissioning of the Class 800 and Class 801 trains for the Great Western main line as part of the Intercity Express Programme (IEP). As part of the contract, GB Railfreight will provide locomotives for transit movements and train crew throughout the test programme. GB Railfreight will support Hitachi Rail Europe through the compatibility process in preparation for the start of testing in March 2015.

GBRf also prides itself in the services that it provides for the London transport network. For example, to haul London Underground 'S' stock, GBRf has taken on nine Class 20 locomotives from various sources, operated in 'top and tail' pairs with translator vehicles to ensure continuous braking.

CONSTRUCTION SERVICES

GBRf has worked with major UK companies to help them get infrastructure projects built. In February 2012, GBRf won a two-year contract with Crossrail tunnelling contractor BFK (BAM/Ferrovial/Kier joint venture) to move over one million tonnes of excavated material from a tunnel portal at Westbourne Park to Northfleet in Kent – involving more than 860 Class-66 hauled trains of JNA bogie ballast box wagons hired from VTG.

PETROCHEMICALS

In December 2011, GBRf secured a major contract with Greenergy, the UK's leading supplier of petrol, biofuel and diesel, to haul petroleum products from the Immingham terminal to Inver Terminal at the Queen Alexandra Dock in Cardiff. GBRf is a crucial part of the logistics chain which ensures that about a fifth of the UK's entire road fuel is delivered to supermarkets, oil companies and forecourts across the country.

SENIOR PERSONNEL

GBRF

MANAGING DIRECTOR
John Smith

GBRf has built a share of around one-third of coal traffic, and has also built up a biomass specialist team and resources. GBRf

Another record year for railfreight

THE MODERN RAILWAY'S REVIEW OF THE RAILFREIGHT MARKET EXPOSES SOME STARTLING TRENDS

It beggars belief. The UK has been mired in recession for the last four years - and yet railfreight is at record levels. 2012/13 saw a 12% increase in tonnage to 113m tonnes, making it the best year since the early 1990s - when the UK still had a large coal industry. Whilst the 52m tonnes of coal moved in 2012/13 is 30% up on the figure two years earlier, it is still a shadow of the over 70m tonnes of the early 1990s. The loss of baseload coal traffic was always expected to deal a mortal blow to the industry, but it has proved far more resilient than many believed possible.

Remarkably, the tonne-mileage moved in 2012/13 is equivalent to that of the early 1970s, when the UK had only a basic motorway system and the biggest lorry allowed on the roads was 32t gross laden weight, compared with the 44t vehicles that now provide the main competition for rail. And the trend continues – Quarter 1 of 2013/14 saw the highest amount of freight moved since detailed records began. Virtually all commodities, except Metals, were up and the star performer was Construction, which was up nearly 20% on the previous quarter, to a level only previously seen during the Olympics building boom. Given that the construction industry is only just reawakening from a deep recession, this is a highly significant result.

POLICY CHANGE

Nevertheless, a commentator well-versed in macro-economic trends, but new to the UK railfreight scene, might be excused from initially painting a gloomy picture of the future. Coal, still nearly half of all railfreight tonnage, is set to decline sharply in the coming years as the country seeks to decarbonise its electricity generation. With gas, new nuclear and renewables set to fill the gap, the prognosis for rail might seem grim.

This would be to miss a small but significant change in government policy in 2013. Biomass was, and still is, seen as an important component of the new fuel mix, but policy now favours conversion of existing large coal-fired stations to biomass rather than the construction of new compact biomass power stations. Whereas rail would struggle to compete for movements to the latter, large scale biomass flows to existing stations by rail are now in prospect.

That this is not an empty policy steer is demonstrated by the substantial private sector investment being made in the biomass supply chain. Major import facilities are being created at Immingham, Tyne, Liverpool and Portbury (Bristol) and the generating groups are installing storage and handling systems at the

Coal traffic has proved remarkably resilient. DB Schenker's Class 66 No 66081 winds its way past Cardiff Canton depot with the 12.39 Aberthaw power station to Avonmouth coal train on 11 July 2013. Stewart Armstrong

power stations. Drax Power – the leader in biomass usage - has gone a step further and commissioned a fleet of innovative high capacity covered hopper wagons to move biomass (essentially wood chips or pellets) from the ports.

None of these investments come cheap, and would not be made for short term, price-driven reasons – biomass is here to stay and is likely be good business for the Freight Operating Companies (FOCs) for years to come. Further, biomass has a lower calorific value than coal and is less dense, so more trains are needed to generate the same amount of electricity. High cube hoppers and longer trains help with the density issue, but the basic equation remains valid.

True, there have been power station closures in 2013 – notably Didcot and Cockenzie – and there are more to come, but the electricity supply industry is set to remain a significant market for rail. Indeed, with growing concerns about the limited amount of spare capacity in the electricity supply system – even before economic growth drives demand higher - the decline of coal may yet prove to be slower than expected. It would be a 'brave' minister (as Sir Humphrey would have said) who would risk the lights going out – or impose peak demand power rationing – in pursuit of decarbonisation, however sound that may be in the long run. Further, the rapid growth of shale gas and oil production in the USA has led to a significant fall in the world price of coal. It is currently an attractive option for generators (hence the rise in UK coal movements over the past year) and there is thus an economic driver for keeping coal generation as high as permitted, as well as the security of supply issue.

NEW EQUIPMENT INVESTMENT

The promising future of UK railfreight is also evidenced by the amount of investment being made by the industry in new equipment and infrastructure. When was the last time that orders for four different types of new freight locomotives were placed in the same year? Not since the Modernisation Plan, for sure, but 2013 saw DRS ordering Class 88 electro-diesels and Class 68 diesels, GBRf ordering more Class 66s, and Colas tipped to order Class 70s. The numbers of each type ordered may not be as large as would have occurred under British Rail, but collectively are significant.

It is interesting that these orders are being placed by the smaller FOCs rather than the market leaders, DB Schenker and Freightliner. In part it is due to customers seeing that the smaller players are more than capable of providing the service they require, and spreading their business over a wider range of suppliers – this is particularly true of infrastructure and coal. However, this is only part of the story and each of the FOCs investing in new locos has a good record of developing new business and expanding the total rail market.

The two big players each have a reserve of locos currently working in mainland Europe – notably France and Poland - which could be replaced by other traction and repatriated if required to meet growing UK demand. This could well prove to be the case with Freightliner, which continues to grow its business, but would seem unlikely in the case of DB Schenker. A long running dispute with its drivers in 2012 damaged DB Schenker customer relations and has resulted in the loss of significant Infrastructure and Charter business during 2013. These losses seem likely to cancel out progress being made elsewhere, in Intermodal and Construction.

Even before these latest losses DBS had almost a third of the 250 Class 66s working overseas, and has started to export Class 92 electrics for use in Bulgaria and Romania. The latter move has raised eyebrows since, whilst the '66s' were financed by private capital under EWS and can reasonably be deployed wherever the company sees fit, the costly '92s' were - along with wagons and terminals - gifted to DBS's predecessor as part of the 'sale' (for a negative price) of the Railfreight Distribution Channel Tunnel business by the UK government. At a time when growing use of electric traction is being encouraged in the UK, the export of such taxpayer-funded assets is seen by some as, at the very least, questionable.

Meanwhile, as a short term measure before the Class 88s are delivered, DBS is hiring a number of '92s' to DRS to haul Intermodal trains on the West Coast main line (WCML) – each electric releasing two '66s' for other DRS work. In parallel, the DBS programme to refurbish and reinstate around a quarter of the excellent Class 60s, for use on the heaviest Construction, Metals and Petroleum trains continues, displacing further '66s'. Demand for locos to haul additional Intermodal trains can thus probably be met from the Class 60 cascade.

WAGON INVESTMENT

Wagon investment is also taking place. As well as the Drax biomass hoppers mentioned earlier, a new breed of length-efficient Ecofret, or Shortliner, 40ft container carriers are entering service with Freightliner. With the proportion of 20ft boxes dropping inexorably on many routes, the FOC can be left with a single 40ft container on many of its standard 60ft wagons. Not only does this waste train space, it hits fuel efficiency as wind eddies caused by the 20ft gaps significantly increase rolling resistance. The improved efficiency of the Ecofret and longer container trains, made possible by infrastructure enhancements, are permitting some impressive payloads of 50 containers or more on one train. Granted, wagon charges will be higher, but other costs are largely unchanged and profitability accordingly better.

Elsewhere, additional car carriers are entering the country from France for service with STVA, many on the frequent trains of Jaguars from Halewood to Southampton. Others are employed on a new flow of imported Renault cars and vans from Southampton that commenced in mid 2013, using DBS's residual Network (formerly Enterprise) service. Whilst relatively small scale, given the number of cars imported through Southampton – all of which previously moved inland by road - this is an important bridgehead.

INFRASTRUCTURE

In parallel, Network Rail is investing significant sums of money (largely from UK government) in enhancing its freight infrastructure. In some cases, such as the flyover rapidly taking shape at Shaftholme Junction north of Doncaster, the driver is increased passenger capacity (in this case on the East Coast main line), but in others the key beneficiaries are the FOCs and their customers. Uppermost in this category must be Ipswich North Chord (nee the Bacon Factory curve) which, when commissioned in early 2014, will permit container trains from Felixstowe to the Midlands and the North to avoid a time-consuming and length-restricting run-round at Ipswich yard. Further north, the new North Chord at Nuneaton to facilitate access onto the WCML by trains from Felixstowe, was commissioned in early 2013.

Less dramatic, but equally important, are a series of improvements taking place on the route from Southampton to the Midlands and the North. Gauge enhancement to permit 9ft 6in containers to travel on standard height wagons (W10 gauge) is complete to Birmingham and the WCML and is currently being implemented on the NE-SW route towards Doncaster and Leeds. Closer to the port, a new Up loop is being created just to the south of Eastleigh to allow better regulation of container trains through this key junction. Further north, the Down goods loop is (after 50 years) being reinstated between Oxford station and Wolvercote Junction.

Welcome as the latter project is, with the forthcoming – and very welcome – reopening of the route to Bletchley and the WCML, plus Great Western electrification, Oxford remains a problem without a solution. Unlike the clear strategic thought applied to Reading five or more years ago - and now coming to fruition in such an impressive manner

- there appears to be a lack of clarity surrounding Oxford. The key, as ever, is separating out the traffic flows to minimise conflicting moves, including turnback sidings between Up and Down lines for terminating services.

Yet, nearly two years on from approval of the Bletchley route, there is still no solution incorporating electrification, Chiltern's London service and the new link to the WCML (and Midland main line) for both freight and passenger. It is now being suggested that the current layout will be electrified 'as is', only to be pulled apart again a few years later to cater for East-West services – hardly a cost-effective approach to infrastructure enhancement and one which would leave Network Rail open to accusations of wasting public money.

PORTS

Perhaps the most impressive freight infrastructure investments are taking place off the network and largely out of the public eye, at Felixstowe and Thames Haven. The brand new London Gateway container port (on the site of the former Shell oil refinery) is on target for commissioning Phase 1 by the end of 2013. Indeed, a stricken ZIM container vessel, looking for a place to land boxes and undergo repairs, was handled in September, in advance of formal opening, with both DB Schenker and Freightliner running trains at short notice to move boxes to inland destinations.

The scale of London Gateway can only be described as profoundly impressive. With a river frontage around two kilometres long and the first of two rail terminals boasting six loading tracks, each a full one kilometre long, DP World is clearly looking to take a sizeable share of the UK deep sea market. This alone would make it a key location for UK railfreight, but the inclusion of a large area on the landward side of the port for rail-served warehousing makes it doubly so. Already, Marks & Spencer has announced a one million square foot distribution centre at the location, complementing a similar rail-connected facility being commissioned at Castle Donington in the East Midlands. In due course, the distribution park at Gateway will have its own intermodal terminal, separate from the initial facility, which will serve deep sea boxes moving directly inland from the port.

The Port of Felixstowe commissioned its new North Terminal in mid 2013, including a new rail terminal designed to accommodate 35 wagon trains and including a traverser to releasing incoming locomotives, thereby saving the length normally required for pointwork leading to a headshunt. Such is demand for rail services from Felixstowe that the original North terminal (now, logically, the Centre terminal), which was to be mothballed against future growth, remains open and works alongside the new North terminal and the expanded South terminal.

Railfreight 'Quote of the year' must go to Clemence Cheng, CEO of Hutchison Ports UK (owner of Felixstowe) who, appearing in front of the Transport Select Committee, was invited to comment on accessibility to the port. No doubt to the considerable surprise of the Committee, Mr Cheng responded that, although the recently-announced improvements to the A14 road were welcome, container lorries make up only about 3% of traffic on the road and the scheme was not that important to him. He was seeing great demand to move freight from road to rail and, accordingly, more important was improving the rail links to Felixstowe, such as extra capacity, longer trains and electrifying the line to Peterborough and Nuneaton. A finer accolade to the future of railfreight in the UK would be hard to imagine.

With ABP also investing in additional berths and cranes at Southampton and a major expansion at Liverpool getting under way (with a similar scheme at Bristol in prospect), there is clearly substantial extra container capacity coming on stream at UK ports. With economic activity starting to recover, the timing of this is propitious but, in the short term, there will be surplus capacity. Given the attractions of Felixstowe, London Gateway and Southampton, it seems likely that the pain will be felt elsewhere and industry feeling is that it will be Thamesport and Tilbury that will take the hit.

Freightliner is rumoured to be pulling out of the former – unsurprisingly since only one feeder shipping line remains – and Tilbury is losing to Gateway a long-standing refrigerated service. This is surprising as Tilbury's traditional strength in this market, based on fruit from South Africa and so on, was seen as its best card in resisting its new down-river competitor. Maybe Tilbury's future will be more in short-sea and feeder container services from Rotterdam and other continental ports. Quite which lines (if any) will see fit to transfer from the Southeast ports, close to the key shipping routes, to Liverpool or Bristol very much remains to be seen.

DOMESTIC INTERMODAL

Notwithstanding the M&S developments mentioned above, and Sainsbury's building a one million square foot rail-connected warehouse at Daventry, domestic intermodal traffic somewhat plateaued in 2013. Tesco, the pack leader, is consolidating and fine-tuning its major rail expansion of the last couple of years and the next big strategic step for retail goods by rail seems set for 2014/15 when M&S and Sainsbury's start operation. In the meantime, the Co-op is moving an increasing proportion of its goods by rail – around half of its Anglo-Scottish traffic is now on rail via Daventry. Elsewhere, a second train to Inverness was rumoured to be in the offing. This would complement the existing Tesco train and would convey chilled and refrigerated goods for most of the supermarket retailers.

Also in Scotland, autumn 2013 saw an extended trial movement of bulk whisky from Speyside, using Elgin as the railhead, to the Central Scotland bottling plants. This follows a study carried out by HITRANS, the Highlands and Islands Strategic Transport Partnership, in 2012 which, with the full co-operation of all the major distillers, identified substantial potential to take heavy trucks off the A9 and Speyside roads – easily enough for a decent size daily train with bulk spirit alone, let alone associated products such as barley and casks. Hopefully, the trial will demonstrate the viability of the rail option and see a permanent transfer from road.

BULK SECTORS

Turning to the Industrial bulk sectors, a mixed picture emerges. Petroleum has recovered a little from the decline over the past few years. The changes appear to reflect volumes of sales at the pump, which dropped markedly as the recession hit, but are recovering somewhat as the economy improves. As a marginal carrier (pipeline and coastal shipping are prime), rail's fortunes are particularly vulnerable to market fluctuations.

In contrast, Metals has seen a

Further expansion for retail goods by rail is in the offing. Direct Rail Services Class 66/4 No 66421 passes Headstone Lane on 14 August 2013, with mainly Tesco containers in tow, forming an intermodal working from Daventry to Tilbury. Ken Brunt

decline in fortunes. An economic recession always hits the steel industry hard, as consumer demand for cars and washing machines drops away and the construction industry stops buying structural steel and cladding for commercial buildings. A decline in railfreight volumes of steel is thus almost inevitable but, conversely, volumes pick up again quickly as the economy recovers.

The market-driven decline has been exacerbated, paradoxically, by the steel industry doing better – Tata's blast furnace rebuild at Port Talbot has come good and is producing record tonnages. Whilst it was down, and during the period when initial teething problems were being overcome, DBS were moving substantial tonnages of slab from ports and SSI at Lackenby to keep

the Port Talbot and Llanwern rolling mills going. That boost to railfreight volumes has now ceased.

Modal switch has both helped and hindered metals carryings. Volumes of scrap are down, as the quantity of scrap required by the UK steel industry has declined with plant closures, for example of Thames Steel at Sheerness. The replacement flows of scrap to the ports for export is more road-orientated and new scrap export facilities at Southampton and Tilbury are served solely by road, at least at present.

Conversely, the use of rail for steel exports to the Continent is increasing, not – sadly – via the Channel Tunnel but via Tilbury. The twice weekly tinplate train from Trostre is set to run more frequently and also carry steel coil from Port Talbot and Llanwern. At Tilbury both products are offloaded to road trailers for the journey to destinations in the Benelux etc, via Ro-Ro ferries. On imports, Colas Rail has started to move automotive coil for BMW from Boston to the Swindon railhead, complementing its existing Boston - Washwood Heath service and DBS's service from South Wales to Swindon.

CONSTRUCTION

The big success story, as trailed at the head of our review, is Construction. The Olympics building boom drove volumes to record levels and, as expected, business fell off as the Games approached. The decline was, however, temporary and the upward trajectory has resumed with a vengeance. True, Crossrail spoil – being moved by GBRf from

RAIL FREIGHT ALLIANCE LAUNCHED

The UK's five major Rail Freight operating companies and Network Rail announced in October the formation of The Rail Freight Alliance.

The formation was endorsed by the Rail Delivery Group after a framework and set of strategy objectives were agreed by the Rail Delivery Group's Freight Group; with a view to delivering a sustainable and flourishing rail freight sector in the UK - delivering whole-industry cost savings, developing 'smarter use' of the network, and a sustainable charging framework for freight.

Peter Maybury, Chair of the RDG Freight Group said: 'The creation of The Rail Freight Alliance is an important step-forward for the rail freight sector. The Alliance will give the rail freight sector a stronger voice in the rail industry and give an opportunity to resolve some significant issues that remain for the sector.'

Paul McMahon, Freight Director, Network Rail said: 'I'm delighted that The Rail Freight Alliance has been agreed. Greater collaboration between the operators and Network Rail will enable us all to better address the challenges and the opportunities that the sector faces in the next five years and beyond.'

The five operating companies in the alliance are DB Schenker Rail UK, Freightliner Group, GB Railfreight, Direct Rail Services and Colas Rail.

Paddington to Northfleet – is providing a boost, but things are buoyant across the board.

As well as established flows running at a high level, new flows are emerging. Castle Cement has replaced imports via Avonmouth with a new rail flow from Clitheroe – restoring a presence in the Bristol market lost when the Speedlink flow from Ketton ceased in the 1980s. Another new flow that commenced in mid 2013 was aggregates from Moreton on Lugg to the former coal depot at West Drayton, hauled by GBRf. Waiting in the wings is a cross-Kent flow of gravel from Lydd to Ridham (near Sittingbourne) for Brett Aggregates, which is expected to start during 2014.

In an encouraging development, a new customer has started using rail – a rare event in an industry dominated by established majors, most of whom use rail to some degree. The new customer is Lynch – a big player in the London muck-shifting market. Using Devon & Cornwall Railways as haulier (with a refurbished Class 56 at the sharp end), Lynch has set up a loading point at the former Willesden Euroterminal to which its lorries feed spoil from all over Central London for despatch by rail to Calvert.

Amongst the Construction majors, the merger between Lafarge and Tarmac was approved by the Competition Commission, but with conditions. Foremost amongst these were that the new grouping had to divest itself of certain assets to limit market share and, after a bidding process, these were acquired by Indian entrepreneur Lakshmi Mittal, owner of Europe's largest steel company - ArcelorMittal. The new grouping was named Hope Construction Materials and includes Hope Cement Works and Dow Low quarry in the Peak District, with railhead terminals at Theale, Walsall and Dewsbury (cement), plus Banbury and Stevenage (aggregates).

Accordingly, several long-established flows have changed source to reflect the new groupings, with Westbury for example now fed from Tunstead instead of Hope. A few conundrums have emerged – the aggregates terminals mentioned above are designed to be fed by Self Discharging Trains, but these have remained with Lafarge-Tarmac. Similarly, Hope Cement works - which has tight planning restrictions on road output – needs more rail terminals than it was gifted in the carve-up. Some short-term supply agreements were put in place to cover a transitional period, but it will be intriguing to see what results from the new groupings.

The improved efficiency of Freightliner's 40ft long Ecofret / Shortliner wagon and longer container trains are permitting some impressive payloads. Freightliner

Equally interesting is the emerging picture surrounding the movement of domestic waste from the main urban areas. It seems that the long established West London flows, from Brentford to Appleford and Northolt to Calvert, will switch to a new Energy-from-Waste (EFW) plant at Avonmouth, whilst North London waste - the existing flow from Cricklewood plus, potentially, the tonnage currently incinerated at Edmonton - will be dealt with by a new EFW plant at Calvert. On Merseyside, where rail has not previously featured, a new long term contract has been signed that will see two trains a day running from the Potter Group terminal at Knowsley to an EFW plant on Teesside. This in spite of a new incinerator being built at Runcorn to which, it appears, Manchester's waste will run in lieu of landfill at Roxby on Humberside.

Every sign, then, that the future for UK railfreight, for both the bulk and intermodal businesses, is bright. Ups and downs there will inevitably be, but the trend is firmly upward.

FREIGHT OPERATOR FINANCES

The freight industry continued its recovery from the impact of the recession during 2011/12, with a sharp increase in to operating and pre-tax profits, according to analysis undertaken by consultants TAS in 'Rail Industry Monitor'.

Cash operating profits more than doubled, from below £24.7m to just above £63.8m, with margins improving from 3.1% to 7.2%.

The combined turnover of the companies analysed was 11.9% higher at £890.1m, whilst the rise in operating costs was restricted to 7.2%, taking the total to £826.3m. Improved returns on pension scheme assets met that the industry recorded £3.6m worth of interest earnings, compared with the previous year's £7.0m outflow. As a result, pre-tax profits more than trebled, reaching £67.5m at a margin of 7.6% (last year: £17.7m at 2.2%).

TAS also reports on market share, as measured by turnover. DB Schenker retains the lion's share of the business, with 54.0%, down from 54.6% last year, and from over 80% in the late 1990s. Freightliner was next with 32.1%, down by 0.6%. The two post privatisation new entrants, Eurotunnel's GB Railfreight subsidiary and Direct Rail Services, have steadily built up their market shares over the last decade, reaching 8.2% and 5.6% respectively. Both saw small increases in their share after slipping back in 2010/11.

GB RAILFREIGHT

This was the company's first full year under the ownership of Europorte SAS, a subsidiary of Eurotunnel, who acquired it from FirstGroup during 2010. The company traded at sharply increased margins – though comparisons are complex since the previous figures only covered nine months. On an estimated annualised basis, turnover was up by 26% but operating costs were 23% higher.

PERIOD TO:	31/12/11	31/12/10
	£000	£000
Turnover	73,056	43,596
Operating Costs:	68,685	42,109
Operating Profit:	4,371	1,487
Operating Margin:	6.0%	3.4%
Turnover per Employee	£211,757	£142,938
Rolling stock lease	11,433	6,702

DIRECT RAIL SERVICES

The company improved its performance sharply during the year as strong revenue growth outstripped rising operating costs. Additional income was gained from a widened customer base featuring retail logistics support as well as infrastructure work.

PERIOD TO:	31/03/12	31/03/11
	£000	£000
Turnover	50,243	43,311
Operating Costs:	47,560	41,634
Operating Profit:	2,683	1,677
Operating Margin:	5.3%	3.9%
Turnover per Employee	£173,252	£148,325
Rolling stock lease	5,477	5,502
Revenue Grant	1,203	1,193

DB SCHENKER INTERNATIONAL

The DB Schenker Channel Tunnel through freight operation further improved its results, even though there was a reduction in turnover of 12% - a setback following the previous year's one-third expansion. Even so, the business continued to record substantial operating and pre-tax losses as the cross-channel railfreight market failed to reach critical mass.

PERIOD TO:	31/12/11	31/12/10
	£000	£000
Turnover	29,077	33,078
Operating Costs:	33,463	42,979
Operating Profit:	(4,386)	(9,901)
Operating Margin:	-15.1%	-29.9%
Turnover per Employee	£143,946	£187,943

DB SCHENKER

The company improved its operating result during the year ahead of exceptional items, as turnover increased by over 12% whilst the cost of the extra business was kept to around 5%.

PERIOD TO:	31/12/11	31/12/10
	£000	£000
Turnover	452,000	401,000
Operating Costs:	413,000	391,000
Operating Profit:	39,000	10,000
Operating Margin:	8.6%	2.5%
Turnover per Employee	£164,723	£129,690

FREIGHTLINER

The intermodal company improved its cash profits during the year, as turnover again grew following recovery in container traffic volumes – however, margins were very slightly lower

PERIOD TO:	31/03/12	26/03/11
	£000	£000
Turnover	177,503	163,504
Operating Costs:	168,521	154,995
Operating Profit:	8,982	8,509
Operating Margin:	5.1%	5.2%
Turnover per Employee	£158,626	£148,236
Rolling Stock Lease	9,038	9,361

FREIGHTLINER HEAVY HAUL

The trading environment was still challenging for the coal, aggregates and infrastructure division of the Freightliner Group.

The company increased cash profits during the year, but traded at slightly lower margins as the percentage rise in costs outstripped otherwise strong revenue growth.

PERIOD TO:	31/03/12	26/03/11
	£000	£000
Turnover	108,241	96,711
Operating Costs:	95,050	84,307
Operating Profit:	13,191	12,404
Operating Margin:	12.2%	12.8%
Turnover per Employee	£178,321	£155,985
Rolling stock lease	13,996	13,869

 SCHENKER

LARGEST RAIL FREIGHT OPERATOR

DB Schenker Rail UK Ltd is Britain's largest rail freight operator. Formerly English, Welsh & Scottish Railway (EWS), the company was acquired in 2007 by Deutsche Bahn (DB - German Rail).

Employing around 31,700 people, DB Schenker Rail operates in 15 countries, generating revenues of Euro 4.9billion in 2012.

DB Schenker Rail UK is part of Region West, along with Euro Cargo Rail (ECR), created in France by EWS in 2005, and Transfesa in Spain. It employs around 4,000 people, and as well as undertaking rail freight operations provides a range of passenger haulage, engineering support, technical and hire services nationwide.

In October 2013 the company signalled its intention to undertake a realignment from a business segment structure to a dedicated sales and production organisation, with principal changes taking effect in January 2014. Its main business areas are:

- Industrial, moving coal, other fuels and heavy industrial materials, such as metals and petroleum products.
- Construction, conveying products for the construction and infrastructure markets, operating waste trains and providing rail industry services for Network Rail, infrastructure contractors and other train operating companies.
- Logistics, providing intermodal, international and logistics services.

DB Schenker Rail UK has been focusing strongly on developing its international logistics activities. Its innovative twice-weekly service between Barking in east London and Wroclaw, Poland, was launched in 2012: running over the HS1 high-speed line between London and the Channel Tunnel, it enables continental gauge wagons to reach the capital. Haulage is provided by Class 92 electric locomotives modified to operate over HS1. The 1,250-mile journey to Poland takes around 50 hours.

International traffic using classic routes to and from the Channel Tunnel includes a weekly intermodal service between Hams Hall in the West Midlands and Padua, Italy, and a train running five times per week between Hams Hall and Domodossola. Some traffic is taken north from Hams Hall to Mossend in Scotland. Steel slabs for rail manufacture are conveyed from Scunthorpe to Ebange in France for Tata Steel, sometimes with finished rail as a return load. Bottled water from France is brought in to Daventry and a weekly train of china clay slurry for paper-making runs from Antwerp to Irvine. In addition there is a long-established flow of Ford car components between Valencia and Dagenham.

The automotive sector provides healthy business, with movements of new Jaguar Land Rover vehicles for export from Halewood and Castle Bromwich to Southampton, and BMW Minis from Cowley to Southampton and Purfleet, while Ford cars imported via Dagenham generate further significant flows.

In Scotland DB Schenker Rail UK was selected as the preferred operator for trials to return movements of whisky to rail, led and part-funded by the Highlands and Islands Transport Partnership (HITRANS). Twice-weekly trials conveying the spirit in tank containers from Elgin to Grangemouth via Aberdeen ran from September to November 2013.

DB Schenker Rail UK runs regular trains of deep sea containers from Southampton and Felixstowe, serving Birch Coppice in the Midlands, Doncaster, Trafford Park and Wakefield. The number of containers it carries passing though Southampton has increased to more than 60,000 per year, leading to the establishment of a new office facility in the city that also handles bookings for all its intermodal services.

In September 2013 DB Schenker Rail UK operated the first train out of the new DP World London Gateway deep-sea port on the north bank of the Thames Estuary. Ahead of the formal opening of the port, it was arranged to convey containers from the fire-damaged cargo ship ZIM Rotterdam after it was diverted for safety reasons. The train ran to DB Schenker Rail UK's Trafford Park terminal in Manchester.

Regular DB Schenker Rail UK services from the port to Trafford Park and Daventry began with its opening in November 2013. An agreement with DP World London Gateway calls for at least four pairs of rail freight services a day. DB Schenker Rail UK says it is also pursuing the development of services from London Gateway to mainland Europe using the Channel Tunnel.

Late 2012 saw DB Schenker Rail UK launch D2D, an integrated transport service from the quayside direct to the warehouse for retail and manufacturing customers who wish to increase their use of rail freight for capacity, environmental and cost reasons.

The company continues to fulfil the Ministry of Defence's Strategic Rail Capability and Mainline Rail Freight Services haulage contract. This covers haulage of the MoD's own wagons, as well as providing specialist services utilising its own wagon fleet. Some movements are combined with other traffic, forming a residual wagonload network.

A DB Schenker Class 66 locomotive hauls an intermodal train. DB Schenker Rail (UK)

DB Schenker Rail UK operates Royal Mail postal trains, running seven services a day between London, Warrington and Glasgow using Class 325 mail EMUs. In 2013 a weekday postal service was reintroduced on the East Coast main line linking London and Tyneside, again using Class 325 units. It also holds the Network Rail Infrastructure Monitoring contract, operating test trains across the system, some using Network Rail's own traction.

Up to 600 DB Schenker Rail UK trains a week move heavy raw materials, such as metals, iron ore and petroleum products. In the last-mentioned category there are significant flows from complexes on Humberside and Robeston in Wales, as well as movements from Fawley and Grangemouth. The company also operates more than 700 trains per week for the power generation industry and has contracts with British Energy, Drax Power, E.ON, EDF Energy, International Power, RWE npower, Scottish & Southern Energy and ScottishPower.

DB Schenker Rail UK runs numerous services to support steel manufacturing in Britain, serving key sites at Scunthorpe, in South Wales and on Teesside, with Tata Steel the major customer. The country's only remaining railborne flow of imported iron ore runs between Immingham and Scunthorpe, and there is an extensive network of inter-plant and finished steel services. Scrap metal traffic is also handled, mainly destined for Cardiff.

A shuttle service is provided for Tata Steel connecting its steelworks at IJmuiden in the Netherlands with its Trostre plant in South Wales to convey steel coils for the packaging industry. The wagons return to Tata's Llanwern site for back-loading with traffic for IJmuiden.

Up to 400 trains a week run for the construction and waste industries. A contract with Mendip Rail covers operation of trains carrying up to 4,000 tonnes of stone from the Mendips quarries of Aggregates Industries (Merehead) and HeidelbergCement subsidiary Hanson (Whatley), some of these using the shippers' own locomotives and wagons. DB Schenker Rail UK has a contract with Cemex UK covering its rail freight haulage requirements for aggregates and coal. The Lafarge Tarmac quarry at Mountsorrel in Leicestershire is also served and sea-dredged aggregates are moved from Thames-side terminals for Brett Aggregates and Marcon.

Other commodities carried include china clay from production sites in Cornwall for Imerys, with traffic both for export locally and for Stoke on Trent, and cement, including a new flow introduced in 2013 between the Hanson plant at Clitheroe and Avonmouth. The last-mentioned supplements a service to Mossend. Sand is conveyed from Middleton Towers in Cambridgeshire to Ellesmere Port and Monk Bretton, and trains of domestic and industrial waste are operated from various points in London to landfill sites at Appleford near Oxford and Calvert.

SENIOR PERSONNEL

DB SCHENKER RAIL (UK)

CHAIRMAN Alain Thauvette
CHIEF EXECUTIVE OFFICER Geoff Spencer
MD, LOGISTICS Dr Carsten Hinne
HEAD OF SALES Neil McDonald
HEAD OF PRODUCTION Graham Young

Services provided for the rail industry include a seven-year infrastructure haulage contract with Network Rail - both scheduled movements of materials such as ballast and rail and trains run in association with infrastructure maintenance and renewals.

The company is also active in the passenger sector. In 2013 it continued to provide locomotives for overnight sleeper trains operated by ScotRail, for Chiltern Railways 'Mainline' services and an Arriva Trains Wales Holyhead-Cardiff train. It additionally supplies traction for the Orient Express luxury train, as well as for charter services and as standby power for the East Coast franchise.

The core of the diesel traction fleet is drawn from 250 EMD-built Class 66 locomotives leased from Angel Trains, although more than 70 of these have been despatched for use by Euro Cargo Rail in France and other DB Schenker companies, notably in Poland. Also leased from Angel are 30 Class 67 125mph locomotives originally acquired for express mail duties, now used on charter passenger services or hired out to franchised TOCs as well as to a limited extent for light freight.

Changes in traffic have led to reduced use of the ex-BR heavy-haul Class 60 locomotives, though a continuing role is seen, and in a £3million programme, 21 have been undergoing heavy overhaul and refurbishment. There are also six Class 59/2s used on Mendips aggregates traffic.

Electric traction comprises UK-based members of a fleet of 30 Class 92 dual-voltage machines plus 25 Class 90s, although the number of both in service is dictated by traffic demands. The Class 92s operate freight services through the Channel Tunnel as well as over DC- and AC-electrified networks, with five despatched to Bulgaria and Romania for use by other DB Schenker Rail subsidiaries.

Other recent fleet developments include modification of 72 60ft intermodal wagons for services to and from London Gateway, reducing deck height to one metre to carry more Hi-cubes on W10 routes. A high-capacity dry-bulk hopper wagon has also been developed to meet the needs of power generators introducing biomass and other alternative fuels. ■

COLAS RAIL FREIGHT

Colas Rail Freight is part of the Colas Group, a subsidiary of the French-based multinational Bouygues. Operations began in 2007 and include the UK legs of trains for French National Railways subsidiary Captrain UK. Among commodities carried are inbound consignments of steel for the automotive industry from Boston docks, transferred in covered wagons to Washwood Heath, Birmingham.

In 2011 Colas began moving coal in HHA wagons for UK Coal from its Park Wall opencast mine, near Wolsingham, County Durham, to Tata Steel at Scunthorpe and Ratcliffe Power Station for E.ON. Subsequently the company has conveyed coal from Avonmouth to Ratcliffe. In 2012 Colas commenced a 12-month contract (since extended) for Air BP moving aviation fuel from the Ineos refinery at Grangemouth in Scotland to Prestwick Airport, Linkswood in Fife and the Rolls Royce factory in Derby. Tank wagons leased by Air BP from VTG are used for these flows.

Also undertaken is haulage of timber for building materials manufacturer Kronospan. Regular trains run to the company's plant at Chirk from Baglan Bay in South Wales and Carlisle, with occasional loads from Teigngrace near Newton Abbot and Ribblehead. Logs are conveyed in Dutch-registered IWA wagons converted from former CargoWaggons and rebuilt former 'Rover Cube' vehicles.

In 2013 Colas began operating engineering materials trains for Network Rail. Part of the National Delivery Service network, these include Hoo Junction-Whitemoor, Hoo Junction-Eastleigh, Eastleigh-Westbury and Westbury-Hackney (Newton Abbot) circuits. The company also provides traction for trains serving Network Rail engineering work.

The traction fleet comprises five Class 66s, three Class 47s and operational members of a pool of six Class 56s plus one on hire. By late 2013 four Class 56s had been returned to traffic. In 2012 Colas acquired Cardiff-based vehicle maintenance company Pullman Rail, strengthening its capability to maintain its own fleet and expand services for other owners and operators.

HEAD OF FREIGHT Simon Ball

Freightliner's Class 70 No 70017 approaches Bristol Parkway with a Wentloog to Southampton intermodal train on 9 July 2013. Stewart Armstrong

Freightliner®

INTERMODAL AND HEAVY HAUL

Freightliner Group is owned by Bahrain-based investment firm Arcapita, which in 2008 acquired the company from previous owners 3i, Electra Private Equity and Freightliner management and staff. It has two rail operating subsidiaries in Britain: Freightliner Ltd the leading intermodal rail freight haulier with 81% of the UK deep-sea rail-borne container market; and Freightliner Heavy Haul (FHH), specialising in bulk commodities. Freightliner Maintenance Ltd is the Group's third UK subsidiary. UK subdivisions include Logico, offering bespoke rail space to new markets.

An Australian subsidiary, Freightliner Australia, was created in 2009, and Freightliner Poland Ltd was set up in 2005. In 2013 the Group further expanded its portfolio with the acquisition of European intermodal operator ERS Railways. The group employs more than 1,900 people.

FREIGHTLINER LIMITED

Freightliner Ltd is the UK's largest rail carrier of maritime containers, operating from the major deep-sea ports of Felixstowe, Seaforth, Southampton, Thamesport and Tilbury. Services run to 14 strategically located rail freight interchanges, nine of which are terminals owned and operated by Freightliner. Operating a road fleet of more than 300 vehicles, the company offers port-to-door and door-to-port services around the clock. It moves around 3,000 containers per day on more than 100 services to and from deep-sea ports, with 37 direct route offerings.

Main locations are:

- Ports: Felixstowe, Seaforth (Liverpool), Southampton, Thamesport (Isle of Grain) and Tilbury.
- Inland terminals: Birmingham, Bristol, Wentloog (Cardiff), Wilton (Cleveland), Coatbridge (Glasgow), Doncaster, Leeds, Liverpool and Manchester.
- Independent terminals served include Birch Coppice (Birmingham International Freight Terminal), Daventry (DIRFT), Hams Hall (Birmingham) and Ditton (Widnes).

Logico provides bespoke intermodal haulage to freight movers, manufacturers, retailers, importers/exporters, tank operators, freight forwarders, and transport operators. It offers regular space on services without the need to make a long-term commitment.

Maritime traffic at Southampton has benefited from W10 gauge enhancements to clear the route from the port to the West Midlands for 9ft 6in containers. Similar work has cleared the Felixstowe to Nuneaton (F2N) route for W10, boosting traffic opportunities at the Suffolk port. A further significant development will be commissioning in 2014 of a new 1 km chord linking the East Suffolk line and the Great Eastern main line in Ipswich to avoid trains to using the F2N route having to reverse there.

Freightliner maintains relationships with a number of the world's leading shipping lines including OOCL, Hamburg Sud, Evergreen, Hapag-Lloyd, MSC, China Shipping and ZIM. It has the largest intermodal contract in the UK with Maersk Line, the container arm of the Danish conglomerate A P Moller-Maersk.

An increase in container volumes by rail to northwest England has resulted from a contract renewed in 2012 between Freightliner and MSC (UK) Ltd. The carrier also has an agreement with logistics company CMA CGM to convey containers for the Asda supermarket chain, initially between Southampton and Wilton.

FREIGHTLINER HEAVY HAUL

Established in 1999, Freightliner Heavy Haul (FHH) has a turnover of over £100million, with more than 600 employees. It operates around 1,200 trains per week using a fleet of 85 locomotives and more than 1,400 wagons. Sectors served include coal, aggregates and minerals, cement, scrap metal, domestic waste and infrastructure services, securing approximately 30% of the bulk rail freight market and moving more than 20 million tonnes annually.

The company's largest bulk market is coal. It serves all the UK's rail-connected coal-fired power stations from opencast sites and collieries in Britain, and from import terminals including Ellesmere Port, Hull, Hunterston, Immingham, Liverpool and Portbury. In 2012 a long-term agreement was reached with EDF Energy to transport coal to its power stations at Cottam and West Burton. FHH has also been anticipating power generators' future needs: at the end of 2011 it unveiled an HHA coal hopper wagon modified by WH Davis to carry biomass, with covers fitted to ensure the product is kept dry during transit.

In the aggregates sector, FHH's clients include Lafarge Tarmac, Aggregate Industries and Hanson. Significant volumes for Aggregate Industries are carried from the quarry at Bardon Hill and from Neath Abbey Wharf. Sand is moved from Wool in Dorset to Neasden and limestone is conveyed from Tunstead in the Peak District to several coal-fired power stations for emissions cleaning processes.

A recast of services that followed the 2013 merger of Lafarge and Tarmac also saw the start of FHH cement flows from Tunstead to West Thurrock and Westbury, in addition to established flows.

FHH works with Greater Manchester Waste Disposal Authority (GMWDA) and Viridor moving

SENIOR PERSONNEL

FREIGHTLINER GROUP

CHIEF EXECUTIVE OFFICER Russell Mears (in photo)
MD, FREIGHTLINER LTD Adam Cunliffe
MD, HEAVY HAUL Paul Smart
ENGINEERING DIRECTOR Tim Shakerley
CORPORATE DEVELOPMENT DIRECTOR Dom McKenna

municipal waste to a landfill site at Roxby Gullet, Scunthorpe. At a future date, FHH will take Solid Recovered Fuel from new facility at Longley Lane, Manchester, to a Combined Heat and Power plant at Runcorn, following a move away from the use of landfill by GMWDA. FHH also runs a containerised household waste service from Cricklewood in north London to Calvert.

Potash and rock salt are moved between a mine at Boulby, on the Cleveland coast, and Tees Dock and Middlesbrough and FHH has a multi-year contract with steelmaker Celsa to transport scrap metal from Dagenham to Cardiff, generating three trains per week.

In the infrastructure sector, FHH provides support for Network Rail, including haulage of high-output ballast cleaning and track renewal systems, ballast movements and operation of the major distribution centre at Basford Hall, Crewe. Activities include support for infrastructure renewals and maintenance programmes.

MAINTENANCE

A separate entity dedicated to repair and maintenance of traction and rolling stock, Freightliner Maintenance Ltd (FML) was established in April 2006, when it took over the assets and staff of LNWR's former Leeds Midland Road depot, together with field engineering support. As well as Freightliner's locomotives, FML maintains coal hoppers used by FHH and Lafarge Tarmac cement wagons. There is a dedicated traction and rolling stock maintenance facility for Freightliner Ltd at Southampton.

Freightliner's overall UK fleet totals 137 Class 66 and 19 Class 70 diesels – with electric locomotives of Class 86 (16), and Class 90 (10), plus shunters. The 19 Class 70 PowerHaul diesel locomotives from GE Transportation are divided between the intermodal (8) and FHH (11) businesses.

The UK wagon fleet totals more than 3,000, of which some 1,700 are container flats. In 2012 Freightliner ordered from VTG 43 twin-platform Ecofret 'Shortliner' wagons each comprising a twin set of two 40ft deck length sections manufactured by Greenbrier in Poland. These provide more capacity for increasingly common 40ft containers and reduce the incidence of unused space on the 60ft wagons that make up the bulk of the fleet.

DIRECT RAIL SERVICES

A wholly owned subsidiary of the Nuclear Decommissioning Authority (NDA), Direct Rail Services Limited (DRS) was established in 1995 to provide British Nuclear Fuels Limited with a strategic rail transport service.

Intermodal freight services include trains operated for Tesco in conjunction with Stobart Rail from Daventry to Mossend, Daventry to Barking and Tilbury and Daventry to Wentloog near Cardiff, all running six days per week. A Mossend-Daventry service runs five days per week and a Daventry-Grangemouth train seven days a week, both for The Malcolm Group. In addition, on behalf of John G Russell, DRS operate two services from Daventry-Coatbridge, one running six days per week and the other five days per week.

In Scotland DRS operates two intermodal services out of Grangemouth – a short-haul consist of shipping containers to Elderslie running five days a week and an Aberdeen train seven days a week carrying mainly Asda and Tesco supermarket traffic. There is also a service six days a week conveying Tesco swapbodies between Mossend and Needlefield intermodal terminal, Inverness.

Rail industry services form a significant part of DRS activities. Among these are seasonal operations for Network Rail, including running autumn railhead treatment trains, crewing MPVs for weed control, winter snow clearance using its own snowplough-fitted locomotives and overhead line 'ice breaking' with Network Rail-owned Class 86/9 electric locomotives. The company also provides traction for trains operated for Network Rail to monitor infrastructure, and convey engineering materials.

DRS provides traction for the Northern Belle luxury train under a five-year contract from April 2011, with traction usually provided by Class 47s painted in Northern Belle livery. The company provides traction for other operators' passenger charter services and also has a small fleet of Mk2 coaches, recently refurbished.

In December 2012 DRS commenced a contract with Virgin Trains to provide 'Thunderbird' locomotives for rescue services on the West Coast main line. Class 57/3 machines from a pool of six are located in key strategic locations.

DRS is introducing a newcomer to the British traction scene in the shape of 15 Vossloh Eurolight Class 68 Bo-Bo diesel locomotives. Adapted specifically for the UK network from a design unveiled for European operations in 2010, they are powered by a Caterpillar C175-16 3,755hp engine with ABB transmission featuring AC traction motors and individual axle inverter drives.

An even more radical traction departure was signalled by an order confirmed in September 2013 for ten bi-mode Class 88 locomotives. Also to be supplied by Vossloh in Spain with delivery due in 2015, these will be rated at 5,360 hp when taking power from a 25 kV AC supply and at 900 hp when operating in diesel mode from a Caterpillar 12-cylinder engine.

Used principally for long-distance intermodal services are 19 Class 66s, most leased from Macquarie European Rail but with five ex-Fastline machines from Beacon Rail. There are nine Class 57s (eight leased from Porterbrook and one owned) plus six ex-Virgin Class 57/3s leased from Porterbrook, and 11 active Class 47s.

The operational Class 37 fleet totals 26, with more stored or under refurbishment. There are also eight Class 20s in service, with more in store.

In 2013 DRS began operating some Anglo-Scottish intermodal services with Class 92 electric locomotives hired from DB Schenker Rail.

Traction maintenance is carried out at DRS's headquarters depot at Carlisle Kingmoor and at its Crewe Gresty Bridge facility. New facilities have been provided at the latter to service the Class 68s. Maintenance services are also provided for other operators.

SENIOR PERSONNEL

DIRECT RAIL SERVICES

MANAGING DIRECTOR Neil McNicholas
DIRECTOR OF COMMERCIAL AND BUSINESS DEVELOPMENT Chris Connelly
OPERATIONS AND COMPLIANCE DIRECTOR Jeffery Marshall
ENGINEERING AND TERMINALS DIRECTOR Tony Bush
FINANCE AND RESOURCES DIRECTOR John Bamforth

'Topped & tailed' by Direct Rail Services Class 37s Nos 37259 and 37611, a test train from Derby to East Ham depot waits at Barking. Brian Morrison

On hire to Network Rail, West Coast Railways Class 33/0 No 33029 'Glen Loy' leads Snow and Ice Treatment vehicles through Paddock Wood on 22 February 2013, with Class 37/5 No 37516 on the rear. Bill Turvill

DEVON & CORNWALL RAILWAYS LIMITED

Devon & Cornwall Railways is an open access freight operator owned by British American Railway Services Limited, itself formed by Iowa Pacific Holdings, an American shortline railroad holding company.

Other BARS subsidiaries include locomotive hire and track maintenance company RMS Locotec, the Weardale Railway linking Bishop Auckland with Wolsingham and Eastgate, and the Dartmoor Railway between Yeoford and Meldon.

BARS acquired Hanson Traction Ltd, the provider of main line railway locomotives, engineering and maintenance services during 2010.

While it was created initially with a view to handling movements between private infrastructure and Network Rail-controlled lines, DCR has operated many freight flows such as scrap metal traffic from Shipley and Stockton on Tees to the Celsa plant at Cardiff and aggregates from Peak Forest to Leeds, as well as coal. It began a new contract in 2013, hauling spoil from a loading point at the former Willesden Euroterminal to Calvert.

It also handles rolling stock movements on behalf of other operators and supplies locomotives on hire. In Autumn 2013 it applied to Office of Rail Regulation (ORR) for a licence to run charter trains - intending to supply drivers and locomotives for this market.

The operational fleet includes four Class 56 locomotives and four Class 31s.

WEST COAST RAILWAY COMPANY

West Coast Railway Company (WCR) has been a licensed train operating company since 1998, when it became the first privately-owned company to obtain a licence, under rail privatisation, allowing it to co-ordinate and run its own trains without third-party involvement. With its main base at Carnforth, Lancashire, it specialises in operating charter trains, both in its own right and on behalf of tour operators, using classic and modern diesels and historic steam locomotives.

It runs regular steam-hauled trains including the 'Jacobite' (Fort William-Mallaig) and the 'Scarborough Spa Express' (York-Scarborough).

WCR owns, maintains and operates diesel locomotives and over 80 passenger vehicles (including the last 10 Pullman carriages to be built, in 1965). Steam locomotives it operates include GWR 'Hall' No 5972 'Olton Hall' - 'Hogwarts Castle' in the Harry Potter films.

RIVIERA TRAINS

Riviera Trains Ltd, formed in 1996, is a prominent independent charter train provider, working closely with leading charter operating companies, and it also provides quality locomotives and coaching stock to support the additional requirements of train operating companies. It operates from a main base at Crewe, and has a sizeable fleet of coaches.

Riviera Trains operates with DB Schenker as part of the Charter Alliance, which was launched in April 2007, as a 'one stop shop' for the provision of coaching stock for franchised train operating companies and charter trains.

Charter trains include mixed rakes of First and Standard Class coaches for enthusiast and 'days out' railtours, and full rakes of First Class vehicles with at-seat dining for luxury VIP charters.

Direct Rail Services' Class 47s Nos 47790 'Galloway Princess' and 47832 'Solway Princess' top and tail the Northern Belle on 16 August 2012, passing Old Linslade with the 07.18 working from London Euston to Edinburgh. Ken Brunt

INNOVATION AND ENVIRONMENT

IN ASSOCIATION WITH

KNORR-BREMSE

Community Rail: where next?

COMMUNITY RAIL IS NOW AN ESTABLISHED PART OF THE RAILWAY SCENE. BUT SUCCESS HAS ALSO HIGHLIGHTED SOME PROBLEMS. MODERN RAILWAYS COLUMNIST, AND COMMUNITY RAIL PARTNERSHIP CHAIRMAN, ALAN WILLIAMS REVIEWS PROGRESS AND OFFERS SOME POINTERS FOR THE FUTURE

In the ten years since the then Strategic Rail Authority (SRA) first published its Community Rail Development Strategy, community rail activity has literally exploded across the country. Today, there are no less than 38 Community Rail Partnerships (CRPs), of which 34 have so far been formally designated by the Department for Transport, with others in hand. Together, they support and promote 72 lines. There are well over a thousand individual station adoption groups in England, Wales and Scotland and it is fair to say that it is now hard to find a branch or secondary line which does not in some way enjoy volunteer support from the local community.

As a result of this activity, the increase in ridership on community-supported lines has outstripped national figures for most of the last decade, with the total number of journeys on designated lines increasing by 61.6 per cent. On some individual lines, the growth has been much more – an astonishing 209 per cent on the Truro-Falmouth line; 163 per cent on the Oxenholme-Windermere connection (which is now to be electrified); 155 per cent on the Preston-Ormskirk line, 151 per cent on the Exeter-Barnstaple line, and even 108 per cent on the inner urban Bristol Temple Meads-Severn Beach branch, giving the lie to the oft heard assumption in some railway circles that community rail activity is only about supporting bucolic rural branch lines!

OBJECTIVES

Adopted by the Department for Transport (DfT) when it succeeded the SRA, the objectives of the Community Rail Strategy have remained essentially the same ever since – increasing patronage, freight use and net revenue; managing costs down; and greater involvement of the local community in the running of the railway. DfT subsequently added a fourth objective, of enabling rail to play a larger role in economic and social regeneration. And it is clear from the figures that two of the objectives – increasing patronage and involving the community – have been handsomely attained, not only at almost no cost to the railway but also, by increasing revenue, reducing the often considerable subsidy on such lines. But managing costs down has proved more difficult because CRPs have often found the rail industry resistant to change.

Initially proposed only for lines in England, the value of Community Rail Partnerships has subsequently been recognised by the Welsh Assembly and, most recently, by the Scottish Government. It emphasised its support for community rail in its recent High Level Output statement for Control Period 5 (2014-19) by encouraging the creation of more Community Rail Partnerships in Scotland and requiring the rail industry 'to work with them to establish facilities and services that address local needs'. This is in fact rather more than has until now been the case elsewhere in the UK. In the past, there has been no requirement from the DfT for franchise operators to work with CRPs, and as a result some of the present clutch of train operating companies (TOCs) have proved notably less supportive of CRPs than others.

STANDARDS

Even where TOCs are supportive, CRPs report that - whilst there is enthusiasm for promotion of services and fares, and for 'soft' initiatives such as improving the environment of stations - getting the industry to engage with them on such issues as rolling stock provision, timetable planning or fares structures has proved rather more difficult, as has

An East Midlands Trains Class 156 diesel multiple-unit at Wilsford, near Ancaster on the Poacher Line - a route supported by the Grantham to Skegness Community Rail Partnership, set up in 2005. East Midlands Trains

interface with Network Rail on such matters as line speeds and the whole issue of standards for signalling and permanent way provision on lower-speed secondary lines.

In the second iteration of the frankly still disappointing 'Alternative Solutions' Route Utilisation Strategy, Network Rail (NR), while acknowledging the work of CRPs, commented that 'there is little evidence, however, of cost savings being achieved through community rail initiatives. It has not been demonstrated on a wide scale that operations, maintenance and renewals costs have been influenced by the present application of the community rail concept'.

That, retort furious CRPs, is not for the want of trying, but because TOCs in general and NR in particular simply will not engage in serious discussion on any really entrepreneurial thinking; TOCs tend to want to keep to their franchise commitments and no more, while NR sticks resolutely to system-wide standards for signalling, track and operation.

In its response to the 'Alternative Solutions' RUS, the Association of Community Rail Partnerships (ACoRP), the umbrella organisation for community rail activity, of which almost all CRPs and many station adoption groups are members, puts it in rather more measured but no less forceful tones, noting that 'the intractability of the industry mitigates against innovative and cost effective ideas' and that as part of the risk-averse railway culture, there is an often unjustified 'fear of Health and Safety legislation among those who genuinely want to make projects happen.'

Echoing this, Somerset County Council proposed that Network Rail should permit lower cost secondary infrastructure where suitable for community rail projects, and several responses, including that from the Lancaster and Skipton Rail User Group, called for a simplified, lower cost process for authorising minor infrastructure projects on community lines. In similar vein, the Esk Valley Community Rail Partnership reported that, despite having secured third party funding, it had to withdraw from a scheme to restore an abandoned signalbox at Glaisdale for community use because the guarantees and safety and legal undertakings required by Network Rail, which proved to be the same as for major multi-million pound redevelopments, were simply too onerous for a CRP. With NR planning to close hundreds of signalboxes in the next few years, many of which are on community lines, this is likely to be a recurrent problem.

RESPONSE

There can be no doubt that, ten years on, the community rail concept has substantially exceeded original expectations and is now well established. With more than 3,000 active supporters nationwide embracing several hundred miles of railway and scores of stations, it is the size of one of the smaller train operating companies. But it is clear that it is also at something of a crossroads. It can't just go on promoting lines. As ACoRP General Manager Neil Buxton points out, many lines are now reaching a performance plateau where CRPs have done everything they can to improve services but are now limited by lack of rolling stock or other investment. On some lines, success has been so great there is now a concern about future capacity.

That concern is expressed by some community rail supporters as a feeling that the effort is rather one-sided. They have, they argue, significantly increased ridership, sometimes to the extent of creating new capacity problems, but the industry has been unwilling – or perhaps unable – to respond with improved services or additional rolling stock.

There is also frustration that a substantial part of the increased ridership goes unrecorded because of the combined effects of poor revenue collection – ironically on some lines a result of huge overcrowding at peak periods but on others simply poor staffing – unreliability of on-train ticket issuing systems, and the questionable accuracy of the LENNON ticket sales recording system. Many community rail activists, supported by actual passenger counts at stations and on trains, believe that the impressive growth figures of recent years nevertheless considerably understate the true picture. And lost revenue aside, this is important to them, because the DfT tends to judge the success or otherwise of each CRP on LENNON figures.

INTEGRAL

One encouraging development for the future is that ACoRP believes it has now persuaded DfT to incorporate support for community rail as an integral part of Invitations to Tender for future franchises, rather than just as a 'nice to have' as in the past, enabling ACoRP and individual CRPs to talk seriously with potential franchise operators. But beyond that, it will need all parts of the industry, and especially Network Rail, to have the courage and commitment to engage fully with the community rail movement if the full benefits are to be attained. Neil Buxton believes there has to be a further step-change in understanding what local railways are actually delivering. He suggests tying them more closely into the localism and devolution agenda would be one way forward. In the wake of the Localism Act 2011, which seeks to devolve powers from central government and increase community involvement in decision making, the Government

A busy scene at Crediton on the Exeter-Barnstaple 'Tarka line', supported by the Devon & Cornwall Rail Partnership and the line's rail association. Network Rail

is pushing hard for sustainable local communities.

But in reality they cannot survive without access to appropriate and affordable transport. With the increasing centralisation of services like hospitals, colleges and shopping centres, perhaps it is time to consider how they might contribute financially to local rail services. As voluntary organisations, CRPs often have access to sources of funding not normally available to TOCs or Network Rail. There are many places where modest, well-targeted, jointly funded investment could make a sizeable difference to local rail services.

I suspect the success of community rail in the next ten years will be judged not so much on the number of further new passengers it has attracted as on the amount of new investment it has been able to corral. But there is a snag. The industry – and DfT – needs to remember that there is no such thing as a free lunch. Despite the quite considerable additional value created for TOCs – a recent report showed that volunteers in the community rail sector add value to the industry worth a staggering £27 million each year – most CRPs are as poor as church mice. Most currently rely on handouts from supporters, already cash-strapped local authorities, or their own fund-raising activities, and many struggle to even raise sufficient funds to employ a Community Rail Officer. That is something that needs to be addressed if community rail is to continue to progress, because CRPs will increasingly need help in developing bids for third party funding or if they contemplate entering the fearsome Network Rail GRIP process for new projects.

The original SRA vision for community rail embraced the concept of micro-franchising, whereby CRPs might eventually take over and run certain lines, and some of the original half dozen CRPs were set up on this basis. When DfT assumed responsibility for the Community Rail Strategy, it was soon relegated firmly to the 'too difficult' box. Nevertheless, it has re-emerged again in some quarters as part of the localisation agenda, particularly on some lines in the north of England where there is a fear that the five Integrated Transport Authorities might dominate the proposed Rail North organisation to the detriment of local lines outwith the five conurbations. But generally, I sense that full micro-franchising is not something that most supporters of community rail feel equipped to deal with, or for which they are confident there would be sufficient financial support.

The message is clear. CRPs have grown up. They are no longer content to be mere cheerleaders, the unpaid marketing arm of TOCs. They feel they have now earned the right to be involved in the planning and specification process of the lines they support. But will the industry listen? ■

RAIL SECTOR OUTLINES TOUGH ENVIRONMENTAL TARGETS

Long-term targets to further improve the environmental performance of the rail sector have been outlined by the International Union of Railways (UIC) and the Community of European Railway and Infrastructure Companies (CER).

The targets represent the improvements the sector feels it can achieve through its own voluntary endeavours, separate to any requirements laid down by EU and member state legislation. They build on the agreement already made in 2008 by rail companies to commit to a sector-wide cut of 30% of specific CO2 emissions from rail traction for 1990 to 2020.

According to the European Environment Agency's 2012 annual TERM (Transport and Environment Reporting Mechanism) report, transport is still responsible for nearly one-quarter of EU greenhouse gas (GHG) emissions, and the 2011 EU Transport White Paper laid down a reduction target of at least 60% of transport GHG emissions between 1990 and 2050. However, the TERM report points out that transport GHG emissions fell by only 0.4% between 2009 and 2010, and energy consumption in transport actually rose slightly by 0.1% in 2011 compared to 2010.

The UIC and CER strategy is built around four key topics: climate protection, energy efficiency, exhaust emissions, and noise emissions. It sets out objectives for the rail sector to meet by 2030, and more general aims for the longer target of 2050.

On climate protection, the strategy says that, by 2030, the railways should reduce their specific average CO2 emissions (emissions per passenger-km or tonne-km) from train operations by 50% compared to 1990. They should also not exceed the total amount of CO2 emissions compared to 1990, even taking into account projected growth in rail traffic. By 2050, the railways will aim for completely carbon-free train operation.

On energy efficiency the document says railways should reduce their specific energy consumption from train operations by 30%, by 2030 compared to 1990, while by 2050 the aim is for this to have reached 50%.

On exhaust emissions the strategy's aim is that railways should, by 2030, reduce their total emissions of nitrogen oxides and particulates by 40% in absolute terms compared to 2005, while by 2050 they will aim to have zero emissions of nitrogen oxides and particulates from trains.

On noise, the strategy comments that, by its nature, this is a harder area to set targets for. The aim is that, by 2050, noise and vibrations will no longer be considered a problem for the railways, with noise levels that are socially and economically acceptable and allow for 24-hour passenger and goods operations.

UIC and CER have established an Environmental Target Monitoring System to measure improvements.

CER Executive Director Libor Lochman said: 'By establishing its own voluntary strategy, the rail sector is showing that it is a responsible and forward thinking low-carbon mode of transport, whose role should be enhanced as part of the wider move towards cleaner transport. Modal shift to rail from higher-emitting modes could further increase these advantages, and produce the biggest benefit for society and the environment.'

Proven in service throughout the world including in Dubai where EP2002 provides consistent, accurate stopping at platform screen door equipped platforms. INSET: Smaller and lighter than conventional brake control, EP2002 is also faster and easier to commission.

Knorr-Bremse EP2002 Distributed Brake Control

In operational use on trains in the UK and around the world, Knorr-Bremse EP2002 is an 'intelligent' Distributed Brake Control (DBC) system which delivers per bogie or axle control in a unique package. Smaller, lighter and easier to install and commission than conventional brake control systems, EP2002 has set new standards in rail vehicle brake control.

MECHATRONIC TECHNOLOGY

Designed and manufactured by Knorr-Bremse in the UK, EP2002 uses an advanced mix of mechanical and electronic elements (mechatronics) to optimise brake performance across the entire train. It does this through the use of "intelligent" valves continuously communicating with each other and self-compensating in real time to address variable operating conditions such as passenger loading and wheel spin and slide.

EP2002 delivers not only optimised brake control but also very accurate brake control. This ability is especially important when used, for example, on driverless metro systems such as Dubai Metro where consistently accurate stopping at platforms equipped with platform screen doors is essential.

The three EP2002 valve types, known as the Smart, Gateway and RIO, make up the family of EP2002 products which are harmonised to deliver the system's outstanding performance.

The EP2002 Smart Valve contains all of the mechatronics to deliver Service Brake, Emergency Brake and Wheel Slide Protection (WSP) control on an individual bogie. The EP2002 Gateway Valve delivers all of the functions of the Smart Valve and in addition provides both the interface of the EP2002 system with the Train Management System and also the management of the whole train braking effort, including the Dynamic Brake. The network of communication required between the EP2002 Gateway and Smart Valves is provided by a dedicated Brake Bus. Each EP2002 Smart Valve provides service brake control in accordance with demands, distributed by the EP2002 Gateway Valve. The EP2002 RIO Valve delivers all of the functions of the EP2002 Smart Valve but with additional interfaces to wired train lines (both analogue and digital).

WORLD CLASS MANUFACTURE AND TEST

The advanced, mechatronic technology used in EP2002 requires equally advanced manufacturing and test techniques and facilities.

The UK based manufacturing and test facility must deliver outstanding quality but also the volumes required to satisfy demands for a system which is increasingly specified for trains around the world.

Knorr-Bremse has established what can only be described as a laboratory type facility in the UK for EP2002 where the product is both manufactured and tested. This facility was the first in the world to achieve the prestigious TÜV certification for a manufacturing facility. The EP2002 product itself is also fully TÜV certificated.

Within this advanced facility, EP2002 is manufactured for a specific customer application. This is an important point; although EP2002 contains a 'family' of valve types each system application is bespoke to the train type it is to be employed to serve.

Testing is also carried out in the similar state of the art UK based facilities. The automated TESRA test rig, designed and built especially for this purpose, is used to replicate the various electronic parts of an EP2002 valve. By connecting these valves together a simulated EP2002 network can be created. The result is that the EP2002 Distributed Brake Control System 'thinks' that it in the real service environment in which it will operate on the train and interacts as such with the test simulation. Knorr-Bremse engineers can therefore verify performance in a simulated environment before giving an OK to release into customer service.

GLOBAL APPLICATIONS

There are over 20,000 EP2002 valves in service today throughout the world including on London Underground and on ScotRail Class 380 commuter trains in the UK. Further afield, EP2002 is in daily service on for example, Hong Kong, Shanghai and Singapore Metros. These valves have proven to be extremely reliable in service but are supported with the unique EP2002 Brakes Explorer Software. This integrated diagnostic software, specially developed to support the EP2002 system, facilitates the integration of individual EP2002 Valves to check on their 'health' status, on train. It is also possible to view the status of the entire train system, using Ethernet technology, in 'real time.' The Brakes Explorer software is easy to use and is actually integrated with the EP2002 Valve meaning that any standard PC browser can be used to access the interface. There is no need for any additional tools or software. In the unlikely event of a potential or actual failure arising EP2002 values can be quickly changed trackside, minimising any operational disruption.

LOWER COSTS WITH HIGHER PERFORMANCE

From the start, EP2002 was designed and developed to answer the increasing demands being made by high traffic, urban mass transit systems, including the demands for high safety levels, excellent performance and lower life-cycle costs.

In comparison to conventional rail brake control technology the same high safety standards are achieved by EP2002, but it is more economical to operate, requires less space, is lighter and its decentralised layout improves systems performance.

The result is an extremely safe and robust system with reduced life cycle costs. This is as a result of the actual number of components being significantly reduced and lower maintenance and overhaul regimes especially adapted to the individual needs of operators. Decentralised installation, close to the bogie, means reduced piping requirements and improved pneumatic performance, with shorter brake reaction times.

The Major Projects award for 2013 went to First Great Western, for its work to increase capacity and offset overcrowding on its network focused on London Paddington. Network Rail

Innovation recognised by *Modern Railways* awards

Interim Franchise Director at the Department for Transport, Pete Wilkinson, was guest of honour at Modern Railways' 2013 Railway Industry Innovation Awards presentation in London on 28 June. The Modern Railways sponsored awards are the longest running such scheme in the rail industry, and one of the most prestigious, drawing entries from the full range of companies active in today's railways.

Pete Wilkinson has had a long career in the rail industry, spanning the privatisation of British Rail's train operating units, leading franchise procurements for the Strategic Rail Authority and also franchise and concession bidding both here in the UK and abroad. He has also been the Principal Advisor to Network Rail on alliancing and was the Commercial Advisor to Richard Brown's independent review of franchising. He joined the Department in 2013 to help kick-start the paused franchising programme. The scale and immediacy of the programme are such that the department was keen to bring in someone with Peter's expertise, and a new franchising programme published in March 2013, which he discussed in his presentation to the Railway Industry Innovation Awards audience, provided a widely welcomed new blueprint for the passenger rail industry.

MAJOR AWARD

The Major Projects award for 2013 went to First Great Western, whose staff have used their close knowledge of the industry's resources to increase capacity and offset overcrowding. First Great Western saw potential in non-standard trains, and in buffet cars which the company converted into full passenger vehicles - while also refreshing other vehicles, recruiting and training staff, installing gatelines, and developing new maintenance and driver training regimes.

The judges believed the operator has showed commendable resourcefulness in increasing capacity to offset overcrowding.

Also shortlisted was the £7.6million redevelopment of Swansea station. Funded by the Welsh Government, Network Rail and the Department for Transport's National Stations Improvement Programme, Swansea has gained a wide range of benefits including improved accessibility and passenger facilities, security and retailing. The use of copper in the design recognises the local industrial heritage.

ENVIRONMENT

The Innovation Award for the Environment was presented to Northern for its carriage washer

improvement programme. Working with Rail Order, Henkel and Koti-Dawson, Northern has improved its train cleaning facilities, not only to improve the exterior cleanliness of its trains, but also to achieve some big environmental savings.

CrossCountry was commended for reducing the environmental impact of a new accommodation building for its traincrew, the Lamp Block at Birmingham New Street. Network Rail was commended for environmental work on the capacity expansion project at the Stockley flyover on the Great Western main line.

PASSENGER EXPERIENCE

The Innovation Award for Passenger Experience, sponsored by Arriva, was won by Ayoupa's 'Commuter' transport planning and journey monitoring app. A collaboration between Pascal Simplice of Ayoupa Ltd and Ben Stewart of Caution Your Blast Ltd, it provides passengers with better information support for complex journeys to realise wider benefits within the environment and transport industry.

The transformation of the Heathrow Express fleet was commended, alongside Southern's project 'Try a Train Day and See Where it Can Take You'.

ENGINEERING AND SAFETY

The Innovation Award for Engineering and Safety, sponsored by the Railway Industry Association, was won by Southeastern's train engineering wiki, which contains more than 50,000 words of technical knowledge, manuals and processes supported by more than 30,000 images. The wiki has transformed the way maintenance work is allocated, analysed and reported. The system is believed to be the most advanced and sophisticated found in any industry.

Unipart Rail was commended for its new modular level crossing installation system, as was Signalling Solutions' work on level crossing obstacle detection

The award for Operations & Performance went to London Overground Rail Operations Ltd for its use of e-reader technology for operations notices. With wi-fi capability installed at depots, this innovation has streamlined the dissemination of essential and critical information for the smooth and safe running of the network, bringing significant financial savings and reducing impact on the external environment.

The Chiltern Mainline Mk3 coach project carried out by Wabtec Rail was commended, as was Garrandale's work on Network Rail's winterisation train.

SMALL SCALE

The Innovation Award for a Small Scale project was won by c2c's use of Quick Response (QR) codes to help in monitoring the performance of every train heating and air-conditioning unit, more than doubling the amount of information captured. A bespoke smartphone programme is used to send immediate reports, at a minimal cost.

Commended was Southeastern's 'Workmate' social networking/ intranet, and STEvan - the Southern Training and Education van.

The award for Innovation in a Cross-Industry project was won by Greater Anglia for its London 2012 Olympics and Paralympics focus. Working in partnership with Network Rail, Transport for London and other industry colleagues, the company offered high standards of assistance and service to customers, including international visitors. A dedicated, co-ordinated and targeted approach addressed planning and preparation through active management, aiming to create a real Olympic spirit and focus. Commended were ScotRail's electrification of the Paisley Canal line, and the South Yorkshire tram-train project.

'GOLDEN SPANNERS' FOR ROLLING STOCK EXCELLENCE

The eleventh annual review of traction and rolling stock fleet reliability is published in the January 2014 issue of Modern Railways magazine. An awards luncheon the previous November - one of the Modern Railways Fourth Friday Club events - sees 'Golden Spanners' awarded to the best performers, with gold (best in class), silver (most improved) and bronze (fastest incident recovery) categories.

The brainchild of Roger Ford, Industry & Technology Editor of Modern Railways, the awards divide the national rolling stock fleet into categories: Pacers; Ex BR EMUs; Ex BR DMUs; InterCity, New-generation DMUs and New-generation EMUs with Spanners for each category awarded based on actual performance data, Miles Per Technical Incident (MTIN) from the Association of Train Operating Companies. The awards are widely credited within the industry as contributing to improvements in train reliability.

Specialist traction motor and MA set repairer Houghton International are sponsors of the Golden Spanner Awards 2013.

The 2013 Major Project award went to First Great Western. Left to right are Richard French, Alison Stone and Rishi Ravidran of FGW, with prize presenter Haydn Abbott, Chairman of the Railway Industry Innovation Awards judging panel. Tony Miles

The Environment award was won by Northen Rail's washplant improvement programme. Left to right: Danny Grayson and Marc Silverwood from Northern, Steve Metcalfe of Railorder, and prize presenter Peter Wilkinson of the Department for Transport. Tony Miles

GOLDEN WHISTLES AWARDS

Skilful operators can make the trains run safely and on time – and the best operators deserve recognition.

For this reason the Institution of Railway Operators and Modern Railways magazine joined forces to launch the Golden Whistles Awards. These awards acknowledge best practice and congratulate railway operators that have done a good job by rewarding them with that ultimate symbol of smart operating – a whistle!

The Golden Whistles, based on objective data, emulate the successful Golden Spanners Awards already run by Modern Railways. There are categories for: Operational Safety, Operational Performance, and Managing Disruption, with awards for best performance and most improved performance in several categories.

Based on nominations from their peers, Golden Whistles are also awarded to the Outstanding Individual Operator of the Year, and Best Operating Team of the Year.

A panel of senior railway executives interpret the data and ensure fair play.

The 2014 Golden Whistles Awards will be presented at the January meeting of the Modern Railways Fourth Friday Club.

THE FOURTH FRIDAY CLUB

The Modern Railways Fourth Friday Club provides a unique networking forum for executives from all sectors in the railway industry. There are club meetings on five Fridays in each year, the season running from September to June. The club was the idea of 'Modern Railways' Editor, James Abbott who is also Club Secretary.

Since the first meeting in 2003, the growing reputation of the Club for attracting senior policy makers and top railway managers as guest speakers has seen membership expand rapidly.

For more information, see 4thfriday.co.uk

The tenth InnoTrans will take place from 23 to 26 September 2014. InnoTrans

Earls Court hosts Infrarail 2014

Earls Court 2 in London will be the venue for 2014's Infrarail exhibition, bringing together leading companies from all parts of the rail infrastructure supply sector. The tenth of these shows takes place from 20 to 22 May 2014 and provides a unique opportunity for visitors to learn more about the latest innovations from the industry's suppliers as Britain's national network embarks on its next round of investments.

Many Infrarail features will be familiar to anyone who has previously attended one of these events or its sister exhibition Railtex, with company stands showcasing the very latest in the systems, products and services needed for building and maintaining the railway's fixed assets, as well as those for underground and light rail systems. The exhibition hall will also be the setting for The Yard – an area for the presentation of larger vehicles and plant, and The Track – lengths of track for product displays and presentations. Also present will be the Recruitment Wall, highlighting participating companies' skills needs and job opportunities.

Alongside the exhibition, an extensive programme of major project updates, technical presentations and discussion groups will enable visitors to gain informed insights into policy developments and trends in rail infrastructure technology. These will be open free of charge to everyone attending the show. An added highlight will be a keynote address delivered each day by a leading industry figure.

Social aspects of the event include the opening day's Networking Reception welcoming exhibitors and show visitors and the popular Infrarail Awards dinner on 21 May, recognising significant achievements by companies taking part in the exhibition.

In a new development, the first Civil Infrastructure & Technology Exhibition (CITE) will take place alongside Infrarail. CITE will provide exhibitors with a showcase for the equipment, products and services needed for constructing and maintaining vital national infrastructure such as roads, ports, airports, utilities and communications networks. Visitors will be able to move freely between the two exhibitions, which will be located in the same hall.

As usual, entry to Infrarail will be free for pre-registered visitors. Registration via the show website www.infrarail.com will open a couple of months ahead of the event. For non-registered visitors an entrance fee will be payable on the door.

The website is frequently updated and provides the latest list of exhibiting companies, plus details of all associated activities including keynote addresses, technical seminars and project updates as they are finalised.

Infrarail 2014 will include The Yard –for presentation of larger vehicles and plant - and The Track – for product displays and presentations. Infrarail

INNOTRANS 2014 - MORE EXHIBITION SPACE

The tenth InnoTrans rail industry exhibition will take place in Berlin from 23 to 26 September 2014.

At the last event, 2,515 companies from 49 countries presented their rail industry innovations to 126,110 trade visitors who came from 140 countries. The five sections at InnoTrans are Railway Technology, Railway Infrastructure, Public Transport, Interiors and Tunnel Construction.

By autumn 2013, more than 90 per cent of the display area occupied at the last event was booked and, at around 50 per cent, participation by international exhibitors was high. For example, the US Railway Engineering-Maintenance Suppliers Association (REMSA) is organising a combined stand and will occupy double the display space at the last event. The Japan Overseas Rolling Stock Association (JORSA) will also be represented on a combined stand. Once again, Japan will be taking up an entire hall.

Kazakhstan will be taking part in the event in Berlin for the first time, where it will be represented by the Tengiz Trans Group, the independent leasing company for rolling stock. DCD, a rolling stock manufacturer from South Africa, is among the newcomers at InnoTrans 2014.

The new CityCube Berlin, a multi-purpose hall for trade fairs, conferences and events, will be providing two extra exhibition floors covering 6,000 square metres each for InnoTrans. The building will be on the site of the former Deutschlandhalle, next door to the south entrance of the exhibition grounds.

InnoTrans is organised by Messe Berlin GmbH. More details are available online at www.innotrans.com

KEY PROJECTS AND CONSULTANTS

IN ASSOCIATION WITH

COSTAIN

Electrification on the Great Western main line will soon extend beyond the stretch installed for the opening of Heathrow Express in 1998. Network Rail

ATKINS

UK ELECTRIFICATION: A ONCE IN A LIFETIME OPPORTUNITY

It has been several decades since main line railway electrification projects were high profile in the UK but now they are, again, top of the agenda. With £10 billion to be invested in electrifying key routes on the UK railway network during Control Periods 5 and 6, passengers will enjoy faster, greener, quieter and more reliable journeys for generations to come. Design, engineering and project management consultancy Atkins knows about the value of electrifying railways and, crucially, how to do it successfully having been involved in many UK electrification projects.

The previous two years have seen the company secure important electrification contracts. It is now delivering the design for the Great Western Electrification Programme (GWEP) and the Midland main line. Atkins also undertook the multidisciplinary design for the entire Edinburgh Glasgow Improvement Programme (EGIP) and is now working with Carillion to deliver Key Output 4 (Springburn to Cumbernauld) under EGIP.

Speaking about Atkins' vision, Ben Dunlop, director of electrification said: 'We have a strong reputation in UK railway electrification built up over many years and the opportunities in front of us are very exciting. The contracts we have secured so far have enabled us to collaborate with our industry colleagues to develop solutions and share knowledge across projects. In addition, our leadership of industry wide working groups such as Safe by Design places us right at the heart of shaping the future ways of working and creating new ideas. One of our key innovations has been the development of our electrification design tools which are delivering real efficiency benefits throughout the design process. With a ten year programme ahead of us we plan to win more work which will provide engineers and engineering managers with a chance to join an innovative team which is at the forefront of electrification in the UK.'

In terms of delivery, Atkins is breaking new ground with GWEP. Having been appointed Lead Design Organisation (LDO) in partnership with Parsons Brinckerhoff, the team is responsible for the design and systems integrator aspects of the scheme. The build requirements of the project are formidable: 22,000 piles, masts and associated wiring will need to be installed along the route between London and Cardiff by 2017. But, as Russell Jackson, Atkins' regional director leading the LDO contract explains, managing the thousands of decisions that will be made on the scheme over the next three years is even more of a challenge.

'We've taken engineering management tools used on other major rail programmes, and further developed them to help the team deliver on GWEP,' Russell explained. 'On a smaller project, achieving requirements and managing interfaces can be managed very easily, without specialist techniques and skills. But with the sheer scale and tremendous complexity of GWEP this isn't possible - so we're using systems that augment traditional tools to ensure engineering management hits the sweet spot of delivery. As GWEP progresses, the whole project will be led this way, so that together, all the work streams align to the common goals of our staged entry into service plans. The checks and balances that have been built into the engineering management will not only keep the project on track but ensure that client expectations are met.'

Collaboration between all parties on GWEP is making this possible. By working in partnership the systems and engineering management philosophy can be weaved throughout every aspect of the scheme as all the delivery teams have bought into the idea. Speaking about the future of the project, Russell said: 'GWEP is a fantastic project to be involved in. It has so many aspects to it from leading safety by design for major new electrification, to finding solutions for complex engineering, stakeholder and innovation challenges. The question here is "what does all this mean for the industry?" and because GWEP is such an industry leading programme, that is something that we will be looking to provide an answer for very soon.'

For further information on the electrification vacancies available at Atkins visit: www.atkinsglobal.com/careers/electrical

Ben Dunlop, Atkins' director of electrification

Russell Jackson, Atkins' regional director leading the LDO contract.

Completed in September 2013, the new 75,000 sq ft King's Cross Square is the final part of the £550m redevelopment of King's Cross station, revealing the station's full historic façade. Network Rail

Key Projects

GREAT WESTERN ROUTE MODERNISATION

The major modernisation now under way on the Great Western main line includes electrification, resignalling and the rebuilding of Reading station and the area's track layout area. Provision is also being made for the possible extension of Crossrail from Maidenhead to Reading.

Electrification of the main line to Bristol and to Cardiff, announced in 2011, supplements the scheme to Newbury and to Oxford (to be completed in 2016), extending electrification from Didcot through to Bristol Temple Meads both via Chippenham and via Bristol Parkway, and to Cardiff Central (by 2017). The line from Cardiff to Swansea was added in July 2012.

Electrification of all the Valleys services from Cardiff, including those to Ebbw Vale Parkway and Maesteg via the Vale of Glamorgan, has also been included in 2014-19 plans.

GW - READING

Network Rail's £895m project to transform Reading's railway system achieved major milestones in 2013. Costain, in joint venture with Hochtief, was awarded a contract worth approximately £80m, one of the one of the largest on the project, to enhance station capacity by constructing five new platforms, as well as a new passenger 'transfer deck' linking platforms to new entrance buildings on the north and south side of the station. There are a total of 19 new escalators to platforms.

At Easter 2013, during a four-day line closure, as many as 2,000 personnel from several organisations – 500 from Costain and its contractors – were busy at the station, including commissioning of a major new signalling system and track works. Costain's main tasks were to demolish an old bridge over the tracks, open the five new platforms on the north side of the station, and refurbish a further two, with construction of platform buildings, new platform surfacing and canopies.

The 100-metre transfer deck was constructed in three sections beside the tracks. The first 50-metre, 729-tonne section was pushed 28 metres out over the railway over four nights in July 2012, the second section in August and the third section was erected in situ.

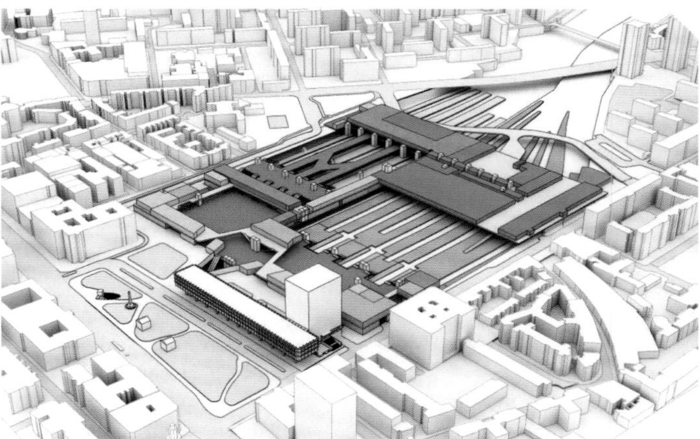

HS2 Ltd revealed in 2013 new proposals for its London Euston terminus which would avoid knocking down and rebuilding the entire station and lowering all platforms. Platforms 9 and 10 would be removed so that adjacent platforms can be lengthened, resulting in 13 long platforms. HS2 Ltd

Grade separation at the east end of the station will allow trains to and from the Waterloo lines to reach the north side of the station. Further grade separation, elevating the main lines west of the station, will enable freight flows (in particular) to and from the line to Basingstoke to cross to the relief lines towards Didcot without obstructing the main lines.

To enable this to happen, the train maintenance facility has been relocated west of Reading station and had its capacity enhanced.

INTERCITY EXPRESS PROGRAMME (IEP)

The Intercity Express Programme 'comprises the infrastructure, rolling stock and franchise changes needed to replace services operated by the ageing fleet of HST sets. The new trains will be faster, with higher

The new transfer deck in place at Reading station - transforming capacity and accessibility. Network Rail

capacity, more comfortable and more environmentally friendly services that will support growth on some of the busiest main line routes'. So said the Department for Transport, describing its original £4.5bn contract with Agility Trains as part of the Intercity Express Programme. They will be built at a new factory in Newton Aycliffe, County Durham.

The initial ideas date from 2005 and Agility Trains (a consortium of Hitachi Rail Europe Ltd and John Laing plc) was appointed preferred bidder in February 2009.

In summer 2010, Agility Trains put forward a revised proposal for a mixed IEP fleet, some all electric trains and some with a combination of straight electric and diesel power under the floor (bi-modes) - aimed at meeting the DfT's interest in preserving through services away from the electrified network without operating diesel traction under the wires for appreciable distances.

In the initial contract signed in July 2012, Agility Trains is responsible for the construction of 92 complete trains totaling 596 vehicles, together with maintenance depots in Bristol, Swansea, Old Oak Common and Doncaster. Agility Trains will also maintain the trains, with the train operating company (TOC) responsible for operations. The TOC will pay Agility Trains a Set Availability Payment for each train that reports for duty each day and remains reliable during the operational period. The Department is providing Agility Trains with a Usage Guarantee that there will be a TOC in place to make use of the trains.

IEP PHASES

Phase 1 trains will operate on the Great Western franchise and will consist of 189 vehicles formed into 21 nine-car electric only trains and 180 vehicles formed into 36 five-car bi-mode trains (total 369 vehicles and 52 trains).

They will operate services from London Paddington to Bristol, Swansea, Cheltenham Spa and Hereford. Hitachi's Newton Aycliffe factory is expected to be fully operational by 2016, with the first IEP trains entering revenue earning service in 2017.

Phase 2 trains will operate on the East Coast franchise and will consist of 60 vehicles formed into 12 five-car electric only trains, 50 vehicles formed into 10 five-car bi-modal trains and 117 vehicles formed into 13 nine-car bi-mode trains, total 227 vehicles and 35 trains.

These will operate services from London King's Cross to Leeds, York, Newcastle, Edinburgh, Aberdeen and Inverness, with deliveries from 2018. The 5-car sets will be able to work in pairs.

The option of a further order was taken up in July 2013 for a further 270 vehicles consisting of 30 nine-car electric only trains for the East Coast. These will replace the Class 91+Mk4 formations.

The contract to finance, supply and maintain the whole fleet takes the total value of the IEP programme to £5.8bn.

THAMESLINK

The Thameslink Programme is a £6bn project to deliver a high capacity, north-south spine railway through central London. With a scheduled completion in 2018, Thameslink will provide greater capacity, higher frequencies, new services and improved access to central London from a range of destinations within London and across southeast England.

Major benefits from the works include a capacity increase in the core section between St Pancras Thameslink and Blackfriars to 24 trains per hour, mostly 12-cars.

The enhanced route will serve around a threefold increase in the number of stations and provide significant relief to existing systems, with capacity for future growth.

The Thameslink programme comprises three main elements:

- Major infrastructure works to provide platforms to accommodate trains of 12-car 20 metre vehicles and the removal of key capacity bottlenecks.
- The specification and procurement of new rolling stock.
- Changes to the existing and the letting of new railway franchises to accommodate the new Thameslink services.

Large-scale works include the now completed rebuilding of Blackfriars station. This is the first station to span the Thames, providing direct passenger access to both the north and south banks. Farringdon

rebuilding for Thameslink is also complete; in future it will become a major interchange with Crossrail as well as London Underground.

THAMESLINK - LONDON BRIDGE RECONSTRUCTION

The aim of the current phase of major works at London Bridge is to remove bottlenecks, improve passenger facilities and significantly improve passenger capacity. Main features include conversion of six high-level through platforms and nine low-level terminal platforms to nine high-level through and six low-level terminal.

A new approach viaduct and two-track bridge over Borough High Street have now ben completed, to feed the new high-level station tracks.

Costain was appointed as principal contractor for the station work by Network Rail, supported by WSP and Hyder Consulting for design. Balfour Beatty Rail has been appointed as principal contractor for the track work and Siemens was awarded the signalling design and installation contract.

A new and very large station concourse, 70m wide and 150m deep, will be underneath the tracks at street level, running at right angles to the tracks, with new entrances both in Tooley Street to the north and St Thomas Street to the south. Escalators will rise directly to all platforms, with lifts as an alternative.

Large scale work began in Summer 2013, with the first new platform scheduled to open in Spring 2014. During 2015/16 Charing Cross services will not stop at London Bridge, and similarly for Cannon Street services in 2016/17. In Summer 2018 the whole station will be complete.

The National Skills Academy for Construction has awarded project status to the redevelopment of London Bridge Station, with Network Rail and main contractor Costain agreeing targets to train 40 apprentices, 71 work placements, 22 graduates and 80 new employees during the four-year project. Each person will receive an average of four days' accredited skills training per year.

THAMESLINK - POWER AND SIGNALLING

The AC overhead line equipment is being reconfigured and the power supply strengthened. There is a new substation at Elstree & Borehamwood and another in the DC area at Ludgate (near Blackfriars).

Overhead electrification has been extended to City Thameslink. A crossover allows trains from the north to be reversed here.

To allow trains to proceed at closer intervals, there is now bi-directional signalling throughout between Kentish Town and Blackfriars. The European Train Control System will be overlaid to provide automatic operation when infrastructure work in the London Bridge area is completed.

A high-capacity Kirow crane is use during the major remodelling at Reading at Easter 2013. Network Rail

THAMESLINK - TRAINS

The order was placed for new trains for Thameslink with a consortium of Siemens plc and Cross London Trains on 27 June 2013. The first of these Class 700 units will be in service by the end of 2016 and the whole fleet by the end of 2018. The trains consist of 55 12-car and 60 8-car dual-voltage Desiro City units. The contract worth c£1.6bn includes the construction of new depots at both Three Bridges and Hornsey.

THAMESLINK - SERVICES

Service provision proposals have varied considerably over the years. As provisionally put forward by Network Rail in their Route Strategy for London & South East in 2011, there would be 24 peak trains per hour through the central section. Of these, 14 would originate on the Brighton lines, and 10 on the South Eastern. Similarly, 16 would terminate on the Midland, and 8 on the Great Northern.

The merging of train services to access the central area between

St Pancras International and Blackfriars will take place at Midland Road Junction (between the Midland and Great Northern lines north of St Pancras). A new grade separated junction at Bermondsey will facilitate the separation of Brighton and South Eastern services.

From 2019, Farringdon will be an important interchange and the only station where London Underground, Thameslink and Crossrail meet. There will be a maximum of 160 trains an hour on all routes combined. These will provide direct services to Heathrow, Gatwick and Luton airports, to Liverpool Street for Stansted, and to St Pancras for international rail services.

CROSSRAIL

The Crossrail project will deliver a new integrated railway through central London from Maidenhead and Heathrow in the west through tunnels under central London with stations at Paddington, Bond Street, Tottenham Court Road, Farringdon, Liverpool Street and Whitechapel, then to Stratford and on out to Shenfield north of the Thames, and to Canary Wharf, Custom House, Woolwich and Abbey Wood to the south. The joint sponsors are the Department for Transport and Transport for London (TfL) which set up a company, Crossrail Ltd, to act as the delivery agent.

Crossrail Ltd is a wholly-owned TfL subsidiary. The company manages the entire programme for the two project sponsors. This includes the partners involved with specific elements of the programme, including Network Rail and London Underground.

CROSSRAIL - SERVICES

New Crossrail services will provide direct links on this network, with up to 24 peak trains per hour in the central section and 12 an hour off-peak. An estimated 160,000 passengers will be carried in the morning rush hour. The total length of the Crossrail system is 118.5km, including 31.5km in tunnels. 38 stations will be served directly.

Crossrail is the biggest transport project in Europe, facilitating economic growth as a very significant capacity addition to the network. Overall, the benefits of Crossrail are now estimated to be worth at least £42bn in current prices to the national GDP over the next 60 years.

CROSSRAIL - CIVIL WORKS

Crossrail trains are to use a 21km diameter twin bore tunnels under the centre of London. Construction started in 2009, with the Canary Wharf station site. This is being built below the water of North Dock and will have pedestrian links to Poplar and Canary Wharf DLR stations, and Canary Wharf Jubilee Line station. The lead contractor and project manager is Canary Wharf Contractors Ltd.

The five pairs of tunnels to be constructed are Royal Oak to Farringdon west (6.1km); Limmo Peninsula (Royal Docks) to Farringdon east (8.3km); Stepney Green to Pudding Mill Lane (2.7km); Limmo Peninsula to Victoria Dock Portal (0.9km); Plumstead to North Woolwich (2.6km). Of the eight Tunnel Boring Machines (TBMs), six are of the earth pressure balance type for use in clay, the other two of the slurry type for boring through the chalk of the 2.6km tunnel under the Thames.

Each Tunnel Boring Machine is operated by a tunnel gang of around 20 people, 12 on the TBM itself and eight working from the rear. As the TBMs move forward, pre-cast concrete segments are built in rings behind them.

The main civil engineering works are planned for completion in 2017, with the fitting out of stations and testing to continue afterwards. All tunnel drives are expected to be complete by the end of 2014, tunnel portals and shafts in 2016, with stations at various times up to 2018.

The station works in particular have to be undertaken in relation to works needed at existing stations where there are interchanges, and there are separate schemes where Network Rail is in the lead. One scheme of particular note is the complete reconstruction of the Airport Junction flyovers, where services to Heathrow diverge.

CROSSRAIL - POWER SUPPLY CONTRACT

Crossrail has awarded the contract for the high voltage traction power supply contract to the AC Joint Venture (Alstom Transport and Costain Limited).

The scope of works includes the provision of traction power, distributed within Crossrail's central section extending from Royal Oak Portal in the west to Pudding Mill Lane in the east, splitting at Stepney Green Junction and running to Plumstead Portal in the southeast.

The works will involve the construction of a feeder station at Pudding Mill Lane where power from the 400 kV National Grid network will be converted down to 25 kV before being fed into the overhead line equipment that will power the new Crossrail trains. A separate feeder station will be constructed by Network Rail at Kensal Green.

Four high voltage auto transformer stations will be also constructed at Westbourne Park, Stepney Green, Custom House and Plumstead to maintain the voltage along the line.

TABLE 1: COMPARATIVE JOURNEY TIMES

JOURNEY	CROSSRAIL	LONDON UNDERGROUND
Heathrow-Canary Wharf	43min	70min
Heathrow-Tottenham Court Road	31min	52min
Ealing Broadway-Liverpool Street	20min	37min
Abbey Wood-Tottenham Court Road	22mn	45min*

** also using Southeastern trains*

CROSSRAIL - NETWORK RAIL

Network Rail is responsible for the design, development and delivery of those parts of Crossrail on the existing network. This includes the upgrading of 70km of track, redeveloping 28 stations and renewing 15 bridges, as well as removing spoil from the tunnel excavations by rail.

Layout changes and turnback capability will be provided at Maidenhead, Slough, West Drayton, Hayes & Harlington, Ilford, Chadwell Heath, Gidea Park and Shenfield. Old Oak Common depot will be remodelled.

Platform extensions are required at over 20 stations, including Abbey Wood, Ilford, Romford and Ealing Broadway. The trains themselves will need to be equipped with selective door opening for use at some stations.

Electrification on all four tracks will take place west of Airport Junction, itself to be substantially rebuilt, and signalling renewed. There will be a new diveunder for freight at Acton yard. At Paddington, there will be a major reworking of platforms and interchange between the Crossrail station and main line platforms.

A new platform taking shape at Stalybridge during the autumn 2012 remodelling, an early part of Northern Hub capacity improvements. Network Rail

CROSSRAIL - DELIVERY

Crossrail is employing up to 14,000 people during the present peak time of construction; it will provide an estimated 1,000 jobs directly when fully operational. The company's skills strategy supports the use of local labour and the tunnelling academy.

Over 60% of Crossrail funding comes from Londoners and London-based business through direct contributions from the City of London, BAA, Canary Wharf Group and a London Business Rates Supplement and planning development levy. The government is providing about £5bn by means of a grant from the Department for Transport. The funding package is designed to strike a fair balance between businesses, passengers and taxpayers.

CROSSRAIL - TRAINS

'To ensure value for money, Crossrail's intention is that the new trains are based upon technology already developed by the worldwide rolling stock market for deployment on other railways. A revolutionary new train design is not required.' In the running are Bombardier, CAF and Hitachi, Siemens having withdrawn in 2013. It is anticipated that the £1bn contract between the successful bidder and TfL for around 60 trains and the Old Oak Common depot will be let in 2014.

Each train will be a maximum length of about 200m. Assuming this equates to 10x20m vehicles, the requirement for around 450 seats is thus a mere 45 per car. Overall capacity including standing will be 1,500. Acceleration will be up to 1 metre per second, comparable with a Metro. Trains will be air-conditioned. They will be operated at 25kV AC, but with potential for fitment with third rail pick up.

Crossrail's trains will operate in Automatic Train Operation mode with Automatic Train Protection in the central section, but will need to feature existing train protection systems until the European Train Control Systems IETCS) is installed at either end on Network Rail. The new trains will be wholly publicly funded.

Crossrail route control will be based at Liverpool Street in the first instance, and later at a new centre at Romford.

CROSSRAIL - OPERATIONS AND SIGNALLING

Crossrail signalling and control systems will enable a 24tph service to be operated during the peak between Paddington and Whitechapel, but they must be designed to support enhancement to 30tph through this section at a later date.

The operation of Crossrail services will be let as a concession by Transport for London's London Rail, similar to that let for London Overground. Companies shortlisted are: Arriva Crossrail Ltd; Keolis/GoAhead; MTR Corporation (Crossrail) Ltd; and National Express Group plc.

The successful bidder will be appointed at the end of 2014 and will operate the existing Liverpool Street-Shenfield, Paddington-Maidenhead and Heathrow Connect services from dates related to franchise renewals. The new rolling stock fleet will be introduced first onto Great Eastern main line services in 2017 and then progressively elsewhere. This will be 'well in advance of services commencing through Crossrail's central section'. Full Crossrail operation starts December 2019.

HIGH SPEED 2

High Speed 2 (HS2) is a planned new north-south railway promoted and built in two phases. HS2 Ltd, the company responsible for developing and promoting it, is wholly owned by the Department for Transport.

Phase One plans are for a new high-speed line from London Euston to north of Birmingham, where it will link with the existing West Coast main line allowing fast services direct to destinations including Manchester, Liverpool, Crewe, Preston and Glasgow. New high-speed trains are to serve Birmingham city centre (Curzon Street) and an interchange with Birmingham International and Birmingham Airport, designed to serve the wider West Midlands. At Old Oak Common in west London, a new interchange is to connect HS2 with Crossrail, the Great Western main line and the Heathrow Express.

The proposals for Phase Two would see the line extended north and east, to join the West Coast main line south of Wigan and the East Coast main line south of York. On a Manchester leg, there would be stations at Manchester Airport High Speed and Manchester Piccadilly (adjacent to existing station). A separate branch would serve an East Midlands station at Toton (near Nottingham), Sheffield Meadowhall and Leeds New Lane.

Passengers would be able to travel from central London to Birmingham in 49 minutes rather than 1 hour 24 minutes today, and from London to Manchester in 1 hour 8 minutes (2 hours 8 minutes today).

HS2 would provide new links between regional cities, and directly connect eight out of the 10 largest cities: London, Birmingham, Manchester, Liverpool, Glasgow, Edinburgh, Sheffield and Leeds.

Manchester and Birmingham airports would be served directly, with the planned interchange at Old Oak Common offering a connection to Heathrow airport. The potential also remains, 'pending decisions after the Airports Commission's report and the strength of the supporting evidence', to provide a direct link in Phase Two from the Midlands and the North to Heathrow Airport. An HS1/ HS2 link will provide for direct train services from the HS2 network to mainland Europe.

HS2 is designed for a top speed of 250mph. Plans envisage services running at up to 225mph, seen as becoming the standard for new high speed trains. For future operation at 250mph, noise and other impacts would be considered first. New stations on the line would be built to accommodate 400m long trains, each capable of carrying up to 1,100 passengers. A 14 trains per hour capability in Phase One (12 in the initial specification), is expected to rise to 18 trains per hour in Phase Two.

Choices made in the design of HS2 have been detailed in consultation documents for Phase One and Phase Two.

Network Rail estimates that over 100 cities and towns could benefit from new or improved services as a result of capacity released on the existing rail network. Opportunities include additional London commuter services from places such as Watford, Milton Keynes, Rugby and Northampton; new commuter services into Birmingham, Leeds and

VISION FOR HIGH SPEED BRITAIN

- HS2 STATION
- HS2 DESTINATION SERVED BY HS2 CLASSIC COMPATIBLE SERVICES
- CORE HIGH SPEED NETWORK (PHASES ONE AND TWO)
- HS2 CONNECTION TO EXISTING RAIL NETWORK
- CLASSIC COMPATIBLE SERVICES
- EXISTING LINES WITH POTENTIAL FOR FUTURE CONNECTION TO HS2

Manchester; new longer distance services, such as new and better links between Bradford, Lincoln, Shrewsbury and London; and between Leeds and Cambridge; and more paths for rail freight (at least an extra 20 West Coast main line freight paths).

The strategic case published by the Department for Transport in October 2013 sets out how both phases of HS2 can deliver the government's objectives - for Phase One the emphasis is 'towards additional capacity' and Phase Two 'emphasises better connectivity'.

It says evidence shows that incremental improvements to existing railways would not achieve objectives, in particular, failing to provide sufficient additional capacity to meet long term demand on north-south railways, with insufficient capacity for intercity travel, commuters and freight. They would, says the report, fail to offer a robust solution to the problem of poor service performance, particularly on the West Coast main line which suffers from unacceptably high levels of unreliability; and would significantly disrupt services on existing lines as construction work is carried out, and over a period of many years if a substantial multi-route programme was contemplated.

The government updated the benefit to cost ratio (BCR) of the railway in October 2013, valuing it at 2.3 to one - 'similar to Crossrail and higher than the benefit cost ratio for some other major projects when approved, such as Thameslink and the Jubilee Line extension'. The BCR would increase to 4.5:1 if rail demand continued to rise until 2049, said the government.

Given the scale of HS2, permission for the scheme to go ahead will be sought through a 'hybrid' Bill process (combination of Public and Private Bill procedures). A bill approving expenditure on detailed design, land acquisition, compensation, and preparatory works was anticipated to achieve Royal Assent by the end of 2013.

The Government announced in June 2013 a potential funding requirement for HS2 of £42.6bn, at 2011 prices (£21.4bn for Phase One and £21.2bn for Phase Two – including a total contingency for both phases of £14.4bn). The government agreed with HS2 Ltd that the target price for the construction of Phase One is not the £21.4bn funding allocation but £17.16bn, and no spending above this can take place 'without the explicit agreement of the Department for Transport, working with HM Treasury'.

Subject to gaining the necessary powers, it is intended to start construction in 2016/17.

An HS2 Growth Task Force has been established to maximise growth on the back of HS2. The task force is looking at development opportunities around stations, wider regeneration in station places, working with the supply chain and increasing skills and apprenticeships to meet the demands of HS2.

EDINBURGH-GLASGOW IMPROVEMENTS PROGRAMME (EGIP)

The aim of the infrastructure improvements in the Scottish Government's High Level Output Statement of 2007 was to deliver reliability, capacity, attractiveness and journey time savings across the network generally.

After revisions, EGIP now initially consists of the electrification of the Edinburgh-Falkirk High-Glasgow Queen Street line - but first the line from Springburn to Cumbernauld, in time for the Glasgow Commonwealth Games in 2014. Electrification to Stirling and Alloa/Dunblane, and via Falkirk Grahamston is intended later.

With reconstruction of Glasgow Queen Street, platforms would be lengthened for 8-car trains: the fastest journey times between there and Edinburgh will be 42 minutes.

A new Edinburgh Gateway station is to be built on the Fife lines (only) to provide interchange with the Edinburgh Trams and their service to Edinburgh Airport.

Paisley Canal line electrification was completed in December 2012.

NORTHERN HUB

The Northern Hub is about targeted investment to stimulate economic growth by upgrading the rail network. Proposals were launched by Network Rail in 2010. Piecemeal authorisation took place, with the scheme fully funded by July 2012.

Main improvements include two new platforms (15 and 16), on the Oxford Road lines at Manchester Piccadilly to allow more trains to run through rather than terminate. Construction of the Ordsall

CONSULTANT FILES: SUPPORTING RAIL DEVELOPMENTS

AECOM

AECOM is a global provider of professional technical and management support services, with international experience of a wide range of rail disciplines, such as network and systems enhancements, operations, infrastructure maintenance, rail engineering and policy and strategy. AECOM is a 40 per cent partner in the Transcend joint-venture team, providing strategic management services for the London Crossrail project.

ATKINS

Atkins is one of the world's leading design, engineering and project management consultancies, employing some 18,000 people across the UK, North America, Middle East, Asia Pacific and Europe. Atkins is a leader in rail engineering and systems design, providing expertise from experience and in-depth knowledge. From development and maintenance of existing systems to the implementation of new schemes, it helps clients through the entire project lifecycle to maximise value and outcomes.

Key rail projects include providing architectural and engineering design services on Crossrail. Atkins and Heriot-Watt University are collaborating on a Centre of Excellence for High Speed Rail.

ARUP

Arup is a global firm of designers, engineers, planners and business consultants which provides a full range of professional services. Arup's portfolio includes all modes of rail, ranging from high speed through to urban transport systems and freight.

Projects undertaken by Arup range in scope from master/strategic planning and total rail infrastructure improvement programmes requiring multi-disciplinary teams, to the application of singular, specialist skills such as operations, planning, permanent way, traction power, signalling, communications, acoustics, station design and tunnelling.

PARSONS BRINCKERHOFF

Parsons Brinckerhoff is the professional services division of Balfour Beatty, the international infrastructure services organisation that also provides construction services, support services, and infrastructure investments.

Parsons Brinckerhoff is a leader in developing and operating infrastructure around the world, offering skills and resources in strategic consulting, planning, engineering, programme/construction management, and operations for all modes of infrastructure, including transportation, power, buildings and infrastructure, water and the environment.

BECHTEL

Founded in 1898, Bechtel is a major engineering, construction, and project management company, active around the world. Major UK projects in which Bechtel has been involved include the West Coast route modernisation, and the Jubilee Line Extension. It was part of the Rail Link Engineering consortium creating High Speed 1; is involved in modernising the London Underground; and is part of the Project Delivery Partner team for the central tunnel section of Crossrail, and Network Rail's Delivery Partner for its Crossrail and Reading programmes.

CAPITA

Capita's property and infrastructure business (previously Capita Symonds) provides a multidisciplinary service for guided transport systems. With a core of experienced rail engineers it focuses on providing the specialist skills required by major railway clients.

The business designed tunnels and portals for Crossrail, putting together a multi-disciplinary team - civils, architects and M&E engineers. A joint venture with Ineco has won a design contract for HS2 covering approximately 78km of route.

DELTARAIL

DeltaRail is a software and technology company dedicated to the needs of the rail industry, with its principal activity in signalling control software. The company's strategy focuses on its three core areas of 'On Operations', 'On Track' and 'On Train'.

On Operations activity includes signalling, with the next

Curve is to provide a direct route between Manchester Piccadilly and Manchester Victoria. Selective track doubling will increase capacity between Leeds and Liverpool and between Sheffield and Manchester, and Manchester Victoria is to be rebuilt as a single transport interchange.

The net result will be an ability to run more and faster trains on key routes, thus also reducing journey times, plus an increase in the scope for the provision of direct rail services to Manchester Airport.

ELECTRIFICATION

In October 2010 the Chancellor George Osborne confirmed that the coalition government would proceed with the electrification of the lines between Liverpool, Manchester, Preston and Blackpool.

In the High Level Output Statement (HLOS) of July 2012 the government confirmed that the electrification would cover the Chat Moss route from Liverpool to Manchester Victoria (the original Stephenson route), plus Huyton to Wigan, Manchester to Euxton Junction and Preston to Blackpool North.

Network Rail expects to complete Manchester to Liverpool and Huyton to Wigan by December 2014, Preston to Blackpool by May 2016 and Manchester to Euxton Junction by December 2016. In each case there is the ancillary work of bridge reconstructions and similar.

Also to be electrified, after a November 2011 announcement, is the North Trans Pennine route from Manchester Victoria/Guide Bridge to Huddersfield, Leeds and York (Colton Junction). Subsequently, Leeds to Selby, which also provides a south-facing connection to the East Coast Main Line, was added in July 2012. This programme creates numerous diversionary electrified routes, as well as allowing the use of electric trains on services currently provided by diesel traction.

THE ELECTRIC SPINE

Electrification of the Midland main line north of Bedford has been under scrutiny since 2009, but without commitment. This and rather more was achieved with the High Level Output Statement (HLOS) of July 2012, which refers to action to be taken during Control Period 5 (2014-19). The aim is the creation of an 'Electric Spine', a high capacity 25kV AC electrified passenger and freight route from Southampton via Oxford and the Midlands to South Yorkshire. The routes to be electrified are:

- Southampton-Basingstoke (presently electrified at 750V DC third-rail);
- Basingstoke-Reading (section thence to Oxford covered by GW electrification);
- Oxford-Leamington Spa-Coventry-Nuneaton;
- Oxford-Bletchley-Bedford (improved/reopened line);
- Bedford-Nottingham/Derby and Derby-Sheffield;
- Kettering-Corby.

That includes the whole of the Midland main line, but not yet a connection to either Doncaster or Leeds. Other possibilities for electrification are the Erewash Valley line, the Matlock branch, north of Corby to Syston and minor works in the London area. The Secretary of State has left these to the industry to propose for CP6, and also the Midland route from Derby to Birmingham and Bristol. Completion of the latter would see most of the CrossCountry network electrified.

The Secretary of State was looking for gauge clearance work for large containers as well as links to adjacent electrified routes, depots and freight facilities. Another priority is to provide sufficient capacity for freight traffic on the Ipswich-Nuneaton flow where this crosses the Electric Spine at Leicester.

The Southampton-Basingstoke section is seen as a pilot scheme for the longer term systematic upgrade of the whole of the third-rail network south of the Thames to 25kV AC overhead electrification throughout.

EAST-WEST RAILWAY

The Electric Spine builds on earlier schemes, notably Chiltern Railways' Evergreen 3 project. By building a new chord from south of Bicester North station to Bicester Town and upgrading the line thence to Oxford, this will enable services to be offered from London Marylebone. A new station will be constructed at Oxford Parkway.

This scheme is linked with the East-West Railway project, to restore local services between Oxford, Bletchley and beyond: the first phase is being undertaken as a combined project by Chiltern Railways and Network

---

generation signalling control system IECC Scalable, as well as operational planning software and management services.

On Track includes world class products such as TracklineTwo for track geometry measurement, with solution partners in Spain, the USA, India and Australia actively promoting these products.

On Train activity includes the train maintenance optimisation and structures consultancy, disciplines which align well with the VIEW and XVPlus products in the train maintenance market.

CH2M HILL AND HALCROW

Employee-owned CH2M HILL is one of the world's leading consulting, design, design-build, operations, and programme management companies serving government, civil, industrial and energy clients, employing over 30,000 people worldwide. Its work is concentrated in the areas of water, transportation, environmental, energy, facilities and resources.

Having operated in the UK for over 20 years, it acquired Halcrow in 2011 and now employs over 3,300 people in the UK. CH2M HILL is working on some of the most iconic infrastructure programmes including High Speed 2, and was one of the leading partners in the delivery partner for the London 2012 Olympic and Paralympic Games.

INTERFLEET TECHNOLOGY

A member of the SNC-Lavalin group of companies, Interfleet Technology is an international rail technology consultancy group. Founded in 1994, it delivers business benefits in the areas of rolling stock, railway systems and strategic railway management.

Interfleet's rolling-stock engineering expertise is established worldwide, with strength-in-depth across all areas from strategy to technical. It has significantly augmented its capabilities in rail infrastructure and train-control systems, to offer integrated cross-sector consultancy support. New capabilities in areas such as Track, Electrification & Power, the Built Environment and Signalling are being applied to several new projects, such as shaping the national delivery plan for ERTMS.

JACOBS CONSULTANCY

Jacobs is one of the world's largest and most diverse providers of technical services. Jacobs UK provides a comprehensive passenger and freight consultancy service to the rail sector covering the full spectrum of railway infrastructure requirements, from project development, preliminary appraisal and feasibility studies through to detailed design, implementation and operational management advice.

Jacobs is the sponsors' Project Representative for Crossrail, designed the new Stockley flyover for Network Rail and Crossrail, and won an engineering design framework package for phase two of High Speed 2.

LLOYD'S REGISTER

A specialist team of railway experts within the Lloyd's Register Group provides a wide range of expert advisory and assurance services to improve the safety, performance, quality and management of rail systems.

Services offered include expert advice in rolling stock, signalling systems, safety engineering, human factors, energy efficiency, project management, software testing, power systems, civil engineering and asset management; plus independent assurance; training; and conditioning monitoring systems.

MOTT MACDONALD

In its global transport business Mott MacDonald has some 3,000 professional staff from a wide range of related disciplines. It provides rail engineering consultancy services through teams based in the UK and internationally. Its technical engineering disciplines cover all aspects of railway systems and infrastructure. It also specialises in applying advanced simulation techniques.

The project portfolio includes the Channel Tunnel, West Coast route modernisation, London Underground, high-speed rail including High Speed 1, and light rapid transit in cities such as London, Birmingham, and Manchester.

A 'factory on rails' will speed up work to electrify the Great Western main line. Network Rail worked with German manufacturer Windhoff to build the High Output Plant system (HOPS) - this is the piling rig which vibrates steel piles into the ground. Network Rail

Rail. It is anticipated that Marylebone-Oxford services will commence in 2016. New services are to include spurs to Aylesbury and to Milton Keynes Central, due to start in 2017.

BORDERS RAILWAY

This project is to reinstate a 35-mile rail link from Edinburgh through Midlothian to Tweedbank in the Scottish Borders, the northern part of the Waverley route which was closed completely in January 1969. The line is to join the existing network at Newcraighall, and seven new stations are being built at Shawfair, Eskbank, Newtongrange, Gorebridge, Stow, Galashiels and Tweedbank. This is to be a mainly single track railway, with three dynamic passing loops.

In September 2011, Network Rail agreed to take on the Borders Railway project, the previous bidders having withdrawn. Around 1,000 people were at work on the project in 2013. It is intended that track work will be completed in late 2014, with 2015 as the target for opening.

The throughout journey time between Edinburgh Waverley and Tweedbank is estimated at 55 minutes. It is intended that the basic service will be hourly, half hourly at peak.

BIRMINGHAM NEW STREET

The present station is used by 140,000 passengers a day, more than twice the number for which it was designed.

The station buildings are being completely renewed. The £600m project doubles passenger capacity and delivers a hugely larger concourse, with platforms made accessible by over 30 new escalators and more then 15 public lifts. There will be a new station façade, better pedestrian links to and through the station with eight new entrances. The whole is expected to provide a major economic stimulus to the area.

The first part of the new station concourse together with two of the new entrances was opened to the public in April 2013 - the half-way stage, with completion expected in 2015.

The New Street Gateway project is funded by Network Rail, Birmingham City Council, Advantage West Midlands, Centro and the Department for Transport. The scheme is being delivered by Network Rail in partnership with Mace.

CONSULTANT FILES: SUPPORTING RAIL DEVELOPMENTS

NETWORK RAIL CONSULTING

The new international rail consultancy business, Network Rail Consulting, says it is setting out to harness the vast range of skills and experience available within Network Rail to demonstrate British expertise overseas, and be an international ambassador for Britain's rail industry. It will also wants to help channel innovation back into Network Rail's core business, helping deliver a better value railway for Britain.

It offers consultancy services across the full spectrum of Network Rail's expertise, including institutional and policy advice, strategic planning, asset management, operations and maintenance, and infrastructure projects.

NICHOLS GROUP

The Nichols Group is a UK consultancy specialising in areas including strategy, programme management and project management. Since its formation in 1975, Nichols has been involved in many transport schemes in the UK including the Docklands Light Railway and Jubilee Line Extension. The group has advised and assisted in implementing programme management and in restructuring major capital rail investment programmes, amongst them the West Coast Route Modernisation and Thameslink. Nichols is a partner in the Transcend team working in programme management for the London Crossrail project.

ONYXRAIL

Onyxrail Ltd is an independent turnkey enhancement and maintenance provider to the rail traction and rolling stock industry, providing high quality managed solutions at its own facilities or client depots, enabling a complete service at the line of route.

Project management and procurement teams, with technology partners, provide comprehensive projects delivered locally at the point of need. Onyxrail also assists higher technology OEMs with route to market services in the UK, and through its sister company provides a range of castings, forgings, fabrications and machined components.

STEER DAVIES GLEAVE

Steer Davies Gleave is a leading independent transport consultancy providing services to government, operators, regulators, promoters, financiers and other interest groups.

Expertise includes rail demand and revenue forecasting, financial modelling, rail operations & costing, rail strategy development & implementation, business case preparation, public consultation, outreach & stakeholder engagement, rail project delivery & appraisal, procurement, rail franchise bidding, specification & evaluation, performance regime design, rail pricing and fares.

VOSSLOH KIEPE UK

Vossloh Kiepe UK (formerly known as Transys Projects Limited) specialises in integration engineering and rolling stock enhancement.

Its wide range of capabiliites includes engineering, consultancy and design packages, turnkey solutions, technology enhancements, product support, refurbishment of rail vehicles, and traincare.

URS/SCOTT WILSON

URS Corporation, with its headquarters in San Francisco, is a leading provider of engineering, construction and technical services.

URS Scott Wilson offers consultancy services that cover all aspects of rail infrastructure planning, design, project management, construction supervision and asset maintenance. Specialist multi-disciplinary railway engineering skills are combined with extensive planning, environment and management expertise.

YORK EMC SERVICES

York EMC Services Ltd is an established market leader for the provision of EMC services to the railway industry.

York EMC Services offers a range of consultancy, testing and training services, specifically designed for the railway industry. The company has a solid track record of solving EMC problems and demonstrating EMC for major railway projects around the world.

INFRASTRUCTURE MAINTENANCE & RENEWAL

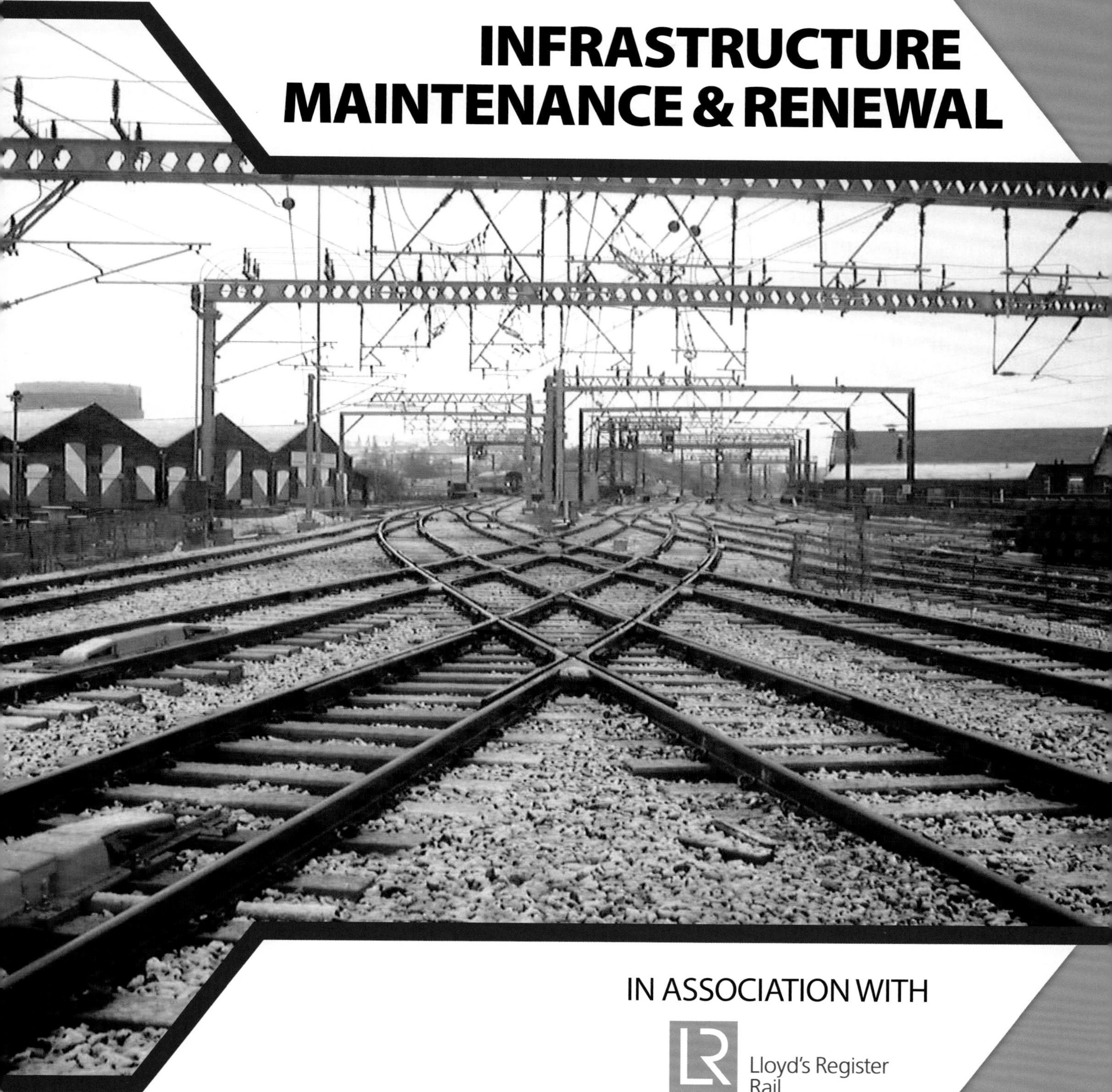

IN ASSOCIATION WITH

Lloyd's Register Rail

Crossrail - one of the first large-scale projects built and brought into use in accordance with the Interoperability specifications. As Notified Body and Assessment Body for the Central Section, Lloyd's Register will be helping to guide the project through the complex regulatory and approvals processes. 1,000 tonne tunnel-boring machine Elizabeth broke into one of Europe's largest mined caverns, 40m below Stepney Green, on 6 November 2013. Crossrail

Staying ahead of project development

It might be a mere 18 months since it first opened its doors, but Lloyd's Register's office on Derby's Pride Park is already preparing for a makeover.

A new brand identity is being rolled out across more than 200 offices world-wide to reflect how the Lloyd's Register Group, which can trace its roots back to 1760, has continued to evolve in recent years.

'The Group has experienced significant growth over the past five years, and we now support a much wider range of industries and have a much stronger emphasis on technology-led services', says Martin Giles, Managing Director of Lloyd's Register's UK rail business. 'So it was time for a refreshed identity - one that is more suited to the digital age, but still draws upon our rich heritage.' (The 'LR' portrayed in the new logo is based on the stamp first used by its surveyors in 1884 as a quality mark on steel).

And over the same five year period the UK rail business has also undergone change, including the move to its new flagship office in 2012 that provided a much larger base from which to grow its technical service teams.

LEADING THE WAY IN INDEPENDENT ASSURANCE

Of course the Lloyd's Register name is synonymous with assurance, and of late has been leading the way in the rail sector, securing key roles on projects such as Crossrail, Thameslink and the Great Western Integrated Programme, as well as further afield on Etihad Rail, the Guangzhou-Hong Kong rail link and Danish rail network's conversion to ERTMS.

Martin attributes this success to Lloyd's Register's 'pragmatic' approach to assurance.

'There are two or three ways of working as a Third Party: sit back and wait for the project's suppliers and system developers to complete their work before we start, or stick by our belief that by joining a project from the outset we can actually help reduce overall costs and prevent costly delays at later stages'.

'Ultimately, all a project manager wants is to complete the acceptance or certification process as efficiently as possible. Our philosophy helps because we stay ahead of the project's development, explaining where and why a certain aspect will not achieve acceptance. We're not a "box-ticking" organisation - we won't turn up and just say "that's not acceptable" - and this is extremely valuable for clients, particularly if going through the process for the first time'.

Crossrail is a case in point, as it is one of the first large-scale projects in the UK to be built and brought into use in accordance with the Interoperability specifications. As the Notified Body and Assessment Body for the Central Section, Lloyd's Register will be helping to guide the project through the complex regulatory and approvals processes by playing a 'pathfinder' role and advising on the extent to which regulations - both existing and emerging - apply.

INDUSTRY WITH A REKINDLED APPETITE FOR INNOVATION

Though renowned for assurance, it is the technical consultancy services that have experienced the strongest growth since the move to DE24.

'The rail industry has rediscovered its appetite for new ideas, and in particular for ways to operate more efficiently. We are seeing increased demand for innovation across every aspect of a railway, from traction technologies and in-cab train control, to predictive maintenance, asset management and infrastructure monitoring. These are technical areas in which we have a lot of specialist expertise to offer'.

Indeed, recent projects, such as the design of a new biomass freight wagon for Drax Power station, the largest of its kind, demonstrates just how far Lloyd's Register's services now extend beyond the assurance roles it is traditionally known for.

AN ORGANISATION WITH A CLEAR PURPOSE

As part of the Lloyd's Register Group, the rail business is ultimately owned by the Lloyd's Register Foundation, a charity that supports engineering-related education programmes, including the UK's National Skills Academy for Railway Engineering (NSARE). This, believes Martin, is key to its overall longevity.

'We've got an important ethos within Lloyd's Register which is 'do something that matters' and that's very important to our staff. We are a home for people who, by nature, want to continually improve things, and our independent status means our experts are free to be absolutely impartial in the advice they give.

'And the more successful we are, the more our Foundation can support the development of skills and technologies in the railway,' says Martin, 'and that is important to all our staff'.

'Challenging but achievable' five years

The Office of Rail Regulation's (ORR's) Periodic Review 2013 (PR13) determines the outputs ORR expects Network Rail to deliver, the income the company will receive and the incentives it will face, for the five years of Control Period 5 (CP5), which runs from 1 April 2014 to 31 March 2019.

Network Rail's revenue comes from access charges which are paid by train operators to use its track and stations. Income is also received direct from governments, as network grants, in lieu of access charges. The company also gets income from other sources such as property. In the PR13 decisions ORR assumes around 30% of revenue will be from access charges, 60% from network grant and 10% from other sources.

An important part of the process involves the Secretary of State for Transport (for England & Wales) and the Scottish Ministers providing ORR with their requirements in terms of high level output specifications (HLOSs) and statements of funds available (SoFAs). They published these in summer 2012.

The final determination published in October 2013 sets out ORR's conclusions on PR13. It considers that the determination is challenging but achievable for Network Rail in terms of efficiency, value for money and deliverability. ORR says it should also improve safety and it takes account of long-term needs as well as the short-term – that is to say, it is sustainable. ORR also believes it incentivises Network Rail to efficiently manage costs it can control and provides appropriate protections against risk.

The starting point for the package is the outputs the company is required to deliver. Network Rail must continue to meet its legal safety obligations, improving safety where reasonably practicable. The determination makes specific provision to address significant safety risks, with extra funding to reduce the risk at level crossings, for example by enabling the closure of more crossings. There will be new funding to improve the safety of those working with high voltage electricity on the railway, and more funding for civils assets to improve their condition and to reduce the risk from failures of earthworks, bridges and other structures. Maintenance efficiency savings will be phased in to give Network Rail more time to introduce new ways of working.

There will be a major programme of improvement works with existing projects such as Crossrail, the Edinburgh-Glasgow improvement programme (EGIP) and Thameslink completed, the completion of new projects such as the electrification of the Welsh Valley Lines and the expansion of the Northern Hub programme centred on Manchester.

Although passenger and freight demand will be growing, Network Rail should deliver this programme while ensuring that 92.5% of trains arrive on time nationally by 2019 (as measured using the Public Performance Measure), compared to 90.7% today. It will also reduce disruption to passengers (by 8%) and freight customers (by 17%) from engineering works over the control period, despite the major enhancements programme.

ORR has also set outputs for Network Rail's asset management – its management of the network infrastructure. This is fundamental to the company's ability to improve performance and efficiency, to ensure the longer term sustainability of its assets and deliver its outputs in CP5 and beyond.

There will be new outputs for the quality of asset data, outputs to improve asset management capability, and for the delivery of the ORBIS (Offering Rail Better Information Services) programme which will increase the effectiveness with which Network Rail deploys its asset knowledge to make decisions.

In addition to the regulated outputs, ORR will also be expecting Network Rail to improve its

Keltbray successfully completed the first phase of the main demolition work at London Bridge station in August 2013 - part of Keltbray's £25 million contract for Costain and Network Rail, helping to create an improved and more spacious station as part of the Thameslink Programme. Keltbray

approach to the environment, both to reduce its own impact on the environment and to improve the resilience of the network to climate change.

ORR says it will be monitoring indicators such as asset condition and asset performance, that give early warning of possible problems in the future, and more of this monitoring will be at the Network Rail route level which will make it clear how well different parts of the network are performing. ORR will also monitor progress on 'enablers', which measure how Network Rail is building its long term capability in areas such as managing capital programmes. All data on indicators and enablers will be published with comment on trends in ORR's Network Rail Monitor.

NETWORK RAIL ORGANISATION

Network Rail's operation of the railway is organised by ten geographic zones or 'Routes' under a structure first implemented in May 2004. They cover Anglia, East Midlands, Kent, London North Eastern, London North Western, Scotland, Sussex, Wales, Wessex, and Western.

Each route managing director in effect runs their own infrastructure railway business with significant annual turnover and resources, with a supporting centre to help make the most of economies of scale. 'The railway still needs to be planned and operated as a network which operates seamlessly. And we must maintain the company's focus on efficient and effective management of long-life railway assets,' said Network Rail Chief Executive, Sir David Higgins.

The route managing directors have responsibility for issues including safety; all customer service matters; asset management outputs and spend; operations; planning and delivering maintenance; and delivery of some renewals and enhancements.

In a further initiative, Network Rail began discussions with several train operating companies about new ways of working ever closer - 'alliances' taking different forms depending on the kind of railway in each area and the views of the operator.

A deep alliance with South West Trains (SWT) goes further than other arrangements, enabled by a strong geographic overlap between the Network Rail management unit and the train operator. An alliance governance board has representatives from both SWT and Network Rail, and SWT's Managing Director is also MD of the alliance team. Train and infrastructure operations answer to one boss.

A new National Centre in Milton Keynes unites many of Network Rail's national teams and functions under one roof to support the new, more powerful business units.

INFRASTRUCTURE PROJECTS

Network Rail has also moved to a new, commercially focused, regionally based projects delivery business – Network Rail Infrastructure Projects – with four regional Directors and three programme Directors responsible for delivery of major renewal and enhancement work in their area. They manage their own profit and loss and will be charged with winning work under a proposed new competitive structure.

There is also a focus on developing the client capability within Network Rail to clearly define project outputs and work with delivery organisations much earlier in the project lifecycle. These changes should enable improved specification of output requirements, better integration of these into route plans, and greater discipline in the interface with the delivery team. This in turn should help to facilitate greater innovation, including through earlier engagement with the supply chain and through improved project-based partnerships with customers.

Where appropriate, says Network Rail, it will invite other organisations to tender for work in competition with Infrastructure Projects, enabling benchmarking of capital project delivery.

Network Rail Consulting was established in 2012, aimed at bringing further skills into the company, with further opportunities to benchmark against market competitors.

ASSET MANAGEMENT SAVINGS

Network Rail plans a series of changes in asset policies to improve the value for money of the railway in Control Period 5:

- Track - less complete renewal, more refurbishment, more preventative maintenance and more track treated for an overall reduction in whole life cost and spend in CP5.
- Signalling - targeted approach to renewal rather than full resignalling; integration of the renewal work bank with operating strategy and the European Rail Traffic Management System.
- Telecoms - more effective obsolescence management and technology change; greater use of partial renewal intervention where appropriate.
- Electrical Power & Fixed Plant - prioritised based on condition and criticality in terms of impact on service outputs.
- Drainage - improved drainage asset condition on high criticality routes, maintained condition elsewhere and contribution to improved track quality with

Network Rail has been installing over 100 miles of new lineside fencing between Rugby and London Euston as part of a package of projects worth nearly £40m, aimed at improving the reliability of the infrastructure and punctuality of train services on the West Coast main line. Network Rail

consequent reduction in delay minutes; improvements in overall track quality by reduced track maintenance interventions and savings in abortive renewal costs; reduced flooding leading to improved safety and reduced delay minutes.

- Buildings - the ability to target the required CP5 performance outcomes - less spend on major station train sheds, buildings and platforms and more spend on canopies; key assets are managed in a sustainable manner, maintaining long term condition and thereby securing the long term functionality of the asset.
- Structures - improved consistency in managing bridge strength & critical condition risks; increased emphasis on maintenance and minor works.

INFRASTRUCTURE CONTRACTORS

While Network Rail carries out the bulk of maintenance work in-house, it has relied on contractors for track renewals and infrastructure projects work, and work on stations and structures, and aims to reinvigorate relationships with suppliers for Control Period 5. Some of the main contractors are featured below.

AMEY

Amey's rail sector services include design, advisory and inspection services in signalling, electrification and power, track and civil engineering structures, as well as installation, renewals and enhancements services. Amey is part of Ferrovial, the major European services and construction group.

In 2012 Amey won a £700m contract for electrification of the Great Western main line. The contract covers Maidenhead to Bristol and Cardiff, Newbury and Oxford.

Working with partner Colas, Amey brings together planning, design and operations skills for track renewals and fulfilled Network Rail's CP4 High Output Track Renewals contract.

Amey was awarded responsibility for Network Rail's Civil Examination Framework Agreement throughout the network, worth about £250m over five years - making it the largest provider of consultancy services to Network Rail. Amey also has specialist skills in customer information, telecoms and security.

BABCOCK RAIL

Babcock Rail - formerly First Engineering - is a leading player in the UK rail infrastructure market and the largest conventional track renewals company in CP4.

It carries out a wide of range of rail infrastructure work, including track renewal, power and signalling contracts throughout Great Britain.

In the Network Rail Partnership Awards 2013, Babcock was highly commended for development of the Network Rail Advanced Apprenticeship Scheme, while Babcock and ScotRail were highly commended for the electrification of the Paisley Canal line, in a groundbreaking alliance.

A joint venture of Babcock, Costain and Alstom, formed to bid for major electrification projects, was awarded a £48m contract with Network Rail in 2013 for phase three of the West Coast power supply upgrade.

Track renewal as part of the £282million investment programme in the Doncaster-Lincoln-Peterborough route is being carried out by an alliance of Babcock and Carillion.

BALFOUR BEATTY

Balfour Beatty Rail provides rail infrastructure services across the life-cycle of rail assets, from feasibility studies and planning, design and implementation to maintenance and asset management globally.

Innovative 'Mission Room' technology adopted by the company was awarded the 2013 Safety Award at the Network Rail Partnership Awards - providing virtual access to sites, it significantly reduces the need for costly and hazardous site visits.

Track Partnership, a collaboration with London Underground and Balfour Beatty, has successfully launched the first new sleeper on the Underground in 30 years - a high quality sleeper, produced by Cemex Rail Solutions which provides improved reliability, greater longevity and offers faster installation.

Network Rail awarded Balfour Beatty a design and build contract to replace the existing overhead wire electrification equipment for 1.7km near St. Pancras (Low Level) station with a reduced depth conductor beam in 2013.

A contract in excess of £130 million to build two miles of the Crossrail route and Abbey Wood station was awarded to Balfour Beatty in 2013, following involvement in the design phase for which Balfour Beatty was awarded BS11000 certification for collaborative working.

Work on the £47m scheme to remove a major bottleneck at Hitchin was completed in June 2013. The new flyover carries trains towards Cambridge, which previously had to leave the East Coast main line on a flat junction. Network Rail

Network Rail also awarded a contract to Balfour Beatty for the upgrade for Crossrail of a 12 mile section between West Drayton and Maidenhead.

Network Rail awarded Balfour Beatty the £50m North West Electrification Phase 2 contract, and Balfour Beatty will deliver the track remodelling for the London Bridge area as part of the Thameslink programme, a contract also worth circa £50m.

BAM NUTTALL

BAM Nuttall is Network Rail's main contractor for the delivery of the new Borders Railway. The £220m contract includes detailed design and construction works.

BAM Nuttall also won the Network Rail civils contract to build a dive under at Acton freight yard in Ealing for Crossrail. It was also involved in enabling works for the 2012 Olympics, and was responsible for Civil and M&E works in the upgrade of Neasden depot, the largest depot on the London Underground network.

CARILLION

Carillion plc is one of the UK's leading support services and construction companies, employing around 40,000 people.

A Network Rail investment programme got under way in 2013 to reduce delays caused by overhead line failures on the busiest section of the West Coast main line. The £7.6m package is being delivered by a specialist team of engineers from Network Rail, SPL Powerlines UK and ABC (Alstom, Babcock, Costain). Network Rail

The contract for track work for the upgrade of Reading station and the surrounding railway, worth in the region of £20m, was awarded to Carillion. Network Rail also awarded Carillion the contract to carry out a £43m expansion of Peterborough station.

Network Rail in 2013 awarded Carillion the contract to electrify the Cumbernauld-Glasgow Queen Street line. The £40m contract will see over 50km of railway electrified.

Bombardier Transportation and Carillion have launched a new UK joint venture, named Infrasig. It combines Bombardier technology for both conventional and ETCS signalling solutions, with the UK rail experience of Carillion to deliver signalling and multi-disciplinary projects.

Carillion started work in 2012 on the Stockley viaduct project in west London to allow Crossrail services to operate to and from Heathrow. Carillion has also been awarded contracts by Network Rail for Crossrail West Inner Track Improvements, and Crossrail Old Oak Common / Paddington Approaches / Intercity Express Programme work - together worth some £122 million.

Carillion's £120m Key Output 2 contract for Thameslink involves fitting out of twin 650 metre tunnels underneath the Regents Canal and connecting the East Coast main line to Thameslink.

Network Rail awarded Carillion a £15.6m contract to replace Loughor viaduct between Swansea and Gowerton, completed in 2013.

Carillion has opened a training centre, for rail engineers to develop skills needed to help deliver a £2 billion electrification expansion programme by Network Rail - part of a network of centres operated under a co-operation agreement between Carillion Rail and SPL Powerlines.

COLAS RAIL

Colas Rail Ltd was created in May 2007 after Amec Spie Rail was taken over by the French infrastructure company Colas, part of the Bouygues group.

Colas Rail combines the engineering skills of specialist businesses to provide total solutions in all aspects of railway infrastructure, from high speed rail systems to light and urban rail. It is also active in freight train operation (see 'Freight and Haulage' section).

The AmeyColas joint venture commenced work under the Network Rail's new high output track renewals contract in 2010 and also delivers conventional track renewals.

Colas Rail and UK Power Networks Services (UKPN Services) are combining their core skills and expertise to deliver a total rail electrification solution to meet the forthcoming programme of infrastructure enhancement.

Colas's on-track plant fleet includes 14 principal S&C machines, which with additional compact and plain line machines provide Colas with what it believes to be the largest most advanced on-track plant fleet in the UK.

Colas runs an extensive suite of courses for personnel who work on Network Rail infrastructure, including track safety and permanent way, electrification, safety training, and railway operations.

A new division, Colas Rail Europe, was formed in 2011, incorporating all Colas Rail businesses across Europe (excluding France) with the purpose of exploring new opportunities.

COSTAIN

Costain will carry out the station redevelopment at London Bridge as part of the congestion-busting Thameslink programme, a contract worth circa £400m.

Costain, in the ATC joint venture with Alstom and TSO, has been awarded a contract worth approximately £300m to design, fit-out and commission the railway systems in Crossrail's tunnel network. Under the contract, ATC will design and install track, overhead lines and mechanical and electrical equipment to fit out the 21km of twin tunnels currently being bored under the streets of London.

The fit-out works start in 2014, and will be carried out within the entire tunnelled and surface sections of the Crossrail route between Royal Oak, Pudding Mill Lane and Plumstead portals.

Costain, in Joint Venture with Alstom, was also awarded the £15m contract for the design, construction and commissioning of the system that will provide traction power for the trains in the central tunnelled section of the Crossrail scheme.

The Costain Skanska joint venture (CSJV) won Crossrail's first 'Whole Project Award' under the CEEQUAL sustainability in civil engineering award scheme for the Royal Oak Portal contract in west London. CSJV also won a contract to provide intermediate tunnel shafts for Crossrail.

A Costain/Hochtief joint venture is principal contractor for the station work as part of Network Rail's Reading remodelling.

The Costain Laing O'Rourke joint venture won the Sustainable Excellence title at the 2013 Network Rail Partnership Awards for its work to bring the Grade II-listed Farringdon station up to modern standards and prepare it for current and future expansion.

Among the sustainability aspects noted by the judges were: diversion of 100% of waste from landfill; high recycled content of steel and concrete; a 700 sq m 'living roof' on the new integrated booking hall to provide foraging grounds for black redstarts; and sensitive handling of heritage considerations.

Costain, as part of the ABC Electrification Joint Venture with Alstom and Babcock, has also started work on the collaborative delivery of Phase Three of Network Rail's West Coast Power Supply Upgrade.

SPENCER

Spencer Rail Infrastructure provides quality multi-disciplinary engineering services to the UK and international markets - supporting and enhancing the operational infrastructure of heavy rail and light rail networks.

Recent projects include the design, construction and fit out of a new modular design building to house the Thames Valley Signalling Centre; a £30m project to extend station platforms on South West Trains routes; the design and build of an architecturally award winning station at St Helens Central; and design and construction of a major new rail depot facility on behalf of East Midlands Trains.

VOLKERRAIL

VolkerRail, part of the Netherlands-based Volker Wessels group, is a comprehensive multi-disciplinary rail infrastructure contractor. Capabilities include design, manufacture and construction; life time maintenance and asset inspection management; heavy rail rigid and ballasted track systems; light rail on-street track systems; signalling design, installation and testing; electrification, overhead line and line side civil engineering works; and high and low voltage power distribution systems.

The overall railway capability is enhanced by the plant and welding division, and the fleet of on-track plant consists of beaver lightweight, On Track Machines and S&C tampers, Kirow rail mounted cranes, ballast regulators, rail mounted excavators, mobile work platforms, Colmar lifting machines, an array of rail mounted support and inspection vehicles, and specialist welding equipment including flash butt and gauge corner restoration.

VolkerRail, as part of the M-Pact Thales consortium with Laing O'Rourke and Thales UK, was awarded contracts to provide Manchester Metrolink Phase 3a and 3b extensions.

Network Rail has awarded VolkerRail a £15.5m contract to remodel Acton yard, including a diveunder, as part of the Crossrail programme.

VolkerRail has also won a contract for Phase 1 of the Sheffield Supertram rail replacement work, and is part of the Staffordshire Alliance carrying out the Stafford Area Improvements Programme. In 2013 it successfully completed the rail systems element of the Hitchin Grade Separation Project.

Sister company VolkerFitzpatrick is carrying out a Network Rail contract for a major enhancement of Gatwick Airport station, which includes the implementation of a new platform, as well as layout changes designed to increase the flexibility of operation.

Stabilisation works on Hessle foreshore were carried out for Network Rail in 2013 by Construction Marine Ltd. A First TransPennine Express train from Hull passes the work in July 2013. Network Rail

SIGNALLING AND CONTROL

IN ASSOCIATION WITH

SIEMENS

SIEMENS

SIEMENS RAIL AUTOMATION

In May 2013, Siemens completed the acquisition of Invensys Rail, incorporating the company into its worldwide Rail Automation organisation. As a business unit within the Siemens Mobility and Logistics division, Siemens Rail Automation is a global leader in the design, installation and commissioning of track-side and train-borne signalling and train control solutions. Its portfolio includes train control, computer-based interlockings, operations control systems, components, track vacancy detection, level-crossing protection, rail communications and cargo automation for both passenger and freight rail operators.

Siemens Rail Automation employs over 9,500 people worldwide, 1,300 of whom operate from a network of offices across the UK - in Chippenham, London, Croydon, Poole, Birmingham, Ashby-de-la-Zouch, York and Glasgow - delivering both main line and mass transit programmes.

For 170 years, the company has been at the heart of many of the world's major rail networks, and continues to successfully deliver some of the UK's largest transport infrastructure projects. With proven technologies and a successful track record in the delivery of large scale, complex programmes it is currently working on the Thameslink, Crossrail and Reading schemes, having recently commissioned the Walsall and Crewe-Shrewsbury projects, as well as the nine-year Victoria Line Upgrade programme for London Underground.

The Thameslink programme is one of Britain's largest ever resignalling projects. Scheduled for completion in December 2018, the core requirement of the project is to deliver a state of the art, high volume, high-capacity railway through the City of London - within the constraints of Victorian infrastructure.

Siemens commissioned the final phase of Thameslink Key Output 1 in 2012, with a conventionally signalled railway now operating through the Thameslink Core Area, providing a capacity of up to 20 trains per hour. Having moved on to Thameslink Key Output 2, the scope of the company's work now includes the detailed design, installation, testing and commissioning of signalling and telecoms systems for the remodelled London Bridge Station and the outlining areas. The programme includes the introduction of a European Train Control System (ETCS) solution, which will be overlaid in the London Bridge area to enable all train movements to be controlled automatically, delivering 24 trains per hour in each direction on the Thameslink core route at the programme's completion.

At the same time, the company is also delivering signalling and train control solutions for the core Crossrail area and for the integration with Network Rail infrastructure at its fringes. Providing 21 kilometres of new railway under the city of London, Crossrail will deliver up to 24 trains per hour in the core central section area during the peak, with 200 million passengers annually using the Crossrail service.

The signalling programme will see the implementation of a Communications-Based Train Control (CBTC) solution, as well as integration with Network Rail's European Rail Traffic Management System (ERTMS). This will enable Crossrail trains to travel on both the new central section and the existing rail network. Final commissioning of this six-year project is scheduled to take place in 2018.

In 2012, Siemens commissioned the final asset replacement stage of the Victoria Line Upgrade programme. This marked the completion of a challenging nine-year programme, which saw the replacement of all the Victoria Line's rolling stock and signalling and provided a '33 trains per hour' service. The project represented a first for London Underground in that it required migration from one Automatic Train Operation system to another, with Siemens' Distance to Go-Radio trackside equipment being overlaid on to the legacy signalling system.

Throughout the project, the Victoria Line remained operational during the day, limiting disruption to passengers and ensuring a smooth transition from the legacy to the new system. The programme has delivered significantly improved capacity, performance and reliability for London Underground and its passengers. ■

Siemens Rail Automation's modular signalling system has been installed on the Crewe to Shrewsbury route.

Communications technology has progressively extended the length of railway that can be operated by a single signaller. This is Stockport Edgeley signalling centre, with Ansaldo equipment. Network Rail

SIGNALLING
Major technology challenges ahead

A SERIES OF NEW SIGNALLING AND CONTROL SYSTEMS IS DUE TO BE INTRODUCED ON BRITAIN'S RAILWAYS IN JUST A FEW YEARS, WRITES ROGER FORD, INDUSTRY & TECHNOLOGY EDITOR OF *MODERN RAILWAYS*.

Signalling and control of railways in the UK is at the start of the biggest technical change since the introduction of Solid State Signalling (SSI) and the Integrated Electronic Control Centres (IECCs) 25 years ago. It contrasts with the decade following privatisation which saw a combination of over-optimism and technical naïveté when it came to signalling.

This resulted in a number of expensive and abortive schemes, including moving block signalling and a new control centre for the West Coast main line. A drive to replace the pioneering British developed solid-state interlocking (SSIs) with later European Computer Based Interlockings on the main line network was ultimately unsuccessful.

Network Rail is now installing the latest generation SSI architecture running on modern hardware platforms from Siemens (formerly Invensys) and Signalling Solutions Ltd (SSL - Alstom/Balfour Beatty joint venture). Technical stability has been restored to signalling's primary role of vital safety and innovation is focusing on meeting the commercial, operational and financial needs of the railway.

COST

Ever since Beeching, lightly used lines have been under pressure to reduce costs. As with the rest of the railway, regional routes are enjoying steady growth in ridership, but railway reviews, such as that by Sir Roy McNulty, continue to highlight their disproportionate subsidy per passenger mile.

Cutting the cost of the infrastructure remains essential, and signalling technology is already playing a major role – both in terms of savings on the cost of renewals and also subsequent operation. Network Rail commissioned its two Modular Signalling (ModSig) pilot schemes in 2013, and during 2014 will be evaluating the operational performance and assessing whether the cost target are being met.

Signalling projects are evaluated in terms of cost per Signalling Equivalent Unit (SEU). An SEU is a single item of equipment, such as a signal or point-head. When ModSig was launched, the cost per SEU for main line signalling schemes was around £200,000, and the aim was to reduce this to £150,000.

Initial reports suggests that this target had been achieved on the pilot schemes. As further schemes roll out, Network Rail is looking for further reductions to around £125,000/SEU. Note that the interlockings used on these schemes are 'ready for ETCS' (European Train Control System), with the prospect of further cost reductions.

ModSig exploits Network Rail's Fixed Telephone Network (FTN) to control local signalling from a remote centre. SSL's Ely-Norwich schemes is controlled from Cambridge signalling centre, while Siemens' Crewe-Shrewsbury resignalling is controlled from Cardiff.

Other elements of ModSig include lightweight, low energy, LED signals, containerised units housing all the power supplies, communications interfaces and other systems required for each location, and pre-wired and tested components which can simply be plug connected after delivery to site.

CROSSINGS

ModSig uses the new MCB-OD (Manually Controlled Barrier with Obstacle Detection) level crossing. This replaces signallers checking that the road is clear using CCTV.

MCB-OD uses radar and lasers to scan the crossing to ensure that it is clear of obstacles during and after closure. MCB-OD is not limited to ModSig, and is currently being rolled out across the network.

RAIL OPERATING CENTRE LOCATIONS

EXISTING LOCATIONS

1	Derby
2	Gillingham
3	Cardiff
4	Edinburgh
5	Didcot
6	Glasgow

NEW BUILDINGS

7	Romford
8	Three Bridges
9	York
10	Manchester
11	Rugby
12	Basingstoke

CHANGE TO ROC NOT NOW PLANNED

- Ashford IECC
- West Midlands signalling centre (Saltley)

CONTROL

Communications technology has progressively extended the length of railway that can be operated by a single signaller. The length of route that the original lever-operated mechanical signalboxes could control was determined by the strength of the signallers and the length of wire and rodding they could move.

Power signalboxes followed, with colour light signals and point motors over a wide area controlled by switches on the track diagram. The 1990s in Britain saw the arrival of the (Integrated Electronic Control Centre) with signallers seated at workstations setting routes on visual display screens using a tracker ball or mouse.

Now Network Rail is taking the IECC concept to the next stage to exploit the cost saving made possible by FTN and other technical developments. There are currently 800 signalling locations, and over the next 30 years, control of most of the railway will be transferred to just 12 Rail Operating Centres. About 80% of the change will have been completed by 2029. Network Rail says a review of the business case means that Ashford IECC and West Midlands Signalling Centre will now not become ROCs.

Control of power on electrified lines will also be concentrated using modern SCADA (supervisory control and data acquisition) remote control systems. The Manchester ROC will control the AC-electrified network, with Three Bridges responsible for the 750V DC network south of the Thames

Network Rail expects that the ROCs will reduced the disruption due to reactionary delays, by faster recovery after service disruption. More reliable performance and better train regulation should also allow more trains to be run.

SMART TRAIN CONTROL

Central to reducing the operator workload in the IECC was Automatic Route Setting (ARS). This name understates the capabilities of what, from its inception, has been an intelligent traffic management system running advanced decision-making strategies to ensure that optimal routing decisions can be made, even under disrupted conditions.

Starting with the Liverpool Street IECC in 1989, ARS is now running at 13 installations on Network Rail setting over 150,000 routes a day.

To support the ROC concept, Network Rail is procuring a new Traffic Management System (TMS). Features will include real time planning, prediction and resolution of pathing conflicts. This will see train graphs introduced as a regulation tool in the UK for the first time.

Contracts, with a combined value of £20 million have been awarded to Signalling Solutions Ltd, Hitachi Rail Europe and Thales UK to develop prototype software. All three companies had demonstrations, based on the Leeds network, running during 2013.

Production contracts will follow the three-month evaluation of the individual demonstrators which was completed during 2013. TMS is scheduled to start rolling out across the network starting in 2014.

ETCS

Signalling itself provides the greatest technical challenge for Network Rail and train operators in the form of the European Train Control System (ETCS). Network Rail is committed to progressively introducing ETCS Level 2 across the network as existing signalling is renewed.

ETCS Level 2 provides cab signalling, replacing lineside signals. Local interlockings are connected to the Radio Block Centre (RBC). The train's location is determined by balises, or transponders mounted on the track.

Interlockings are monitored by the RBC which generates

Network Rail completed a £100m project to remodel and resignal Nottingham station and its approaches in August 2013, including this new platform. The whole Nottingham area is now controlled by one Alstom Smartlock interlocking at East Midlands Control Centre, Derby. Network Rail

movement authority messages. A message is sent to a train when the route has been set, all locking is in place and the conditions for the train movement have been satisfied.

A screen in the train cab displays the distance that the train has permission to travel plus the maximum speed. It also shows the braking point if the train will be required to slow or come to a halt. If the train is not braked, ETCS intervenes, providing Automatic Train Protection.

INSTALLATION

Network Rail is planning to introduce ETCS progressively, starting with the Great Western main line (GWML) from 2016. An incremental policy has been adopted because of the wide variety of traction and rolling stock using the route.

First, signalling on the GWML will be replaced with SSI and conventional colour light signals. This will then be overlaid with ETCS. The first trains to run under ETCS will be the new IEP fleet of Hitachi Super Express Trains which will be supplied with ETCS equipment already fitted. In 2015 when all trains on the route have ETCS, the signals will be removed.

A similar 'overlay' approach is planned for the Thameslink central core between St Pancras and London Bridge. Starting with colour light signals, ETCS will then be overlaid, giving drivers the benefit of cab signalling.

But human factors analysis suggest that at the planned frequency of 24 trains/hr Automatic Train Operation (ATO) will be necessary for reliable running. As a result, when ETCS is operational, there will be a further overlay of ATO, the first application of ETCS in this mode.

Crossrail, the new east-west cross-London tunnelled railway, has adopted a different philosophy. As with Thameslink, trains will enter the tunnel from conventionally-signalled routes, including ETCS on the GWML. To reduce the risk associated with ETCS, Crossrail engineers have decided to use a proven metro-style radio Communications Based Train Control (CBTC) system with ATO for the 13-mile tunnel itself. The system will be supplied by Siemens.

At each end, trains will switch between systems 'on the fly'. Thus a Crossrail train approaching the western tunnel portal outside Paddington and running under ETCS Level 2 will switch automatically to the Siemens CBTC. Managing this interface is part of the Siemens contract.

ECML CHALLENGE

Next in the Network Rail programme will he the southern end of the East Coast main line between Kings Cross and Doncaster, starting in 2018. This will be the first part of the network to be fitted with ETCS as a direct replacement for conventional colour light signalling. When installation is completed, all trains using the route will have to be ETCS-fitted.

While the new Hitachi Super Express trains for East Coast will be supplied ready equipped, existing passenger and freight cabs will need to be retrofitted with ETCS. This is likely to be the biggest technical challenge. Apart from the difficulties of interfacing new electronics equipment with the traction and braking systems of existing locomotives and trains, there are already concerns about the availability of contractors to carry out the work.

Meanwhile Network Rail has established the European Rail Traffic Management System (ERTMS) National Integration Facility (ENIF) on the Hertford North loop line. (ERTMS consists of ETCS and GSM-R, the GSM mobile communications standard for railway operations). Class-313 EMU No 313121 has been converted to a laboratory train and is now being used to check the compatibility of different makes of trainborne and track-mounted systems and equipment. ■

Hitachi's onboard ETCS (European Train Control System) solution successfully connected to the Network Rail Cambrian Line signalling system, and achieved ETCS Level 2 operation, during trials in 2013. Locomotive No 97301 locomotive was successfully retro-fitted with the Hitachi onboard system to prove interoperability with other systems currently in use. Hitachi

The ETCS National Integration Facility (ENIF) at Hitchin utilises a five-mile stretch of the down line on the Hertford Loop. Network Rail

ETCS TESTING PROGRESS

Network Rail says its testing programme for cab signalling has enjoyed a successful start, and entered its second phase at the test centre in Hitchin in autumn 2013.

The European Rail Traffic Management System and its signalling component ETCS (European Train Control System) will form the basis of future signalling schemes on the network.

Starting with an overlay on the Great Western main line in CP5 and the southern end of the East Coast main line in CP6, ETCS will revolutionise the way trains are run in Britain; bringing new levels of control, capacity, efficiency, economy and safety.

Network Rail's client Simon Whitehorn said: 'ETCS will have a huge impact on the railway and it's vital we thoroughly test our equipment to get it right first time. Testing has gone very well and even in the first few days we were able to get the the cab and trackside equipment communicating and complete the planned tests.

'The kit on the train is supplied by SSL, and therefore it was their trackside equipment that was first in line for testing. That has been completed successfully and we're now in the process of testing Infrasig's equipment.

'Switching the test facility on was a big moment for the team and it's a big step towards eventually rolling cab signalling out across the country.'

The ETCS National Integration Facility (ENIF) at Hitchin utilises a five-mile stretch of the down line on the Hertford Loop between Molewood tunnel and Langley South junction, controlled from a new structure in the former Hitchin goods yard. The test facility will be used by Network Rail for 18 months to examine four suppliers' trackside ETCS equipment, using a converted Class 313 laboratory train.

Siemens and Ansaldo's trackside equipment will follow in the testing programme, and Network Rail's work at Hitchin will continue until the track and train are handed over to the Thameslink programme. This will allow them to test systems in advance of equipping the line from St Pancras to Blackfriars with ETCS and automatic train operation.

ETCS provides train drivers with a target speed, including movement authority, on a screen in the cab. The train 'knows' where it is through a combination of trackside equipment and on-board sensors, while instructions from the control centre are conveyed through the GSM-R (Global System for Mobile - Railway) signal.

By signalling each train according to its braking and accelerating capabilities, it will allow more capacity to be squeezed out of the current network, and also bringing considerable cost savings over traditional lineside resignalling schemes.

Signalling on the Hertford Loop is controlled from a new WestCAD workstation at King's Cross power signalbox, with control of the test track switching to ENIF at Hitchin with the turn of a key.

SIGNALLING RENEWALS AND ENHANCEMENTS

Network Rail awarded framework agreements of up to seven years in 2012, to deliver railway signalling projects worth approximately £1.5bn. This is part of wider reforms to its infrastructure business, says Network Rail, with a greater focus on partnership with suppliers and a restructuring of the way the company delivers capital projects.

The frameworks, which cover the majority of signalling renewals and enhancements across England, Scotland and Wales, were awarded to:

- Siemens Rail Automation (formerly Invensys Rail,
- Signalling Solutions,
- Atkins.

The framework agreements form the backbone of a programme to modernise and maintain safety-critical railway signalling systems and are designed to deliver efficiency savings across the company's signalling work bank over the next seven years, through further reductions in unit costs.

Simon Kirby, Network Rail managing director, infrastructure

ROUTE-BASED SIGNALLING FRAMEWORK AGREEMENTS

FRAMEWORK AREA	PRIMARY CONTRACTOR	SECONDARY CONTRACTOR
Scotland	Siemens	SSL
Central (west)	Siemens	SSL
Central (east)	SSL	Siemens
Wales & West	Siemens	SSL
Great Western (inner)	SSL	Siemens
Great Western (outer)	SSL	Siemens
Anglia & Kent	Atkins	SSL
Sussex & Wessex	Atkins	Siemens

The converted Class 313 electric multiple-unit which is the laboratory train for the ETCS National Integration Facility. Network Rail projects, said: 'These new frameworks represent a seven-year commitment by suppliers, allowing us to work closely with them to develop long-term plans for work to be carried out more quickly and efficiently. The length of the agreements, coupled with a visible workload, will provide much-needed stability throughout the supply chain and drive further cost savings and innovation across our signalling renewals and enhancements activities.'

In line with Network Rail's new approach to supplier engagement, the frameworks incorporate collaborative working in order to deliver the necessary efficiencies. Integrated design teams and a reduction in man-marking will remove costly duplication of effort, while smoothing of peaks and troughs in Network Rail's work bank will allow better use of suppliers' resources.

The frameworks appoint both a primary and secondary supplier for each area. This provides the flexibility needed to meet the significant increase in volumes required over the life of the framework and provides an alternative in each area if the primary supplier does not have the capacity. The agreements also provide the option to competitively tender up to 20pc of the predicted workload each year.

EARS UPS PPM

DeltaRail has announced that its Enhanced Automatic Route Setting (EARS) system has attained Network Rail approval, with the process taking just 14 weeks. Delta Rail says EARS is the first approved ARS to NR10120 in the world, fully compliant without derogation.

Building on DeltaRail's proven ARS, which automatically routes trains without the need for signaller intervention, EARS introduces improved features for the live signalling environment and an online system that allows user configuration and simulation of ARS.

One of the great advances of EARS is that the signaller can use a range of performance enhancing functions such as mandatory sequences, standard timing patterns and train priorities. EARS then allows the user the option to simulate them in an online environment to ensure operational performance is optimised before deploying to the live environment.

During the pilot, there was a significant drop in delay minutes and an increased public performance measure (PPM) across the pilot area.

SSL AWARDED GREAT WESTERN RESIGNALLING CONTRACT

Signalling Solutions Limited (SSL), the Alstom/Balfour Beatty Rail joint venture company, has been awarded three contracts by Network Rail totalling around £140m to renew the signalling system controlling major areas of the Great Western main line.

SSL will deliver the design, supply, installation, testing and commissioning of the renewed signalling around the areas of Oxford, Swindon and Bristol as well as the associated power system. In addition to the renewal of life expired equipment, the projects are being driven by the requirement to prepare the line for electrification and for the overlay of ERTMS.

The works will include the supply of five Smartlock 400, the powerful interlocking product developed by parent company Alstom. This leading edge product has already been deployed in a number of locations around the UK rail network.

ETCS provides train drivers with a target speed, including movement authority, on a screen in the cab. Network Rail

TELENT RETB CONTRACT

telent has been awarded the RETB (Radio Electronic Token Block) contract for Scotland's Far North and West Highland Lines by Network Rail, to deliver a replacement radio infrastructure. This is to accommodate reallocation of the existing radio frequencies to allow changes to European TV, and allow operational enhancements to the signalling operation.

The next generation RETB system will be implemented on single track lines from Glasgow to Oban via Fort William and from Inverness to the North Coast of Scotland.

The project includes the replacement of radio base station equipment at 46 sites and radio units on over 100 trains, including 5 steam locomotives, and must be completed to allow the existing radio frequencies to be reallocated in December 2015.

A key feature of telent's approach is the migration solution. It is essential that both the existing system and the new system operate in parallel to allow uninterrupted service during the transition phase.

Part of the work will be on one of Network Rail's highest installations White Corries, 3,563 ft above sea level, where some parts of the mountain range are only accessible by either helicopter or track mounted Land Rovers.

As the principal contractor, telent will co-ordinate all aspects of the work, including the initial trial to prove system performance and leading to product acceptance and system safety case approval.

New signal structures provided at Nottingham during the summer 2013 remodelling, which created the additional platform in the background. East Midlands Trains

LIGHT RAIL AND METRO

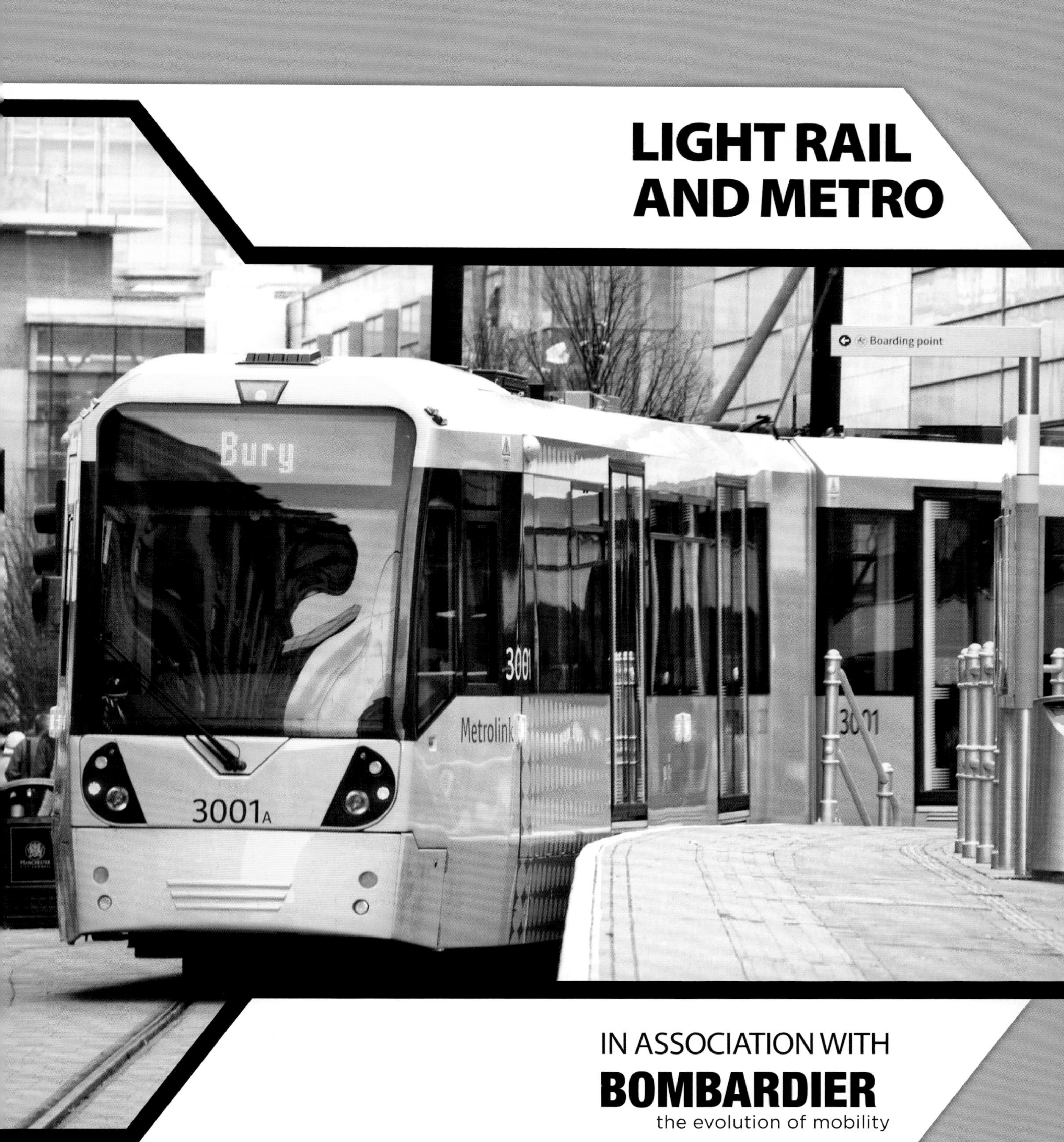

IN ASSOCIATION WITH

BOMBARDIER

the evolution of mobility

The new *FLEXITY* 2 for Queensland's Gold Coast Rapid Transit system. Bombardier

Latest international technology for Blackpool

THE BEGINNING OF AN EXCITING FUTURE FOR THE NEXT GENERATION OF TRAMWAYS WORLDWIDE

In April 2012 sixteen *BOMBARDIER FLEXITY* 2 trams went into revenue service in Blackpool proving an instant success with tram passengers. Blackpool and Lancashire County Councils have purchased the world's most advanced tram technology from Bombardier to revitalise Britain's most traditional tram system and is operating the new vehicles on the Blackpool and Fleetwood tramway.

At the 2013 Light Rail Awards held in London, Bombardier Transportation won the coveted award for Manufacturer of the Year. Taking this prestigious award for the third year running after winning Worldwide Supplier of the Year in 2010, Bombardier impressed the judges with its commitment to technological innovation, reliability and customer service – no matter where across the globe. 'This award underscores our capability as a provider of light rail solutions and as a reliable partner for transport operators in the UK, which is a core market for Bombardier Transportation. Our vehicles are already in successful revenue service in Manchester, London-Docklands, London-Croydon and Nottingham, and we recently launched our *FLEXITY 2* tram in Blackpool,' said Germar Wacker, President Light Rail Vehicles, Bombardier Transportation.

The *FLEXITY* 2 tram combines 'the best of the best' in global tram technology and Bombardier's experience in delivering more than 3,500 trams and light rail vehicles to around 100 cities in more than 20 countries. *FLEXITY* 2 is based on the very successful *BOMBARDIER FLEXITY* family of light rail vehicles and combines proven technology with continuous improvement and innovation.

With 127 years of service, Blackpool has the UK's longest running tram operation. As a popular tourist destination, 4 million passengers use the tram annually, with the majority travelling during the busy summer period. While the heritage trams that still operate remain a popular tourist attraction for visitors, with new accessibility regulations coming into effect in 2019, Blackpool and Lancashire County Council began an extensive programme to identify a supplier for a new fleet of vehicles, which would enable ease of access and comfort for all passengers.

The new *FLEXITY* 2 tram is equipped with Bombardier's industry-leading *BOMBARDIER ECO4* range of technologies, making it an energy efficient and low carbon means of transit.

Combining 100 percent low-floor technology with conventional wheel-set bogies, the *FLEXITY* 2 tram not only guarantees a smooth ride, but also includes some new advanced features, such as touch-screens in the driver's cab, reflecting the latest developments in intelligent digital technology.

Following Bombardier's contract success in Blackpool and Lancashire, the Queensland Government in Australia ordered 14 high-capacity 45 m long, seven-module *FLEXITY* 2 trams for its Gold Coast Rapid Transit system in 2011. As part of the GoldlinQ consortium, Bombardier will also design, build and operate the system. The first two state-of-the-art trams have already arrived in Australia. The Basel Transport Authority BVB placed an order for 60 *FLEXITY* trams in January 2012, the biggest order in its 116-year history. Bombardier Transportation will supply 48 *FLEXITY* 2 trams for the cities of Ghent and Antwerp to the Flemish operator De Lijn. The total number of *FLEXITY* 2 trams ordered to date now stands at 138.

Based on the highly successful *FLEXITY* platform with a strong reputation for performance and reliability, the *FLEXITY* 2 tram combines proven features and innovation in a single vehicle. It sets the highest standards in the areas of comfort, safety and environmental protection.

Each Blackpool tram is 32.2 m long and 2.65 m wide, with five sections and three bogies. The trams can carry approximately 74 seated passengers, with additional wheelchair and pushchair space plus standing room.

The technical advantages include an improved carbody concept, with good corrosion protection (essential for the seafront environment in which the vehicles operate) and an enhanced bogie design, the *BOMBARDIER FLEXX* Urban 3000 bogie.

Principal features are as follows:

- Leading-Edge Technology - The combination of 100% low-floor technology and conventional wheel-set bogies ensures a low unsuspended mass on the bogie, which results in
  - ultra-smooth running qualities
  - low noise levels and vibrations
  - a more comfortable ride for passengers
  - reduced track maintenance costs for the operator.

  Furthermore an advanced Intelligent Driver's Desk includes 2 touch screen displays.
- Enhanced Safety - The *FLEXITY* 2 tram provides the best possible protection for both passengers and driver with vehicles equipped to the highest standards for collision and fire damage.
- Customised design - The *FLEXITY* 2 tram provides operators to individually shape cityscapes and get good value for money: creative customisation based on standardised components.
- Environmental Excellence - The latest flagship tram in the Bombardier portfolio is equipped with energy-saving technologies from the *ECO4* portfolio.
- Improved repairabilty - An intelligent repairability concept and various smart functions make the *FLEXITY* 2 tram easier to repair. This means significant savings of time and money for the operator.

The exciting future of the next generation of trams worldwide has begun.

INNOVATIVE TRAMS AND LIGHT RAIL VEHICLES FOR THE UK

The *BOMBARDIER FLEXITY** family encompasses the industry's most comprehensive portfolio of tram and light rail solutions, ranging from 100% low-floor trams to high-capacity light rail vehicles as well as dual-mode solutions. In the UK, operators in Blackpool, London and Manchester have opted for trams and light rail vehicles from the market leader.

The *FLEXITY* 2 trams, which have been in successful revenue service in Blackpool since April 2012, incorporate the 'best of the best', bringing the outstanding, proven features of Bombardier trams into one vehicle. In Manchester, tram operator, Transport for Greater Manchester has ordered 94 *FLEXITY SWIFT* light rail vehicles to date, which significantly ease congestion in the busy Greater Manchester city centre. In London, the Croydon Tramlink System operates 24 *FLEXITY* Swift light rail vehicles on its 28-km network. And linking the centre of London with the eastern Docklands area, the Docklands Light Railway operates 94 Bombardier-built vehicles proving enormously popular and reliable during the London Olympics 2012.

www.bombardier.com

BOMBARDIER
the evolution of mobility

Impression of a Sheffield tram-train. Vossloh

Light rail expansion continues

More people used light rail and metro transport in 2012/13 than ever before, though several systems saw a fall in patronage. In Olympic and Paralympic year, London's Docklands Light Railway dominated, with 16pc growth. Recent extensions in Greater Manchester resulted in a 12pc gain in journeys.

System expansion continues also on Midland Metro and in Nottingham, while Sheffield's extension is a tram-train pilot scheme, getting to grips with the feasibility of mixing the operation of urban street trams with the general purpose railway.

The core of the oldest of the 'modern' systems, the Tyne & Wear Metro, has now been in operation for over 30 years. Others too find themselves in need of serious expenditure, including the Glasgow Subway, one of the world's oldest underground metros, dating back to an initial cable-hauled system of 1896. The builders of the circular route omitted to include track transition curves, and the result can still be detected in the motion of the trains. The current modernisation is to improve the transitions where possible. Renewal in Blackpool has now been completed and the rebuilding of traffic is under way.

Completion of Edinburgh's Tram line is now expected in the first half of 2014 - much reduced from the network originally envisaged, with a fleet purchased for the more extensive scheme.

New approaches such as driverless operation (established on DLR and planned for the Glasgow Subway), the tram-train, and ultra light rail (Stourbridge) are slowly gaining ground. What new applications will be found for these and other developments as time progresses?

LIGHT RAIL AND METRO NETWORKS

KEY STATISTICS	2012/13	2011/12
Passgr journeys (millions)	3.7	1.1
Passenger km (millions)	16.0	3.3
Passenger revenue (£m 2012/13 prices)	5.0	1.7

The sole surviving traditional tramway in Britain, now much changed after modernisation, has an 18km route, mostly on reserved track along the seafront, with street running in Fleetwood. The infrastructure and the trams are owned by Blackpool Borough Council, but are operated under contract by the municipally-owned Blackpool Transport Services Ltd.

The recent renewals programme required extensive closures, and traffic and income suffered, but an upturn in fortunes is demonstrated in the statistics above.

A new depot was built at Starr Gate for the 16 Bombardier 'Flexity 2' trams, each with five articulated sections, and a substantial 32.2m long. Each has 74 seats and a standing capacity of 148. They are fully accessible, with new level platforms at stops, which were reduced in number to 37. This and the higher performance trams have reduced end-to-end journey times to under the hour.

Two thirds of the £102m funding came from the government, the rest equally from Blackpool Borough and Lancashire County councils. About £33m was required for the new trams. Ten of the old fleet have been retained for special operations.

Transport for Lancashire (TfL) is a private/public body to develop, approve and fund major transport schemes. Based on the devolved budget anticipated from the Department for Transport for 2015/16, a priority is to spend £16.4m on building a tramway branch to Blackpool North rail station. £1.8m would be sourced locally.

KEY STATISTICS	2012/13	2011/12
Passenger journeys (millions)	100.0	86.1
Passenger km (millions)	509.8	455.5
Passenger revenue (£m 2012/13 prices)	124.9	106.7

The original section of London's Docklands Light Railway opened in 1987; successive extensions have taken it to a length of 38km with 45 stations. Most trains are now formed of three pairs of the 149 two-section articulated vehicles, each 28.8m long.

This 750V DC third rail system uses underside contact. The DLR has many grade separated junctions, keeping operational conflicts to the minimum, and signalling is by the Thales SelTrac moving block system.

London 2012 provided a boost to traffic, and growth is expected to continue until the opening of Crossrail, after which it is likely to level off.

London Tramlink converted four under-used or disused rail lines around Croydon to light rail, operational from May 2000. The assets are now owned by Transport for London but the 28km system is operated by Tram Operations Ltd, a First Group subsidiary.

There are 24 pairs of articulated K4000 cars built by Bombardier in Vienna, each 30.1m long. Six 32.4m Variobahn trams, with five sections, were delivered by Stadler in 2012: four more were ordered in September 2013 as part of the £30m Wimbledon Tramlink project. This will enable a 12 trams/hr service between Wimbledon and Croydon, increasing frequency and capacity by 50%.

Other parts of the project comprise a second platform at Wimbledon station and twin-tracking existing single track from Beddington Lane to Mitcham Junction by September 2015.

Proposed extensions to Crystal Palace, Morden and Sutton, and from the Beckenham Junction spur to Bromley, are under discussion, as is a new Willow Way stop at Mitcham.

The DLR is operated and maintained by Serco-Docklands under a franchise extended until September 2014. The company is paid a set fee for operating the railway to agreed service standards and receives a share of revenue, though the next concession is expected to have less revenue risk allocated to the operator.

Three concessionaires designed, financed, built and maintained route extensions. TfL in 2011 bought out the London City Airport and Woolwich Arsenal concessions: infrastructure maintenance remains with the former partners though may transfer to the new DLR franchise in 2014. The Lewisham branch is expected to remain with its original concession until expiry in 2021.

Many schemes have been suggested for further extensions, including to Dagenham, Bromley and Euston. Doubling of single track on the Stratford line, including relocating Pudding Mill Lane station, is under way in conjunction with Crossrail.

EDINBURGH TRAMS

Edinburgh Trams will run for 14km between the Airport, Edinburgh Park, Haymarket, St Andrew Square (for Waverley rail station) and York Place. Project management is overseen by Transport Scotland.

Testing began in October 2013, with the infrastructure expected to be handed over to the city council in March 2014. Passenger service is expected by May 2014, with an end-to-end journey of about 30min. The project remained in line with the revised overall budget of £776m approved by the council in September 2011. The twenty seven seven-section trams built by CAF are at 42.8m the longest in Britain.

The council has set out plans for a new integrated organisation, Transport for Edinburgh, initially to consist of local authority owned operators Lothian Buses and Edinburgh Trams.

KEY STATISTICS	2012/13	2011/12
Passgr journeys (millions)	12.6	12.9
Passenger km (millions)	40.2	41.2
Passenger revenue (£m 2012/13 prices)	14.5	14.5

The Glasgow Subway runs for 10.6km in a complete circle, taking 24min. It is wholly underground, apart from Broomloan depot. Two separate running tunnels are to the restrictive diameter of 3.35 metres, and track gauge is a highly unusual 1,220mm (4ft 0in). The three-car trains are just 38.3 metres long.

Originally cable hauled, the Subway was electrified in 1935 and totally refurbished in 1980; now a new modernisation is under way. This is planned to include smartcard ticketing, new driverless trains and associated resignalling, station refurbishment (including new escalators), rail replacement and work on the running tunnels.

The total cost of £290m is being funded with a grant of £246m from Transport Scotland, the balance by owner and operator, Strathclyde Partnership for Transport (SPT). Completion is due in 2018/19: considerable progress has been made on stations and ticketing in advance of the 2014 Commonwealth Games.

KEY STATISTICS	2012/13	2011/12
Passenger journeys (millions)	30.1	28.6
Passenger km (millions)	156.4	148.4
Passenger revenue (£m 2012/13 prices)	22.5	21.5

Metrolink

KEY STATISTICS	2012/13	2011/12
Passenger journeys (millions)	25.0	22.3
Passenger km (millions)	261.7	228.4
Passenger revenue (£m 2012/13 prices)	42.0	34.1

The first phase of Transport for Greater Manchester's Metrolink system created a city centre link between the former heavy rail lines to Bury and Altrincham. A 6km route to Eccles opened in 2000 and, after numerous issues over funding, work on the 'Big-Bang' expansion of the system began in 2009. This will see four new lines constructed, increasing the network from 37 to 95km by 2016, making Metrolink the largest light rail network in the UK, with 92 stops.

The expansion is being paid for from a special transport fund of £1.5bn, drawn from an increase in council tax, contributions from Manchester Airport, increased fares revenue, and the early release of government allocations.

The first new section, the 400m spur to MediaCityUK, Salford Quays, opened in 2010 and in 2011, Trafford Bar to St Werburgh's Road opened.

In June 2012 the Oldham Mumps line opened, extended to Shaw &

CAF-built Edinburgh trams at Gogar depot. City of Edinburgh Council

The new bridge to carry the extended NET route across Nottingham main line station. The existing tram stop is in the background, on the north side of the station. John Sully

New level-access tram stops, like this one at North Pier, have been provided as part of the Blackpool Tramway modernisation. S Knapp

Crompton in December 2012 and Rochdale rail station in February 2013. Work continues on the diversion through Oldham town centre and the rest of the route to Rochdale town centre.

The East Manchester extension to Droylsden opened in February 2013, through key regeneration areas, and serving the Etihad Campus (Manchester City football stadium) and Velodrome. St Werburgh's Road to Didsbury carried its first passengers in May 2013, and the Droylesden to Ashton-under-Lyne section opened in October 2013. The new Tram Management System has been introduced successfully after early problems.

The route from St Werburgh's Road to Manchester Airport is due to open in 2016. Plans for another line to the Trafford Centre retail complex are being developed.

To handle the increased flow of trams through the city centre, a 1.6km Second City Crossing is to be constructed from Deansgate-Castlefield via St Peters Square to Victoria station.

The operator is Metrolink RATP Dev Ltd under a 10-year concession (from 2007), sold by Stagecoach in 2011.

The original 32-strong fleet of T68 and T68a trams is to be replaced, with a fleet of 94 new Bombardier M5000 vehicles to be completed in 2014. This is expected to improve reliability and reduce maintenance costs, with the M5000's lighter weight also reducing energy track costs.

KEY STATISTICS	2012/13	2011/12
Passenger journeys (millions)	4.8	4.9
Passenger km (millions)	50.4	50.9
Passenger revenue (£m 2012/13 prices)	7.8	7.5

Midland Metro's Line 1 follows the former Great Western Railway between Birmingham Snow Hill and Wolverhampton, with 2.3km on-street in Wolverhampton.

Opened in 1999, Midland Metro is operated by National Express company Travel West Midlands, under a renewed six-year agreement signed in 2012. Electrification is 750V DC overhead and the operations centre and depot are at Wednesbury.

Many possible extensions have been suggested, and now under construction by Balfour Beatty is a 1.4km section to Stephenson Street (outside New Street station) in Birmingham, with a £9m viaduct already built by developer Ballymore.

A completely new fleet of 20 Urbos 3 trams is being built by CAF to replace 16 smaller Ansaldo cars. Extensive depot alteration and extension is being undertaken by Morgan Sindall. There will also be electrification and telecoms upgrades.

The new trams are to enter service from February 2014, with the line extension due to open in 2015. The government has provided £72m of the £128m scheme cost.

Public consultation was carried out in 2013 for further extensions, beyond Stephenson Street to Paradise Circus and Centenary Square; and to give greater town centre penetration and transport interchange in Wolverhampton.

KEY STATISTICS	2012/13	2011/12
Passenger journeys (millions)	7.4	9.0
Passenger km (millions)	32.9	40.1
Passenger revenue (£m 2012/13 prices)	8.5	8.5

Nottingham Express Transit's (NET's) Line 1 opened in 1994, from the main line station to Hucknall via the city centre. A short branch leads to Phoenix Park. The depot is at Wilkinson Street.

The original fleet consists of 15 articulated five-section cars of 33.0m built in Derby by Bombardier. Electrification is at 750V DC and each car has 58 seats. About a quarter of all passenger journeys are to or from one of five Park & Ride sites.

Patronage took a serious dip to 7.4 million journeys in 2012/13, well below the peak of 10.2m reached in 2007/08.

Construction of Phase 2 extensions is under way, backed by a government grant of £480m. Separately, Regional Funding Allocations included £7.8m for preparation works. Approval was linked to the introduction of a workplace parking levy.

The extensions continue across the present Nottingham station on a new bridge. Line 2 will run for 7.6km to Clifton and Line 3 will run 9.8km to Toton Lane, both having Park & Ride facilities.

The extended 31km system, due to open by the end of 2014, will more than double the length of the original. The PFI concession to finance, build, operate and maintain Phase 2, and take over Phase 1 for 22 years, was awarded to Tramlink Nottingham, a consortium of tram builder Alstom, operators Keolis and Wellglade (parent of bus company TrentBarton), Vinci Construction UK, and Investors OFI Infravia and Meridiam Infrastructure. Delivery of 22 new Citadis 302 trams started in September 2013.

KEY STATISTICS	2012/13	2011/12
Passenger journeys (millions)	37.0	37.9
Passenger km (millions)	299.3	303.9
Passenger revenue (£m 2012/13 prices)	43.6	42.7

The Tyne & Wear Metro pioneered modern light rail operation in Britain and the initial system serving Newcastle, Gateshead, North and South Tyneside opened in stages from 1980 to 1983. Subsequent extensions to Newcastle Airport in 1991 and Sunderland/South Hylton in 2002 produced a system with 78km of route.

The Metro uses former British Rail lines plus new underground sections in the central area. It can be described as a hybrid, displaying elements of light rail, heavy underground metro, and longer distance higher-speed urban and interurban operation. There is mixed running with National Rail trains between Pelaw and Sunderland.

The system is operated by a 90 strong fleet of six-axle Metrocars built by Metro-Cammell. Each seats 68 and they normally run in pairs. Each unit is 27.8m long. Electrification is at 1,500V DC overhead and the single depot is at Gosforth.

A high of 59.1m passenger journeys was reached in 1985, but then a serious decline led to a low of 32.1m journeys in 2000/01. In the subsequent recovery journey levels exceeded 40 million, but have declined slowly.

In 2010, government confirmed a £580m funding package, with £350m for the Metro 'All Change' renewal and modernisation programme, plus £230m for operating subsidy. Nexus split Metro into operations and infrastructure companies.

DB Regio Tyne & Wear, now part of DB's Arriva group, won the operating concession. Commencing in April 2010, it runs until 2017, extendable to 2019. The Metrocars are undergoing a 'three-quarter life' refurbishment, but are projected to be replaced in 2019 along with signalling.

Nexus, wholly owned by the Passenger Transport Executive, continues to own the Metro and sets fares and services, paying DB Regio a performance based fee related to service quality and revenue protection targets.

Major track replacement work in August 2013 required a 27-day closure of 16km of railway.

The Tyne & Wear Local Transport Plan for 2011-21 notes that the distinction between Metro and heavy rail has become less rigid, which might offer options for further extension of Metro and joint running. A Metro expansion plan is to be consulted on in 2014.

KEY STATISTICS	2012/13	2011/12
Passenger journeys (millions)	14.4	15.0
Passenger km (millions)	93.4	97.0
Passenger revenue (£m 2012/13 prices)	14.4	15.6

The 29km Sheffield network was completed in 1995, roundly half of it fully segregated. The route incorporates some tight geometry, with a minimum horizontal curve radius of 25m and vertical curve of 100m. Maximum gradients are 10pc.

Services are operated by Stagecoach, from the City Centre to Middlewood in the north with a spur to Meadowhall Interchange. In the south the route is to Halfway, with a spur to Herdings Park.

There are 25 Siemens/Duewag cars, 34.8m long - large three-section cars avoiding the need for multiple working or excessively frequent services. Vehicles have 88 seats, with space for around 200 standing.

A £58m tram-train pilot scheme is now well under way. The concept is to run through services from a city tram network to the heavy rail network, doing away with the need for passenger interchange.

Services will originate in Rotherham Parkgate Retail Park and use the freight-only heavy-rail route towards Sheffield (partly single track). The tram-trains will then join the Supertram network via a 400-metre link at Meadowhall South. Network Rail will electrify its part of the route at 750V DC overhead.

Tram-trains will use a new stop at Rotherham Parkgate, their own new section of platform at Rotherham Central, and a new dedicated island platform at Meadowhall South, all 385mm above rail level. They will make the eight mile journey to the Sheffield Cathedral stop in about 25min, with services at 20min intervals.

Seven 37.2m tram-trains are being built by Vossloh in Valencia. These will be 750V DC and 25kV AC dual-voltage vehicles, to accommodate future main line electrification north of Sheffield should it be authorised. Three vehicles will provide the basic service, with three to strengthen existing tram services, and a maintenance spare. Delivery is expected from mid-2015.

Key issues include the wheel/rail interface and profiles, variations in technical standards, vehicle detection for signalling purposes, the use of sanders for adhesion, and the use of magnetic track brakes. A programme of rail replacement that was falling due will include all areas where the tram-trains will operate, and will now use a new rail profile which has a wider and deeper groove, compatible with tram-trains.

The trials are being led by South Yorkshire Passenger Transport Executive in conjunction with the Department for Transport, Northern Rail, Network Rail, and Stagecoach Supertram.

It is anticipated that tram-trains will be operational from early 2016. The trial is for two years, with the expectation that it will become permanent.

ABBEY LINE

Plans for Hertfordshire County Council to lease the electrified 10.5km Watford Junction to St Albans 'Abbey Line' from Network Rail on a long term basis, and convert it to light rail standards, were withdrawn in May 2013, because of difficulties over issues including funding and through ticketing. The council still aspires to achieve a more frequent train service, and plans further investigation of light rail conversion and town-centre route extensions.

THE STOURBRIDGE SHUTTLE

Service provision on the 1km National Rail branch between Stourbridge Junction and Stourbridge Town is by Pre-Metro Operations Ltd (PMOL). The company runs the four wheeled Parry People Mover railcars for franchise holder London Midland, employs the operating staff and maintains the trains.

This Ultra Light Rail operation commenced in 2009. The two Parry People Mover Class-139 PPM-60 units use flywheel-stored energy, charged by a small Ford engine. The 23-seat (and one wheelchair space) vehicles are 9.6m long and weigh a modest 12.5 tonnes. Carrying capacity is about 60, and they have a maximum speed of 45mph. With a running time of 3min, one train makes six return trips in the hour. Reliability is better than 99%.

As a licensed operator with an approved safety case, PMOL plans to provide future tramway and rural rail services.

UKTRAM LTD

UKTram Ltd represents the light rail industry in dealings with government and statutory bodies. The aim is the development of a coordinated and structured approach to regulation, procurement and standardisation. The company is owned in equal shares by the Passenger Transport Executive Group (PTEG), the Confederation of Passenger Transport UK, the Light Rapid Transit Forum, and London Tramlink.

UKTram provides promoters with practical help in preparing schemes, reducing development costs and making the business case.

Northern Line 1995 Stock with driving motor No 51635 leading arrives at Tooting Broadway on 20 April 2013, en route to Morden. Additional trains will be needed for the line's extension to Battersea, and increases in frequency after resignalling and the planned separation of Charing Cross and Bank branches. Brian Morrison

Transport *for* London

TRANSPORT FOR LONDON

Transport for London (TfL) was created in 2000 under the Greater London Authority Act 1999. Directly accountable to the Mayor, Boris Johnson, TfL is responsible for implementing the Mayor's transport strategy and managing transport services in various modes across the capital. It receives part of its income in government grant.

The Chancellor of the Exchequer confirmed in 2013 a six-year settlement. An investment grant of £925m in 2015/16 would rise to £1,007m in 2020/21, with annual borrowing of over £600m for capital investment.

SENIOR PERSONNEL

TRANSPORT FOR LONDON

COMMISSIONER Peter Hendy (in photo)
MANAGING DIRECTOR, LONDON UNDERGROUND AND LONDON RAIL Mike Brown
MANAGING DIRECTOR, FINANCE Steve Allen
MANAGING DIRECTOR, PLANNING Michele Dix

The Mayor had committed to efficiencies totalling £9.8bn to 2017/18. He said the grant settlement for 2015-16 represented a reduction of support for TfL of 8.5pc.

TFL COMPANIES

London Underground is TfL's principal rail operation. In the 2012/13 year, the Underground carried a record 1,229million people nearly two and a half times the 1982 figure of 498m journeys.

London itself is growing quickly; a population of 7.8m in 2011 is expected to increase to 8.9m by 2031, plus a forecast 800,000 new jobs. Something over four million passengers a day is thus likely to become the norm. This gives an additional urgency to the upgrade programme of replacing life-expired assets with modern technology, which in turn allows capacity to be increased.

Several TfL companies have public transport responsibilities related to rail. London Underground Ltd is responsible for operating the Underground network and serves 270 stations. Docklands Light Railway Ltd owns the land on which the DLR is built and is responsible for the operation of the railway.

Transport Trading Ltd is the holding company for all TfL's operating transport companies, and receives revenues from the sales of Travelcards and similar. By law, TfL can only carry out certain activities through a limited liability company which is a TfL subsidiary, or which TfL formed alone or with others. Rail for London Ltd (London Rail), Docklands Light Railway Ltd and Crossrail Ltd are three such subsidiaries; others include the London Transport Museum.

LONDON UNDERGROUND

London Underground's operational structure is based on the network's lines. The Chief Operating Officer is responsible for the running of the Underground and for nearly 12,000 operational and support staff across the network. The Chief Operating Officer leads a team which can be divided into three main areas.

The Line General Managers are responsible for day to day management and performance of their respective lines. The Network Services division aims to deliver long-term improvements to the overall operating performance, while Operational Upgrades staff are the Chief Operating Officer's representatives for all matters affecting the operational railway, to ensure that what is delivered is fit for purpose and that he is ready to accept new assets and systems into use.

LU's fundamental objective is to provide a safe and reliable service. This means assets that consistently perform well, correctly trained staff, and the ability to recover swiftly from delays when they do occur.

This results in a number of challenges to deliver a safe service day-in, day-out, irrespective of the reliability of ageing and often obsolete assets; to use the investment programme to make good deficiencies in asset quality and to build in sufficient new capacity to meet future demand expectations; and to maintain customer service during the biggest rebuilding programme that the Underground has ever seen.

To illustrate the scale of what the company achieves, Table 1 shows the 15 busiest stations on the system, in descending order. The figures represent the annual usage during 2012, being the summated

KEY STATISTICS
LONDON UNDERGROUND

	2011/12	2012/13
Passenger journeys (millions)	1,171	1,229
Passenger km (millions)	9.519	10,099
Passenger revenue (£m 2012/13 prices)	2,008	2,125

totals of entry and exit counts taken on different days throughout the year. Passengers interchanging between lines and who thus do not pass through the ticket barriers are excluded.

In this group, Canary Wharf alone has a single Underground line. (The DLR station of the same name is completely separate). This and Stratford are the only stations featured here which are outside the central area.

Only 10 Underground stations have an annual entry/exit count of less than one million passengers a year.

The high rate of passenger growth is evident, with the figures for 2012 being 10.8pc above those for only two years earlier.

In view of the debate over airport capacity in the southeast, it is instructive to record the use of the Piccadilly Line's Heathrow stations (Table 2). Usage of all four airport stations together at 16.83m is very similar to that of the inner-suburban station of Highbury & Islington, with its 16.77m users. Hatton Cross is used mainly by airport workers.

Airport use of London Underground is not therefore overwhelming, but Underground services are of course supplemented by the Heathrow Express/Heathrow Connect services to London Paddington.

PEAK AND OFF PEAK

Table 3 sets out the maximum number of trains needed to maintain the service at various time periods. Noticeable is the varying extent to which the numbers required reduce from the Monday to Friday peak to the midday period; overall, 81pc are still running. The Saturday service requires slightly more trains but there are reduced operations on Sundays. Train loadings have thus become more constant, with the variations between peak and off peak diminishing. Encouraging off peak travel is nowadays not a major solution to capacity problems.

Where Automatic Train Operation (ATO) has been introduced, overall journey times have been shortened. This allows the same number of trains to offer a more intensive service. Throughout London Underground, train formations remain constant for each line; there are no longer any sections served by shorter three or four car trains.

The Asset Performance team manages the upkeep and repair of the eight lines formerly part of the Metronet consortium. This includes trains, stations, signalling, track, tunnels, bridges and structures, lifts and escalators, and other related assets. The Jubilee, Northern and Piccadilly lines are maintained by the wholly-owned Tube Lines subsidiary (another former private group).

TRANSFORMATION OF THE TUBE

The key elements of the 'Transforming the Tube' programme are to replace most train fleets to increase fleet reliability and capacity; replace signalling assets to reduce service delays and increase network capacity; reduce the backlog of track investment to reduce safety risks and increase capacity by removing speed restrictions; renew infrastructure assets to maintain a safe service, reduce the risks of flooding, and the service limitations caused by speed or weight restrictions; and modernise stations by replacing fire systems, public address, CCTV, and lifts and escalators.

A critical feature of line upgrades is to enable LU to provide capacity for future (or even present) demands. By the end of the current programme, the Underground will have delivered up to an additional 30pc capacity. Beyond this, there is a continuous requirement to keep assets in a state of good repair.

TABLE 2: LU PASSENGERS AT HEATHROW

STATION	PASENGER NUMBERS
Heathrow Terminals 1,2,3	7.80m
Heathrow Terminal 4	2.44m
Heathrow Terminal 5	3.64m
Hatton Cross	2.95m
Total, LU Heathrow stations	16.83m

(LU annual station usage, entries and exits combined, 2012)

TABLE 1: LU STATION USAGE – TOP 15 IN 2012

STATION	PASENGER NUMBERS
Waterloo	88.16m
Victoria	82.96m
King's Cross St Pancras	80.97m
Oxford Circus	80.55m
London Bridge	67.15m
Liverpool Street	64.23m
Stratford	50.96m
Canary Wharf	48.94m
Bank & Monument	47.75m
Paddington	46.33m
Piccadilly Circus	42.36m
Leicester Square	38.51m
Bond Street	38.07m
Euston	37.53m
Hammersmith (both stations)	37.29m
Total, top 15 stations, 2012	**851.76m**
Equivalent usage for 2011	**821.78m**
Equivalent usage for 2010	**768.71m**

(LU annual station usage, entries and exits combined)

Work on this scale inevitably requires some service disruptions. Total blockades are now seen as an efficient way of delivering upgrades while minimising disruption to passengers, and are likely to become more common.

London Underground and Crossrail have awarded a major contract to Otis for the procurement and maintenance of new escalators throughout their 30 year life. At least 50 heavy duty metro-type will be installed on LU over the next 10 years. A further 57 are for Crossrail. A major aim is to improve their reliability, given that they are mostly operational for 20 hours a day. The whole life cost of a single escalator including design, building and maintenance is around £2.5m.

Balfour Beatty has a £220m contract lasting until 2016 to carry out track renewal work on the Bakerloo, Central and all sub-surface lines. The work covers replacement of ballasted track, points and crossings, including all ancillary signalling and drainage works.

For ventilation, shafts and fans at stations will mostly have to suffice at stations in deep level tunnels for the time being. There is a difference between what is comfortable and what is safe, but platform cooling has been installed at Green Park (cool water from boreholes) and Oxford Circus (chilling units of top of an adjacent building), delivering air at around 18ºC.

TABLE 3: LU LINES – TRAINS REQUIRED

LINE	MON-FRI AM PEAK	MON-FRI MIDDAY	SATURDAY	SUNDAY
Bakerloo	33	29	29	27
Central	79	66	65	61
Circle/Hammersmith & City	32	30	30	30
District	76	59	61	58
Jubilee	57	42	49	41
Metropolitan	49	35	35	35
Northern	91	72	72	72
Piccadilly	79	68	69	68
Victoria	37	30	30	30
Waterloo & City	5	3	3	no service
Total trains	538	434	443	422
As index	100	81	82	78

(LU maximum number of trains required, 2013)

Jubilee Line 1983 Stock and Metropolitan Line S8 Stock, respectively led by driving cars Nos 96123 and 21105, head south past Neasden depot on 26 September 2012. The depot has been upgraded to provide maintenance facilities for the new Metropolitan Line trains, and further upgrading is planned for heavy maintenance of the entire S-stock fleet of 191 trains. Ken Brunt

The fares system on all TfL services is now dominated by the Oyster smartcard. Oysters can be loaded with Travelcards, or they can be used on a pay as you go basis. Cash fares are still available, but are priced typically at twice the Oyster levels.

MORE TRAINS

Metropolitan Line services are now provided entirely with the new Bombardier-built S8 rolling stock. Deliveries are now concentrating on S7 trains for the Hammersmith & City, Circle and Edgware Road-Wimbledon District Line services. (S8 and S7 refer to the number of vehicles in the train). It will then be the turn of the main District Line to receive a new fleet. Once deliveries are complete, the S stock upgrade will have resulted in a virtually uniform fleet of 191 new trains for all the sub-surface lines. Bombardier won a contract in 2011 to provide moving-block communication-based train control for the sub-surface lines.

New trains are expected to be procured next for the Piccadilly Line (1973 stock), but later spending rounds will have to address the Bakerloo (whose 1972 stock is the network's veteran) and the Central/ Waterloo & City Lines (both 1992 stock).

Fleet replacement on the deep tube lines will also be accompanied by the installation of moving block control (already installed on the Jubilee Line by Thales, which is also installing it on the Northern Line).

EXTENSIONS AND IMPROVEMENTS

Beyond the current investment programme, crowding on the LU network will remain. Schemes will be subjected to a thorough value for money and feasibility analysis and considered in the light of funding constraints.

Longer-term enhancements and extensions have been proposed. Approval is being sought for a Northern Line extension from Kennington to Battersea, partly funded by developers, which could open in 2020. Separation of the line's Charing Cross and City routes to increase capacity, with a signalling upgrade to 28-32tph, is also proposed. This and the Battersea extension will require a larger fleet to supplement the present 1995 stock, and additional trains to increase frequencies on the Jubilee Line are also likely to be part of a single procurement exercise.

Restored Metropolitan No 1 made a number of journeys as part of the London Underground's 150th anniversary celebrations. It is seen on 13 January 2013, passing Farringdon station, which was connected 150 years earlier to King's Cross, Euston and Paddington by the world's first underground railway, opening to the public on 10 January 1863. Transport for London

CROXLEY LINK

The double track Croxley rail link, approved in 2013, will reroute the Watford branch of the Metropolitan Line, via a new viaduct and a station at Cassio Bridge, to join the revived Croxley Green branch. With another new station at Watford Vicarage Road, trains will continue to Watford Junction.

The £117m scheme is funded by the Department for Transport (65pc), Hertfordshire County Council (29pc) and third parties and expected to become operational in 2016, when Watford (Metropolitan) station will close.

CROSSRAIL 2

Two variations of Crossrail 2, on a northeast to southwest axis are under consideration (to follow on from Crossrail 1 see 'Key Projects' section). The Metro option would be a new wholly underground railway between Alexandra Palace and Wimbledon via Euston and Victoria. The Regional option would be a combined underground and overground railway from both Alexandra Palace and Cheshunt (or beyond) in Hertfordshire with a junction at Angel, via Euston and Victoria, to Wimbledon and various possible destinations in southwest London and Surrey. Extensions at both ends would be over Network Rail tracks. Construction could take place from 2020 with public opening in the early 2030s.

LONDON RAIL

TfL's London Rail deals with the National Rail network in London. Its main responsibilities are to oversee major new rail projects, including those relating to London Overground, managing the Overground concession and also the operation of the Docklands Light Railway and Tramlink. It supports and develops Crossrail, as well as the Thameslink scheme, and seeks to influence and support National Rail's contribution to an integrated public transport system. It liaises with the freight industry to support the sustainable movement of goods.

LONDON OVERGROUND

The orbital London Overground network combines new and rebuilt lines with sections that share or have adopted parts of National Rail routes.

It is operated by London Overground Rail Operations Ltd (LOROL) whose concession (not a franchise) has been extended until 2016. The company is a 50/50 consortium of the Mass Transit Railway of Hong Kong and Arriva. The concession awarded by TfL has been presented as a first step in relation to National Rail services around the capital generally. The aim is to offer a similar style of frequency and service quality to that of the Underground setting of fares, procurement of rolling stock and decisions on service levels are retained by TfL.

All electric services are operated by four-car units. Dual voltage AC/DC units (Class 378/2) are used from Stratford to Richmond, plus Willesden Junction to Clapham Junction. DC-only trains (Class 378/1), are used from Highbury & Islington via Dalston Junction to New Cross, Clapham Junction, West Croydon and Crystal Palace; also Euston to Watford. Diesel operated (by 2-car Class 172/0 trains) is the Gospel Oak-Barking line.

Demand growth has resulted in orders for extra vehicles to strengthen all 57 electric trains to five cars. The future electrification of the Gospel Oak-Barking line has now been confirmed and planning work is under way.

NATIONAL RAIL DEVOLUTION

The Mayor has argued for the devolution of decision making and funding allocations for London's National Rail services to TfL, arguing that London Overground has demonstrated TfL's ability to leverage extra investment, increase service levels and improve passenger satisfaction.

The government in 2013 announced the intention to devolve the Liverpool Street to Chingford, Enfield Town and Cheshunt via Southbury services to the Mayor (not those via the Lea Valley).

55 BROADWAY

The home of London Transport, and in recent years London Underground Ltd, above St James's Park station at 55 Broadway is to be vacated and the staff relocated in 2015. Architects are being engaged by TfL to help develop the plans for the Grade 1 listed building, which dates from 1929. The future use seems most likely to be residential.

LONDON TRAVELWATCH

This statutory consumer body, sponsored and funded by the London Assembly, promotes integrated transport policies and presses for higher standards of quality, performance and accessibility.

Chief Executive: Janet Cooke

SENIOR PERSONNEL

LONDON OVERGROUND

MANAGING DIRECTOR Peter Austin (in photo)
OPERATIONS DIRECTOR Stuart Griffin
FLEET DIRECTOR Peter Daw
CUSTOMER SERVICE DIRECTOR David Wornham
CONCESSION DIRECTOR Mark Eaton

KEY STATISTICS

LONDON OVERGROUND

	2011-12	2012-13
Punctuality (0-5min)	96.6%	96.6%
Passenger journeys (millions)	102.6	125.3
Passenger km (millions)	843.8	959.5
Timetabled train km (millions)	7.0	7.6
Route km operated	113.1	124.0
Number of stations operated	55	57
Number of employees	1,171	1,211

INTO EUROPE
renfe
IN ASSOCIATION WITH
CAF

Into Europe

KEITH FENDER, EUROPE EDITOR OF MODERN RAILWAYS MAGAZINE, REVIEWS PROSPECTS FOR THE CONTINENT'S RAILWAYS

The improving economic outlook in much of Europe has had some positive impact on the railways, with passenger numbers continuing to grow in most major countries in 2013 and freight recovering too. Cutbacks in long-term infrastructure plans, particularly in France and Spain, will reduce demand for high-speed trains and equipment, although the supply industry continues to benefit from investment in urban rail systems, plus, in many major EU countries, steady if not spectacular demand for new trains to replace 1970s/80s fleets.

Budget cutbacks continued in some EU economies, with Spain, Bulgaria, Croatia and Slovakia all reducing the number of passenger lines and services supported by public funds. The growth of innovative and open access passenger operations has continued, although the only major new service launched in 2013 was the low cost 'Ouigo' in France. Rail freight in most EU countries has recovered at least partially from the worst of the downturn, and governments, particularly in eastern Europe, are beginning to privatise former national rail freight operators.

Perhaps 2013's single most significant addition to the European railway network, the Marmaray link rail tunnel under the Bosphoros waterway, opened in Istanbul, linking 1,435mm gauge lines in Europe and Asia. The main routes west from Turkey via Bulgaria and Romania or Serbia are being upgraded and electrified– so that through standard-gauge freight trains from Asiatic Turkey (and potentially even Georgia and Iran) will become possible.

PASSENGER COMPETITION DEVELOPS - SLOWLY

Open access passenger operations continued to grow in Italy, the Czech Republic, Germany and Austria, although (with Germany the major exception) legal action by some new operators against the incumbents was common. In the Czech Republic, Leo Express announced plans for services to and within Poland, although these were delayed due to safety case issues. DB subsidiary Arriva started open access suburban services north of Prague as did Czech company KŽC Doprava. The Czech government has announced plans to tender long distance routes that cross regional boundaries (regions were already tendering intra-regional routes).

In Italy, private high-speed operator Nuovo Trasporto Viaggiatori (NTV) started full operation as all 25 Alstom AGV high-speed trains entered service; expansion of NTV services from Milan to Bari on the Adriatic was delayed by track access disputes – this didn't prevent incumbent operator Trenitalia extending its high-speed services to the route. In Austria, open access operator Westbahn cut back parts of its service relying on revenue-sharing with regional transport authorities – because it was not receiving the payments in most cases.

The EC 'Fourth Railway Package' published in 2013 would see domestic rail services liberalised from 2019, with mandatory tendering of publicly funded services, and a stronger split between infrastructure managers and operators (this will not require explicitly separate organizations - nor does the existing EU railway law, as the European Court of Justice clarified during 2013). Operators not fully separated from infrastructure managers in the 'home' market could be denied access in countries having full separation. Several governments appear to be acting to pre-empt or frustrate the aims of the proposals: in France, a major reorganisation is to see infrastructure manager RFF losing its independence and becoming a subsidiary of an expanded SNCF group. The prospect of mandatory tendering has led governments such as Hungary and Finland to award long term operating contracts covering the entire country to the incumbent operator: in countries such as the Czech Republic and Poland, regional and inter regional services are increasingly being tendered in advance of the planned EU deadline.

HIGH SPEED DEVELOPMENTS

In France the budget 'Ouigo' service uses four retrofitted TGV Duplex trains operating, from April 2013, from Marne-la-Vallée Chessy in eastern Paris to Lyon, Montpellier and Marseilles. TGV and AVE services between France and Spain did not start in 2013 despite the new high-speed line in Spain being complete, due to both technical (approvals for AVE trains in France) and political issues. 'Fyra' high-speed services started in late 2012 between Brussels

The first EU freight operator listed on a stock exchange. A PKP Cargo container train on the Inowroclaw-Czestochowa freight line in central Poland in September 2012, with a modernised EU07 electric loco hauling the train. Keith Fender

and Amsterdam, using Ansaldo Breda built V250 EMUs, only to be withdrawn a month later over a wide range of issues. Following assessments of the trains' future reliability, both Belgian and Dutch Railways decided to cancel the contract with Ansaldo Breda and hand the trains back: the dispute was continuing at the end of 2013. As part of a replacement, Eurostar announced it would introduce two London-Amsterdam train pairs from December 2016, using its new Siemens Class 374 Velaro e320 trains which commenced dynamic testing in Belgium during 2013.

The new Bombardier designed, but largely Ansaldo Breda built, Zefiro 360km/h EMU for Trenitalia began test running in Italy; 50 of these are due for delivery from 2014. The on-going approval delays for the new DB Velaro-D Class 407 ICE train in Germany continued with test running in Germany, Belgium and France: introduction, in Germany only, during 2014 seemed possible. Siemens won an order for seven Velaro-D-based trains for Turkish operator TCDD and delivered one of the original German batch to enable test running; the other six will be delivered in 2016. Siemens is building eight more ten-car 250km/h 1,520mm-gauge Velaro-Rus Sapsan trains for Russian Railways (RZD) in 2014 in Germany.

Spain suffered its worst rail accident in 41 years when an Alvia bi-mode high speed multiple-unit derailed at 179 km/h as it left the high speed line at Santiago de Compostela in July 2013. The accident, which killed 79 people, highlighted shortcomings in signalling and speed protection and led to a nationwide review of all similar situations.

FREIGHT STARTS TO RECOVER

In most EU countries, rail freight volumes started to grow in 2013: traffic fell by over 5% in many countries in 2012. Freight levels generally remain below pre-financial-crisis levels of 2007/08, partly reflecting lower economic activity in many countries, plus changes in global energy markets, resulting in less coal mining in countries such as Germany and the Czech Republic: but in some cases rail volume has been replaced by flows of imported coal from port to power station. In Germany, DB introduced a range of noise-mitigation measures, aiming to reduce freight-train noise by 50% by 2020; with higher charges for wagons not fitted with the new 'whisper brakes', incorporating quieter composite brake blocks or pads.

Plans of several governments to sell all or part of (normally profitable) rail freight companies to raise money to fund other expenditure, or to comply with IMF/World Bank 'bail out' terms, have been only partially successful. In Romania, the sale of CFR Marfa by auction collapsed after private operator Grup Feroviar Român (GFR) had been selected as the new owner. In Croatia, which joined the EU in July 2013, the freight business HZ Cargo was sold to GFR. Privatisation of operators in Greece, Bulgaria, Slovakia and Spain was underway at varying speeds in late 2013; in Poland the government successfully listed 49% of PKP Cargo via a share offering. PKP Cargo has indicated it may now acquire stakes in other operators, with those specialising in oil and petrol being of most interest. Belgian Railways (SNCB) confirmed during 2013 that it was in talks over a future partnership for SNCB Logistics led by DB Schenker; a full or partial sale to DB in 2014 is likely.

The Russian Railways (RZD) acquisition of 75% of French logistics operator Gefco from PSA Peugeot Citroën, substantially expanding RZD's activities in western Europe, was completed in early 2013, for Euro 800million. A debate on opening the market in Russia to alternative 'open access' traction providers was underway in late 2013; RZD has said it now regrets the 2012 privatisation of its wagon fleet and is lobbying to avoid any forced sale of part of its locomotive fleet.

ROLLING STOCK MARKET

In Germany, continuing delays with Velaro-D trains were exacerbated by approval delays for the new Bombardier built Intercity Twindexx double deck 160k/h push-pull intercity trains, thought unlikely to enter service before mid 2014. Approval delays in Germany became a talking point across Europe, as, despite government and DB pressure, safety regulator EBA did not speed up or significantly change its processes. DB managed to introduce new Class 430 S-Bahn trains in Stuttgart earlier than planned, only to take them out of service when problems occurred. DB has now ordered 43 Twindexx EMUs from Bombardier, the first due for delivery in 2014.

DB placed the first order under its 2012 framework contract with Polish manufacturer Pesa for 36 Link DMUs for services west of Dortmund: German regional operator NEB also ordered nine Link DMUs in late 2013. DB surprised observers by ordering six 189km/h double-deck push-pull trains for regional services on the Munich-Nuremburg high-speed route from Czech builder Skoda Transportation; the trains will use Skoda F109E locomotives (Czech Class 380) and new design coaches. Hitachi Europe lost out to Bombardier on a contract to renew much of the Hamburg S-Bahn EMU fleet. National Express won its first German contracts and ordered 35 Talent-2 EMUs from Bombardier for services in the Ruhr from 2015. Abellio won two major contracts in eastern Germany and also ordered

ODEG Kiss EMU 445 107 at Berlin Hbf on 4 August 2013. Keith Fender

Leo Express 'Flirt' EMU passing Kolin on 7 July 2013 with a Prague to Ostrava service. Keith Fender

a fleet of 35 Talent-2s for one, but unusually chose to withdraw its offer for the other, DB Regio taking it over. In Berlin, ODEG introduced its Stadler Kiss double-deck EMUs in 2013 and Luxembourg operator CFL will introduce similar EMUs in 2014.

Orders for new multiple units for both regional and intercity services in France were placed during 2013, with the French government announcing a Euro 510 million fund to fund replacement of some of SNCF's existing Intercités fleet; an initial order for 34 of a new Coradia Liner design of bi-mode trains from Alstom was placed in later 2013. Alstom presented the first of 216 Regiolis single-deck EMU/bi-Modes for SNCF, with series deliveries due to start in early 2014: Bombardier presented the first of its Omneo or Regio2N double-deck regional EMUs, with introduction planned for mid 2014. In Belgium, all 120 Siemens built ES60U3 Class 18/19 locos and around half the 305 Desiro ML EMUs on order for SNCB were delivered. Austrian Railways (OBB) announced an order for 100 Desiro ML EMUs during 2013, construction begins in 2014, with final assembly in Austria. Stadler announced an order for 25 double-deck EMUs for services to Russian airports, to be built at a new joint-venture-owned factory in Minsk, Belarus. In Switzerland, Stadler completed delivery of new 'Allegra' EMUs to metre-gauge operator Rhaetische Bahn. In Montenegro three CAF-built EMUs entered service on the newly electrified line from Podgorica to Nikšic.

LOCOMOTIVE ORDERS SCARCE

Bombardier won 2013's only major locomotive order in the EU, DB awarding a new framework contract for up to 450 locos and an immediate order for 130 Traxx AC locos for DB Schenker and passenger operator DB Regio. Diesel loco specialist Voith has completed delivery of the Gravita model to DB Schenker (the last 23 as the 1,800kW Gravita 15L BB, DB Class 265). With limited demand, Voith was seeking a new owner for its loco business. Vossloh experienced a better year, with orders from the UK (ten Class 88 electro-diesels for Beacon Rail/DRS) plus South Africa (70 electro-diesels). Siemens won a series of small orders for its new Vectron electric loco and deliveries were under way of the 23 Vectron DC locos ordered for DB Schenker Polska. Siemens was set to complete delivery of thirteen 1,067mm-gauge BoBoBo electric freight locos, built in Munich, for rail freight operator BHP Billiton Mitsubishi Alliance of Queensland, Australia.

SBB Cargo is taking delivery of thirty Class 923 electro diesel shunting/trip locos from Stadler, which completed delivery of the world's most powerful rack electric locos to MRS Logística in Brazil during 2013. In Croatia rail engineering firm TVZ Gredelj was placed in administration during 2013 but has remained open, supported by US Customer NREC, building twenty

GT26CW-3 model CoCo diesel locos for Moroccan Railways (ONCF) in its Zagreb factory.

1,520MM GAUGE

In Russia Siemens is working with Yekaterinburg based Sinara to build the Desiro-Rus EMU in Russia: most of the 1,470-vehicle total orders are to be built in Russia at a new Euro 400 million production plant: it started assembling the second batch of 16 from kits supplied from Germany during 2013; the first Russian-assembled train should be complete by September 2014. (38 German-built trains are in service). In Estonia private freight operator Estonian Railway Services ordered 15 GE-Evolution-based type-TE33A locos to be built by Lokomotiv Kurastyru Zauyty, a subsidiary of Kazakhstan's national railway KTZ, under licence from GE Transportation. Chinese loco builder CNR Datong Electric Locomotive is to supply 18 more electric locos to Belarus Railways; the 120km/h 25kV AC 7,200kW single-section locos are intended for freight traffic and will work lighter trains than the 12 Class-BKG1 twin-section 9,600kW locos from CNR, delivered in 2013.

INFRASTRUCTURE PLANS

Infrastructure plans in both Spain and France have been cut back, although more high-speed line construction continues in both than anywhere else in Europe. The EC unveiled plans in late 2013 to concentrate future investment on nine defined trans-European (TEN-T) corridors rather than supporting individual schemes: total investment envisaged by 2030 is around Euro 250 billion, much funded by national governments.

In Sweden the final section of the Söderström immersed tunnel was lowered into place in central Stockholm in August 2013; the tunnel connecting the islands of Riddarholmen and Södermalm forms part of the 6km long Citybanan cross-city line due for completion in 2017. Plans for substantial additional rail capacity in the Greater Paris area were backed by the new French government.

GAUGE CONVERSION

In Lithuania the Šeštokai-Marijampolė line, south west of Kaunas, is now being rebuilt to dual 1,435/1,520mm gauge as the first stage of the Rail Baltica project. The intention is for 1,435mm gauge track to reach the Kaunas area in 2015. DB Schenker and Lithuanian Railways (Lietuvos Geležinkeliai (LG)) signed an agreement for the joint development of rail freight. DB Schenker intends to start regular container services between Poland and Lithuania with through 1,435mm gauge services from 2015 to a new terminal outside Kaunas.

Substantial investment is being made in the 'Mediterranean Corridor' project to create a 1,435mm-gauge freight route over the 1,300km between the French border and Algeciras to connect Spain's south coast to the EU 1,435mm gauge network.

Russia hosts the 2014 Winter Olympics in Sochi in February/March 2014 and RZD has built a 48km long line to serve sporting venues as well as a new airport line in Sochi, opened in 2012. Plans for a Moscow-St Petersburg high-speed line have been cancelled, with a line from Moscow east to Kazan via Nizhny Novgorod now planned instead. In Germany, opposition from DB and government to the installation of ETCS was eroded with the announcement that the Emmerich-Basel section of the Rotterdam-Genoa TEN Corridor route would be equipped by 2018. Plans to rebuild the northern end of this route from the Dutch border (linking with the freight-only Betuwe Route) and the major freight centre at Oberhausen were announced.

The first Alstom Pendolino set for PKP Intercity was delivered in August 2013. 20 of the seven-car non-tilting EMUs have been ordered. Alstom

LIGHT RAIL AND METRO

The growth of metro systems and the renewal and expansion of light rail has continued in almost all EU countries. Polish manufacturer Solaris delivered the first of its Tramino trams to Germany with entry into service in Jena expected early in 2014. Siemens was due to deliver eight of its new Avenio trams to Munich operator MVG by early 2014 after MVG decided against additional Stadler Variobahn trams. Bombardier delivered different versions of its Flexity design to small German operators in Strausberg (near Berlin) and Plauen plus larger numbers to major operators such as BVG in Berlin. Most German major cities reported record passenger numbers in 2013. The first of 60 Flexity-2 trams on order for the Swiss city of Basel will be delivered in 2014 as will initial deliveries of 48 Flexity-2 trams for fleet renewal in the Belgian cities of Antwerp and Ghent.

Dutch Railways (NS) became a 49% shareholder in Den Haag tram operator HTM: plans to convert the Schiedam-Hoek van Holland line to metro operation as part of the Randstadtrail network were announced. The tramway in Vélez-Málaga in Spain closed after only six years operation in mid 2012: its trams were leased to Sydney, Australia. In Poznan, Poland the extension of the city's fast tram dedicated alignment with full scale interchange stations opened to the main railway station in September 2013. Poznan has continued to take delivery of Solaris Traminos: substantial numbers of 1970s Polish trams have been replaced by new Bombardier Flexity cars in Krakow, new Pesa Swing trams in Warsaw, and Pesa Twist trams in Częstochowa. Pesa also won a contract to supply 120 Twists to Moscow, to be built with Russian partner Uralwagonzavod for delivery in 2014-15. In the Croatian capital Zagreb, a further batch of Crotram TMK 2200 K trams have entered service during 2013; in Serbia, deliveries of CAF Urbos trams to Belgrade were completed during 2013.

Light rail development in France has continued during 2013, with new tramways in Tours and expansion in Paris. 32 of Alstom's new Citadis Compact trams have been ordered for new lines in Avignon and Aubagne. Plans for a 10km extension of the Mainz network in Germany were agreed in 2013. In eastern Europe the Slovak capital ordered fifteen 32.5-metre long trams from Skoda, which started delivery of similar Type 26Ts to the eastern Hungarian city of Miskolc in late 2013. In Helsinki the first two of 40 new trams being built by Transtech in Kajaani, Finland were delivered in 2013; they will be tested in 2014 before series production begins.

Metro construction in many European capitals has continued on new lines or extensions in Berlin, Prague, Budapest, Milan, Warsaw, Sofia, Kiev, Moscow and Bucharest. Metro extensions in Athens, Kazan and Milan opened during 2013. Siemens delivered the first of its new Inspiro metro trains to Warsaw for the new Line 2 under construction, while Alstom-built Metropolis trains finally entered service in Budapest.

DIRECTORY

THE UK RAIL INDUSTRY IN YOUR HANDS

IN ASSOCIATION WITH

ATKINS

3D Laser Mapping
1a Church St,
Bingham,
Nottingham NG13 8AL
T: 0870 442 9400
F: 0870 121 4605
E: info@3dlasermapping.com
W: www.3dlasermapping.com

3M CPPD
Standard Way,
Northallerton,
N.Yorks DL6 2XA
T: 01609 780170
F: 01609 777905
W: www.copon.co.uk

3M United Kingdom PLC
3M Centre, Cain Rd,
Bracknell,
Berks RG12 8HT
T: 01344 858704
E: railsolutions@mmm.com
W: www.3m.co.uk/railsolutions

360 Vision Technology Ltd
Unit 7, Seymour Court,
Runcorn, Cheshire WA7 1SY
T: 0870 903 3601
F: 0870 903 3602
W: www.360visiontechnology.com

Aardvark Site Investigations Ltd
see screwfast

AATI Rail Ltd
11 Swinborne Drive,
Springwood Ind. Est, Braintree,
Essex, CM7 2YP
T: 01376 346278
F: 01376 348480
E: info@aati.co.uk
W: www.aati.co.uk

Abacus Lighting Ltd
Oddicroft lane,
Sutton in Ashfield,
Notts NG17 5FT
T: 01623 511111
F: 01623 552133
E: sales@abacuslighting.com
W: www.abacuslighting.com

ABA Surveying
Lansbury Est,
Lower Guildford St, Knaphill,
Woking, Surrey GU21 2EP
T: 01483 797111
F: 01483 797211
W: www.abasurveying.co.uk

Abbeydale Training Ltd
26 Stonewood Grove,
Sheffield S10 5SS
T: 0114 230 4400
E: abbeydale.training
@btconnect.com
W: www.abbeydaletraining.co.uk

Abbey Pynford Foundation Systems Ltd
Second Floor, Hille House,
132 St Albans Rd,
Watford WD24 4AQ
T: 0870 085 8400
F: 0870 085 8401
E: info@abbeypynford.co.uk
W: www.abbeypynford.co.uk

ABB Ltd
Daresbury Park,
Daresbury,
Warrington WA4 4BT
T: 01925 741111
F: 01925 741212
E: karen.strong@gb.abb.com
W: www.abb.com/railway

Abbott Risk Consulting Ltd
10 Greycoat Place,
London SW1P 1SB
T: 020 7960 6087
F: 020 7960 6100
E: rail@consultarc.com
W: www.consultarc.com

AB Connectors Ltd
Abercynon,
Mountain Ash,
Rhondda Cynon Taff CF45 4SF
T: 01443 740331
F: 01443 741676
E: sales@ttabconnectors.com
W: www.ttabconnectors.com

Abellio
1 Ely Place, 2nd Floor,
London EC1N 6RY
T: 020 7430 8270
F: 020 7430 2239
E: info@abellio.com
W: www.abellio.com

ABET Ltd
70 Roding Rd, London Ind. Park,
London E6 4LS
T: 020 7473 6910
F: 020 7476 6935
E: sales@abetltd.uk
W: www.abetuk.com

AB Hoses & Fittings Ltd
Units 6-7,
Warwick St Ind Est,
Chesterfield,
Derbys S40 2TT
T: 01246 208831
F: 01246 209302
E: info@abhoses.com
W: www.abhoses.com

Abloy UK
Portobello Works,
School St, Willenhall,
West Midlands WV13 3PW
T: 01902 364500
E: sales@abloy.co.uk
W: www.abloy.co.uk

ABM Precast Solutions Ltd
Ollerton Rd, Tuxford,
Newark, Notts NG22 0PQ
T: 01777 872233
F: 01777 872772
E: precast@abmeurope.com
W: www.abmeurope.co.uk

Abracs Ltd
Glaisdale Rd,
Northminster Business Park,
Upper Poppleton,
York YO26 6QT
T: 01904 789997
F: 01904 789996
E: abracs@abracs.com
W: www.abracs.com

ABS Consulting
EQE House, The Beacons,
Warrington Rd,
Birchwood,
Warrington WA3 6WJ
T: 01925 287300
F: 01925 287301
E: enquiriesuk@absconsulting.com
W: www.eqe.co.uk

Abtus Ltd
Falconer Rd, Haverhill,
Suffolk CB9 7XU
T: 01440 702938
F: 01440 702961
E: chris.welsh@abtus.com
W: www.abtus.com

Access IS
18 Suttons Business Park,
Reading,
Berks RG6 1AZ
T: 0118 966 3333
F: 0118 926 7281
E: carol.harraway@access-is.com
W: www.access-is.com

Accolade Associates
63 Elgar Drove, Shefford,
Beds SG17 5RZ
T: 01462 709854
F: 01462 709854
W: www.accoladeassociates.com

Acetech Personnel Ltd
Pembroke House, Pegasus Bus. Park,
Castle Donnington,
Derby DE74 2TZ
T: 01509 676962
F: 01509 676867
E: rail@acetech.co.uk
W: www.acetech.co.uk

Achilles Information Ltd (Link-Up)
30 Park Gate, Milton Park, Abingdon,
Oxon OX14 4SH
T: 01235 820813
F: 01235 838156
E: link-up@achilles.com
W: www.achilles.com

ACIC International Ltd
14 Blacknest Business Park,
Blacknest,
Nr Alton Hants GU34 4PX
T: 01420 23930
F: 01420 23921
E: sales@acic.co.uk
W: www.acic.co.uk

ACM Bearings Ltd
Derwent Way, Wath West Ind Est,
Rotherham,
S Yorks S63 6EX
T: 01709 874951
F: 01709 878818
E: sales@acmbearings.co.uk
W: www.acmbearings.co.uk

ACOREL S.A.S
Technopar Pole 2000,
3 Rue Paul Langevin,
07130 St Peray, France
T: 0033 475 405979
F: 0033 475 405771
E: info@acorel.com
W: www.acorel.com

ACT Informatics Ltd
One St Peters Rd, Maidenhead,
Berks SL6 1QU
T: 0870 114 9800
F: 0870 114 9801
E: admin@act-consultancy.com

Acumen Design Associates Ltd
1 Sekforde St,
Clerkenwell,
London EC1R 0BE
T: 020 7107 2900
F: 020 7107 2901
E: info@acumen-da.com
W: www.acumen-da.com

Adaptaflex
Station Rd, Coleshill,
Birmingham B46 1HT
T: 01675 468222
F: 01675 464276
E: sales@adaptaflex.com
W: www.adaptaflex.com

ADAS UK Ltd
Woodthorn, Wergs Rd,
Wolverhampton WV6 8TQ
T: 01902 754190
E: david.middleditch@adas.co.uk
W: www.adas.co.uk

Adeo Construction Consultants
Unit 16, Oakhurst Business Park,
Wilberforce Way,
Southwater,
Horsham RH13 9RT
T: 01403 821770
F: 01403 733405
E: enquiries@adeo.uk.com
W: www.adeo.uk.com

Adien Ltd
Delta Court,
Sky Business Park,
Robin Hood Airport,
Doncaster DN9 3GB
T: 01302 802200
F: 01302 802201
E: info@adien.com
W: www.adien.com

ADT Fire & Security
Security House,
The Summit, Hanworth Rd,
Sunbury on Thames TW16 5DB
T: 01932 743229
F: 01932 743047
W: www.tycoint.com

Advance Consultancy Ltd
St Mary's House, Church St,
Uttoxeter ST14 8AG
T: 01889 561510
F: 01889 561591
E: enquiry
@advance-consultancy.com
W: www.advance-consulting.com

Advance Training & Recruitment Services
2nd Floor,
Woodbridge Chambers,
89 Woodbridge Rd,
Guildford
GU1 4QD
T: 01483 361061
F: 01483 431958
M: 07786 968851
E: info
@advance-trs.com
W: www.advance-trs.com

Advantage Technical Consulting
see atkins

Advante Strategic Site Services
4th Floor,
Phoenix House,
Christopher Martin Rd,
Basildon SS14 3HG
T: 01268 280500
F: 01268 293454
E: sales
@advante.co.uk
W: www.advante.co.uk

Advanced Handling Ltd
Northfields Ind. Est,
Market Deeping,
Peterborough
PE6 8LD
T: 01778 345365
F: 01778 341654
E: sales@
advancedhandling.co.uk
W: www.advancedhandling.co.uk

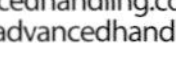

Advanced Selection Ltd
Cooper House,
The Horsefair,
Romsey,
Hants SO31 8JZ
T: 02380 744455
F: 01794 518549
E: sam
@advancedselect.co.uk
W: www.advancedselect.co.uk

AECOM
AECOM House,
63-77 Victoria St,
St Albans,
Herts
AL1 3ER
T: 0161 602 7515
E: dan.rodgers
@aecom.com
W: www.aecom.com

Aedas Group Ltd
5-8 Hardwick St,
London
EC1R 4RG
T: 020 7837 9789
F: 020 7837 9678
E: london
@aedas.com
W: www.
aedas.com

The 2014 Modern Railway Directory - The most comprehensive directory of businesses involved in the operation of the UK rail industry

KEY TO SYMBOLS

TRAIN OPERATORS
Passenger and Freight Train Operators, TOC Owning Groups, Railway, Metro and Tramway Operators, Rail Tour Operators, Passenger Transport Authorities/Executives, Freight Forwarders/Brokers.

ROLLING STOCK MANUFACTURE, SUPPLY AND DELIVERY
Locomotive, Carriage and Wagon Manufacture, Locomotive, Wagon and Coaching Stock Hire, Chartering, Rolling Stock Leasing Companies, Heavy Haulage, Replacement Buses and Vehicle Hire.

CIVILS, PLANT & EQUIPMENT
Civil Engineering, Construction, Projected Developments, Buildings & Building Refurbishment, Plant, Tools, Architects, Surveying, Welding, Paints & Coatings, Clothing & Boots, Chemicals and Lubricants, Scaffolding.

INFRASTRUCTURE - Infrastructure Maintenance and Renewal, Workshop Equipment, Carriage Washing, Weighing & Lifting, Fencing & Security, Lighting (except rolling stock), Platforms, Cable Management, Power Supply, Freight Terminals, Car Parking, Cleaning, Grafitti Removal, Pest Control, Ticketing, CCTV, Test Facilities, Fares and Collection.

ROLLING STOCK MAINTENANCE/ PARTS - Locomotive, Carriage and Wagon Maintenance, Component supply, Lighting and Cabling, Decals and Transfers, De-Icing, Sanding, Upholstery, Disposal, Textiles, Fuel Technology and Carpeting.

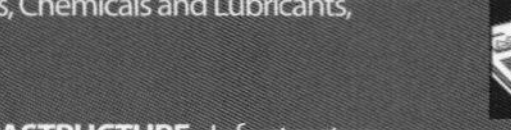

CONSULTING
Consultants, Legal Services, Economists, Industry Reporting, Insurance, Accreditation & Compliance, Verification & Validation, Assessment, Test & Development, Systems & Software, IT Services, Data Management, Financial Services, Solutions and Turnkey Providers, Vehicle Acceptance and Project Management, Research Organisations, legal and administrative services.

SIGNAL & TELECOMMUNICATION
S&T Installation and Equipment, Wireless Technology and Datacoms.

PERSONNEL SERVICES, TRAINING & HEALTH
Recruitment and Training Companies/Consultancies, Personnel Supply, Retirement and Convalescence, Training Simulators, Medical Services and Religious/ Spiritual support, Pension Schemes.

INDUSTRY BODIES
Trade Associations, Alliances and Authorities, Advisory Boards, Government Departments, Customer Organisations, Accident Investigators, Campaigning Organisations, Passenger Watchdogs, Trade Unions, Port Authorities and Development Agencies.

MISCELLANEOUS
Conferences & Exhibitions, Catering, Property, Journey Planning, In-Train Entertainment, Photography, Mapping, Lost Property and Video & Film Production.

AEG Power Solutions Ltd
Vision 25,
Electric Ave,
Enfield,
Middx EN3 7GD
T: 01992 719200
F: 01992 702151
E: kevin.pateman@aegps.com
W: www.aegps.com

Aegis Engineering Systems Ltd
29 Brunel Parkway,
Pride Park,
Derby DE24 8HR
T: 01332 384302
F: 01332 384307
E: info@aegisengineering.co.uk
W: www.aegisengineering.co.uk

Aggregate Industries UK Ltd
Bardon Hill,
Coalville,
Leics LE67 1TL
T: 01530 510066
F: 01530 510123
W: www.aggregate-uk.com

Aggreko UK Ltd
2 Voyager Drive,
Cannock,
Staffs WS11 8XP
T: 08458 247365
F: 01543 437772
E: enquiries
@aggreko.co.uk
W: www.
WWaggreko.co.uk

AEI Cables Ltd
Durham Rd, Birtley,
Chester-le-Street,
Co. Durham DH3 2RA
T: 0191 410 3111
F: 0191 410 8312
E: info@aeicables.co.uk
W: www.aeicables.co.uk

Aerco Ltd
17, Lawson Hunt Ind. Park,
Broadbridge Heath,
Horsham,
W. Sussex RH12 3JR
T: 01403 260206
F: 01403 259760
M: 07767 002298
E: chenderson@aerco.co.uk
W: www.aerco.co.uk

Aerial Facilities Ltd
Aerial House,
Asheridge Rd,
Chesham,
Bucks HP5 2QD
T: 01494 777000
F: 01494 777002
E: sales@aerial.co.uk
W: www.aerialfacilities.com

Aerosystems International
see bae systems

AES
The Old Warehouse,
Park St,
Worcester WR5 1AA
T: 01905 363520
E: contact@aesco.co.uk
W: www.aesco.co.uk

Agant Ltd
T: 020 8123 9401
E: contactus@agant.com
W: www.agant.com

AGD Equipment Ltd
Avonbrook House,
Masons Rd,
Stratford upon Avon,
Warks CV37 9LQ
T: 01789 292227
F: 01789 268350
E: info@
agd-equipment.co.uk
W: www.agd-equipment.co.uk

Agilent Technologies UK Ltd
610 Wharfedale Rd,
IQ Winnersh,
Wokingham,
Berks RG41 5TP
T: 0118 927 6504
E: jason_saw@agilent.com
W: www.agilent.com

Agility Trains
7th Floor,
40 Holborn Viaduct,
London EC1N 2PB
T: 020 7970 2700
E: enquiries@agilitytrains.com
W: www.agilitytrains.co.uk

Aikona Management Ltd
Windsor House,
Lodge Place,
Sutton SM1 4AU
T: 020 8770 9393
F: 020 8770 9555
E: training@aikona.com
W: www.aikonatraining.com

Ainscough
Bradley Hall,
Bradley Lane,
Standish,
Lancs WN6 0XQ
T: 01257 473423
F: 01257 473286
E: heavy.cranes@ainscough.co.uk
W: www.ainscough.co.uk

Airquick (Newark) Ltd
Brunel Business Park,
Jessop Close,
Newark,
Notts NG24 2A
T: 01636 640480
F: 01636 701216
E: info@airquick.co.uk
W: www.airquick.co.uk

Airscrew Ltd
see ametek

Airtec International Ltd
40, Couper St,
Glasgow G4 0DL
T: 0141 552 5591
F: 0141 552 5064
E: akilpatrick@airtecintl.co.uk
W: www.airtecinternational.com

Alan Dick Communications Ltd
Unit 11, Billet Lane,
Normanby Enterprise Park,
Scunthorpe DN15 9YH
T: 01724 292200
F: 01724 292556
E: robert.illsley@alandickcomms.com
W: www.alandick.com

Albatros UK
Unit 9, Garamonde Drive,
Clarendon Ind Park, Wymbush,
Milton Keynes MK8 8DF
T: 01908 305740
F: 01908 577899
E: sales@raildoorsolutions.co.uk
W: www.raildoorsolutions.co.uk

Alcad
1st Floor, Unit 5, Astra Centre,
Edinburgh Way,
Harlow,
Essex CM20 2BN
T: 01279 772555
E: carter.sarah@alcad.com
W: www.alcad.com

Alcatel-Lucent
Voyager Place, Shoppenhangers Rd,
Maidenhead SL5 2PJ
T: 01628 428221
F: 01628 428785
M: 07917 577971
E: olivier.andre@alcatel-lucent.com
W: www.alcatel-lucent.com/
railways

Alcoa Fastening Systems (Huck)
Unit 7, Stafford Park 7,
Telford TF3 3BQ
T: 01952 204603
E: matthew.dowd@alcoa.com
W: www.afsglobal.net

Alcontrol
Units 7&8,
Hawarden Business Park,
Manor Rd, Hawarden,
Deeside, Cheshire CH5 3LD
T: 01244 528700
F: 01244 528791
W: www.alcontrol.com

Alert Safety Technologies
Nasmyth Buildings,
Nasmyth Ave,
East Kilbride,
Glasgow G75 0QR
T: 01355 272828
F: 01355 272788
E: sales@alertsafety.net
W: www.alertsafety.net

Alfred Mc Alpine Plc
see carillion

ALH Rail Coatings
Station Rd, Birch Vale,
High Peak,
Derbys SK22 1BR
T: 01663 746518
F: 01663 746605
E: help@dowhyperlast.com
W: www.hyperlast.com

All Clothing & Protection Ltd
Units 6&7, Manor Park Ind Est,
Station Rd South, Totton,
Hants SO40 9HP
T: 02380 428003
F: 02380 869333
E: sales@allclothing.co.uk
W: www.allclothing.co.uk

Allelys Heavy Haulage
The Slough, Studley,
Warks B80 7EN
T: 01527 857621
F: 01527 857623
E: robert@allelys.co.uk
W: www.allelys.co.uk

Allen & Douglas Corporate Clothing
see sartoria

Alliance Rail Holdings
88 The Mount, York YO24 1AR
T: 01904 628904
E: info@alliancerail.co.uk
W: www.alliancerail.co.uk

Allies & Morrison
85 Southwark St,
London SE1 0HX
T: 020 7921 0100
F: 020 7921 0101
E: info@alliesandmorrison.com
W: www.alliesandmorrison.com

Alltask Ltd
Alltask House,
Commissioners Rd, Strood,
Kent ME2 4EJ
T: 01634 298000
M: 07837 188717
E: nick.covell@alltask.co.uk
W: www.alltask.co.uk

Alltype Fencing Specialists Ltd
Ye Wentes Wayes, High Rd,
Langdon Hills, Essex SS16 6HY
T: 01268 545192
F: 01268 545260
E: alltypefencing@btinternet.com
W: www.alltypefencing.com

Alpha Adhesives & Sealants Ltd
Llewellyn Close, Sandy Lane Ind. Est.,
Stourport-on-Severn,
Worcs DY13 9RH
T: 01299 828626
F: 01299 828666
E: sales@alpha-adhesives.co.uk
W: www.alpha-adhesives.co.uk

Alphatek Hyperformance Coatings Ltd
Head Office & Works, Unit A5,
Cuba Ind. Est, Bolton Rd North,
Ramsbottom, Lancs BL0 0NE
T: 01706 821021
F: 01706 821023
E: railcoatings@alphatek.co.uk
W: www.alphatek.co.uk

Alpha Trains (UK) Ltd
Egginton House, 25-
28 Buckingham Gate,
London SW1E 6LD
T: 020 7073 9026
F: 020 7073 9046
E: info@alphatrains.eu
W: www.alphatrains.eu

Alstom Transport
PO Box 70, Newbold Rd, Rugby,
Warks CV21 2WR
T: 01788 545654
F: 01788 546440
E: jo.doxey@transport.alstom.com
W: www.transport.alstom.com

Altran UK Ltd
2nd Floor Offices, 22 St Lawrence St,
Southgate, Bath BA1 1AN
T: 01225 466991
F: 01225 496006
E: info-uk@altran.com
W: www.altran.co.uk

Alucast Ltd
Western Way,
Wednesbury,
W.Midlands WS10 7BW
T: 0121 556 6111
F: 0121 556 6111
E: aes@alucast.co.uk
W: www.alucast.co.uk

Aluminium Special Projects Ltd (ASP Group)
Unit 39, Second Ave,
The Pensnett Estate,
Kingswinford,
W.Midlands DY6 7UW
T: 01384 291900
F: 01384 400344
E: david@aspgroup.co.uk
W: www.aspgroup.co.uk

Aluminium Structures
Unit 5a, Aviation Park, Flint Rd,
Saltney Ferry,
Chester CH4 0GZ
T: 01244 531889
F: 01244 539412
E: info@allystructures.co.uk
W: www.allystructures.co.uk

Alvey & Towers
Bythorn House, 8 Nether St,
Harby,
Leics LE14 4BW
T: 01949 861894
E: office@alveyandtowers.com
W: www.alveyandtowers.com

Amalgamated Construction Ltd (AMCO)
Whaley Rd, Barugh,
Barnsley,
S.Yorks S75 1HT
T: 01226 243413
F: 01226 320202
E: info@amco.co.uk
W: www.amco.co.uk

Ambassador Train Travel
PO Box 79, Ventnor PO38 9BP
T: 01983 853708
E: info@ambassadortraintravel.co.uk
W: www.ambassadoetraintravel.co.uk

Amber Composites
94 Station Rd, Langley Mill,
Nottingham NG16 4BP
T: 01773 530899
F: 01773 768687
E: sales@ambercomposites.co.uk
W: www.ambercomposites.co.uk

AMCL Systems Engineering Ltd
221 St John St, Clerkenwell,
London EC1V 4LY
T: 020 7688 2561
F: 020 7688 2829
E: sky.crockford@amcl.com
W: www.amcl.com

Ameron UK Ltd
Bankside, Hull HU5 1SQ
T: 01482 341441
F: 01482 348350
E: sales.uk@ameron-bv.com
W: www.ameron-bv.com

Amery Construction Ltd
Amery House, Thirdway,
Wembley,
Middx HA9 0EL
T: 020 8903 1020
F: 020 8903 1560
E: reception@ameryrail.co.uk
W: www.ameryrail.co.uk

Ametek Airscrew
111 Windmill Rd,
Sunbury-on-Thames TW16 7E
T: 01932 765822
F: 01932 761098
E: mail.airscrew@ametek.co.uk
W: www.ametekaerodefense.com

Amey
The Sherard Building,
Edmund Halley Rd,
Oxford OX4 4DQ
T: 01865 713100
F: 01865 713357
E: ais@amey.co.uk
W: www.amey.co.uk
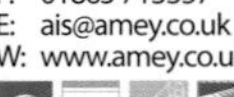
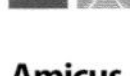
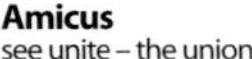

Amicus
see unite – the union

AMOT
Western Way,
Bury St Edmunds,
Suffolk IP33 3SZ
T: 01284 762222
F: 01284 760256
E: info@amot.com
W: www.amot.com

Amphenol Ltd
Thanet Way, Whitstable,
Kent CT5 3JF
T: 01227 773200
F: 01227 276571
E: info@amphenol.co.uk
W: www.industrial-amphenol.com

AMPL Ltd
see carillion

Amtrain Midlands Ltd
A38 Southbound, Fradley, Lichfield,
Staffs WS13 8RD
T: 01283 792633
F: 01283 792622
E: info@amtrain.co.uk
W: www.amtrain.co.uk

AMT Sybex Ltd
The Spirella Building, Bridge Rd,
Letchworth Garden City,
Herts SG6 4ET
T: 01462 476400
F: 01462 476401
E: info@amt-sybex.com
W: www.amt-sybex.com

Anders Elite Ltd
Dashwood House, 69, Old Broad St,
London EC2M 1NQ
T: 020 7256 5555
F: 020 7256 9898
E: rail@anderselite.com
W: www.anderselite.com

Anderson Precision Gearing Ltd
Flemington Industrial Park,
Motherwell ML1 2NT
T: 01698 260000
F: 01698 252010
E: enquiries@apg-gears.com
W: www.apg-gears.com

Anderton Concrete Products Ltd
Anderton Wharf, Soot Hill, Anderton,
Northwich, Cheshire CW9 6AA
T: 01606 79436
F: 01606 871590
E: sales@andertonconcrete.co.uk
W: www.andertonconcrete.co.uk

Andrew Muirhead & Son Ltd
273-289 Dunn St,
Glasgow G40 3EA
T: 0141 554 3724
F: 0141 554 3724
E: sales@muirhead.co.uk
W: www.muirhead.co.uk

Andrews Signs and Engravers
Units 9-10,
The Bull Commercial Centre,
Stockton-on-the-Forest,
York YO32 9LE
T: 01904 400800
W: www.andrewssigns.co.uk

Angel Trains Limited
Portland House,
Bressenden Place,
London SW1E 5BH
T: 020 7592 0500
F: 020 7592 0520
E: communications@angeltrains.co.uk
W: www.angeltrains.co.uk

Anixter Adhesives
3 Edmund St, Sheffield S2 4EB
T: 0114 275 5884
F: 0114 275 7169
E: enquiries@anixteradhesives.com
W: www.infast.com

Anixter (UK) Ltd
Unit A, The Beacons,
Warrington Rd, Risley,
Warrington WA3 6GB
T: 0870 242 2822
F: 01925 848006
E: railsales@anixter.com
W: www.anixter.com

Ansaldo STS
8-10 Great George St,
London SW1P 3EA
T: 020 7340 6100
W: www.ansaldo-signal.com

Antagrade Electrical Ltd
Victoria Building,
Lewin St,
Middlewich,
Cheshire CW10 9AT
T: 01606 833299
F: 01606 836959
E: enquiries@antagrade.co.uk
W: www.antagrade.co.uk

Antal International Network
170 Lanark Rd West,
Currie,
Edinburgh EH14 5NY
T: 0870 428 1745
F: 0870 428 1745
E: edinburgh@antal.com
W: www.antal.com

Antislip Antiwear Treads Int.
see aati
APB Group Ltd Ryandra House,
Ryandra Business Park,
Cheadle,
Stoke-on-Trent ST10 1SR
T: 01538 755377
F: 01538 755010
E: apbgroup@aol.com

APD Communications Ltd
Newlands Centre,
Inglemire Lane, Hull HU6 7TQ
T: 01482 808300
F: 01482 803901
E: info@apdcomms.com
W: www.apdcomms.com

Aperio Ltd
see fugro aperio

Apex Cables Ltd
St Johns Rd,
Meadowfield Ind Est,
Durham DH7 8RJ
T: 0191 378 7908
F: 0191 378 7809
E: apex@apexcables.co.uk
W: www.apexcables.co.uk

A Plant
see ashtead

Appleyards Consulting
72, Brighton Rd,
Horsham,
West Sussex RH13 5BU
T: 08705 275201
F: 08705 143047
E: mail@appleyards.co.uk
W: www.appleyards.co.uk

Allied Card Technology Ltd
Langley Gate,
Kington Langley,
Chippenham,
Wilts SN15 5SE
T: 01249 751200
F: 01249 751201
E: info@weareact.com
W: www.weareact.com

Applied Inspection Ltd
Bridge House, Bond St,
Burton upon Trent DE14 3RZ
T: 01283 515163
F: 01283 539729
E: ted@appliedinspection.co.uk
W: www.appliedinspection.co.uk

Application Solutions (Safety & Security) Ltd
Unit 17, Cliffe Ind. Est,
Lewes, E Sussex BN8 6JL
T: 01273 405411
F: 01273 405415
E: contactus@asl-control.co.uk
W: www.asl-control.co.uk

APT Skidata Ltd
The Power House,
Chantry Place, Headstone Lane,
Harrow,
Middlesex HA3 6NY
T: 020 8421 2211
F: 020 8428 6622
E: d.murphy@aptskidata.co.uk
W: www.aptcontrols-group.co.uk

Aqua Fabrications Ltd
Belmont House, Garnett Place,
Skelmersdale, Lancs WN8 9UB
T: 01695 51933
F: 01695 51891
W: www.aquafab.co.uk

Aquarius Railroad Technologies Ltd
Old Slenningford Farm,
Mickley, Ripon,
N Yorks HG4 3JB
T: 01765 635021
F: 01765 635022
E: enquiries@railrover.com
W: www.railrover.com

Arbil Lifting Gear
Providence St, Lye,
Stourbridge,
West Midlands DY9 8HS
T: 01384 424006
F: 01384 898814
E: info@arbil.co.uk
W: www.arbil.co.uk

Arcadia Alive Ltd
Parkfield House, Park St,
Stafford ST17 4AL
T: 0845 260 0126
F: 01785 214921
E: talk@arcadiaalive.com
W: www.arcadiaalive.com

Arcadis EC Harris
10 Furnival St, London EC4A 1YH
T: 020 7216 1000
W: www.arcadis-uk.com

Archer Signs & Panels Ltd
Unit 6 Daniels Way, Hucknall,
Nottingham NG15 7LL
T: 0115 927 3100
F: 0115 976 1110
E: brian@archersigns.co.uk
W: www.archersigns.co.uk

Areva Risk Management Consulting Ltd
Suite 7, Hitching Court,
Abingdon Business Park,
Abingdon, Oxon OX14 1RA
T: 01235 555755
F: 01235 525143
E: abingdon@arevarmc.com
W: www.arevarmc.com

Aries Power Solutions Ltd
Oaklands, Flordon Rd,
Creeting St Mary,
Ipswich IP6 8NH
T: 01449 720842
F: 01449 722846
E: john@ariesgen.co.uk
W: www.generating-sets.co.uk

Arlington Fleet Services Ltd
Railway Works, Campbell Rd,
Eastleigh, Hants SO50 5AD
T: 02380 696789
F: 02380 629118
E: info@arlington-fleet.co.uk
W: www.arlington-fleet.co.uk

ARM Engineering
Langstone Technology Park,
Langstone Rd, Havant,
Hants PO9 1SA
T: 02392 228228
F: 02392 228229
E: marketing@arm.co.uk
W: www.arm.co.uk

Arriva CrossCountry
see crosscountry trains

Arriva plc
1 Admiral Way,
Doxford International
Business Park, Sunderland SR3 3XP
T: 0191 520 000
F: 0191 520 4001
E: enquiries@arriva.co.uk
W: www.arriva.co.uk

Arriva Trains Wales
St Mary's House, 47 Penarth Rd,
Cardiff CF10 5DJ
T: 0845 606 1660
E: customer.relations@arrivatrainswales.co.uk
W: www.arrivatrainswales.co.uk

Arrow Cleaning & Hygeine Solutions
Rawdon Rd, Moira, Swadlincote,
Derbys DE12 6DA
T: 01283 221044
F: 01283 225731
E: sales@arrowchem.com
W: www.arrowchem.com

Arrowvale Electronics
Arrow Business Park, Shawbank Rd,
Lakeside, Redditch, Worcs B98 8YN
T: 01527 514151
F: 01527 514321
E: sales@arrowvale.co.uk
W: www.arrowvale.co.uk

Artel Rubber Company
Unit 11, Waterloo Park,
Wellington Rd, Bidford on Avon,
Warks B50 4JH
T: 01789 774099
F: 01789 774599
W: www.artelrubber.com

Arthur D Little Ltd
Unit 300, Science Park, Milton Rd,
Cambridge CB4 0XL
T: 01223 427100
F: 01223 427101
E: info.adl@adlittle.com
W: www.adl.com

Arthur Flury AG
CH-4543 Deitingen,
Switzerland
T: 0041 32613 3366
F: 0041 32613 3368
E: info@aflury.ch
W: www.aflury.ch

Arup
The Arup Campus, Blythe Gate,
Blythe Valley Park, Solihull,
West Midlands B90 8AE
T: 0121 213 3412
F: 0121 213 3001
E: rail@arup.com
W: www.arup.com/rail

Ashley Group
704 London Rd, North Cheam,
Sutton, Surrey SM3 9BY
T: 020 8644 4416
F: 020 8644 4417
E: colin@ashleygroup.co.uk
W: www.ashleygroup.co.uk

Ashtead Plant Hire Co Ltd (APlant)
102 Dalton Ave, Birchwood Park,
Birchwood, Warrington WA3 6YE
T: 0870 050 0797
F: 01925 281005
E: enquiries@aplant.com
W: www.aplant.com

Ashurst
Broadwalk House, 5 Appold St,
London EC2A 2HA
T: 020 7859 1897
F: 020 7638 1112
W: www.ashurst.com

ASL Contracts
see pitchmastic

ASLEF
75-77 St Johns St, Clerkenwell,
London EC1M 4NN
T: 020 7324 2400
F: 020 7490 8697
E: info@aslef.org.uk
W: www.aslef.org.uk

Aspec Engineering Ltd
Unit P1, Dales Manor Business Park,
Babraham Rd, Sawston,
Cambridge CB22 3TJ
T: 01223 836710
F: 01223 836294
E: info@aspec.co.uk
W: www.aspec.co.uk

Aspin Foundations Ltd
The Freight Yard, Hemel Station,
London Rd, Hemel Hempstead,
Herts HP3 9BE
T: 01442 236507
F: 01442 239096
E: info@aspingroup.com
W: www.aspingroup.com

Aspire Rail Consultants
see keltbray aspire

Asset international Structured Solutions
Stephenson St,
Newport NP19 4XH
T: 01633 637505
F: 01633 290519
E: koh@assetint.co.uk
W: www.assetint.co.uk

Asset-Pro Ltd
Concorde House,
24 Cecil Pashley Way,
Shoreham Airport,
W.Sussex BN43 5FF
T: 0845 120 2046
F: 01444 448071
E: info@asset-pro.com
W: www.asset-pro.com

Associated British Ports
150 Holborn,
London EC1N 2LR
T: 0207 430 1177
F: 020 7430 1384
E: pr@abports.co.uk
W: www.abports.co.uk

Associated Rewinds (Ireland) Ltd
Tallaght Business Park,
Whitestown,
Dublin 24, Ireland
T: 00353 1 452 0033
F: 00353 1 452 0476
E: sales@associatedrewinds.com
W: www.associatedrewinds.com

Associated Train Crew Union
PO Box 647, S72 8XU
T: 01226 716417
E: admin@atcu.org.uk
W: www.atcu.org.uk

Association of Community Rail Partnerships (ACoRP)
The Old Water Tower,
Huddersfield Railway Station,
St Georges Sq,
Huddersfield HD1 1JF
T: 01484 548926
F: 01484 481057
E: info@acorp.uk.com
W: www.acorp.uk.com

Association of Railway Training Providers (ARTP)
Kelvin House,
RTC Business Park,
London Rd,
Derby DE24 8UP
T: 01332 360033
F: 01332 366367
E: artp@neway-training.com
W: www.artp.co.uk

Association of Train Operating Companies (ATOC)
200 Aldersgate St,
London EC1 4HD
T: 020 7841 8062
E: enquiry@atoc.org
W: www.atoc.org

Association for Project Management
150 West Wycombe Rd,
High Wycombe,
Bucks HP12 3AE
T: 01494 460246
F: 01494 528937
E: info@apm.org.uk
W: www.apm.org.uk

Astrac Safety Training Solutions Ltd
Unit 2, Victoria Rd,
Stoke on Trent ST4 2HS
F: 01782 411490
M: 07878 041285
E: train@astractraining.co.uk
W: www.astractraining.co.uk

AST Recruitment Ltd
First Floor, Chase House, Park Plaza,
Heath Hayes,
Cannock,
Staffs WS12 2DD
T: 01543 331331
M: 07967 594097
E: iperry@ast-recruit.com
W: www.astrecruitment.co.uk

ATA Rail
see catalis

ATEIS UK Ltd
10 Hacche Lane Business Park,
Pathfields,
South Molton,
Devon EX36 3LH
T: 0845 652 1511
F: 0845 652 2527
E: neil.voce@ateis.co.uk
W: www.ateis.co.uk

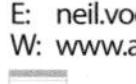

Athena Project Services
Mill Lane,
Barrow on Humber,
North Lincs DN17 7BD
T: 01469 533333
F: 01469 532233
E: david.tyerman@athenaprojectservices.com
W: www.athenaprojectservices.com

Atkins
Euston Tower,
286 Euston Road,
London NW1 3AT
T: 020 7121 2000
F: 020 7121 2111
E: rail@atkinsglobal.com
W: www.atkinsglobal.com

Atlantic Design Projects Limited
Branch Hill Mews, Branch Hill,
London NW3 7LT
T: 020 7435 1777
E: cg@atlanticdesign.uk.com
W: www.atlanticdesign.uk.com

Atlantis International Ltd
see karcher

Atlas Copco Compressors Ltd
Swallowdale Lane,
Hemel Hempstead, Herts HP2 7HA
T: 01442 261201
F: 01442 234791
E: gba.info@uk.atlascopco.com
W: www.atlascopco.co.uk

Atlas Copco Tools
Swallowdale Lane,
Hemel Hempstead,
Herts HP2 7EA
T: 01442 261202
F: 01442 240596
E: toolsuk_info@uk.atlascopco.com
W: www.atlascopco.co.uk

Atlas Rail Components
3.14 Warwick Mill,
Warwick Bridge,
Carlisle, Cumbria CA4 8RR
T: 01228 210167
F: 01228 510965
E: rpotter@atlasrail.co.uk
W: www.atlasrail.co.uk

ATOS Origin
4 Triton Square, Regents Place,
London NW1 3HG
T: 020 7830 4447
E: ukwebenquiries@atos.net
W: www.atos.net/transport

At Source QX Ltd
18 Eve St, Louth,
Lincs LN11 0JJ
T: 01507 604322
F: 01507 608513
E: mick@sourceqx.com
W: www.protecthear.co.uk

Aura Graphics Ltd
Venture House,
2 Arlington Square,
Downshire Way,
Bracknell RG12 1WA
T: 0845 052 5241
F: 0845 052 5242
E: info@auragraphics.com
W: www.auragraphics.com

AUS Ltd
1 Dearne Park Ind Est,
Park Mill Way,
Clayton West,
Huddersfield HD8 9XJ
T: 01484 860575
F: 01484 860576
E: sales@aus.co.uk
W: www.aus.co.uk

Austin Reynolds Signs
Augustine House,
Gogmore Lane,
Chertsey,
Surrey KT16 9AP
T: 01932 568888
F: 01932 566600
E: sales@austinreynolds.co.uk
W: www.austinreynolds.com

Autobuild Ltd
see pelma services and autobuild ltd

Autoclenz Holdings Plc
see react beyond cleaning

Autodrain
Wakefield Rd,
Rothwell Haigh,
Leeds LS26 0SB
T: 0113 205 9332
F: 0113 288 0999
E: mark@autodrain.net
W: www.autodrain.net

Autoglass
1 Priory Business Park,
Cardington,
Bedford MK44 3US
T: 01234 273636
E: debbie.barnes@autoglass.co.uk
W: www.autoglass.co.uk

Autoglym PSV
Letchworth Garden City,
Herts SG6 1LU
T: 01462 677766
F: 01462 686565
E: npro@autoglym.com
W: www.autoglym.com

Autolift GmbH
Mayrwiesstasse 16,
5300 Hallwang - Salzburg
T: 0043 662 450588 11
F: 0043 662 450588 18
E: a.foelsce@autolift.info
W: www.autolift.info

AVE Rail Products
see compin uk

Avery Weigh-Tronix
Foundry Lane, Smethwick,
West Midlands
T: 0845 366 7788
E: info@awtxglobal.com
W: www.awtxglobal.com

Avoidatrench Ltd
Brookes Lane,
Middlewich,
Cheshire CW10 0JQ
T: 01606 831600
F: 01606 831260
W: www.pochins.plc.uk/avoidatrench

Avondale Environmental Services Ltd
Fort Horsted,
Primrose Close,
Chatham, Kent ME4 6HZ
T: 01634 823200
F: 01634 844485
E: info@avondaleuk.com
W: www.avondaleuk.com

Axiom Rail
Lakeside Business Park,
Carolina Way, Doncaster DN4 5PN
T: 0870 140 5000
F: 0870 140 5009
E: sales@axiomrail.com
W: www.axiomrail.com

Axion Technologies
Lokesvej 7-9, 3400 Hilleroed,
Denmark
T: 0045 721 93500
F: 0045 721 93501
E: info@axiontech.dk
W: www.axiontech.dk

Axis Communications (UK) Ltd
Ground Floor, Gleneagles,
Belfry Business Centre, Colonial Way,
Watford WD24 4WH
T: 01923 211417
F: 01923 205589
W: www.axis.com/trains

Axminster Carpets Ltd
Woodmead Rd,
Axminster, Devon EX13 5PQ
T: 01297 630686
F: 01297 35241
E: sales@axminster-carpets.co.uk
W: www.axminster-carpets.co.uk

Axon Bywater
see bywater training

Azea Ltd
6 Dilton Terrace,
Amble, Morpeth,
Northumberland NE65 0DT
T: 01665 714000
E: info@azea.co.uk
W: www.azea.co.uk

Aztec Chemicals
Gateway,
Crewe CW1 6YY
T: 01270 655500
F: 01270 655501
E: info@aztecchemicals.com
W: www.aztecchemicals.com

B3 Cable Solutions
Delauneys House,
Delauneys Rd, Blackley,
Manchester M9 8FP
T: 0161 740 9151
F: 0161 795 8393
E: info@b3cables.com
W: www.b3cables.com

Babcock Rail
Kintail House, 3 Lister Way,
Hamilton International Park,
Blantyre G72 0FT
T: 01698 203005
F: 01698 203006
E: shona.jamieson@babcock.co.uk
W: www.babcock.co.uk/rail

Bache Pallets Ltd
Bromley St, Lye,
Stourbridge DY9 8HU
T: 01384 897799
F: 01384 410306
E: mike@bache-palletsltd.co.uk
W: www.bache-pallets.co.uk

BAE Systems
Marconi Way,
Rochester, Kent ME1 5XX
T: 01634 844400
F: 01634 205100
E: john.hawkins@baesystems.com
W: www.baesystems.com/hybridrive

Alfred Bagnall & Sons (North)
6, Manor Lane, Shipley,
West Yorks BD18 3RD
T: 01274 714800
F: 01274 530171
E: info@bagnalls.co.uk
W: www.bagnalls.co.uk

NG Bailey Rail
Denton Hall, Ilkley,
West Yorks LS29 0HH
T: 0800 140 4400
F: 01943 816117
E: enquiries@ngbailey.co.uk
W: www.ngbailey.co.uk

Baker Bellfield Ltd
Display House, Hortonwood 7,
Telford, Shropshire TF1 7GP
T: 01952 677411
F: 01952 670188
E: sales@bakerbellfield.co.uk
W: www.bakerbellfield.co.uk

Bakerail Services
4 Green Lane, Hail Weston, St Neots,
Cambs PE19 5JZ
T: 01480 471349
F: 01480 218044
E: info@bakerailservices.co.uk
W: www.bakerailservices.co.uk

Baldwin & Francis Ltd
President Park, President Way,
Sheffield S4 7UR
T: 0114 286 6000
F: 0114 286 6059
E: sales@baldwinandfrancis.com
W: www.baldwinandfrancis.com

Balfour Beatty Ground Engineering
Pavilion B, Ashwood Park,
Ashwood Way,
Basingstoke,
Hants RG23 8BG
T: 01256 400400
F: 01256 400401
E: neil.beresford@bbge.com
W: www.bbge.com

Balfour Beatty Rail
86 Station Road,
Redhill,
Surrey RH1 1PQ
T: 01737 785000
F: 01737 785100
E: info@bbrail.com
W: www.bbrail.com

Balfour Kilpatrick Ltd
Lumina Building,
40 Aislie Rd,
Hillington Park,
Glasgow G52 4RU
T: 0141 880 2001
F: 0141 880 2201
E: enquiry@balfourkilpatrick.com
W: www.balfourkilpatrick.com

Ballast Tools (UK) Ltd
7 Pure Offices, Kembrey Park,
Swindon SN2 8BW
T: 01793 697800
F: 01793 527020
E: sales@btukltd.com
W: www.btukltd.com

Ballyclare Ltd
Union House, Hempshaw Lane,
Stockport, Cheshire SK1 4LG
T: 0161 412 0000
F: 0161 412 0001
E: maggie.shaw@ballyclarelimited.com
W: www.ballyclarelimited.com

BAM Nuttall Ltd
St James House, Knoll Rd,
Camberley, Surrey GU15 3XW
T: 01276 63484
F: 01276 66060
E: headoffice@bamnuttall.co.uk
W: www.bamnuttall.co.uk

Bam Ritchies
Glasgow Rd, Kilsyth,
Glasgow G65 9BL
T: 01236 467000
F: 01236 467030
E: ritchies@bamritchies.co.uk
W: www.bamritchies.co.uk

R Bance & Co
Cockrow Hill House,
St Mary's Rd, Surbiton,
Surrey KT6 5HE
T: 020 8398 7141
F: 020 8398 4765
E: admin@bance.com
W: www.bance.com

Bank of Scotland Corporate
155 Bishopsgate, London EC2M 3YB
T: 020 7012 8001
F: 020 7012 9455
W: www.bankofscotland.co.uk/corporate

Baqus Group Plc
2/3 North Mews, London WC1N 2JP
T: 020 7831 1283
F: 020 7242 9512
E: enquiries@baqus.co.uk
W: www.baqus.co.uk

Barclays
1 Churchill Place,
London E14 5HP
T: 020 7116 5214
F: 020 7116 7653
E: rob.riddleston@barclayscorporate.com
W: www.barclays.co.uk/logistics_transport

Barcodes For Business Ltd
Buckland House, 56 Packhorse Rd,
Gerrards Cross SL9 8EF
T: 01753 888833
F: 01753 888834
E: info@barcodesforbusiness.co.uk
W: www.barcodesforbusiness.co.uk

Bardon Aggregates
see aggregate industries

Barhale Construction Plc
Unit 3, The Orient Centre,
Greycaine Rd, Watford,
Herts WD24 7JT
T: 0844 736 0090
F: 01923 474501
M: 07939 997529
E: samantha.davis@barhale.co.uk
W: www.barhale.co.uk

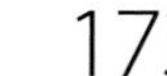

Barker Ross Recruitment
24 De Montford St,
Leicester LE1 7GB
T: 0800 0288 693
F: 0116 2550 811
E: people@barkerross.co.uk
W: www.barkerross.co.uk

Barnshaw Section Bending Ltd
Tipton Rd, Tividale,
Oldbury,
West Midlands
T: 0121 557 8261
F: 0121 557 5323
E: tony.farrington@barnshaws.com
W: www.barnshaws.com

Basic Solutions Ltd
see Int solutions ltd

H S Bassett
Coronet Way, Enterprise Park,
Morriston, Swansea SA6 8RH
T: 01792 790022
F: 01792 790033
E: info@hsbassett.co.uk
W: www.hsbassett.co.uk

BATT Cables
The Belfry, Fraser Rd, Erith,
Kent DA8 1QH
T: 01322 441166
F: 01322 440492
E: battindustrial.sales@batt.co.uk
W: www.batt.co.uk

BCM Glass Reinforced Concrete
Unit 22, Civic Industrial Park,
Whitchurch, Shropshire SY13 1TT
T: 01948 665321
F: 01948 666381
E: info@bcmgrc.com
W: www.bcmgrc.com/railhome

Beacon Rail Leasing Ltd
Floor 28, 30 St Mary Ave,
London EC3A 8BF
T: 020 7015 0030
F: 020 7015 0001
E: rail@beaconrail.com
W: www.beaconrail.com

Beakbane Bellows Ltd
Stourport Rd, Kidderminster,
Worcs DY11 7QT
T: 01562 820561
F: 01562 820560
E: amd@beakbane.co.uk
W: www.beakbane.co.uk

Bechtel Ltd
Bechtel House,
245 Hammersmith Rd,
Hammersmith, London W6 3DP
T: 020 8846 5111
F: 020 8846 4938
E: jgreen2@bechtel.com
W: www.bechtel.com

Beck & Pollitzer
Burnham rd, Dartford,
Kent DA1 5BD
T: 01322 223494
F: 01322 291859
E: dartford@beck-pollitzer.com
W: www.beck-pollitzer.com

Becorit GmbH
PO Box 189,
Congleton, Cheshire CW4 7FB
F: 01270 269000
M: 07866 424869
E: becorit@btinternet.com
W: www.becorit.de

Beejay Rail Ltd
79 Charles St, Springburn,
Glasgow G21 2PS
T: 0141 553 1133
F: 0141 552 5333
E: info@beejayrewinds.com
W: www.beejayrewinds.com

A Belco Engineering
Jubilee Ind. Est., Ashington,
Northumberland NE63 8UG
T: 01670 813275
F: 01670 851141
E: sales@a-belco.co.uk
W: www.a-belco.co.uk

Belden Solutions
Suite 13, Styal Rd,
Manchester M22 5WB
T: 0161 498 3724
F: 0161 498 3762
E: info@belden.com
W: www.belden.com

Bell & Pottinger
Bell & Webster Concrete Ltd
Alma Park Rd, Grantham,
Lincs NG31 9SE
T: 01476 562277
E: bellandwebster@eleco.com
W: www.eleco.com/bellandwebster

Bender UK Ltd
Low Mill Business Park,
Ulverston, Cumbria LA12 9EE
T: 01229 480123
F: 01229 480345
E: info@bender-uk.com
W: www.bender.org.uk

Bentley Systems UK Ltd
North Heath Lane, Horsham,
W Sussex RH12 5QE
T: 01403 259511
W: www.bentley.com

Bernstein Ltd
Unit One, Tintagel Way, Westgate,
Aldridge, West Midlands WS9 8ER
T: 01922 744999
F: 01922 457555
E: sales@bernstein-ltd.co.uk
W: www.bernstein-ltd.co.uk

Berry Sytems
Springvale Business &
Industrial Park,
Bilston,
Wolverhampton WV14 0QL
T: 01902 491100
F: 01902 494080
E: sales@berrysystems.co.uk
W: www.berrysystems.co.uk

Bestchart Ltd
6A, Mays Yard, Down Rd, Horndean,
Waterlooville, Hants PO8 0YP
T: 023 9259 7707
F: 023 9259 1700
E: info@bestchart.co.uk
W: www.bestchart.co.uk

Best Impressions
15 Starfield Rd,
London W12 9SN
T: 020 8740 6443
F: 020 8740 9134
E: talk2us@best-impressions.co.uk
W: www.best-impressions.co.uk

Beta Cable Management Systems Ltd
Nothway Lane,
Newtown Trading Est,
Tewkesbury GL20 8JG
T: 01684 274274
F: 01684 276266
W: www.betacable.com

Bevan Brittan
Fleet Place House,
2 Fleet Place,
Holborn Viaduct,
London EC4M 7RF
T: 0870 194 7710
F: 0870 194 7800
E: martin.fleetwood@bevanbrittan.com
W: www.bevanbrittan.com

Bewator Ltd
see siemens

BF Technology Ltd
Unit 6, Cobham Centre,
Westmead Industrial Est,
Westlea,
Swindon SN5 7UJ
T: 01793 498020
E: sales@bftechnology.co.uk
W: www.bftechnology.co.uk

BHSF Occupational Health Ltd
Banham Court, Hanbury Rd,
Stoke Prior, Bromsgrove,
Worcs B60 4JZ
T: 01527 577242
F: 01527 832618
E: admin@bhsfoh.co.uk
W: www.bhsf.co.uk

Bierrum International Ltd
Bierrum House, High St,
Houghton Regis,
Dunstable,
Beds LU5 5BJ
T: 01582 845745
F: 01582 845746
E: solutions@bierrum.co.uk
W: www.bierrum.co.uk

Bijur Delimon International
Wenta Business Centre,
1 Electric Ave, Innova Science Park,
Enfield EN3 7XU
T: 01432 262107
F: 01432 365001
E: chris.riley@bijurdelimon.co.uk
W: www.bijurdelimon.co.uk

Bingham Rail
Barrow Rd, Wincobank,
Sheffield S9 1JZ
T: 0870 774 5422
F: 0870 774 5423
E: info@trainwash.co.uk
W: www.trainwash.co.uk

Bircham Dyson Bell LLP
50 Broadway, London SW1H 0BL
T: 020 7227 7000
F: 020 7222 3480
E: enquirieslondon@bdb-law.co.uk
W: www.bdb-law.co.uk

Birchwood Price Tools
Birch Park, Park Lodge Rd,
Giltbrook,
Nottingham NG16 2AR
T: 0115 938 9000
F: 0115 938 9010
W: www.birdwoodpricetools.com

Birley Manufacturing Ltd
Birley Vale Ave,
Sheffield S12 2AX
T: 0114 280 3200
F: 0114 280 3201
E: jamestaylor@birleyml.com
W: www.birleyml.com

Birmingham Centre for Railway Research and Education
University of Birmingham,
Gisbert Kapp Building,
Edgbaston,
Birmingham B15 2TT
F: 0121 414 4291
E: j.grey@bham.ac.uk
W: www.railway.bham.ac.uk or www.rruka.org.uk

Birmingham Centre for Railway Research and Education
Rail Technology Unit,
Manchester Metropolitan University,
John Dalton Building, Chester St,
Manchester M1 5GD
T: 0161 247 6247
F: 0161 247 6840
E: j.grey@bham.ac.uk
W: www.rtu.mmu.ac.uk or rruka.org.uk

Birse Rail Ltd
see balfour beatty rail

Blackpool Transport Services
Rigby Rd, Blackpool,
Lancs FY1 5DD
T: 01253 473001
F: 01253 473101
E: enquiries@blackpooltransport.com
W: www.blackpooltransport.com

Bodyguard Workwear Ltd
Adams St,
Birmingham B7 4LS
T: 0121 380 1308
E: sales@bodyguardworkwear.co.uk
W: www.bodyguardworkwear.co.uk / www.railclothing.co.uk

Blom Aerofilms Ltd
The Astrolabe,
Cheddar Business Park, Cheddar,
Somerset BS27 3EB
T: 01934 745820
F: 01934 745825
E: uk.info@blomasa.com
W: www.blomasa.com

Blue I UK Ltd
see peli

BMAC Ltd
Units 13-14, Shepley Ind. Est.,
South Shepley Road, Audenshaw,
Manchester M34 5PW
T: 0161 337 3070
F: 0161 336 5691
E: enquiries@bmac.ltd.uk
W: www.bmac.ltd.uk

BMT Fleet Technology Ltd
12 Little Park Farm Rd, Fareham,
Hants PO15 7JE
T: 01489 553200
F: 01489 553101
E: uk@fleetech.com
W: www.fleetech.com / www.bmrail.com

BNP Paribas Real Estate
One Redcliff St,
Bristol BS1 6NP
T: 0117 984 8480
F: 0117 984 8401
W: www.realestate.bnpparibas.co.uk

BOC
Customer Service Centre,
Priestley Rd, Worsley,
Manchester M28 2UT
T: 0800 111 333
F: 0800 111 555
E: custserv@boc.com
W: www.bocindustrial.co.uk
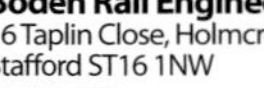

Boden Rail Engineering
16 Taplin Close, Holmcroft,
Stafford ST16 1NW

Boddingtons Electrical
Prospect House,
Queenborough Lane,
Great Notley,
Essex CM77 7AG
T: 01376 567490
F: 01376 567495
E: info@boddingtons-electrical.com
W: www.boddingtons-electrical.com

Bodycote Materials Testing
see exova

Bombardier Transportation UK Ltd
Litchurch Lane, Derby DE24 8AD
T: 01332 344666
F: 01332 289271
W: www.bombardier.com

Bonar Floors Ltd
see forbo flooring ltd

Bond Insurance Services
Salisbury House, 81 High St,
Potters Bar, Herts EN6 5AS
T: 01707 291200
F: 01707 291202
W: www.bond-insurance.co.uk

C F Booth Ltd
Armer St, Rotherham,
S.Yorks S60 1AF
T: 01709 559198
F: 01709 561859
E: info@cfbooth.com
W: www.cfbooth.com

Borders Railway Project
Transport Scotland,
7th Floor, Buchanan House,
58 Port Dundas Rd, Glasgow G4 0HS
T: 0141 272 7100
E: bordersrailway@transportscotland.gsi.gov.uk
W: www.bordersrailway.com

Bosch Rexroth Ltd
15 Cromwell Rd, St Neots,
Cambs PE19 2ES
T: 01480 223253
E: info@boschrexroth.co.uk
W: www.boschrexroth.co.uk

Bosch Security Systems
PO Box 750, Uxbridge,
Middx UB9 5ZJ
T: 01895 878088
F: 01895 878089
E: uk.securitysystems@bosch.com
W: www.boschsecurity.co.uk

Bott Ltd
Bude-Stratton Business Park, Bude,
Cornwall EX23 8LY
T: 01288 357788
F: 01288 352692
E: i-sales@bottltd.co.uk
W: www.bott-group.com

Bovis Lend Lease Consulting
142 Northolt Rd, Harrow,
Middx HA2 0EE
T: 020 8271 8000
F: 020 8271 8026
W: www.bovislendlease.com

Bowen Projects Ltd
1 Portway Close,
Coventry CV4 9UY
T: 02476 695550
F: 02476 695040
E: s.bowen@bowenprojects.co.uk
W: www.bowenprojects.co.uk

Bowmer & Kirkland Ltd
High Edge Court,
Heage, Belper,
Derbys DE56 2BW
T: 01773 853131
F: 01773 856170
E: general@bandk.co.uk
W: www.bowmerandkirkland.com

Boxwood Ltd
15 Old Bailey,
London EC4M 7EF
T: 020 3170 7240
F: 020 3170 7241
E: info@boxwood.com
W: www.boxwood.com

J.Boyle Associates Ltd
Bunch Meadows,
Woodway,
Princes Risborough,
Bucks HP27 0NW
F: 0870 460244
M: 07919 386100
E: info@jba.uk.net
W: www.jba.uk.net

Bradgate Containers
Leicester Rd, Shepshed,
Leics LE12 9EG
T: 01509 508678
F: 01509 504350
E: sales@bradgate.co.uk
W: www.bradgate.co.uk

The Bradley Group
Russell St, Heywood,
Lancs OL10 1NU
T: 01706 360353
F: 01706 366154
E: pce@johnbradleygroup.co.uk
W: www.johnbradleygroup.co.uk

Branch Line Society
53 Kemble Close,
Wistaston,
Crewe CW2 6XN
T: 01270 662396
M: 07921 949228
E: info@branchline.org.uk
W: www.branchline.org.uk

Brand-Rex Ltd
Speciality Cabling Solutions,
West Bridgewater St, Leigh,
Lancs WN7 4HB
T: 01942 265500
F: 01942 265576
E: speciality@brand-rex.com
W: www.brand-rex.com
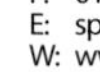
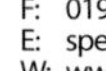
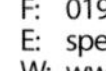
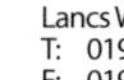

Bratts Ladders
Abbeyfield Rd,
Nottingham NG7 2SZ
T: 0115 986 6851/2221
F: 0115 986 1991
E: stephen@brattsladders.com
W: www.brattsladders.co.uk

Brecknell, Willis & Co Ltd
PO Box 10, Chard,
Somerset TA20 2DE
T: 01460 64941
F: 01460 66122
E: sales@brecknellwillis.com
W: www.brecknellwillis.com
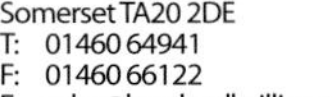

Bridgezone
22 Lower Town,
Sampford Peverill,
Tiverton,
Devon EX16 7BT
T: 01884 822899
E: info@bridgezoneltd.co.uk
W: www.bridgezoneltd.co.uk

Bridgeway Consulting Ltd
Bridgeway House,
Beeston Business Park,
Technology Drive, Beeston,
Nottingham NG9 1LA
T: 0115 919 1111
F: 0115 919 1112
E: enquiries@bridgeway-consulting.co.uk
W: www.bridgeway-consulting.co.uk

Bright Bond (BAC Group)
Stafford Park 11,
Telford,
Shropshire TF3 3AY
T: 01952 208524
F: 01952 290325
E: brightbond@bacgroup.com
W: www.brightbond.com

Britannia Washing Systems
see smith bros. & webb

British American Railway Services (BARS)
Stanhope Station,
Stanhope,
Bishop Auckland,
Co Durham DL13 2YS
T: 01388 526203
E: mfairburn@britamrail.com
W: www.rmslocotec.com

British Geological Survey
Kingsley Dunham Centre,
Keyworth,
Nottingham NG12 5GG
T: 0115 936 3100
F: 0115 936 3200
E: enquiries@bgs.ac.uk
W: www.bgs.ac.uk

British Springs
see gme springs

British Transport Police (BTP)
25 Camden Rd,
London NW1 9LN
T: 020 7830 8800
F: 020 7023 6952
E: first_contact@btp.pnn.police.uk
W: www.btp.police.uk

Briton Fabricators Ltd
Fulwood Rd South,
Huthwaite,
Sutton-in-Ashfield,
Notts NG17 2JW
T: 0115 963 2901
F: 0115 968 0335
E: sales@britonsltd.co.uk
W: www.britonsltd.co.uk

Brixwoth Engineering Co Ltd
Cracton Rd, Brixworth,
Northampton NN5 9BW
T: 01604 880338
F: 01604 880252
E: sales@benco.co.uk
W: www.benco.co.uk

Brockhouse Forgings Ltd
Howard St,
West Bromwich,
West Midlands B70 0SN
T: 0121 556 1241
F: 0121 502 3076
W: www.brockhouse.co.uk

Broadland Rail
7 York Rd, Woking,
Surrey GU22 7XH
T: 01483 725999
W: www.broadlandrail.com

Brown & Mason Ltd
Schooner Court,
Crossways Business Park,
Dartford DA2 6QG
T: 01322 277731
F: 01322 284152
E: b&m@brownandmason.ltd.uk
W: www.brownandmason.com

Browse Bion Architectural Signs
Unit 19/20,
Lakeside Park,
Medway City Est,
Rochester,
Kent ME2 4LT
T: 01634 710063
F: 01634 290112
E: sales@browsebion.com
W: www.browsebion.com

BRP Ltd
see keltbray

Brush Barclay
Caledonia Works,
West Longlands St,
Kilmarnock KA1 2QD
T: 01563 523573
F: 01563 541076
E: sales@brushtraction.com
W: www.brushtraction.com

Brush Traction
PO Box 17,
Loughborough,
Leics LE11 1HS
T: 01509 617000
F: 01509 617001
E: sales@brushtraction.com
W: www.brushtraction.com

Bruton Knowles
Greybrook House,
28 Brook St,
London W1
T: 0845 200 6489
F: 020 7499 8435
E: patrick.downes@brutonknowles.co.uk
W: www.brutonknowles.co.uk

Bryn Thomas Cranes Ltd
421 Chester Rd,
Flint CH6 5SE
T: 01352 733984
F: 01352 733990
E: dylan.thomas@brynthomascranes.com
W: www.brynthomascranes.com

BSP Consulting
12 Oxford St,
Nottingham NG1 5BG
T: 0115 840 2227
F: 0115 840 2228
E: info@bsp-consulting.co.uk
W: www.bsp-consulting.co.uk
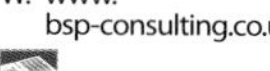

BTMU Capital Corporation
see beacon rail

C Buchanan
see colin buchanan

Buck and Hickman
Siskin Parkway East,
Middlemarch Business Park,
Coventry CV3 4FJ
T: 02476 306444
F: 02476 514214
E: enquiries@buckandhickman.com
W: www.buckandhickman.com

Buckingham Group Contracting Ltd
Silverstone Rd,
Stowe,
Bucks MK18 5LJ
T: 01280 823355
F: 01280 812830
E: mail@buckinghamgroup.co.uk
W: www.buckinghamgroup.co.uk

Buildbase
Gemini One,
5520 Oxford Business Park,
Cowley,
Oxford OX4 2LL
F: 01865 871700
E: tony.newcombe@buildbase.co.uk

Building Business Bridges UK Ltd
B4 Ashville Centre, Hampton Park,
Melksham, Wilts SN12 6ZE
T: 01225 707021
F: 01225 709361
E: hello@bbbuk.co.uk
W: www.bbbuk.co.uk

Bumar SP ZOO
Al Jana Pawla 11, no 11, PL-00-828 Warsaw, Poland
T: 0048 22 311 2512
F: 0048 22 311 2642
E: bumar@bumar.com
W: www.bumar.com

Bupa – Health Care Service Delivery
Battle Bridge House,
300 Grays Inn Rd,
London WC1X 8DU
T: 020 7800 6459/ 0845 600 3476
F: 0207 800 6461
E: lampkine@bupa.com
W: www.bupa.co.uk/business/large-business/occupational-health/railways

Bureau Veritas Weeks
Tower Bridge Court, 224-226 Tower Bridge Rd,
London SE1 2TX
T: 020 7550 8900
F: 020 7403 1590
E: transport.logistics@bureauveritas.com
W: www.bureauveritas.com

Burges Salmon LLP
Narrow Quay House, Narrow Quay,
Bristol BS1 4AH
T: 0117 939 2000
F: 0117 902 4400
E: email@burges-salmon.com
W: www.burges-salmon.com

Burns Carlton Plc
Simpson House, Windsor Court,
Clarence Drive, Harrogate HG1 2PE
T: 01423 792000
F: 01423 792001
E: contactus@burnscarlton.com
W: www.burnscarlton.com

Butler & Young (BYL) Ltd
Unit 3-4 Jansel House, Hitchin Road,
Luton LU2 7XH
T: 01582 404113
F: 01582 483420
E: debbie.clark@byl.co.uk
W: www.byl.co.uk

M Buttkereit Ltd
Unit 2, Britannia Rd, Sale,
Cheshire M33 2AA
T: 0161 969 5418
F: 0161 969 5419
E: sales@buttkereit.co.uk
W: www.buttkereit.co.uk

Bywater Training Ltd
3 Furtho Manor,
Northampton,
Old Stratford MK19 6NR
T: 01908 543900
F: 01908 543999
E: sales@bywatertraining.co.uk
W: www.bywatertraining.co.uk

C2C Rail Ltd
2nd Floor, Cutlers Court,
115 Houndsditch,
London EC3A 7BR
T: 020 7444 1800
F: 020 7444 1803
E: c2c.customerrelations@nationalexpress.com
W: www.c2c-online.co.uk

C2e Consulting
Ludlow House, The Avenue,
Stratford upon Avon,
Warks CV37 0RH
M: 07813 616939
E: ed.sharman@c2econsulting.co.uk
W: www.c2econsulting.co.uk

C3S Projects
Canal Mills, Elland Bridge, Elland,
Halifax HX5 0SQ
T: 01422 313800
E: info@c3s.com
W: www.c3s.com

C4 Industries Ltd
Unit 3-5, Yardley Rd,
Knowsley Ind Park, Kirkby,
Liverpool L33 7SS
T: 0151 548 7900
F: 0151 548 7184
E: paul.lighton@c4-industries.com
W: www.c4-industries.com

Cable & Wireless UK
Lakeside House, Cain Rd, Bracknell,
Berks RG12 1XL
T: 01908 845000
F: 01344 713961
W: www.cw.com

Cablecraft Ltd
Cablecraft House, Unit 3,
Circle Business Centre,
Blackburn Rd, Houghton Regis,
Beds LU5 5DD
T: 01582 606033
F: 01582 475419
E: claire@cablecraft.co.uk
W: www.cablecraft-rail.co.uk

Cable Detection Ltd
Unit 1, Blythe Park, Sandon Rd,
Cresswell, Stoke on Trent ST11 9RD
T: 01782 384630
F: 01782 388048
W: www.cabledetection.co.uk

Cable Management Products Ltd - Thomas & Betts Ltd
CMG House, Station Rd, Coleshill,
Birmingham B46 1HT
T: 01675 468 200
F: 01675 464930
E: info@cm-products.com
W: www.cm-products.com

Cabletec ICS Ltd
Sunnyside Rd,
Weston Super Mare BS23 3PZ
T: 01934 424900
F: 01934 636632
E: sales@cabletec.com
W: www.cabletec.com

CAF
see construcciones

Calco Services Ltd
Melrose House, 42 Dingwall Rd,
Croydon CR0 2NE
T: 020 8655 1600
F: 020 8655 1588
E: careers@calco.co.uk
W: www.calco.co.uk

Calmet Laboratory Services
Hampton House,
1 Vicarage Rd,
Hampton Wick,
Kingston upon Thames KT1 4EB
T: 0845 658 0770
F: 020 8614 8048
E: sales@lazgill.co.uk
W: www.calmet.co.uk

Campaign for Better Transport
12-18 Hoxton St,
London N1 6NG
T: 020 7613 0743
F: 020 7613 5280
E: info@bettertransport.org.uk
W: www.bettertransport.org.uk

Campbell Collins Ltd
Boulton Rd, Pin Green Ind. Area,
Stevenage, Herts SG1 4QX
T: 01438 369466
F: 01438 316465
E: sales@camcol.co.uk
W: www.camcol.co.uk

CAN Geotechnical
Smeckley Wood Close,
Chesterfield Trading Est.,
Chesterfield S40 3JW
T: 01246 261111
F: 01246 261626
E: info@can.ltd.uk
W: www.can.ltd.uk

C & S Equipment Ltd
9d Wingbury
Courtyard,
Leighton Rd,
Wingrave HP22 4LW
T: 01296 688500
F: 020 3070 0055
E: info@candsequipment.co.uk
W: www.candsequipment.co.uk

Cannon Technologies Ltd
Head Office, Queensway,
Stem Lane, New Milton,
Hants BH25 5NU
T: 01425 638148
F: 01425 619276
E: sales@cannontech.co.uk
W: www.cannontech.co.uk

Capita Architecture
90-98 Goswell Rd,
London EC1V 7DF
T: 020 7251 6004
F: 020 7253 3568
E: mervyn.franklin@capita.co.uk
W: www.capitaarchitecture.co.uk

Capita
Capita Symonds House,
Wood St, East Grinstead,
W. Sussex RH19 1UU
T: 01342 327161
F: 01342 315927
M: 07740 757683
E: john.mayne@capita.co.uk
W: www.capitasymonds.co.uk

Capital Project Consultancy Ltd (CPC)
see cpc

Capital Safety Group
Unit 7, Christleton Court,
Manor Park, Runcorn,
Cheshire WA7 1ST
T: 01928 571324
F: 01928 571325
E: csgne@csgne.co.uk
W: www.uclsafetysystems.com

C A P Productions Ltd
The Crescent,
Hockley,
Birmingham B18 5NL
T: 0121 554 9811
F: 0121 554 3791
E: sales@capproductions.co.uk
W: www.capproductions.co.uk
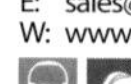

Captec Ltd
11 Brunel Way, Segensworth,
Fareham, Hants PO15 5TX
T: 01489 866066
F: 01489 866088
E: sales@captec.co.uk
W: www.captec.co.uk

Captrain UK Ltd
Asra House, 2nd Floor, 1 Long Lane,
London SE1 4PG
T: 020 7939 1900
F: 020 7939 1901
E: sales@captrain.co.uk
W: www.captrain.co.uk

Cardev International
see ecolube

Cargo-D Ltd
32 Sydney Rd, Haywards Heath,
West Sussex RH16 1QA
T: 01444 300160
F: 0845 051 8771
E: dirk.ottermans@cargo-d.co.uk
W: www.cargo-d.co.uk

Carillion Rail
24 Birch St,
Wolverhampton WV1 4HY
T: 01902 422431
F: 01902 316165
E: railenquiries@carillionplc.com
W: www.carillionrail.com

Carlbro Group
see grontmij

Carlisle Support Services
Wallace House,
4 Falcon Way, Shire Park,
Welwyn Garden City AL7 1TW
T: 01707 824200
E: info@carlislesupportservices.com
W: www.carlislesupportservices.com

Carlow Precast Tanks UK Ltd
Gunnery House, The Royal Arsenal,
Woolwich, London SE18 6SW
T: 01538 753333
F: 0870 493 1409
E: sales@carlowprecasttanks.com
W: www.carlowprecasttanks.com

Carlton Technologies Ltd
Unit 4, Church View Business Park,
Coney Green Rd, Clay Cross,
Chesterfield, Derbys S45 9HA
T: 01246 861330
F: 01246 251466
E: sales@carltontech.co.uk
W: www.carltontech.co.uk

Carson Industries Ltd
IDA Industrial Est.,
Racecourse Rd,
Roscommon, Ireland
T: 00353 9066 25922
F: 00353 9066 25921
E: sales@carsoneurope.com
W: www.carsoneurope.com / www.multiduc.com

Carver Engineering Services Ltd
11 Brunel Close,
Brunel Ind. Est,
Blyth Rd, Harworth,
Doncaster DN11 8QA
T: 01302 751900
F: 01302 757026
E: alan@carvereng.co.uk
W: www.carvereng.co.uk

Cass Hayward LLP
York House, Welsh St,
Chepstow,
Monmouthshire NP16 5UW
T: 01291 626994
F: 01291 626306
E: office@casshayward.com
W: www.casshayward.com

Catalis
see tq catalis

Caterpillar (Progress Rail Services)
Eastfield,
Peterborough PE1 5NA
T: 01733 583000
E: mcdonald_michael@cat.com
W: www.progressrail.com

Cats Solutions Ltd
Two Rushy Platt, Caen View,
Swindon,
Wilts SN5 8WQ
T: 01793 432913
F: 01793 490270
E: sales@cats-solutions.co.uk
W: www.cats-solutions.com

CB Rail S.a.r.l
6 Rue Jean Monnet,
L2180 Luxembourg
F: 020 7158 2701
M: 07595 123440
W: www.cbrail.com

CCD Design and Ergonomics
Northdown House, 11-
21 Northdown St, London N1 9BN
T: 0207 593 2900
E: info@ccd.org.uk
W: www.ccd.org.uk

CCL Rail Training
Scope House, Weston Rd,
Crewe CW1 6DD
T: 01270 252400
E: info@ccltraining.com
W: www.ccltraining.com

CCP Composites
16/32 Rue Henri Regnault,
La Defense 6,
92062 Paris La Defense cedex,
France
T: 00331 4796 9850
F: 00331 4796 9986
M: 07896 094628
E: kevin.louis@ccpcomposites.com
W: www.ccpcomposites.com

CDC Draincare Ltd
Unit 1, Chatsworth Ind. Est, Percy St,
Leeds LS12 1EL
T: 0845 644 6130
E: enquiries@cdc-draincare.co.uk
W: www.cdc-draincare.co.uk

CDL (Collinson Dutton Ltd)
see ghd

CDM-UK
PO Box 7035, Melton Mowbray,
Leics LE13 1WG
T: 01664 482486
F: 01664 482487
E: info@cdm-uk.co.uk
W: www.cdm-uk.co.uk

CDS Rail Ltd
1570, Parkway, Solent Business Park,
Portsmouth PO15 7AG
T: 01489 571771
F: 01489 571555
E: sales@cdsrail.com
W: www.cdsrail.com

Cembre Ltd
Dunton Park,
Kingsbury Rd, Curdworth,
Sutton Coldfield B76 9EB
T: 01675 470440
F: 01675 470220
E: sales@cembre.co.uk
W: www.cembre.co.uk

Cemex Rail Products
Aston Church Rd, Washwood Heath,
Saltley, Birmingham B8 1QF
T: 0121 327 0844
F: 0121 327 7545
W: www.cemex.co.uk

Centinal Group
174 Bromyard Rd, St Johns,
Worcester WR2 5EE
T: 01905 748569
F: 01905 420700
E: les@mfhhydraulics.co.uk
W: www.mfhhydraulics.co.uk

Central Engineering & Hydraulic Services Ltd
T: 01905 748569
F: 01905 420700
E: chris@cehsltd.co.uk
W: www.cehsltd.co.uk

Centregreat Rail Ltd
Ynys Bridge, Heol yr Ynys,
Tongwynlais, Cardiff CF15 7NT
T: 02920 815661
F: 02920 815660
E: rail@centregreat.net
W: www.centregreatrail.co.uk

Centro
Customer Relations,
16 Summer Lane,
Birmingham B19 3SD
T: 0121 200 2787
W: www.centro.org.uk

Charcon
see aggregate industries

Ch2m Hill
43 Brook Green, London W6 7EF
T: 01332 222676
F: 01332 222621
M: 07702 779748
E: chris.hanson@ch2m.com
W: www.ch2m.com

Charles Endirect Ltd
Wessex Way,
Wincanton Business Park,
Wincanton, Somerset BA9 9RR
T: 01963 828400
F: 01963 828401
E: info@charlesendirect.com
W: www.charlesendirect.com

The Chartered Institute of Logistics and Transport (UK) (CILT)
Logistics and Transport Centre,
Earlstrees Court, Earlstrees Rd,
Corby NN17 4AX
T: 01536 740100
F: 01536 740101
E: enquiry@ciltuk.org.uk
W: www.ciltuk.org.uk

Charter Security Plc
Cambridge House, Cambridge Rd,
Barking, Essex IG11 8NR
T: 020 7507 7717
E: info@charter-security.co.uk
W: www.charter-security.co.uk

CHB & W Buildings & Railway Contractors
Unit 9, Skein Enterprises, Hodsall St,
Sevenoaks, Kent TN15 7LM
T: 01732 824687
F: 01732 823285
E: admin@chbw.co.uk
W: www.chbw.co.uk

Chela Ltd
78 Bilton Way, Enfield,
Middx EN3 7LW
T: 020 8805 2150
F: 020 8443 1868
E: tony.philippou@chela.co.uk
W: www.chela.co.uk

Chester le Track Ltd
see the trainline

Chieftain Trailers Ltd
207 Coalisland Rd,
Dungannon,
Co Tyrone BT71 4DP
T: 028 8774 7531
F: 028 8774 7530
E: sales@chieftaintrailers.com
W: www.chieftaintrailers.com

Chiltern Railways
2nd Floor, Western House,
Rickfords Hill, Aylesbury, Bucks
T: 08456 005165
F: 01296 332126
E: marketing@chilternrailways.co.uk
W: www.chilternrailways.co.uk

Chloride Power Protection
see emerson network power

Chubb Systems Ltd
Shadsworth Rd, Blackburn BB1 2PR
T: 0844 561 1316
F: 01254 667663
E: systems-sales@chubb.co.uk
W: www.chubbsystems.co.uk

Cintec International Ltd
Cintec House, 11 Gold Tops,
Newport,
S.Wales NP20 4PH
T: 01633 246614
F: 01633 246110
E: johnbrooks@cintec.co.uk
W: www.cintec.co.uk

CIRAS
Block 2, Angel Square,
1 Torrens St,
London EC1V 1NY
T: 0800 410 1101
E: info@ciras.org.uk
W: www.ciras.org.uk

CITI
Lovat Bank, Silver St,
Newport Pagnell,
Bucks MK16 0EJ
T: 01908 283600
F: 01908 283601
E: bdu@citi.co.uk
W: www.citi.co.uk

Cityspace Ltd
Astley House,
33 Notting Hill Gate,
London W11 3QJ
T: 020 7313 8400
F: 020 7313 8401
E: enquiries@cityspace.com
W: www.cityspace.com

CJ Architecture
Earl Business Centre, Office 20, E3,
Dowry St, Oldham OL8 2PF
T: 0161 620 8834
M: 07845 571351
E: enquiries@cjarchitecture.co.uk
W: www.cjarchitecture.co.uk

CJ Associates Ltd
26 Upper Brook St,
London W1K 7QE
T: 020 7529 4900
F: 020 7529 4929
E: nharrison@cjassociates.co.uk
W: www.cjassociates.co.uk

Clancy Docwra
Clare House, Coppermill Lane,
Harefield, Middx UB9 6HZ
T: 01895 823711
F: 01895 825263
E: enquiries@theclancygroup.co.uk
W: www.theclancygroup.co.uk

R.S. Clare & Co Ltd
8-14, Stanhope St,
Liverpool L8 5RQ
T: 0151 709 2902
F: 0151 709 0518
E: info@rsclare.co.uk
W: www.rsclare.com

Class 40 Preservation Society
38 Watkins Drive,
Prestwich,
Manchester M25 0DS
M: 075000 40145
E: chairman@cfps.co.uk
W: www.cfps.co.uk

CLD Fencing Systems
Unit 11,
Springvale Business Centre,
Millbuck Way,
Sandbach,
Cheshire CW11 3HY
T: 01270 764751
F: 01270 757503
E: sales@cld-fencing.com
W: www.cld-fencing.com

CLD Services
170 Brooker Rd,
Waltham Abbey EN9 1JH
T: 01992 702300
E: contact@cld-services.co.uk
W: www.cld-services.co.uk

Cleartrack
Salcey-EVL Ltd,
The Old Woodyard,
Forest Rd, Hanslope,
Milton Keynes MK19 7DE
T: 01908 516250
E: info@cleartrack.co.uk
W: www.cleartrack.co.uk

Clemtech Rail
9 The Spinney,
Parklands Business Pk,
Forest Rd, Denmead,
Waterlooville,
Hants PO7 6AR
T: 0845 223 5303
F: 0845 223 5313
E: rail@clemtech.co.uk
W: www.clemtech.co.uk

Cleshar Contract Services Ltd
Heather Park House,
North Circular Rd,
Stonebridge,
London NW10 7NN
T: 020 8733 8888
F: 020 8733 8899
E: info@cleshar.co.uk
W: www.cleshar.co.uk

Cleveland Bridge Uk
PO Box 27, Yarm Rd,
Darlington DL1 4DE
T: 01325 381188
F: 01325 382320
W: www.clevelandbridge.com

Clyde Process Ltd
Carolina Court, Lakeside,
Doncaster DN4 5RA
T: 01302 321313
F: 01302 554400
E: dbogovac@clydeprocess.co.uk
W: www.clydeprocess.co.uk

CMCR Ltd
see survey first ltd

CML
see construction marine

CMS Cameron McKenna
Mitre House,
160 Aldersgate St,
London EC1A 4DD
T: 020 7367 2113
F: 020 7367 2000
E: jonathan.beckitt@cms-cmck.com
W: www.law-now.com

Cobham Technical Services (ERA Technology Ltd)
Cleeve Rd,
Leatherhead,
Surrey KT22 7SA
T: 01372 367030
F: 01372 367102
E: era.rail@cobham.com
W: www.cobham.com/technicalservices

Co Channel Electronics
Victoria Rd, Avonmouth,
Bristol BS11 9DB
T: 0117 982 0578
F: 0117 982 6166
E: sales@co-channel.co.uk
W: www.co-channel.co.uk

COE Ltd
Photon House, Percy St,
Leeds LS12 1EG
T: 0113 230 8800
F: 0113 279 9229
E: sales@coe.co.uk
W: www.coe.co.uk

Coffey Geotechnics
Atlantic House, Atls Business Park,
Simonsway, Manchester M22 5PR
T: 0161 499 6800
F: 0161 499 6802
E: julia_cartmell@coffey.com
W: www.coffey.com

COLAS Rail
Dacre House, 19 Dacre Street,
London SW1H 0DQ
T: 020 7593 5353
F: 020 7593 5343
E: enquiries@colasrail.co.uk
W: www.colasrail.co.uk

Colin Buchanan
see skm colin buchanan

Collis Engineering Ltd
Salcombe Rd, Meadow Lane Ind. Est,
Alfreton, Derbys DE55 7RG
T: 01773 833255
F: 01773 520693
E: sales@collis.co.uk
W: www.collis.co.uk

Collis Engineering Civils Division
Salcombe Rd, Meadow Lane Ind. Est,
Alfreton, Derbys DE55 7RG
T: 01773 833255
F: 01773 520693
E: sales@collis.co.uk
W: www.signalhousegroup.co.uk

Comech Metrology Ltd
Castings Rd, Derby DE23 8YL
T: 01332 867700
F: 01332 867707
E: sales@comech.co.uk
W: www.comech.co.uk

Commend UK Ltd
Commend House, Unit 20,
M11 Business Link,
Parsonage Lane,
Stansted,
Essex CM24 8GF
T: 01279 872020
F: 01279 814735
M: 07584 474988
E: sales@commend.co.uk
W: www.commend.co.uk

Compass Group
Rivermead, Oxford Rd,
Denham,
Uxbridge UB9 4BF
T: 01895 554554
F: 01895 554555
W: www.compass-group.co.uk

Compass Tours
46 Hallville Rd,
Liverpool L18 0HR
T: 0151 722 1147
F: 0151 722 0297
E: info@compasstoursbyrail.co.uk
W: www.compasstoursbyrail.co.uk

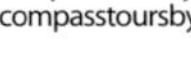

Compass Performance Software
Loughborough Technology Centre,
Epinal Way,
Loughborough LE11 3GE
T: 01509 632625
E: enquiries@sis-limited.co.uk
W: www.sis-limited.co.uk

Competence Assurance Solutions Ltd
221 St John St,
Clerkenwell,
London EC1V 4LY
T: 020 7688 2840
F: 020 7688 2829
E: info@casolutions.co.uk
W: www.casolutions.co.uk

Complete Drain Clearance
49 Weeping Cross,
Stafford ST17 0DG
T: 01785 665909
F: 01785 664944
E: completedrainclearance@yahoo.co.uk
W: www.completedrainclearance.co.uk

Complus Teltronic
see commend uk ltd

Comply Serve Ltd
Number 1, The Courtyard,
707 Warwick Rd, Solihull B91 3DA
T: 0121 711 2185
M: 07547 120619
E: chris.angus@complyserve.com
W: www.complyserve.com

Concept Rail Limited
Unit 5, Hailey Rd,
Hailey Rd. Business Park, Erith,
Kent DA18 4AA
T: 020 8311 3950
F: 020 8312 2066
E: info@conceptrail.com
W: www.conceptrail.com

Conductix-Wampfler Ltd (Insul 8)
1 Michigan Ave, Salford M50 2GY
T: 0161 848 0161
F: 0161 873 7017
E: info.uk@conductix.co.uk
W: www.conductix.co.uk

Confederation of Passenger Transport UK
Drury House, 34-43 Russell St,
London WC2B 5HA
T: 020 7240 3131
F: 020 7240 6565
E: admin@cpt-uk.org
W: www.cpt-uk.org

Consillia Ltd
see donfabs and consillia ltd

Construcciones y Auxiliar de Ferrocarriles SA (CAF)
The TechnoCentre, Puma Way,
Coventry CV1 2TT
T: 02476 158195
F: 0034 914 366008
E: caf@caf.net
W: www.caf.net

Construction Marine Ltd
The Coach House,
Mansion Gate Drive,
Chapel Allerton, Leeds LS7 4SY
T: 0113 262 4444
F: 0113 262 4400
E: info@cml.uk.com
W: www.cml-civil-engineering.co.uk

Containerlift
PO Box 582, Great Dunmow,
Essex CM6 3QX
T: 0800 174 546
F: 0800 174 547
E: joostbaker@containerlift.co.uk
W: www.containerlift.com

Continental Contitech
Chestnut Field House,
Chestnut Field, Rugby,
Warks CV21 2PA
T: 01788 571482
F: 01788 542245
W: www.contitech.co.uk

Cook Rail
see william cook

Cooper and Turner Ltd
Templeborough Works, Sheffield Rd, Sheffield S9 1RS
T: 0114 256 0057
F: 0114 244 5529
E: sales@cooperandturner.co.uk
W: www.cooperandturner.com

Cooper B-Line
Walrow Ind. Est, Highbridge, Somerset TA9 4AQ
T: 01278 783371
F: 01278 789037
E: sales@cooperbline.co.uk
W: www.cooperbline.co.uk

Cooper Bussmann (UK) Ltd
Burton-on-the-Wolds, Leics LE12 5TH
T: 01509 882600
W: www.cooperbussmann.com

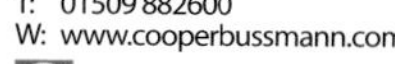

Copon E Wood Ltd
see 3m ppd

Cordek Ltd
Spring Copse Business Park, Slinfold, West Sussex RH13 0SZ
T: 01403 799600
F: 01403 791718
E: sales@cordek.com
W: www.cordek.com

Corehard Ltd
Viewpoint, Babbage Rd, Stevenage, Herts SG1 2EQ
T: 01438 225102
F: 01438 213721
E: info@corehard.com
W: www.corehard.com

Coronet Rail Ltd
see portec rail

Corporate College
Derby College, Prince Charles Ave, Deby DE22 4LR
T: 01332 520145
E: enquiries@derby-college.ac.uk
W: www.corporatecollege.co.uk

Correl Rail Ltd
See sgs correl rail

JB Corrie & Co Ltd
Frenchmans Rd, Petersfield, Hants GU32 3AP
T: 01730 237129
F: 01730 264915
E: mhickman@jbcorrie.co.uk
W: www.jbcorrie.co.uk

Corus Cogifer
See vossloh cogifer uk

Corus Rail Infrastructure Services
see tata steel products

Corys T.E.S.S
74 Rue des Martyrs, 38027 Grenoble, France
T: 0033 476 288200
F: 0033 476 288211
W: www.corys.com

Cosalt Ltd
see ballyclare ltd

Costain Ltd - Rail Sector
Costain House, Vanwall Business Park, Maidenhead, Berks SL6 4UB
T: 01628 842310
E: gren.edwards@costain.com
W: www.costain.com

Cowans Sheldon
The Clarke Chapman Group Ltd, PO Box 9, Saltmeadows Rd, Gateshead NE8 1SW
T: 0191 477 2271
F: 0191 477 1009
E: martin.howell@clarkechapman.co.uk
W: www.cowanssheldon.co.uk

Covtec Ltd
Allens West, Eaglescliffe Logistics Centre, Durham Rd, Eaglescliffe, Stockton on Tees TS16 0RW
M: 07776 148839
E: info@covtec.co.uk
W: www.covtec.co.uk

Coyle Personnel Plc
Hygeia, 66-68 College Rd, Harrow, Middx HA1 1BE
T: 020 8901 6619
F: 020 8901 6706
M: 07899 074370
E: roger@coyles.co.uk
W: www.coylerail.co.uk

CPC Project Services LLP
5th Floor, Quality House, 6-9 Quality Court, Chancery Lane, London WC2A 1HP
T: 020 7539 4750
F: 020 7539 4751
E: andy.norris@cpcprojectservices.com
W: www.cpcprojectservices.com

CP Films Solutia (UK) Ltd
13 Acorn Business Centre, Northarbour Rd, Cosham PO6 3TH
T: 02392 219112
F: 02392 219102
W: www.llumar.eu.com

C P Plus Ltd
10 Flask Walk, Camden, London NW3 1HE
T: 020 7431 4001
F: 020 7435 3280
E: info@cp-plus.co.uk
W: www.cp-plus.co.uk

Craig & Derricott Ltd
Hall Lane, Walsall Wood, Walsall WS9 9DP
T: 01543 375541
F: 01543 452610
E: sales@craiganderricott.com
W: www.craiganderricott.com

Cranfield University
College Rd, Cranfield, Beds MK43 0AL
T: 01234 750111
E: info@cranfield.ac.uk
W: www.cranfield.ac.uk/soe/rail-investgation

Creative Rail Dining
PO Box 10375, Little Waltham, Chelmsford, Essex CM1 9JW
T: 01255 556222
E: graham@creativeraildining.co.uk
W: www.creativeraildining.co.uk

Creactive Design
22 New St, Leamington, Warks CV31 1HP
T: 01926 833113
F: 01926 832788
E: neil@creactive-design.co.uk
W: www.creactive-design.co.uk

Critical Power Supplies Ltd
Unit F, Howlands Business Park, Thame, Oxon OX9 3GQ
T: 01844 340122
E: sales@critical.co.uk
W: www.criticalpowersupplies.co.uk

Critical Project Resourcing Ltd
6 Blighs Rd, Blighs Meadow, Sevenoaks, Kent TN13 1DA
T: 01732 455300
F: 01732 458447
E: rail@cpresourcing.co.uk
W: www.cpresourcing.co.uk

CrossCountry
5th Floor, Cannon House, 18 Priory Queensway, Birmingham B4 6BS
T: 0121 200 6000
F: 0121 200 6003
E: richard.gibson@crosscountrytrains.co.uk
W: www.crosscountrytrains.co.uk

Crossrail Ltd
25 Canada Square, Canary Wharf, London E14 5LQ
T: 0845 602 3813
E: helpdesk@crossrail.co.uk
W: www.crossrail.co.uk

Cross Services Group
Cross House, Portland Centre, Sutton Rd, St Helens WA9 3DR
T: 01744 458000
F: 01744 458099
E: martinclementson@crossgroup.co.uk
W: www.crossgroup.co.uk

Crouch Waterfall & Partners Ltd
Solly's Mill, Mill Lane, Godalming, Surrey GU7 1EY
T: 01483 425314
F: 01483 425814
E: office@cwp.co.uk
W: www.cwp.co.uk

Crowd Dynamics
21 Station Rd West, Oxted, Surrey RH8 9EE
T: 01883 718690
F: 08700 516196
E: enquiries@crowddynamics.com
W: www.crowddynamics.com

Croylek Ltd
23 Ullswater Cres, Coulsdon, Surrey CR5 2UY
T: 020 8668 1481
F: 020 8660 0750
E: sales@croylek.co.uk
W: www.croylek.co.uk

CSC
Royal Pavilion, Wellesley Rd, Aldershot GU11 1PZ
T: 01252 534000
F: 01252 534100
E: uk-consumer@csc.com
W: www.csc.com

CSRE Ltd
78 York St, London W1H 1DF
T: 0207 193 7351
F: 0203 514 2989
E: info@csre.co.uk
W: www.csre.co.uk

Cubic Transportation Systems
AFC House, Honeycrock Lane, Salfords, Redhill, Surrey RH1 5LA
T: 01737 782362
F: 01737 789759
E: jennifer.newell@cubic.com
W: www.cubic.com/cts

Cubis Industries
Lurgan, Co Armagh BT66 6LN
T: 0151 548 7900
F: 0151 548 7184
E: info@cubisindustries.com
W: www.cubisindustries.com

Cudis Ltd
Power House, Parker St, Bury BL9 0RJ
T: 0161 765 3000
F: 0161 705 2900
E: sales@cudis.co.uk
W: www.cudis.co.uk

Cummins
Yarm Rd, Darlington DL1 4PW
T: 01327 886464
F: 0870 241 3180
E: cabo.customerassistance@cummins.com
W: www.everytime.cummins.com

Cyril Sweett
60 Grays Inn Rd, London W1X 8AQ
T: 020 7061 9000
F: 020 7430 0603
E: eryl.evans@sweettgroup.com
W: www.sweettgroup.com

D2 Rail and Civils
1st Floor, Langton House, Bird St, Lichfield WS13 6PY
E: david@d2railandcivils.co.uk
W: www.d2railandcivils.co.uk

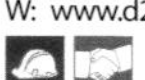

DAC Ltd
Unit 28, Lomeshaye Business Village, Turner Rd, Nelson, Lancs BB9 7DR
T: 01282 447000
F: 0845 280 1915
E: sales@daclimited.co.uk
W: www.daclimited.co.uk

Dailys UK Ltd
see novah

Dalkia Rail
5 Limeharbour Court, Limeharbour, London E14 9RH
T: 01784 496200
F: 01784 496222
E: carol.taylor@dalkia.co.uk
W: www.dalkia.co.uk

Dallmeier Electronic UK Ltd
Dallmeier House, 3 Beaufort Trade Park, Pucklechurch, Bristol BS16 9QH
T: 0117 303 9303
F: 0117 303 9302
E: dallmeieruk@dallmeier-electronic.com
W: www.dallmeier-electronic.com

D&D Rail Ltd
Time House, Time Square, Basildon, Essex SS14 1DJ
T: 01268 520000
F: 01268 520011
E: info@ddrail.com
W: www.ddrail.com

Dartford Composites Ltd
Unit 1, Ness Rd, Erith, Kent DA8 2LD
T: 01322 350097
F: 01322 359438
E: sales@dartfordcomposites.co.uk
W: www.dartfordcomposites.co.uk

Data Display UK Ltd
3 The Meadows, Waterberry Drive, Waterlooville, Hants PO7 7XX
T: 023 9224 7500
F: 023 9224 7519
E: sales@datadisplayuk.com
W: www.datadisplayuk.com

Datasys Ltd
Carrington Business Park, Manchester M31 4ZU
T: 0161 776 4206
M: 07801 497515
E: info@datasys.co.uk
W: www.datasys.co.uk

Data Systems & Solutions
see optimized systems & solutions

Datum - Composite Products
22 Longbridge Lane, Derby DE24 8UJ
T: 01332 386300
F: 01332 385487
M: 07973 621086
E: composites@datum-patterns.co.uk
W: www.datum-patterns.co.uk

David Brice Consultancy
11 Sebastian Ave, Shenfield, Brentwood, Essex CM15 8PN
T: 01277 221422
F: 01277 263614
M: 07721 657521
E: davidpbrice@aol.com
W: www.bricerail.co.uk

David Brown Gear Systems Ltd
Park Gear Works, Lockwood, Huddersfield HD4 5DD
T: 01484 465664
F: 01484 465587
E: soldroyd@davidbrown.com
W: www.davidbrown.com

David Simmonds Consultancy
Suite 14, Millers Yard, Mill Lane, Cambridge CB2 1RQ
T: 01223 316098
E: dsc@davidsimmonds.com
W: www.davidsimmonds.com

David Simmonds Consultancy
7-9 North St. David St , Edinburgh EH2 1AW
T: 0131 524 9475

Davis Langdon – an AECOM Company
MidCity Place, 71 High Holborn, London WC1V 6QS
T: 020 7061 7000
W: www.davislangdon.com/eme

WH Davis Ltd
Langwith Rd, Langwith Junction, Mansfield, Notts NG20 9SA
T: 01623 741600
F: 01623 744474
W: www.whdavis.co.uk

Davis Pneumatic Systems Ltd
Huxley Close, Newnham Ind Est, Plympton, Plymouth PL7 4BQ
T: 01752 336421
F: 01752 345828
E: sales@davispneumatic.co.uk
W: www.davispneumatic.co.uk

dBD Communications
4 Furlongs, Basildon, Essex SS16 4BW
T: 01268 449871
F: 01268 442390
E: npurcell@dbdcom.co.uk
W: www.dbdcom.co.uk

DBK Technitherm Ltd
Unit 11, Llantrisant Business Park, Llantrisant CF72 8LF
T: 01443 237927
F: 01443 237867
E: dbk@dbkt.co.uk
W: www.dbktechnitherm.ltd.uk

DB Schenker
Lakeside Business Park, Carolina Way, Doncaster DN4 5PN
F: 0870 140 5000
E: robert.smith2@dbschenker.com
W: www.rail.dbschenker.com

DC Airco
Flemingstraat 17, 1704 Sl Heerhugowaard, Netherlands
T: 0031 72533 6540
F: 0031 72533 9393
E: info@dcairco.com
W: www.dcairco.com

DCA Design International
19, Church St, Warwick CV34 4AB
T: 01926 499461
F: 01926 401134
E: transport@dca-design.com
W: www.dcatransport.co.uk

Dean & Dyball Rail Ltd
Unit 8, Viewpoint Office Village,
Babbage Rd, Stevenage SG1 2EQ
T: 01438 765360
F: 01438 765361
E: enquiries@deandyball.co.uk
W: www.deandyball.co.uk

Dedicated Micros
1200 Unit, Daresbury Park,
Daresbury, Warrington WA4 4HS
T: 0845 600 9500
F: 0845 600 9504
E: customerservices@dmicros.com
W: www.dedicatedmicros.com/uk

DEG Signal Ltd
Aspect House, Crusader Park,
Warminster, Wilts BA12 8BT
T: 01985 212020
F: 01985 212053
E: info@degsignal.co.uk
W: www.degsignal.co.uk

Delay Attribution Board
1 Eversholt St, 8th Floor,
London NW1 2DN
M: 07515 627708
E: admin@delayattributionboard.co.uk
W: www.delayattributionboard.co.uk

Delimon Denco Lubrication
see bijur delimon international

Dellner Couplers UK Ltd
Heathcote Rd,
Swadlincote,
Derbys DE11 9DX
T: 01283 221122
E: info@dellner.com
W: www.dellner.com

Delta Rail Group Ltd
Hudson House, 2 Hudson Way,
Pride Park,
Derby DE24 8HS
T: 01332 221 000
F: 01332 221 008
E: enquiries@deltarail.com
W: www.deltarail.com

Deltix Transport Consulting
4 Church Hill Drive,
Edinburgh EH10 4BT
T: 0131 447 7764
M: 07917 877319
E: david@deltix.co.uk
W: www.deltix.co.uk

Deltone Training Consultants
Ground Floor, 42-48 High Rd,
South Woodford,
London E18 2QL
T: 020 8532 2208
F: 020 8532 2206
E: sales@deltonetraining.com
W: www.deltonetraining.com

Demco
Heyford Close,
Aldermans Green Ind. Est.,
Coventry CV2 2QB
T: 02476 602323
F: 02476 602116
E: info@mgs.co.uk
W: www.demco.co.uk

Denton Wilde Sapte
One Fleet Place,
London EC4M 7WS
T: 020 7242 1212
F: 020 7246 7777
E: info@dentonwildesapte.com
W: www.dentonwildesapte.com

Department for Transport
Great Minster House,
76 Marsham St,
London SW1P 4DR
T: 020 7944 5409
F: 020 7944 2158
E: fax9643@dft.gsi.gov.uk
W: www.dft.gov.uk

Depot Rail ltd
Mercury House, Willoughton Drive,
Gainsborough, Lincs DN21 1DY
T: 01427 619512
F: 01427 619501
E: sales@drail.co.uk
W: www.depotrail.co.uk

Derby & Derbyshire Rail Forum
Council House, Corporation St,
Derby DE1 2FT
T: 01332 642395
M: 07812 300067
E: debbie.cook@derby.gov.uk
W: www.derbyrailforum.org.uk

Derby Engineering Unit Ltd
Unit 22, Riverside Park,
East Service Rd, Raynesway,
Derby DE21 7RW
T: 01332 660364
F: 01332 675191
E: enquiries@derbyengineeringunit.co.uk
W: www.derbyengineeringunit.co.uk

The Deritend Group Ltd
Cyprus St, Off Upper Villiers St,
Wolverhampton WV2 4PA
T: 01902 392315
F: 01902 390186
E: sales@deritend.co.uk
W: www.deritend.co.uk

Design & Projects Int. Ltd
2 Manor Farm, Flexford Rd,
North Baddesley,
Hants SO52 9FD
T: 02380 277910
F: 02380 277920
E: colin.brooks@designandprojects.com
W: www.railwaymaintenance.com

Designplan Lighting
6 Wealdstone Rd, Kimpton Ind. Est,
Sutton, Surrey SM3 9RW
T: 020 8254 2000
F: 020 8644 4253
E: sales@designplan.co.uk
W: www.designplan.co.uk

Design Triangle Ltd
The Maltings, Burwell,
Cambridge CB25 0HB
T: 01638 743070
F: 01638 743493
E: mail@designtriangle.co.uk
W: www.designtriangle.com

Det Norske Veritas
see dnv

Deuta-Werke GmbH
Paffrather Str. 140,
D-51465 Bergisch Gladbach,
Germany
T: 0049 2202 958 100
F: 0049 2202 958 145
E: support@deuta.de
W: www.deuta.de

Deutche Bahn UK
DB Vertrieb GmbH, Suite 6/7,
The Sanctuary, 23 Oakhill Grove,
Surbiton, Surrey KT6 6DU
W: www.bahn.co.uk

DEUTZ AG - UK & Ireland
Unit 3, Willow Park,
Burdock Close, Cannock,
Staffs WS11 7FQ
T: 01543 438901
F: 01543 438931
E: brocklebank.s@deutz.com
W: www.deutz-driven.co.uk

Devol Engineering Ltd
Clarence St, Greenock,
Strathclyde PA15 1LR
T: 01475 883274
F: 01475 787873
E: elspeth.halley@devol.com
W: www.devol.com

Devon & Cornwall Rail Partnership
School of Geography Earth & Environmental Studies,
University of Plymouth,
Plymouth PL4 8AA
T: 01752 233094
F: 01752 233094
E: railpart@plymouth.ac.uk
W: www.greatscenicrailways.com

Dewalt
210, Bath Rd, Slough SL1 3YD
T: 01753 567055
F: 01753 521312
W: www.dewalt.co.uk

Dewhurst Plc
Melbourne Works, Inverness Rd,
Hounslow, Middx TW3 3LT
T: 020 8607 7300
F: 020 8572 5986
E: railsales@dewhurst.co.uk
W: www.dewhurst.co.uk

DG8 Design and Engineering Ltd
Room 7,
The College Business Centre,
Uttoxeter New Rd, Derby DE22 3WZ
T: 01332 869351
F: 01332 869350
E: tony.devitt@dg8design.com
W: www.dg8design.com

DGauge Ltd
Innovation Centre, 1 Devon Way,
Longbridge Technology Park,
Birmingham B31 2TS
T: 0121 222 5662
E: david.johnson@dgauge.co.uk
W: www.dgauge.co.uk

Diamond Point
Suite 13, Ashford House,
Beaufort Court,
Sir Thomas Longley Rd,
Rochester ME2 4FA
T: 01634 300900
F: 01634 722398
E: john.vaines@dpie.com
W: www.dpie.com

DIEM Ltd
Merseyside Office, 11 Jubilee Rd,
Formby, Merseyside L37 2HN
T: 01704 870461
M: 07737 194686
E: davidinman@diemltd.co.uk
W: www.diemltd.co.uk

Diesel Trains Ltd
Great Minster House,
76 Marsham St,
London SW1P 4DR
T: 020 7944 5409
F: 020 7944 2158
W: www.dft.gov.uk

Difuria Ltd
Wood Lane, Beckingham,
Doncaster DN10 4NR
T: 01427 848712
F: 01427 848056
W: www.difuria.co.uk

Dilax Systems Ltd
3 Calico House,
Plantation Wharf,
London SW11 3TN
T: 020 7326 9821
F: 020 7223 2011
E: nigel.fountain@dilax.com
W: www.dilax.co.uk

The Direct Group
Unit 1, Churnet Court,
Churnetside Business Park,
Harrison Way, Cheddleton,
Staffs ST13 7EF
T: 01538 360555
F: 01538 369100
E: dpl@direct-group.co.uk
W: www.direct-group.co.ukdirect link north

Direct Link North
56 Beverley Gardens,
Wembley,
Middx HA9 9QZ
T: 020 8908 0638
E: keith.gerry@virgin.net
W: www.directlinknorth.com

Directly Operated Railways
4th Floor,
One Kemble St,
London
WC2B 4AN
T: 020 7904 5043
E: enquiries@directlyoperatedrailways.co.uk
W: www.directlyoperatedrailways.co.uk

Direct Rail Services (DRS)
Kingmoor Depot,
Etterby Rd,
Carlisle CA3 9NZ
T: 01228 406600
F: 01228 406601
E: enquiries@drsl.co.uk
W: www.directrailservices.com

Direct Track Solutions Ltd
Unit C, Midland Place, Midland Way,
Barlborough Links, Barlborough,
Chesterfield S43 4FR
T: 01246 810198
F: 01246 570926
E: info@directtracksolutions.co.uk
W: www.directtracksolutions.co.uk

Discover LEDs
PO Box 222,
Evesham,
Worcs WR11 4WT
T: 0844 578 1000
F: 0844 578 1111
E: sales@mobilecentre.co.uk
W: www.mobilecentre.co.uk

Discovery Drilling Ltd
32 West Station Yard,
Maldon,
Essex CM9 6TS
T: 01621 851300
F: 01621 851305
E: enquiries@discoverydrilling.co.uk
W: www.discoverydrilling.co.uk

DLA Piper UK LLP
Princes Exchange, Princes Square,
Leeds LS1 4BY
T: 0113 369 2468
F: 0113 369 2999
E: julie.lang@dlapiper.com
W: www.dlapiper.com

DMC Group
Unit 17, The Capstan Centre,
Thurrock Park Way, Tilbury,
Essex RM18 7HH
T: 01375 845070
F: 01375 841333
E: office@dmccontracts.co.uk
W: www.dmccontracts.co.uk

DML Group
see babcock

DMS Technologies
Belbin's Business Park,
Cupernham Lane, Romsey,
Hants SO51 7JF
T: 01794 525463
F: 01794 525450
E: info@dmstech.co.uk
W: www.dmstech.co.uk

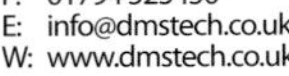

DNH WW Ltd
31 Clarke Rd, Mount Farm, Bletchley,
Milton Keynes MK1 1LG
T: 01908 275000
F: 01908 275100
E: dnh@dnh.co.uk
W: www.dnh.co.uk

DNV (Det Norske Veritas)
Palace House, 3 Cathedral St,
London SE1 9DE
T: 020 7716 6593
F: 020 7716 6738
E: david.salmon@dnv.com
W: www.dnv.com

Docmate Services Ltd
15 Millside Rd, Peterculter,
Aberdeen AB14 0WE
T: 01224 732780
F: 01224 732780
E: info@docmates.co.uk
W: www.docmates.co.uk

Docklands Light Railway
Castor Lane, Poplar,
London E14 0DX
T: 020 7363 9898
F: 020 7363 9708
E: enquire@tfl.gov.uk
W: www.dlr.co.uk

Dold Industries Ltd
11 Hamberts Rd, Blackall Ind Est,
South Woodham Ferrers,
Essex CM3 5UW
T: 01245 324432
F: 01245 325570
E: admin@dold.co.uk
W: www.dold.co.uk

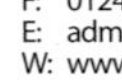

Domnick Hunter Industrial Operations
Dukesway, Team Valley Trading Est.,
Gateshead, Tyne & Wear NE11 0PZ
T: 0191 402 9000
F: 0191 482 6296
E: dhindsales@parker.com
W: www.domnickhunter.com

Donaldson Associates
Eastfield, Church St, Uttoxeter,
Staffs ST14 8AA
T: 01889 563680
F: 01889 562586
E: tunnels@donaldsonassociates.com
W: www.donaldsonassociates.com

Donfabs and Consillia Ltd
The Old Iron Warehouse, The Wharf,
Shardlow, Derby DE72 2GH
T: 01332 792483
F: 01332 799209
E: ian.moss@consillia.com
W: www.trackgeometry.co.uk

Dorman
Wennington Rd,
Southport,
Merseyside PR9 7TN
T: 01704 518000
F: 01704 518001
E: dorman.info@unipartdorman.co.uk
W: www.unipartdorman.co.uk

Donyal Engineering Ltd
Hobsin Ind Est,
Burnopfield,
Newcastle upon Tyne NE16 6EA
T: 01207 270909
F: 01207 270333
E: mike@donyal.co.uk
W: www.donyal.co.uk

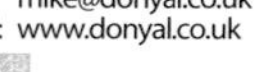

Dow Hyperlast
Station Rd,
Birch Vale,
High Peak SK22 1BR
T: 01663 746518
F: 01663 746605
W: www.dowhyperlast.com

DP Consulting
Unit 4, Tygan House,
The Broadway,
Cheam,
Surrey
T: 0845 094 2380
F: 0700 341 8557
E: info@dpconsulting.org.uk
W: www.dpconsulting.org.uk

DPSS Cabling Services Ltd
Unit 16,
Chiltern Business Village,
Arundel Rd,
Uxbridge UB2 2SN
T: 01895 251010
F: 01895 813133
E: airon.duke@dpsscabling.co.uk
W: www.dpsscabling.co.uk

DRail
see depot rail

Dragados S.A.
Regina House,
2nd Floor,
1-5 Queen St,
London EC4N 1SW
T: 020 7651 0900
F: 020 7248 9044
E: jcruzd@dragados.com
W: www.grupoacs.com

Drum Cussac
8 Hill St,
St Helier,
Jersey JE4 9XB
T: 0870 429 6944
E: risk@drum-cussac.com
W: www.drum-cussac.com

Dual Inventive Ltd
27 Royal Scot Rd,
Pride Park,
Derby DE24 8AJ
T: 01332 346026
E: info@dualinventive.com
W: www.dualinventive.com

DuPont (UK) Ltd
Wedgwood Way,
Stevenage,
Herts SG1 4QN
T: 01438 734061
F: 01438 734836
W: www.rail.dupont.com

Dura Composites
Unit 14, Telford Rd,
Clacton-on-Sea,
Essex CO15 4LP
T: 01255 423601
F: 01255 435426
E: info@duracomposites.com
W: www.duracompositescom

Durapipe
Walsall Rd,
Norton Canes,
Cannock,
Staffs WS11 9NS
T: 01543 279909
E: enquiries@durapipe.co.uk
W: www.durapipe.co.uk

Dyer & Butler Ltd
Mead House,
Station Rd, Nursling,
Southampton SO16 0AH
T: 02380 742222
F: 02380 742200
E: enquiries@dyerandbutler.co.uk
W: www.dyerandbutler.co.uk

Dyer Engineering Ltd
Solution House,
Unit 3,
Morrison & Busty North Ind Est,
Annfield Plain,
Stanley,
Co Durham DH9 7RU
T: 01207 234315
F: 01207 282834
E: paul.dyer@dyer.co.uk
W: www.dyer.co.uk

Dynex Semiconductor Ltd
Doddington Rd,
Lincoln LN6 3LF
T: 01522 500500
F: 01522 500020
E: power_solutions@dynexsemi.com
W: www.dynexsemi.com

Dywidag-Systems International Ltd
Northfield Rd,
Southam,
Warks CV47 0FG
T: 01926 813980
F: 01926 813817
E: sales@dywidag.co.uk
W: www.dywidag-systems.co.uk

EAO Ltd
Highland House,
Albert Drive,
Burgess Hill RH15 9TN
T: 01444 236000
F: 01444 236641
E: sales.euk@eao.com
W: www.eao.com

E A Technology
Capenhurst Technology Park,
Capenhurst, Chester CH1 6ES
T: 0151 339 4181
F: 0151 347 2404
E: john.hartford@eatechnology.com
W: www.eatechnology.com

East Coast Main Line Company ltd
1/18, Great Minster House,
76 Marsham St,
London SW1 4DR
T: 020 7904 5043
E: dorenquiries@dor.gsi.gov.uk
W: www.dft.gov.uk/dor

Eagle Pest Control Services UK Ltd
1 King Alfred Way,
Cheltenham GL52 6QP
T: 01242 696969
F: 01242 696970
E: sales.eagle@mitie.co.uk
W: www.epest.demon.co.uk

East Lancashire Railway
Bolton St Station,
Bury,
Lancs BL9 0EY
T: 0161 764 7790
E: admin@east-lancs-rly.co.uk
W: www.eastlancsrailway.org.uk

East Midlands Trains
Stagecoach Group,
10 Dunkeld Way,
Perth PH1 5TW
T: 01738 442111
F: 01738 643648
E: mail@stagecoachgroup.com
W: www.stagecoachgroup.com

Eaton Electrical Ltd
Reddings Lane,
Tyseley,
Birmingham B11 3EZ
T: 0121 685 2100
M: 07803 740082
E: chrisswales@eaton.com
W: www.eaton.com

EB Elektro UK Ltd
Unit 2, Shireoaks Triangle,
Coach Crescent, Worksop,
Notts S81 8AD
T: 01909 483658
E: william@eb-elektro.co.uk
W: www.eb-elektro.co.uk

EcarbonUK
see electrical carbon uk

Ecolube
Cardev International Ltd,
Ripon Way,
Harrogate HG1 2AU
T: 01423 817200
F: 01423 817400
E: admin@ecolube.co.uk
W: www.ecolube.co.uk

ECT Group
see british american railway services

Eden Brown
222 Bishopsgate,
London EC2M 4QD
T: 020 7422 7300
F: 0845 434 9573
E: london@edenbrown.com
W: www.edenbrown.com

Eden Business Analysis Ltd
23 Station Rd,
Upper Poppleton,
York YO26 6PX
T: 01904 780781
E: neil@edenba.co.uk
W: www.edenba.co.uk

EDF Energy
see uk power networks

Edilon Sedra
see tiflex

Edgar Allen
see balfour beatty

Edmund Nuttall Ltd
see bam nuttall

Edward Symmons
2 Southwark St, London SE1
T: 020 7955 8454
F: 020 7407 6423
E: info@edwardsymmons.com
W: www.es-group.com

EFD Corporate
Blackhill Drive, Wolverton Mill,
Milton Keynes MK12 5TS
T: 08451 285174
E: enquiries@efd-corporate.com
W: www.efd-corporate.com

EFi Heavy Vehicle Brakes
6/7 Bonville Rd, Brislington,
Bristol BS4 5NZ
T: 0117 977 7859
F: 0117 971 0573
E: tonyp@efiltd.co.uk
W: www.efiltd.co.uk

Electrical Carbon UK Ltd
Office 100, Devonshire House,
49 Eldon St,
Sheffield S1 4NR
T: 0114 231 6454
F: 0114 238 5464
E: sales@ecarbonuk.com
W: www.ecarbonuk.com

Electromagnetic Testing Services Ltd (ETS)
Pratts Fields,
Lubberhedges Lane, Stebbing,
Dunmow, Essex CM6 3BT
T: 01371 856061
F: 01371 856144
E: info@etsemc.co.uk
W: www.etsemc.co.uk

Electro Motive
9301 W.55th St,
LaGrange,
Illinois 60525, USA
T: 001 800 255 5355
F: 001 708 387 6626
E: scott.garman@emdiesels.com
W: www.emdiesels.com

Eglin Concourse International
Globe Works,
Victoria Rd,
Sowerby Bridge,
West Yorks HX6 3AE
T: 01422 317601
F: 01422 833857
E: sales@eglinconcourse.com
W: www.eglinconcourse.com

Elan Public Transport Consultancy Ltd
8 The Grange,
Chesterfield S42 7PS
T: 0845 123 5733
E: george.watson@elanptc.com
W: www.elanptc.com

Eland Cables
120 Highgate Studios,
53-79 Highgate Rd,
London NW5 1TL
T: 020 7241 8787
F: 020 7241 8700
E: sales@eland.co.uk
W: www.eland.co.uk

Elcot Environmental
The Nursery, Kingsdown Lane,
Blunsdon,
Swindon SN25
T: 01793 700100
F: 01793 722221
E: peterw@elcotenviro.com
W: www.elcotenviro.com

Eldapoint Ltd
Charleywood Rd,
Knowsley Ind. Prk North,
Knowsley,
Merseyside L32 7SG
T: 0151 548 9838
F: 0151 546 4120
E: paul.wyatt@eldapoint.co.uk
W: www.eldapoint.co.uk

Elite Precast Concrete
Halesfield 9,
Telford TF9 4QW
T: 01952 588888
F: 01952 582011
E: sales@eliteprecast.co.uk
W: www.eliteprecast.co.uk

Eltek Valere UK Ltd
Eltek House, Maxted Rd,
Hemel Hempstead,
Herts HP2 7DX
T: 01442 219355
F: 01442 245894
E: steve.pusey@eltekvalere.com
W: www.eltekvalere.com

Eltherm UK Ltd
Liberta House,
Scotland Hill,
Sandhurst,
Berks GU47 8JR
T: 01252 749910
E: sales@eltherm.uk.com
W: www.eltherm.uk.com

Embedded Rail Technology Ltd
Rosehill House,
Derby DE23 8GG
M: 07967 667020
E: cp@charlespenny.com

EMEG Electrical Ltd
Unit 3, Dunston Place,
Whittington Moor,
Chesterfield,
Derbys S41 8XA
T: 01246 268678
F: 01246 268679
E: enq@emeg.co.uk
W: www.emeg.co.uk

Emergency Power Systems
see emerson network power

Emergi-Lite - Thomas & Betts Ltd
Bruntcliffe Lane,
Morley,
Leeds LS27 9LL
T: 0113 281 0600
F: 0113 281 0601
E: emergi-lite.sales@tnb.com
W: www.emergi-lite.co.uk

Emerson Crane Hire
Emerson House, Freshwater House,
Dagenham, Essex RM8 1RX
T: 020 8548 3900
F: 020 8548 3999
E: liam@emersoncranes.co.uk
W: www.emersoncranes.co.uk

Emerson Network Power
Carley Drive Business Area,
Westfield,
Sheffield S20 8NQ
T: 0114 247 8369
F: 0114 247 8367
E: uk.rail@emerson.com
W: www.emerson.com

Emerson Network Power Chloride Products & Services
George Curl Way,
Southampton SO18 2RY
T: 02380 610311
F: 02380 610852
E: uk.enquiries.chloride@emerson.com
W: www.emersonnetworkpower.com

Emico
Able House, 1 Figtree Hill,
Hemel Hempstead, Herts HP2 5XL
T: 01442 213111
F: 01442 236945
E: contact@emico-rail.com
W: www.emico-rail.com

Enerpac
Bentley Rd South, Darlaston,
West Midlands WS10 8LQ
T: 0121 505 0787
F: 0121 505 0799
E: info@enerpac.com
W: www.enerpac.com

Enersys Ltd
Oak Court,
Clifton Business Park, Wynne Ave,
Swinton, Manchester M27 8FF
T: 0161 794 4611
F: 0161 727 3809
E: enersys.rail@uk.enersys.com
W: www.enersys-emea.com

Engineering Support Group
see esg

Ennstone Johnston
see fp mccann

ENOTRAC UK Ltd
Chancery House,
St Nicholas Way,
Sutton,
Surrey SM1 4AF
T: 020 8770 3501
F: 020 8770 3502
E: sebastien.lechelle@enotrac.com
W: www.enotrac.com

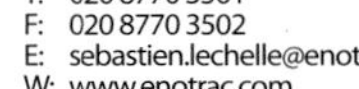

Enplex
310 Green Lane, Ilford,
Essex IG1 1LQ
T: 0870 763 6059
F: 0870 763 6064
E: info@enplex.co.uk
W: www.enplex.co.uk

Entech Technical Solutions Ltd
1st Floor, Hamilton House,
111 Marlowes,
Hemel Hempstead,
Herts HP1 1BB
T: 01442 898900
F: 01442 898990
E: info@entechts.com
W: www.entechts.co.uk

Entec UK Ltd
Atlantic House,
Imperial Way,
Reading RG2 0TP
T: 01189 036686
F: 01189 036261
E: whitr@entecuk.co.uk
W: www.entecuk.com

Entech Technical Solutions Ltd
56 Broadwick St,
London W1F 7AL
T: 0207 434 7370
E: saul@entechts.co.uk
W: www.entechts.co.uk

Enterprise
Trident 1, Trident Park, Basil Hill,
Didcot, Oxon OX11 7HJ
T: 01772 819000
F: 01235 515888
E: john.davies@enterprise.plc.uk
W: www.enterprise.plc.uk

Enterprise Informatics
Old Bridge House,
40 Church St, Staines,
Middx TW18 4EP
T: 01784 426600
F: 01784 426601
W: www.enterpriseinformatics.com

Enterprise Managed Services Ltd
Endeavour House, 1 Lyonsdown Rd,
New Barnet, Herts EN5 1HR
T: 020 8275 8000
F: 020 8449 6536
E: evin.harcombe@enterprise.plc.uk
W: www.enterprise.plc.uk

Environmental Management Solutions Group Holdings Ltd (EMS)
Global House, Geddings Rd,
Hoddesden, Herts EN11 0NT
T: 01992 535445
F: 01992 456435
W: www.emsgroup.org

Environmental Scientifics Group Ltd (ESG)
ESG House,
Bretby Business Park, Ashby Rd,
Burton upon Trent DE15 0YZ
T: 01283 554400
F: 01283 554401
E: sales@esg.co.uk
W: www.esg.co.uk

Environment Hygeine Services (EHS)
32 Clay Hill, Enfield EN2 9AA
T: 020 8367 7350
E: info@pigeonglide.com
W: www.pigeonglide.com

Envirotech
see lh group services

EPC Global
see talascend

EQE International
see abs consulting

ERA Technology Ltd
Cleeve Rd,
Leatherhead,
Surrey KT22 7SA
T: 01372 367345
F: 01372 367359
E: info@era.co.uk
W: www.era.co.uk

Ergonomics & Safety Research Institute (ESRI)
Holywell Building,
Holywell Way,
Loughborough,
Leics LE11 3UZ
T: 01509 226900
F: 01509 226960
E: esri@lboro.ac.uk
W: www.lboro.ac.uk

ERG Transit Systems (UK) Ltd
Unit 1,
Riverside,
Waters Meeting Rd,
They Valley,
Bolton BL1 8TU
T: 01204 384709
F: 01204 384806
E: tim.burke@vix-erg.com
W: www.vix-erg.com

Eric Wright Group
Sceptre House,
Sceptre Way,
Bamber Bridge,
Preston PR5 6AW
T: 01772 698822
F: 01772 628811
E: info@ericwright.co.uk
W: www.ericwright.co.uk

ERM Ltd
2nd Floor,
Exchequer Court,
33 St Mary Axe,
London EC3 8LL
T: 020 3206 5401
F: 020 7465 7272
E: nick.cottam@erm.com
W: www.erm.com

Ernst & Young LLP
1 More London Place,
London SE1 2AF
T: 020 7951 1113
F: 020 7951 3167
E: gfavaloro@uk.ey.com
W: www.ey.com/uk

ESAB (UK) Ltd
Hanover House, Queensgate,
Britannia Rd, Waltham Cross EN8 7TF
T: 01992 768515
F: 01992 788053
E: info@esab.co.uk
W: www.esab.co.uk

ESG
Derwent House,
RTC Business Park,
London Rd,
Derby DE24 8UP
T: 01332 483800
F: 01332 383565
E: sales@esg-rail.com
W: www.esg-rail.com

Esmerk Ltd
County House,
3rd Floor, Friar St,
Reading RG1 1DB
T: 0118 956 5836
F: 0118 956 5850
E: response@esmerk.com
W: www.esmerk.com

ESP Systex Ltd
68-74 Holderness Rd,
Hull HU9 1ED
T: 01482 384500
F: 01482 384555
E: info@espsystex.co.uk
W: www.espsystex.com

ESR Technology Ltd
410 Birchwood Park,
Warrington,
Cheshire WA3 6FW
T: 01925 582491
E: info@esrtechnology.com
W: www.esrtechnology.com

Essempy
1 Phoebe Lane, Church End,
Wavendon, Bucks MK17 8LR
T: 01908 582491
M: 07967 398431
E: norman.price@essempy.co.uk
W: www.essempy.co.uk

ESS Rail
3rd Floor, Regal House,
70 London Rd,
Twickenham TW1 3QS
T: 0845 245 3000
F: 0845 245 3061
E: john.lynch@essengineering.com
W: www.essengineering.com

ETS Cable Components
Units 4/5, Red Lion Business Park,
Red Lion Rd, Tolworth KT6 7QD
T: 020 8405 6789
F: 020 8405 6790
E: sales@etscc.co.uk
W: www.etscc.co.uk

Eurailscout GB Ltd
Unit 2, Kimberley Court,
Kimberley Rd, Queens Park,
London NW6 7SL
T: 020 7372 2973
F: 020 7372 5444
E: info@eurailscout.com
W: www.eurailscout.com

Euro Cargo Rail SAS
Immeuble la Palacio, 25-
29 Place de la Madelaine,
75008 Paris France T:
0033 977 400 000
F: 0033 977 400 200
E: info@eurocargorail.com
W: www.eurocargorail.com

Eurochemi
Kingsbury Park, Midland Rd,
Swadlincote, Derbys DE11 0AN
T: 01283 222111
F: 01283 550177
W: www.eurochemi.co.uk

Eurocom Ltd
1 Glyn St, Vauxhall,
London SE11 5HT
T: 020 7820 8344
E: comms@eurocomltd.co.uk
W: www.eurocomltd.co.uk

Eurolog Ltd
Orlando House, 3 High St,
Teddington TW11 8NP
T: 020 8977 4407
F: 020 8977 3714
E: info@eurolog.co.uk
W: www.eurolog.co.uk

European Friction Industries Ltd (EFI)
6/7 Bonville Rd, Brislington,
Bristol BS4 5NZ
T: 0117 977 7859
E: rail@efiltd.co.uk
W: www.efiltd.co.uk

Europhoenix
W: www.europhoenix.eu

Europe Rail Consultancy Ltd
North Court, Hassocks,
West Sussex BN6 8JS
T: 01273 845583
E: chris.dugdale@europerailconsultancy.com
W: www.europerailconsultancy.com

Eurostar International Ltd
Times House,
Bravingtons Walk,
Regent Quarter,
London N1 9AW
E: press.office@eurostar.co.uk
W: www.eurostar.com

Eurotech Ltd
3 Clifton Court,
Cambridge CB1 7BN
T: 01223 403410
F: 01223 410457
E: sales@eurotech-ltd.co.uk
W: www.eurotech-ltd.co.uk

Eurotunnel
The Channel Tunnel Group Ltd,
UK Terminal,
Ashford Rd,
Folkestone,
Kent CT18 8XX
T: 08443 353535
F: 01303 288784
E: communication.internet@eurotunnel.com
W: www.eurotunnel.com

Eurox
Aqua House,
Buttress Way,
Smethwick B66 3DL
T: 0121 555 7167
F: 0121 555 7168
E: sales.orders@eurox.co.uk
W: www.eurox.co.uk

Eve Trakway Ltd
Bramley Vale,
Chesterfield,
Derbys S44 5GA
T: 08700 767676
F: 08700 737373
E: mail@evetrakway.co.uk
W: www.evetrakway.co.uk

Evergrip Ltd
Unit 4, Flaxley Rd,
Selby YO8 4BG
T: 01757 212744
F: 01757 212749
E: sales@evergrip.com
W: www.evergrip.com

Eversheds
1 Royal Standard Place,
Nottingham NG1 6FZ
T: 0845 497 9797
F: 0845 497 4919
W: www.eversheds.co.uk

Eversholt Rail (UK) Ltd
PO Box 68166,
210 Pentonville Rd,
London N1P 2AR
T: 020 7380 5040
F: 020 7380 5148
E: wendy.filer@eversholtrail.co.uk
W: www.eversholtrail.co.uk

Evolvi Rail Systems Ltd
3rd Floor,
1 new Century Place,
East St,
Reading RG1 4ET
T: 0871 521 9871
E: accountmanagement@evolvi.co.uk
W: www.evolvi.co.uk

EWS
see db schenker

Excalibur Screwbolts Ltd
Gate 3, Newhall Nursery,
Lower Rd, Hockley,
Essex SS5 5JU
T: 01702 206962/207909
F: 01702 207918
E: charles.bickford@screwbolt.com
W: www.excaliburscrewbolts.com

Exide Technologies
see gnb industrial power

Exova (UK) Ltd
6 Coronet Way,
Centenary Park,
Salford M50 1RE
T: 0161 787 3291
F: 0161 787 3251
E: steve.hughes@exova.com
W: www.exova.com

Expamet Security Products
PO Box 14,
Longhill Ind. Est. (North),
Hartlepool TS25 1PR
T: 01429 867366
F: 01429 867355
E: sales@exmesh.co.uk
W: www.expandedmetalfencing.com

Express Electrical
37 Cable Depot Rd,
Riverside Ind Est,
Clydebank G81 1UY
T: 0141 941 3689
F: 0141 952 8155
E: sales@expresselectrical.co.uk
W: www.expresselectrical.co.uk

Express Medicals Ltd
8, City Business Centre,
Lower Rd,
London SE16 2XB
T: 020 7500 6900
F: 020 7500 6910
E: workhealth@expressmedicals.co.uk
W: www.expressmedicals.co.uk

Express Rail Alliance
W: www.expressrailalliance.com

External Solutions Ltd
Unit 2, 5 Elwes St, Brigg,
North Lincs DN20 8LB
T: 01652 655933
F: 01652 655966
E: dawn@external-solutions.co.uk
W: www.external-solutions.co.uk

Exxell (Acorn People)
7 York Rd, Woking, Surrey GU22 7XH
T: 01483 654463
F: 01483 723080
E: sarah.griffiths@acornpeople.com
W: www.acornpeople.com

Factair Ltd
49 Boss Hall Rd, Ipswich,
Suffolk IP1 5BN
T: 01473 746400
F: 01473 747123
E: enquiries@factair.co.uk
W: www.factair.co.uk

Faithful & Gould
Euston Tower, 286, Euston Rd,
London NW1 3AT
T: 020 7121 2121
F: 020 7121 2020
E: info@fgould.com
W: www.fgould.com

Faiveley Transport Birkenhead Ltd.
Morpeth Wharf, Twelve Quays,
Birkenhead, Wirral CH41 1LW
T: 0151 649 5000
F: 0151 649 5001
E: kevin.smith@faiveleytransport.com
W: www.faiveleytransport.com

Faiveley Transport Tamworth Ltd
Darwell Park, Mica Close, Armington,
Tamworth, Staffs B77 4DR
T: 01827 308430
F: 01827 308431
E: brian.harvey@faiveleytransport.com
W: www.faiveleytransport.com

Falcon Electrical Engineering Ltd
Falcon House,
Main St,
Fallin,
Stirlingshire FK7 7HT
T: 01786 819920
F: 01786 814381
E: sales@falconelectrical.com
W: www.falconelectrical.com

Fantuzzi Noell (UK) Ltd
Units 3&4,
Oldham West Business Centre,
Watts Green,
Chadderton,
Manchester OL9 9LH
T: 0161 785 7870
F: 0161 670 6582
E: info@fantuzzi.co.uk
W: www.fantuzzi.co.uk

Farrer Consulting Ltd
see mwh global ltd

Fastrack (Expamet Security Products)
PO Box 14,
Longhill Ind. Est.(North),
Hartlepool TS25 1PR
T: 01429 867366
F: 01429 867355
E: sales@exmesh.co.uk
W: www.expandedmetalcompany.co.uk

Federal Mogul Friction Products (Ferodo)
Chapel-en-le-Frith,
Derbys SK23 0JP
T: 01298 811689
F: 01298 811580
W: www.federalmogul.com

Fencing & Lighting Contractors Ltd
Unit 21,
Amber Drive,
Bailey Brook Ind Est,
Langley Mill,
Derbys NG16 4BE
T: 01773 531383
F: 01773 531921
E: info@fencingandlighting.co.uk

Fenbrook Consulting Ltd
22 Fenbrook Close,
Hambrook,
Bristol BS16 1QJ
T: 0117 970 1773
E: trevor@fenbrook.com
W: www.fenbrook.com

The Fenning Lovatt Partnership Ltd
69-71 Newington Causeway,
London SE1 6BD
T: 020 7378 4812
F: 020 7407 4612
E: mail@fenninglovatt.com
W: www.fenninglovatt.com

Fenton UK
Merlin Way,
North Weald,
Essex CM16 6HR
T: 01992 522555
F: 01992 523444
E: info@fenton.com
W: www.fentonuk.com

Feonic Technology
3a,
Newlands Science Park,
Inglemire Lane,
Hull HU6 7TQ
T: 01482 806688
F: 01482 806654
E: info@feonic.com
W: www.feonic.com

Ferrabyrne Ltd
Fort Rd Ind. Est,
Littlehampton BN17 7QU
T: 01903 721317
F: 01903 430452
E: sales@ferrabyrne.co.uk
W: www.ferrabyrne.co.uk

Ferrograph Ltd
Unit 1,
New York Way,
New York Ind Park,
Newcastle Upon Tyne NE27 0QF
T: 0191 280 8800
F: 0191 280 8810
E: info@ferrograph.com
W: www.ferrograph.com

Fibergrate Composite Structures
5151 Beltline Rd,
Ste 1212,
Dallas,
TX 75254 USA
T: 00 800 527 4043
F: 00 972 250 1530
E: info@fibergrate.com
W: www.fibergrate.com

Fibreglass Grating Ltd
Unit 14,
Telford Rd,
Gorse Lane Ind. Est,
Clacton on Sea,
Essex CO15 4LP
T: 01255 423601
F: 01255 436428
E: info@fibreglassgrating.co.uk
W: www.fibreglassgrating.co.uk

Fibrelite
Snaygill Ind. Est, Keighley Rd,
Skipton, N Yorks BD23 2QR
T: 01756 799773
E: jostott@fibrelite.com
W: www.fibrelite.com

Field Fisher Waterhouse LLP
35 Vine St,
London EC3N 2AA
T: 020 7861 4000
F: 020 7488 0084
E: nicholas.thompsell@ffw.com
W: www.ffw.com

Fifth Dimension Associates Ltd (FDAL)
Suite 18411, 145-157,
St John St, London EC1V 4PW
T: 020 7060 2332
F: 020 7060 3325
E: london@fdal.co.uk
W: www.fdal.co.uk

Findlay Irvine Ltd
Bog Rd, Penicuik,
Midlothian EH26 9BU
T: 01968 671200
F: 01968 671237
E: sales@findlayirvine.com
W: www.findlayirvine.com

Finning (UK) Ltd
Triangle Business Park,
Oakwell Way, Birstall, Batley,
West Yorks WF17 9LU
T: 0113 201 2065
E: oillab@finning.co.uk
W: www.maintain-it.co.uk

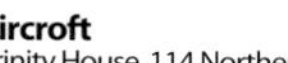

Fircroft
Trinity House, 114 Northenden Rd,
Sale, Cheshire M33 3FZ
T: 0161 905 2020
F: 0161 969 1743
E: hq@fircroft.co.uk
W: www.fircroft.co.uk

The Fire Service College
Moreton-in-Marsh, Glos GL56 0RH
T: 01608 812130
F: 01608 651790
E: dluff@fireservicecollege.ac.uk
W: www.fireservicecollege.ac.uk

First Capital Connect
Hertford House, 1 Cranwood St,
London EC1V 9QS
T: 0845 026 4700
E: customer.relations.fcc@firstgroup.com
W: www.firstcapitalconnect.co.uk

First Choice Protection
see portwest

First Class Partnerships
148 Lawrence St, York YO10 3EB
T: 01904 870792
F: 01904 424499
E: info@firstclasspartnerships.com
W: www.firstclasspartnerships.com

Firstco Ltd
4 Celbridge Mews,
London W2 6EU
T: 020 7034 0833
F: 020 7229 8002
E: info@firstco.uk.com
W: www.firstco.uk.com

First Components Ltd
Wallows Ind Est,
Wallows Rd,
Brierley Hill, DY5 1QA
T: 01384 262068
F: 01384 482383
E: info@firstcomponents.co.uk
W: www.firstcomponents.co.uk

First Engineering Ltd
see babcock rail

First Great Western
Milford House, 1 Milford St,
Swindon SN1 1HL
T: 08457 000125
E: fgwfeedback@firstgroup.com
W: www.firstgreatwestern.co.uk

First Group Plc
395 King St,
Aberdeen AB24 5RP
T: 01224 650100
F: 01224 650140
W: www.firstgroup.com/corporate

First Hull Trains
Europa House, 184 Ferensway,
Hull HU1 3UT
T: 08450 710222
E: customer.services@hulltrains.co.uk
W: www.hulltrains.co.uk

First Procurement Associates
see fpa consulting ltd

First Rail Support Ltd
Unit 20, T
ime Technology Park,
Blackburn Rd,
Simonstone,
Lancs BB12 7TG
T: 01282 688110
F: 01282 688141
E: rail.support@firstgroup.com
W: www.firstgroup.com/firstrailsupport

First Scotrail
Customer Relations,
PO Box 7030,
Fort William PH33 6WX
T: 0845 601 5929
E: scotrailcustomer.relations@firstgroup.com
W: www.firstgroup.com/scotrail

First Trans Pennine Express
Bridgewater House,
60 Whitworth St,
Manchester M1 6LT
T: 08700 005 151
F: 0161 228 8120
E: tpecustomer.relations@firstgroup.com
W: www.tpexpress.co.uk

Fishbone Solutions Ltd
25 Statham St, Darley,
Derbys DE22 1HR
T: 0115 714 3444
F: 020 7942 0701
E: go-fish@fishbonesolutions.co.uk
W: www.fishbonesolutions.co.uk

Fitzpatrick Contractors Ltd
see volker fitzpatrick

FKI Switchgear
see hawker siddley

Fleetech Ltd
12 Little Park Farm Rd, Fareham,
Hants PO15 7JE
T: 01489 553200
F: 01489 553101
W: www.fleetech.com/www.bmrail.com

Flexible & Specialist (FS) Cables
Alban Point, Alban Park,
Hatfield Rd,
St Albans AL4 6JX
T: 01727 840841
F: 01727 840842
E: sales@fscables.com
W: www.fscables.com

Flexicon Ltd
Roman Way, Coleshill,
Birmingham B46 1HG
T: 01675 466900
F: 01675 466901
E: rail@flexicon.uk.com
W: www.flexicon.uk.com

Flint Bishop Solicitors
St Michaels Court,
St Michaels Lane,
Derby DE1 3HQ
T: 01332 340211
E: info@flintbishop.co.uk
W: www.flintbishop.co.uk

Flir Systems Ltd (UK)
2 Kings Hill Ave,
West Malling,
Kent ME19 4AQ
T: 01732 220011
F: 01732 843707
E: flir@flir.com
W: www.flir.com

FLI Structures
Francis & Lewis International,
Waterwells Drive,
Waterwells Business Park,
Gloucester GL2 2AA
T: 01452 722200
F: 01452 722244
E: m.jones@fli.co.uk
W: www.fliscrewpiles.co.uk

Flowcrete UK Ltd
The Flooring Technology Centre,
Booth Lane, Sandbach,
Cheshire CW11 3QF
T: 01270 753000
F: 01270 753333
E: uk@flowcrete.com
W: www.flowcrete.com

Fluor Ltd
Fluor Centre, Riverside Way,
Camberley, Surrey GU15 3YL
T: 01276 62424
F: 01276 26762
W: www.fluor.com

Fluke UK Ltd (Tracklink)
52 Hurricane Way,
Norwich NR6 6JB
T: 020 7942 0700
F: 020 7942 0701
E: industrial@uk.fluke.nl
W: www.fluke.co.uk

Focus 2000 Infrared Ltd
5a Lodge Hill Business Park,
Westbury-sub-Mendip,
Somerset BA5 1EY
T: 01749 870620
F: 01749 870622
E: sales@focus2k.co.uk
W: www.focus2k.co.uk

Fone Alarm Installations Ltd
59 Albert Rd North, Reigate RH2 9EL
T: 01737 223673
F: 01737 224349
E: enquiries@fonealarm.co.uk
W: www.fonealarm.co.uk

Forbo Flooring Ltd
High Holborn Rd, Ripley,
Derbys DE5 3NT
T: 01773 740615
F: 01773 744142
E: bob.summers@forbo.com
W: www.uk.bonarfloors.com

Ford & Stanley Ltd
44 Royal Scot Rd,
Pride Park,
Derby DE24 8AJ
T: 01332 344443
E: daniel.taylor@fordandstanley.com
W: www.fordandstanley.com

Ford Components Manufacturing Ltd
Unit 2,
Monkton Business Park North,
Mill Lane, Hebburn,
Tyne & Wear NE31 2JZ
T: 0191 428 6600
F: 0191 428 6620
E: shaun.gribben@ford-components.com
W: www.ford-components.com

Foremost Logan Ltd
Kersey Hall, Tannery Rd,
Combs, Stowmarket,
Suffolk
T: 01449 742450
F: 01449 771207
E: info@foremostlogan.com
W: www.foremostlogan.com

ForgeTrack Ltd
Thistle House, St Andrew St,
Hertford SG14 1JA
T: 01992 500900
F: 01992 589495
E: sales@forgetrack.co.uk
W: www.forgetrack.co.uk

Forward Chemicals Ltd
PO Box 12, Tanhouse Lane,
Widnes,
Cheshire WA8 0RD
T: 0151 422 1000
F: 0151 422 1011
E: salesandservice@forwardchem.com
W: www.forwardchem.com

LB Foster Rail Technologies (UK) Ltd
Stamford St,
Sheffield S9 2TX
T: 0114 256 2225
F: 0114 261 7826
E: uksales@lbfoster.com
W: www.lbfoster.co.uk

Fourway Communications Ltd
Delamere Rd, Cheshunt,
Herts EN8 9SH
T: 01992 629182
F: 01992 639227
E: enquiries@fourway.co.uk
W: www.fourway.co.uk

FPA Consulting Ltd
1 St Andrew's House, Vernon Gate,
Derby DE1 1UJ
T: 01332 604321
F: 01332 604322
E: johnb@fpaconsulting.co.uk
W: www.fpaconsulting.co.uk

FP McCann
Brascote Lane, Cadeby,
Nuneaton, Warks CV13 0BE
T: 01455 290780
F: 01455 292189
E: scarson@fpmccann.co.uk
W: www.fpmccann.co.uk

Frankham Consulting Group Ltd
Irene House,
Five Arches Business Park,
Maidstone Rd, Sidcup,
Kent DA14 5AE
T: 020 8309 7777
F: 020 8306 7890
E: enquiries@frankham.com
W: www.frankham.com

Franklin + Andrews
Sea Containers House,
20 Upper Ground,
London SE1 9LZ
T: 020 7633 9966
F: 020 7928 2471
E: enquiries@franklinandrews.com
W: www.franklinandrews.com

Frauscher UK
Suite 5,
Yeovil Innovation Centre,
Barracks Close,Copse Rd,
Yeovil, BA22 8RN
T: 01935 385905
F: 01935 385901
M: 07590 099582
E: richard.colman@uk.frauscher.com
W: www.frauscher.com

Frauscher Selectrail (UK) Ltd
Unit 58,
Basepoint Business Centre,
Isidore Rd,
Bromsgrove B60 3ET
T: 01527 834670
F: 01527 834671
E: info@frauscher-selectrail.com
W: www.frauscher-selectrail.com

Frazer Nash Consultancy Ltd
Stonebridge House,
Dorking Business Park,
Station Rd,
Dorking,
Surrey RH4 1JH
T: 01306 885050
F: 01306 886464
E: r.jones@fnc.co.uk
W: www.fnc.co.uk

Freeman Williams zLanguage Solutions Ltd
College Business Centre,
Uttoxeter New Rd,
Derby DE22 3WZ
T: 01332 869342
F: 01332 869344
E: abi@freemanwilliams.co.uk
W: www.freemanwillams.co.uk

Freeth Cartwright LLP
2nd Floor, West Point,
Cardinal Square,
10 Nottingham Rd,
Derby DE1 3QT
T: 0845 634 9791
F: 0845 634 1732
E: mike.copestake@freethcartwright.co.uk
W: www.freethcartwright.co.uk

FreightArranger Ltd
West View, Brownshill, Stroud,
Glos GL6 8AQ
T: 01453 367150
W: www.freightarranger.co.uk

Freight Europe (UK) Ltd
Asra House, 4th Floor, 1 Long Lane,
London SE1 4PG
see captrain uk ltd

Freightliner Group Ltd
3rd Floor, The Podium, 1 Eversholt St,
London NW1 2FL
T: 020 7200 3900
F: 020 7200 3975
E: pressoffice@freightliner.co.uk
W: www.freightliner.co.uk

Frequentis UK Ltd
Gainsborough Business Centre,
2 Sheen Rd,
Richmond upon Thames TW9 1AE
T: 020 8973 2616
E: marketing@frequentis.com
W: www.frequentis.com

Freshfields Bruckhaus Deringer LLP
65 Fleet St, London EC4Y 1HT
T: 0207 936 4000
F: 0207 832 7001
W: www.freshfields.com

Freyssinet Ltd
Innovation House, Euston Way,
Town Centre, Telford,
Shropshire TF3 4LT
T: 01952 201901
F: 01952 201753
E: kevin.bennett@freyssinet.co.uk
W: www.freyssinet.co.uk

Frimstone
Ashcraft Farm, Main Rd,
Crimplesham, Norfolk PE33 9EB
T: 0845 177 9900
E: enquiries@frimstone.co.uk
W: www.frimstone.co.uk

CB Frost & Co Ltd
Green St, Digbeth,
Birmingham B12 0NE
T: 0121 773 8494
F: 0121 772 3584
E: info@cbfrost-rubber.com
W: www.cbfrost-rubber.com

FS Cables
see flexible & specialist

Fuchs Lubricants (UK) Plc
New Century St, Hanley,
Stoke on Trent ST1 5HU
T: 08701 203700
F: 01782 202072
E: contact-uk@fuchs-oil.com
W: www.fuchslubricants.com

Fuelcare Ltd
Suite 1, The Hayloft, Blakenhall Park,
Barton under Needwood,
Staffs DE13 8AJ
T: 01283 712263
F: 01283 262263
E: sales@fuelcare.com
W: www.fuelcare.com

Fugro Aperio Ltd
Focal Point, Newmarket Rd,
Bottisham,
Cambridge CB25 9BD
T: 0870 600 8050
F: 0870 800 8040
E: info@fugro-aperio.com
W: www.fugro-aperio.com

Fujikura Europe Ltd
C51 Barwell Business Park,
Leatherhead Rd,
Chessington,
Surrey KT9 2NY
T: 020 8240 2000
F: 020 8240 2010
E: sales@fujikura.co.uk
W: www.fujikura.co.uk

Fujitsu
W: www.fujitsu.com/uk/industries/rail

Funkwerk Information Technologies York Ltd
see trapeze group rail ltd

Furneaux Riddall & Co Ltd
Alchorne Place,
Portsmouth,
Hants PO3 5PA
T: 02392 668624
F: 02392 668625
E: info@furneauxriddall.com
W: www.furneauxriddall.com

Furrer + Frey
4th Floor, Hamilton House,
Mabledon Place,
London WC1H 9BB
T: 020 7953 0250
E: ndolphin@furrerfrey.ch
W: www.furrerfrey.ch

Furse - Thomas & Betts Ltd
Wilford Rd,
Nottingham NG2 1EB
T: 0115 964 3700
F: 0115 986 0538
E: enquiry@furse.com
W: www.furse.com

Furtex
see holdsworth

Fusion People Ltd
2nd/3rd Floor, Aldermary House,
10-15 Queen St, London EC4N 1TX
T: 020 7653 1070
F: 020 7653 1071
E: rail@fusionpeople.com
W: www.fusionpeople.com

Future Rail (formerly Future Welding)
The Rowe, Stableford,
Staffs ST5 4EN
T: 01782 411800
E: futureraildesign@gmail.com
W: www.futurerail.co.uk

Gabriel & Co Ltd
1 Cromwell Rd, Smethwick,
West Midlands B66 2JT
T: 0121 555 7615
F: 0121 555 1922
E: john.gabriel@gabrielco.com
W: www.gabrielco.com

GAI Tronics (Hubbel Ltd)
Brunel Dr., Stretton Business Park,
Burton upon Trent DE13 0BZ
T: 01283 500500
F: 01283 500400
E: sales@gai-tronics.co.uk
W: www.gai-tronics.co.uk

Galliford Try Rail
Crab Lane, Fearnhead,
Warrington WA2 0XR
T: 01925 822821
F: 01925 812323
E: ron.stevenson@gallifordtry.co.uk
W: www.gallifordtry.co.uk

Gamble Rail
see ketbray

Ganymede Solutions Ltd
26 Hershel St, Slough SL1 1PA
T: 01753 820810
F: 0870 890 1894
E: gary.hewett@ganymedesolutions.co.uk
W: www.ganymedesolutions.co.uk

Gardiner & Theobald
32, Bedford Square,
London WC1B 3JT
T: 020 7209 3000
F: 020 7209 3359
E: p.armstrong@gardiner.com
W: www.gardiner.com

Gardner Denver Ltd
Claybrook Drive, Washford Ind. Est,
Redditch, Worcs B98 0DS
T: 01527 838200
F: 01527 521140
E: hydrovane-info.uk@gardnerdenver.com
W: www.hydrovane.co.uk

Garic Ltd
Kingfisher Park, Aviation Rd,
Pilsworth, Bury BL9 8GD
T: 0844 417 9780
F: 0161 766 8809
E: sales@garic.co.uk
W: www.garic.co.uk

Garrandale Ltd
Alfreton Rd, Derby DE21 4AP
T: 01332 291676
F: 01332 291677
E: info@garrandale.co.uk
W: www.garrandale.co.uk

GarrettCom Europe Ltd
Haslar Marine Technology Park,
Haslar Rd, Gosport PO12 2AU
T: 0870 382 5777
F: 0870 382 5098
E: john.ward@garrettcom.co.uk
W: www.garrettcom.co.uk

Gates Power Transmission
Tinwald Downs Rd,
Heath Hall,
Dumfries DG1 1TS
T: 01387 242000
F: 01387 242010
E: mediaeurope@gates.com
W: www.gates.com

Gatwick Express
see southern

Gatwick Plant Ltd
Woodside Works,
The Close, Horley,
Surrey RH6 9EB
T: 01293 824777
F: 01293 824077
E: transport@gatwickgroup.com
W: www.gatwickgroup.com

GAV Access Covers
PO Box 85, Nuneaton,
Warks CV11 9ZT
T: 02476 381090
F: 02476 373577
E: gavmet@aol.com
W: www.gav-solutions.com

GB Railfreight
15-25 Artillery Lane,
London E1 7HA
T: 020 7904 3393
F: 020 7983 5113
E: gbrfinfo@gbrailfreight.com
W: www.gbrailfreight.com

Geatech S.p.A
Via Del Plazzino 6/B,
40051 Altedo (BO) Italy
T: 0039 051 6601514
F: 0039 051 6601309
E: info@geatech.it
W: www.geatech.it

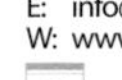

Geismar UK Ltd
Salthouse Rd,
Brackmills Ind. Est.,
Northampton NN4 7EX
T: 01604 769191
F: 01604 763154
E: sales@geismar.co.uk
W: www.geismar.com

Geldards LLP
Number One, Pride Place,
Pride Park,
Derby DE24 8QR
T: 01332 331631
F: 01332 294295
E: roman.surma@geldards.co.uk
W: www.geldards.co.uk

Gemma Lighting
Victoria St,
Mansfield,
Notts NG18 5RW
T: 01623 415601
F: 01623 420484
E: marketing@gemmalighting.com
W: www.gemmagroup.com

GenQuip Plc
Aberafan Rd, Baglan Ind. Park,
Port Talbot SA12 7DJ
T: 01639 823484
F: 01639 822533
E: sales@genquip.co.uk
W: www.genquip.co.uk

Genwork Ltd
see bache pallets

Geodesign Barriers Ltd
2 Montgomery Ave, Pinehurst,
Swindon SN2 1LE
T: 01793 538565
M: 07890 983239
E: britt.warg@palletbarrier.com
W: www.geodesignbarriers.com

Geoff Brown Signalling Ltd
The Cottage, Old Lodge,
Minchinhampton, Stroud GL6 9AQ
T: 07977 265721
E: geoffbrownsignalling@btinternet.com

GeoRope
Arumindarrich, West Laroch,
Ballachulish,
Argyll PH49 4JG
T: 01855 811224
E: kam@geo-rope.com
W: www.geo-rope.com

Geosynthetics Ltd
Fleming Rd, Harrowbrook Ind.Est.,
Hinckley, Leics LE10 3DU
T: 01455 617139
F: 01455 617140
E: sales@geosyn.co.uk
W: www.geosyn.co.uk

Geotechnical Engineering Ltd
Centurion House,
Olympus Park, Quedgeley,
Glos GL2 4NF
T: 01452 527743
F: 01452 729314
E: geotech@geoeng.co.uk
W: www.geoeng.co.uk

Geotechnics Ltd
The Geotechnical Centre,
203 Torrington Ave, Tile Hill,
Coventry CV4 9AP
T: 02476 694664
F: 02476 694642
E: mail@geotechnics.co.uk
W: www.geotechnics.co.uk

GE Transportation Systems
Inspira House, Martinfield,
Welwyn Garden City,
Herts AL7 1GW
T: 01707 383700
F: 01707 383701
W: www.getransportation.com

Getzner Werkstoffe GmbH
Herrenaus, A-6706 Burs,
Austria
T: 0043 5552 2010
F: 0043 5552 201899
E: sylomer@getzner.at
W: www.getzner.at

GGB UK
Wellington House, Starley Way,
Birmingham Int. Park,
Birmingham B37 7HB
T: 0845 230 0442
F: 0121 781 7313
E: greatbritain@ggbearings.com
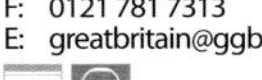

GGR Group Ltd
Broadway Business Park, Broadgate,
Chadderton, Oldham OL9 0JA
T: 0161 683 2580
F: 0161 683 4444
E: info@ggrgroup.com
W: www.ggrrail.com

GGS Engineering (Derby) Ltd
Atlas Works, Litchurch Lane,
Derby DE24 8AQ
T: 01332 299345
F: 01332 299678
E: sales@ggseng.com
W: www.ggseng.com

GHD Ltd
6th Floor, 10 Fetter Lane,
London EC4A 1BR
T: 020 3077 7900
E: sue.jackson@ghd.com
W: www.ghd.com

Gifford
see ramboll uk ltd

Giken Europe BV
Room 302, Burnhill Bus. Centre,
Kingfisher House, Elmfield Rd,
Bromley, Kent BR1 1LT
T: 0845 260 8001
F: 0845 260 8002
E: info@giken.co.uk
W: www.giken.com

Gilbarco Veeder-Root
Crompton Close, Basildon,
Essex SS14 3BA
T: 0870 010 1136
F: 0870 010 1137
E: uksales@gilbarco.com
W: www.gilbarco.com

Gioconda Limited
Unit 10, Woodfalls, Gravelly Lane,
Laddingford, Maidstone,
Kent ME18 6DA
T: 01622 872512
E: mail@gioconda.co.uk
W: www.gioconda.co.uk

Glasdon UK Ltd
Preston New Rd, Blackpool,
Lancs FY4 4UL
T: 01253 600414
F: 01253 792558
E: sales@glasdon-uk.co.uk
W: www.glasdon.com

Glenair UK Ltd
40 Lower Oakham Way, Mansfield,
Notts NG18 5BY
T: 01623 638100
F: 01623 638111
E: cbaker@glenair.co.uk
W: www.glenair.com

Glentworth Rail Ltd
Long Lane, Hawthorn Hill,
Maidenhead, Berks SL6 3TA
T: 01628 639823
F: 01628 639823
E: alistair.forsyth@glentworth.co.uk
W: www.glentworth.co.uk

Global Crossing (UK) Telecommunications Ltd
see level 3 communications

Globalforce UK Ltd
The Willows, College Avenue, Grays,
Essex RM17 5UN
T: 01375 380629
F: 01375 381995
E: graham@globalforceuk.co.uk
W: www.globalforceuk.co.uk

Global House Training Services Ltd
35a Astbury Rd,
London SE15 2NL
T: 020 7639 3322
E: contact@globalhouse.co.uk
W: www.globalhouse.co.uk

Global Rail Support
8 Curzon Lane,
Alvaston,
Derby DE24 8QS
T: 01332 601596
F: 01332 727494
E: ask@globalrailsupport.com
W: www.globalrailsupport.com

GME Springs
Boston Place, Foleshill,
Coventry CV6 5NN
T: 02476 664911
F: 02476 663020
E: sales@gmesprings.co.uk
W: www.gmesprings.co.uk

GMPTE
2 Piccadilly Place,
Manchester M1 3BG
T: 0871 200 2233
E: publicity@gmpte.gov.uk
W: www.gmpte.com

GM Rail Services Ltd
65 Somers Rd, Rugby,
Warks CV22 7DG
T: 01788 573777
F: 01788 551138
E: dwhitley@gmrail.co.uk
W: www.gmrail.co.uk

GMT Manufacturing Ltd
Old Gorsey Lane,
Wallasey CH44 4AH
T: 0151 630 1545
F: 0151 630 8555
E: info@gmt.co.uk
W: www.gmt.co.uk
no web

GMT Rubber-Metal-Technic Ltd
The Sidings, Station Rd, Guiseley,
Leeds LS20 8BX
T: 01943 870670
F: 01943 870631
E: sales@gmt.gb.com
W: www.gmt-gb.com

GNB Industrial Power (UK) Ltd
Mansell House, Aspinall Close,
Middlebrook, Horwich,
Bolton BL6 6QQ
T: 0845 606 4111
F: 0845 606 4112
E: sales-uk@eu.exide.com
W: www.gnb.com

GNER
see alliance rail holdings

GNWR
see alliance rail holdings

Go Ahead Group plc
Head Office, 4 Matthew Parker St,
Westminster, London SW1H 9NP
T: 020 7799 8999
F: 020 7799 8998
E: enquiries@go-ahead.com
W: www.go-ahead.com

Goldline Bearings Ltd
Stafford Park 17, Telford,
Shropshire TF3 3DG
T: 01952 292401
F: 01952 292403
E: sales@goldlinebearings.co.uk
W: www.goldlinebearings.com

Gordon Services Ltd
Unit 8, Daws Farm, Ivy Barn Lane,
Ingatestone,
Essex CM4 0PX
T: 01277 352895
F: 01277 356115
E: enquiries@gordonservicesltd.co.uk
W: www.gordonservicesltd.co.uk

Goskills
see people 1st

GOS Tool & Engineering Services Ltd
Heritage Court Rd,
Gilchrist Thomas ind. Est,
Blaenavon,
Torfaen NP4 9RL
T: 01495 790230
F: 01495 792757
E: enquiries@gosengineering.co.uk
W: www.gosengineering.co.uk

Go-Tel Communications Ltd
see samsung electronics

Govia
Go-ahead Group Rail,
Go-ahead House, 26-28 Addiscombe Rd, Croydon,
Surrey CR9 5GA
E: contact@go-ahead-rail.com
W: www.govia.info

Gradus Ltd
Park Green, Macclesfield,
Cheshire SK11 7LZ
T: 01625 428922
F: 01625 433949
E: imail@gradusworld.com
W: www.gradusworld.com

Grammer Seating Systems Ltd
Willenhall Lane Ind. Est., Bloxwich,
Walsall WS3 2XN
T: 01922 407035
F: 01922 710552
E: david.bignell@grammer.com
W: www.grammer.com

Gramm Interlink
17-19 High St, Ditchling,
East Sussex BN6 8SY
F: 01275 846397
M: 07827 947086
W: www.gramminerlinkrail.co.uk

Gramos Applied Ltd
Spring Rd,
Smethwick, West Midlands B66 1PT
T: 0121 525 4000
F: 0121 525 4950
E: info@gramos-applied.com
W: www.gramos-applied.com

Grand Central Railway Co. Ltd.
River House, 17 Museum Street,
York YO1 7DJ
T: 01904 633307
F: 01904 466066
E: customer.services@grandcentralrail.com
W: www.grandcentralrail.co.uk

Grant Rail Group
see volker rail

Grant Thornton UK LLP
Melton St, Euston Square,
London NW1 2EP
T: 0141 223 0731
E: taylor.ferguson@uk.gt.com
W: www.grant-thornton.co.uk

Grass Concrete Ltd
Duncan House, 142 Thornes Lane,
Thornes, Wakefield WF2 7RE
T: 01924 379443
F: 01924 290289
E: info@grasscrete.com
W: www.grasscrete.com

Graybar Ltd
10 Fleming Close,
Park Farm Ind. Est,
Wellingborough,
Northants NN8 6QF
T: 01933 676700
F: 01933 676800
E: sales@graybar.co.uk
W: www.graybar.co.uk

Greater Anglia
11th Floor , One Stratford Place,
Montfitchet Rd, London E20 1EJ
T: 020 7904 4031
F: 020 7549 5999
E: firstname.surname@greateranglia.co.uk
W: www.greateranglia.co.uk

Greenbrier Europe/Wagony Swidnica SA
Ul Strzelinska 35,
58-100 Swidnica,
Poland
T: 0048 74 856 2000
F: 0048 74 856 2035
E: europeansales@gbrx.com
W: www.gbrx.com

Green Leader Ltd
21 Foxmoor Close, Oakley,
Basingstoke,
Hants RG23 7BQ
T: 01256 781739
M: 07944 855611
E: nmoore@greenleader.co.uk
W: www.greenleader.co.uk

GreenMech Ltd
Mill Ind. Park, Kings Coughton,
Alcester, Warks B49 5QG
T: 01789 400044
F: 01789 400167
E: sales@greenmech.co.uk
W: www.greenmech.co.uk

Grimshaw Architects
57 Clerkenwell Rd,
London EC1M 5NG
T: 0207 291 4141
E: info@grimshaw-architects.com
W: www.grimshaw-architects.com

Groeneveld Uk Ltd
The Greentec Centre,
Gelders Hall Rd,
Gelders hall Ind. Est,
Shepshed,
Leics LE12 9NH
T: 01509 600033
F: 01509 602000
W: www.groeneveld-group.com

Grontmij
Grove House,
Mansion Gate Drive,
Leeds LS7 4DN
T: 0113 262 0000
F: 0113 262 0737
E: enquiries@grontmij.co.uk
W: www.grontmij.co.uk

Groundwise Searches Ltd
Suite 8, Chichester House,
45 Chichester Rd,
Southend on Sea SS1 2JU
T: 01702 615566
F: 01702 460239
E: mail@groundwise.com
W: www.groundwise.com

GroupCytek
The Oast House, 5 Maed Lane,
Farnham,
Surrey GU9 7DY
T: 01252 715171
F: 01252 713271
E: projects@groupcytek.com
W: www.groupcytek.com

Gummiwerk
see strail

Gunnebo UK Ltd
PO Box 61, Woden Rd,
Wolverhampton WV10 0BY
T: 01902 455111
F: 01902 351961
E: marketing@gunnebo.com
W: www.gunnebo.com

Gutteridge, Haskins & Davey Ltd
see ghd

h2gogo Ltd
The Heights, 59-65 Lowlands Rd,
Harrow,
Middx HA1 3AW
T: 01494 817174
E: info@h2gogo.com
W: www.h2gogo.com

Hadleigh Castings Ltd
Pond Hall Rd, Hadleigh,
Ipswich,Suffolk IP7 5PW
T: 01473 827281
F: 01473 827879
E: data@hadleighcastings.com
W: www.hadleighcastings.com

Hafren Security Fasteners
Unit 23, Mochdre Industrial Park,
Newtown,
Powys SY16 4LE
T: 01686 621300
F: 01686 621800
E: security@hafrenfasteners.com
W: www.hafrenfasteners.com

Haigh Rail Ltd
60 Grange Drive,
Hoghton,
Preston PR5 0LP
T: 01254 854432
M: 07875 847602
E: chris@haighrail.com
W: www.haighrail.com

Haki Ltd
Magnus,
Tame Valley Ind. Est,Tamworth,
Staffs B77 5BY
T: 01827 282525
F: 01827 250329
E: info@haki.co.uk
W: www.haki.co.uk

Hako Machines Ltd
Eldon Close, Crick,
Northants NN6 7SL
T: 01788 825600
F: 01788 823969
E: sales@hako.co.uk
W: www.hako.co.uk

Halcrow Group Ltd
44 Brook Green,
London W6 7BY
T: 01332 222620
E: chris.hanson@ch2m.com
W: www.halcrow.com

Halfen Ltd
Humphrys Rd,
Woodside Est.,Dunstable,
Beds LU5 4TP
T: 0870 531 6300
F: 0870 531 6304
E: info@halfen.co.uk
W: www.halfen.co.uk

KJ Hall Chartered Land & Engineering Surveyors
30 Church Rd,
Highbridge,
Somerset TA9 3RN
T: 01278 794600
F: 01278 785562
E: admin@kjhsurvey.co.uk
W: www.kjhsurvey.co.uk

HallRail
see trackwork

Halo Rail
See Stewart Signs,

Harmill Systems Ltd
Unit B1,
Cherrycourt Way,
Leighton Buzzard,
Beds LU7 4UH
T: 01525 851133
F: 01525 850661
E: david.flint@harmill.co.uk
W: www.harmill.co.uk

Harp Visual Communications Solutions
Unit 7,
Swanwick Business Centre,
Bridge Rd,
Lower Swanwick,
Southampton SO31 7GB
T: 01489 580011
F: 01489 580022
E: sales@harpvisual.co.uk
W: www.passengerinformation.com

Harrington Generators International (HGI)
Ravenstor Rd,
Wirksworth,
Matlock,
Derbys DE4 4FY
T: 01629 824284
F: 01629 824613
E: sales@hgigenerators.com
W: www.hgigenerators.com

E C Harris
ECHQ, 34 York Way,
London N1 9AB
T: 020 7812 2000
F: 020 7812 2001
W: www.echarris.com

Harry Fairclough Construction
Howley Lane, Howley,
Warrington WA1 2DN
T: 01925 628300
F: 01925 628301
E: post@harryfairclough.co.uk
W: www.harryfairclough.co.uk

Harry Needle Railroad Company
Barrow Hill Depot, Campbell Drive,
Barrow Hill, Chesterfield S43 2PR
T: 01246 477001
F: 01246 477208
M: 07917 777871
E: hnrcbh@aol.com
W: www.harryneedlerail.com

Harsco Rail Ltd
Unit 1, Chewton St, Eastwood,
Notts NG16 3HB
T: 01773 539480
F: 01773 539481
E: uksales@harsco.com
W: www.permaquip.com

Harting Limited
Caswell Rd, Brackmills Ind. Est,
Northampton NN4 7PW
T: 01604 827500
F: 01604 706777
E: gb@harting.com
W: www.harting.com
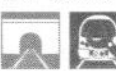

The Haste Partnership
10 The Croft, Sheriff Hutton,
York YO60 6SQ
T: 01347 878034
E: richardhaste@aol.com
W: www.icrg.co.uk

Hawker Siddley
Switchgear Ltd, Unit 3,
Blackwood Ind. Est., Newport Rd,
S.Wales NP12 2XH
T: 01495 223001
F: 01495 225674
E: nigel.jones@hss-ltd.com
W: www.hss-ltd.com

Hawkgrove Ltd
Bloomfield, Coalpit Lane,
Stoke St Michael,
Somerset BA3 5JT
T: 01373 837900
E: mike.duberry@hawkgrove.co.uk
W: www.hawkgrove.co.uk

Hayley Rail
48-50 Westbrook Rd,
Trafford Park,
Manchester M17 1AY
T: 0161 877 3005
F: 0161 755 3425
E: phil.mccabe@hayley-group.co.uk
W: www.hayley-group.co.uk

HBM Test & Measurement
1 Churchill Court, 58 Station Rd,
North Harrow,
Middx HA2 7SA
T: 020 8515 6100
F: 020 8515 6149
E: info@uk.hbm.com
W: www.hbm.com

John Headon Ltd
Hivernia, Jackson's Hill, St Mary's,
Isles of Scilly
T: 01720 423540
M: 07840 102666
E: john@johnheadonltd.co.uk
W: www.johnheadonltd.co.uk

Healthcare Connections Ltd
Nashleigh Court, 188 Severalls Ave,
Chesham, Bucks HP5 3EN
T: 08456 773002
F: 08456 773004
E: sales@healthcare-connections.com
W: www.healthcare-connections.com

Health, Safety & Engineering Consultants Ltd (HSEC)
70 Tamworth Rd,
Ashby de la Zouch,
Leics LE65 2PR
T: 01530 412777
F: 01530 415592
E: hsec@hsec.co.uk
W: www.hsec.co.uk

Heath Lambert Group
Transportation Division,
133 Houndsditch,
London EC3A 7AW
T: 020 7560 3819
F: 020 7560 3294
E: mhawkes@heathlambert.com
W: www.heathlambert.com/projects

Heathrow Connect
6th Floor,
50 Eastbourne Terrace,
Paddington,
London W2 6LX
T: 020 8750 6600
F: 020 8750 6615
W: www.heathrowconnect.com

Heathrow Express
See Heathrow Connect
W: www.heathrowexpress.com

Hert Trace Ltd
Mere's Edge,
Chester Rd,
Helsby,
Frodsham,
Cheshire WA6 0DJ
T: 01928 726451
F: 01928 727846
E: nil.malone@heat-trace.com
W: www.heat-trace.com

Heavy Haul Power International GmbH
Steigerstrasse 9,
99096 Erfurt,
Germany
T: 0049 361 43046714
F: 0049 361 2629971
E: richard.painter@hhpi.eu
W: www.hhpi.eu

Hedra
See Mouchel

Hegenscheidt MFD GmbH & CO KG
Hegenscheidt Platz,
D-41812 Erkelenz,
Germany
T: 0049 2431 86279
F: 0049 2431 86480
E: info@niles-simmons.de
W: www.hegenscheidt-mfd.de

Hellermann Tyton
Robeson Way, Altrincham Road,
Wythenshawe, Manchester
M22 4TY
T: 0161 947 2200
F: 0161 947 2220
W: www.hellermanntyton.co.uk

Henkel Loctite
Technologies House,
Wood Lane End,
Hemel Hempstead, Herts HP2 4RQ
T: 01442 278100
F: 01442 278293
W: www.loctite.com

Henry Williams Ltd
Dodsworth St, Darlington,
Co. Durham DL1 2NJ
T: 01325 462722
F: 01325 381744
E: info@hwilliams.co.uk
W: www.hwilliams.co.uk

Hepworth Rail International
4 Merse Rd, North Moons Moat,
Redditch, Worcs B98 9HL
T: 01527 60146
F: 01527 66836
E: markjones@b-hepworth.com
W: www.b-hepworth.com

Hering UK LLP
Wessex House, Oxford Rd, Newbury,
Berks RG14 1PA
T: 01635 814490
F: 01635 814491
W: www.heringinternational.com

Herrenknecht AG
Schlehenweg 2, 77963 Schwanau,
Germany
T: 0049 7824 3020
F: 0049 7824 3403
E: info@herrenknecht.com
W: www.herrenknecht.com

Hertford Controls Ltd
14 Ermine Point, Gentlemens Field,
Westmill Rd, Ware, Herts SG12 0EF
T: 01920 467578
F: 01920 487037
E: info@hertfordcontrols.co.uk
W: www.hertfordcontrols.co.uk

Hexagon Metrology Ltd
Halesfield 13, Telford,
Shropshire TF7 4PL
T: 0870 446 2667
F: 0870 446 2668
E: enquiry.uk@hexagonmetrology.com
W: www.hexagonmetrology.com/uk

Hid Global Hiflex Fluidpower
Howley Park Rd, Morley,
Leeds LS27 0BN
T: 0113 281 0031
F: 0113 307 5918
E: sales@hiflex-europe.com
W: www.dunlophiflex.com

The Highgate Partnership
Joel House, 19 Garrick St,
London WC2E 9AX
T: 020 7010 7750
F: 020 7010 7751
W: www.highgatepartners.com

High-Point Rendel Limited
61 Southwark St,
London SE1 1SA
T: 020 7654 0400
F: 020 7654 0401
E: london@hprworld.com
W: www.hprworld.com

High Speed 1 Ltd
see hs1 ltd

High Speed 2 |ltd
see hs2 ltd

High Voltage Maintenance Services Ltd
Unit A, Faraday Court, Faraday Rd,
Crawley, West Sussex RH10 9PU
T: 0845 604 0336
F: 01293 537739
E: enquiries@hvms.co.uk
W: www.hvms.co.uk

Hill Cannon (UK) LLP
Royal Chambers, Station Parade,
Harrogate HG1 1EP
T: 01423 562571
F: 01423 530018
E: harrogate@hillcannon.com
W: www.hillcannon.com

Hillfort Communications Ltd
3 Campion Way, Lymington,
Hants SO41 9LS
T: 01590 670912
F: 01590 688341
E: hillfort@doc2prod.demon.co.uk

Hill McGlynn
See Ranstadt CPE

Hilti (GB) Ltd
No1 Trafford Wharf Rd, Trafford Park,
Manchester M17 1BY
T: 0800 886 100
F: 0800 886 200
E: gbsales@hilti.com
W: www.hilti.co.uk

Hima-Sella Ltd
Carrington Field St,
Stockport SK1 3JN
T: 0161 429 4500
F: 0161 476 3095
E: sales@hima-sella.co.uk
W: www.hima-sella.co.uk

Hiremasters
See Quickbuild

Hiremee Ltd
York Way, Royston, Herts SG8 5HJ
T: 01763 247111
F: 01763 247222
E: info@hiremee.co.uk
W: www.hiremee.co.uk

Hitachi Capital Vehicle Solutions Ltd
Kiln House, Kiln Rd, Newbury,
Berks RG14 2NU
T: 01635 574640
W: www.hitachicapitalvehiclesolutions.co.uk

Hitachi Rail Europe Ltd
40 Holborn Viaduct,
London EC1N 2PB
T: 020 7970 2700
F: 020 7970 2799
E: rail.enquiries@hitachirail-eu.com
W: www.hitachirail-eu.com

HOCHTIEF (UK)Construction Ltd
Epsilon, Windmill Hill Business Park,
Whitehill Way,
Swindon SN5 6NX
T: 01793 755555
F: 01793 755556
E: enquiries@hochtief.co.uk
W: www.hochtief.co.uk

Hodge Clemco Ltd
Orgreave Drive,
Sheffield S13 9NR
T: 0114 254 8811
F: 0114 254 0250
E: sales@hodgeclemco.co.uk
W: www.hodgeclemco.co.uk

Hodgson & Hodgson Group Ltd
Crown Business Park,
Old Dalby,
Melton Mowbray,
Leics LE14 3NQ
T: 01376 555200
E: info@hodgsongroup.co.uk
W: www.acoustic.co.uk/h&h/rail

Hogia Transport Systems Ltd
St James House,
13 Kensington Square,
London W8 5HD
T: 020 7795 8156
E: gary.umpleby@hogia.com
W: www.hogia.com

HOK International Ltd
Qube, 90 Whitfield St,
London W1T 4EZ
T: 020 7636 2006
F: 020 7636 1987
E: samantha.davis@hok.com
W: www.hok.com

Holdfast Level Crossings Ltd
Brockenhurst,
Cheap St,
Chedworth,
Cheltenham,
Glos GL54 4AA
T: 01242 578801
F: 01285 720748
M: 07970 656143
E: request@railcrossings.co.uk
W: www.railcrossings.co.uk

Holdsworth Fabrics Ltd
Hopton Mills,
Mirfield,
West Yorks WF14 8HE
T: 01924 490591
F: 01924 495605
E: info@camirafabrics.com
W: www.holdsworthfabrics.com

Holland Company
1000 Holland Drive, Crete,
Illinois 60417 USA
T: 001 708 672 2300
F: 001 708 672 0119
E: sales@hollandco.com
W: www.hollandco.com

Holmar Rail Services
Kendal House, The Street,
Shadoxhurst,
Ashford,
Kent TN26 1LU
T: 01233 731007
F: 01233 733221
W: www.holmar.co.uk

Holophane Rail Solutions
T: 01908 649292
F: 01908 367618
E: info@holophane.co.uk
W: www.holophane.co.uk

Homegrown Timber (Rail) Ltd
Courtlands,
Antlands Lane,
Shipley Br,
Surrey RH6 9TE
T: 01293 821321
F: 01293 772319
E: rail@homegrowntimber.com
W: www.homegrowntimber.com
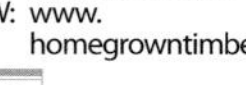

Hoppecke Industrial Batteries Ltd
2 Lowfield Drive,
Centre 500,
Newcastle,
Staffs ST5 0UU
T: 01782 667300
W: www.hoppecke.com

Hosiden Besson Ltd
11 St Josephs Close,
Hove,
East Sussex BN3 7EZ
T: 01273 861166
F: 01273 777501
E: info@hbl.co.uk
W: www.hbl.co.uk

Houghton International
Fisher St, Walker,
Newcastle upon Tyne NE6 4LT
T: 0191 234 3000
F: 0191 263 7873
E: info@houghtoninternational.com
W: www.houghton-international.com

Howells Railway Products Ltd
Longley Lane, Sharston Ind. Est.,
Wythenshawe, Manchester M22 4SS
T: 0161 945 5567
F: 0161 945 5597
E: info@howells-railway.co.uk
W: www.howells-railway.co.uk

HP Information Security
3200 Daresbury Park, Daresbury,
Warrington WA4 4BU
T: 01925 665500
F: 01925 667200
E: salessupport.infosec@hp.com
W: www.hp.com
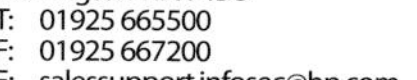

HPR Consult
See High Point Rendel

HS1 Ltd
12th Floor, One Euston Square,
40 Melton St,
London NW1 2FD
T: 020 7014 2700
E: wendy.spinks@highspeed1.co.uk
W: www.highspeed1.co.uk

HS2 Ltd
2nd Floor, Eland House,
Bressenden Place,
London SW1E 5DU
T: 020 7944 4908
E: hs2enquiries@hs2.org.uk
W: www.hs2.org.uk

HSBC Rail (UK)
See Eversholt Rail Lrd

HS Carlsteel Engineering Ltd
Crabtree Manorway South,
Belvedere,
Kent DA17 6BH
T: 020 8312 1879
F: 020 8320 9480
E: sales@hscarlsteel.co.uk
W: www.hscarlsteel.co.uk

HSS Training Ltd
Circle House, Lostock Rd,
Davyhulme,
Manchester M41 0HS
T: 0845 766 7799
F: 0161 877 9074
E: training@hss.com
W: www.hsstraining.com

Huber + Suhner (UK) Ltd
Telford Rd, Bicester,
Oxon OX26 4LA
T: 01869 364100
F: 01869 249046
E: info.uk@hubersuhner.com
W: www.hubersuhner.co.uk

Hull Trains
See First Hull Trains

Human Engineering Ltd
Shore House, 68, Westbury Hill,
Westbury-on-Trym,
Bristol BS9 3AA
T: 0117 962 0888
F: 0117 962 9888
W: www.humaneng.net

Human Reliability
1 School House, Higher Lane,
Dalton, Lancs WN8 7RP
T: 01257 463121
F: 01257 463810
E: dembrey@humanreliabilty.com
W: www.humanreliability.com

Hunslet Barclay
See Brush Barclay

Hunslet Engine Co
See LH Group Services

Husqvarna Construction Products
Unit 4, Pearce Way,
Bristol Rd,
Gloucester GL2 5YD
T: 0844 844 4570
E: husqvarna.construction@husqvarna.co.uk
W: www.husqvarna.co.uk

Hutchinson Team Telecom Ltd
See Indigo Telecom Group

Hyder Consulting (UK) Ltd
Manning House,
22 Carlisle Place, London SW1P 1JA
T: 020 3014 9000
F: 020 7828 8428
E: mahmoud.alghita@hyderconsulting.com
W: www.hyderconsulting.com

Hydrex Equipment UK Ltd
see txm plant ltd

Hydro Aluminium Extrusions Ltd
Pantglas Ind. Est., Bedwas,
Caerphilly CF83 8DR
T: 0870 777 2262
F: 02920 863728
E: sales.haeuk@hydro.com
W: www.hydro.com/extrusion/uk

Hydrotech Europe Ltd
Beaufort Court, 11 Roebuck Way,
Knowlhill, Milton Keynes MK5 8HL
T: 01908 675244
F: 01908 397513
W: www.hydro-usl.com

Hydrotechnik UK Ltd
Unit 10, Easter Lane, Lenton,
Nottingham NG7 2PX
T: 01159 003550
F: 01159 705597
E: sales@hydrotechnik.co.uk
W: www.hydrotechnik.co.uk

Hypertac UK
36-38 Waterloo Rd,
London NW2 7UH
T: 020 8450 8033
F: 020 8208 3455
E: info@hypertac.co.uk
W: www.hypertac.co.uk

IAD Rail Systems
see network rail

Ian Catling Consultancy
Ash Meadow, Bridge Way,
Chipstead CR5 3PX
T: 01737 552225
F: 01737 556669
E: ic@catling.com
W: www.catling.com

Ian Riley
See Riley & Son

IBI Group
Kemp House, 152-160 City Rd,
London ECIV 2NP
T: 020 7017 1850
F: 020 7251 8339
E: enquiriesuk@ibigroup.com
W: www.ibigroup.com

I C Consultants Ltd
58 Prince's Gate, Exhibition Rd,
London SW7 2QA
T: 020 7594 6565
F: 020 7594 6570
E: consultants@imperial.ac.uk
W: www.imperial-consultants.co.uk

ICEE
20 Arnside Rd, Waterlooville,
Hants PO7 7UP
T: 02392 230604
F: 02392 230605
E: sales@icee.co.uk
W: www.icee.co.uk

Icomera UK
Innovation Centre Medway,
Maidstone Rd, Chatham,
Kent ME5 9FD
T: 0870 446 0461
E: sales@icomera.com
W: www.icomera.com

Icon Silentbloc UK Ltd
Wellington Rd,
Burton upon Trent,
Staffs DE14 2AP
T: 01283 741700
F: 01283 741742
E: info@iconpolymer.com
W: www.iconpolymer.com

Icore International Ltd
220 Bedford Avenue,
Slough SL1 4RY
T: 01753 896600
F: 01753 896601
E: cristophebigare@zodiacaerospace.com
W: www.zodiacaerospace.com

ID Computing Ltd
ID Centre, Lathkill House,
rtc Business Park,
London Rd.
Derby DE24 8UP
T: 01332 258880
F: 01332 258823
E: info@idcomputing.co.uk
W: www.idcomputing.co.uk

Ideas Limited (Integration Design Ergonomics Applications Solutions)
PO Box 193, Thame, Oxon OX9 0BR
T: 01844 216896
F: 0970 460 6190
E: info@ideas.ltd.uk
W: www.ideas.ltd.uk

IET
See Institution of Engineering & Technology

IETG Ltd
Cross Green Way,
Cross Green Ind. Est., Leeds LS9 0SE
T: 0113 201 9700
F: 0113 201 9701
W: www.ietg.co.uk

IGP
See PSV Glass

Ilecsys
Tring Ind. Est, Upper Icknield Way,
Tring, Herts HP23 4JX
T: 08444 770990
F: 01442 828399
E: pjd@ilecsys.co.uk
W: www.ilecsys.co.uk

ILME UK Ltd
50 Evans Rd, Venture Point, Speke,
Merseyside L24 9PB
T: 0151 336 9321
F: 0151 336 9326
E: sales@ilmeuk.co.uk
W: www.ilmeuk.co.uk

Imagerail
Reservoir House,
Wetheral Pasture,
Carlisle CA4 8HR
T: 01768 800208
E: andrew@imagerail.com
W: www.imagerail.com

In2rail Ltd
Hobbs Hill, Rothwell,
Northants NN14 6YG
T: 01536 711804
M: 07980 104571
E: pm@in2rail.co.uk
W: www.in2rail.co.uk

Inbis Ltd
Club St, Bamber Bridge,
Preston,
Lancs PR5 6FN
T: 01772 645000
F: 01772 645001
W: www.inbis.com

Inchmere Design
Inchmere Studios,
Grange Park, Chacombe,
Banbury, Oxon OX17 2EL
T: 01295 711801
E: mark@inchmere.co.uk
W: www.inchmere.co.uk

Incorporatewear
Edison Rd,
Hams Hall National
Distribution Park,
Coleshill B46 1DA
T: 0844 257 0530
F: 0844 257 0591
E: info@incorporatewear.co.uk
W: www.incorporatewear.co.uk

Independent Glass Co Ltd
540-550 Lawmoor St,
Dixons Blazes Ind. Est,
Glasgow G5 0UA
T: 0141 429 8700
F: 0141 429 8524
E: toughened@ig-glass.co.uk
W: www.independentglass.co.uk

Independent Rail Consultancy Group (IRCG)
E: info@ircg.co.uk
W: www.ircg.co.uk

Indigo Telecom Group
Field House, Uttoxeter Old Rd,
Derby DE1 1NH
T: 01332 375570
F: 01332 375673
E: sales@indigotelecomgroup.com
W: www.indigotelecomgroup.com

Industrial Door Services Ltd
Adelaide St, Crindau Park,
Newport,
Gwent NP20 5NF
T: 01633 853335
F: 01633 851989
E: enquiries@indoorserv.co.uk
W: www.indoorserv.co.uk

Industrial Flow Control Ltd
Unit 1, Askews Farm Lane, Grays,
Essex RM17 5XR
T: 01375 387155
F: 01375 387420
E: sales@inflow.co.uk
W: www.inflow.co.uk

Inflow
See Industrial Flow Control Ltd

Infodev EDI Inc.
1995 Rue Frank-Carrel, Suite 202,
Quebec G1N 4H9 Canada
T: 001 418 681 3529
F: 001 418 681 1209
E: info@infodev.ca
W: www.infodev.ca

Infor
1 Lakeside Rd, Farnborough,
Hants GU14 6XP
T: 0800 376 9633
F: 0121 615 8255
E: ukmarketing@infor.com
W: www.infor.co.uk

informatica Software Ltd
6 Waltham Park,
Waltham Rd,
White Waltham,
Maidenhead,
Berks SL6 3JN
T: 01628 511311
F: 01628 511411
E: ukinfo@informatica.com
W: www.informatica.com

Informatiq
Gresham House,
53 Clarendon Rd,
Watford WD17 1LA
T: 01923 224481
F: 01923 224493
E: permanent@informatiq.co.uk
W: www.informatiq.co.uk

Infotec Ltd
The Maltings, Tamworth Rd,
Ashby De La Zouch, Leics LE65 2PS
T: 01530 560600
F: 01530 560111
E: sales@infotec.co.uk
W: www.infotec.co.uk

Infra Safety Services
See ISS Labour

INIT Innovations in Transportation Ltd
49 Stoney St, The Lace Market,
Nottingham NG1 1LX
T: 0870 890 4648
F: 0115 989 5461
W: www.init.co.uk

Initial Facilities -Transport Sector
13-27 Brunswick Place,
London N1 6DX
T: 0800 0778963
E: if-contact-uk@rentokil-initial.com
W: www.initial.co.uk

Initiate Consulting Ltd
9 Gainsford St,
Tower Bridge, London SE1 2NE
T: 020 7357 9600
F: 020 7357 9604
E: info@initiate.uk.com
W: www.initiate.uk.com

Inline Track Welding Ltd
Ashmill Business Park, Ashford Rd,
Lenham, Maidstone ME17 2GQ
T: 01622 854730
F: 01622 854731
E: david.thomson@fsmail.net

InnoTrans – a trade fair organised by Messe Berlin GmbH,
Messedamm 22, D-14055 Berlin,
Germany
T: 0049 303038 2376
F: 0049 303038 2190
E: innotrans@messe-berlin.de
W: www.innotrans.com

Innovative Railway Safety Ltd
Ty Penmynydd, Llangennith,
Swansea SA3 1DT
M: 07974 065798
E: paul@inrailsafe.co.uk
W: www.inrailsafe.co.uk

Innovative Support Systems Ltd (ISS)
15 Fountain Parade, Mapplewell,
Barnsley, S Yorks S75 6FW
T: 01226 381155
F: 01226 381177
E: enquiries@iss-eng.com
W: www.iss-eng.com

The Input Group
101 Ashbourne Road,
Derby DE22 3FW
T: 01332 348830
F: 01332 296342
E: info@inputgroup.co.uk
W: www.inputgroup.co.uk

Insight Security
Unit 2, Cliffe Ind. Est,
Lewes,
E Sussex BN8 6JL
T: 01273 475500
F: 01273 478800
E: info@insight-security.com
W: www.insight-security.com

Insituform Technologies Ltd
Roundwood Ind. Est.,
Ossett,
West Yorks WF5 9SQ
T: 01924 277076
F: 01924 265107
E: jbeech@insituform.com
W: www.insituform.co.uk

Inspectahire Instrument Co. Ltd
Unit 11,
Whitemyres Business Centre,
Whitemyres Ave,
Aberdeen AB16 6HQ
T: 01224 789692
F: 01224 789462
E: enquiries@inspectahire.com
W: www.inspectahire.com

Install CCTV Ltd
10 Rochester Court,
Anthonys Way, Rochester,
Kent ME2 4NW
T: 01634 717784
F: 01634 718085
W: www.installcctv.co.uk

Installation Project Services Ltd
53 Ullswater Crescent, Coulsdon,
Surrey CR5 2HR
T: 020 8655 6060
F: 020 8655 6070
E: sales@ips-ltd.co.uk
W: www.ips-ltd.co.uk

Institute of Railway Research
University of Huddersfield,
Queensgate,
Huddersfield HD1 3DH
T: 01484 472030
M: 07760 197819
E: irr.info@hud.ac.uk
W: www.hud.ac.uk/irr

Institute of Rail Welding
Granta Park,
Great Abingdon,
Cambridge CB21 6AL
T: 01223 899000
F: 01223 894219
E: tim.jessop@twi.co.uk
W: www.iorw.co.uk

Institution of Civil Engineers (ICE)
One Great George St,
Westminster,
London SW1P 3AA
T: 020 7222 7722
E: communications@ice.org.uk
W: www.ice.org.uk
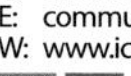

Institution of Engineering& Technology
Michael Faraday House,
Six Hills Way,
Stevenage SG1 2AY
T: 01438 767359
F: 01438 767305
E: cthomason@theiet.org
W: www.theiet.org
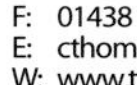
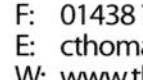

Institution of Mechanical Engineers (IMechE)
1 Birdcage Walk,
Westminster,
London SW1H 9JJ
T: 020 7222 7899
F: 020 7222 4557
E: railway@imeche.org.uk
W: www.imeche.org.uk

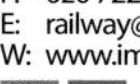

Institution of Railway Operators
The Moat House,
133 Newport Rd,
Stafford ST16 2EZ
T: 01785 248113
E: info@railwayoperators.co.uk
W: www.railwayoperators.co.uk

Institution of Railway Signal Engineers (IRSE)
4th Floor,
1 Birdcage Walk,
Westminster,
London SW1H 9JJ
T: 020 7808 1180
F: 020 7808 1196
E: hq@irse.org
W: www.irse.org

Intamech Ltd
see Arbil

Intec (UK) Ltd
York House,
76-78 Lancaster Rd,
Morecambe,
Lancs LA4 5QN
T: 01524 426777
F: 01524 426888
E: intec@inteconline.co.uk
W: www.inteconline.co.uk

Integrated Transport Planning Ltd
50 North Thirtieth St,
Milton Keynes MK9 3PP
T: 01908 259718
F: 01908 605747
E: wheway@itpworld.net
W: www.itpworld.net

Integrated Utility Services
16 Toft Green,
York YO1 6JT
T: 01904 685678
E: railenquiries@ius.biz
W: www.ius.biz

Integrated Water Services Ltd
Park Lane West, Tipton,
Dudley DY4 8LH
T: 0121 520 1006
F: 0121 521 2811
E: nickitasmith@integrated-water.co.uk
W: www.integrated-water.co.uk

Intelligent Data Collection Ltd
4 Pocketts Yard, Cookham,
Berks SL6 9SL
T: 0845 003 8747
E: info@intelligent-data-collection.com
W: www.intelligent-data-collection.com

Intelligent Locking Systems
Bordesley Hall,
Alvechurch,
Birmingham B48 7QA
T: 01527 68885
F: 01527 66681
E: info@ilslocks.co.uk
W: www.ilslocks.co.uk

Intelligent Radio Solutions (IRIS) Ltd
Networks House,
32 Stephenson Rd,
St Ives,
Cambs PE27 3WT
T: 01223 906052
E: info@intelligentradiosolutions.com
W: www.intelligentradiosolutions.com

Interface Fabrics Ltd
See Holdsworth

Interfaces
2 Valley Close,
Hertford SG13 8BD
T: 01992 422042
E: reg.harman@ntlworld.com

Interfleet Technology Ltd- a member of the SNC-Lavalin Group
Interfleet House,
Pride Parkway,
Derby DE24 8HX
T: 01332 223 000
F: 01332 223 001
E: grace.m@interfleet.co.uk
W: www.interfleet.co.uk

Intermodality LLP
6 Belmont Business Centre,
East Hoathly,
Lewes,
East Sussex BN8 6QL
T: 0845 130 4388
F: 01825 841049
W: www.intermodality.com

Intermodal Logistics
Cedar House, Glade Rd,
Marlow,
Bucks SL7 1DQ
T: 01234 822821
F: 01628 486800
E: derekbliss@intermodallogistics.co.uk
W: www.intermodallogistics.co.uk

International Rail
PO Box 153, Alresford,
Hants SO24 4AQ
T: 0871 231 0790
F: 0871 231 0791
E: sales@internationalrail.com
W: www.internationalrail.com

International Transport Intermediaries Club Ltd
see itic

Intertrain (UK) Ltd
Intertrain House, Union St,
Doncaster DN1 3AE
T: 01302 815530
F: 01302 815531
E: intertraininfo@intertrain.biz
W: www.intertrain.biz

Invensys Rail Ltd
see siemens rail automation

Ionbond Ltd
Unit 36, Number One Ind Est,
Medomsley Rd,
Consett DH7 6TS
T: 01207 500823
F: 01207 590254
E: maria.beadle@ionbond.com
W: www.ionbond.com

Iosis Associates
15 Good Shepherd Close,
Bishop Rd,
Bristol BS7 8NF
T: 0117 370 6313
M: 07968 947021
E: pwt@iosis.org.uk
W: www.iosis.org.uk

Ipex Consulting
Rose Cottage, Woodcroft Lane,
Woodcroft, Chepstow NP16 7QB
M: 07767 436467
E: info@ipexconsulting.com
W: www.ipexconsulting.com

I-Plas Ltd
Ridings Business Park,
Hopwood Lane,
Halifax HX1 3TT
T: 0845 459 9352
F: 0845 459 9354
E: enquiries@i-plas.co.uk
W: www.i-plas.co.uk

IQPC
Anchor House,
15-19 Bitten St,
London SW3 3QL
T: 020 7368 2363
F: 020 7368 9301
E: enquire@iqpc.co.uk
W: www.iqpc.co.uk

Iridium Onboard
Clue House, Petherton Rd,
Hengrove,
Bristol BS14 9BZ
T: 01275 890140
W: www.iridiumonboard.com

Irish Traction Group
31 Hayfield Rd, Bredbury,
Stockport SK6 1DE
M: 07713 159869
E: info@irishtractiongroup.com
W: www.irishtractiongroup.com

IRL Group Ltd
Unit C1, Swingbridge Rd,
Loughborough,
Leics LE11 5JD
T: 01509 217101
F: 01509 611004
E: info@irlgroup.com
W: www.irlgroup.com

Ironside Farrar
111 McDonald Rd,
Edinburgh EH7 4NW
T: 0131 550 6500
E: mail@ironsidefarrar.com
W: www.ironsidefarrar.com

ISC Best Practice Consultancy Ltd
Lower Market Hall Offices, Market St,
Okehampton, Devon EX20 1HN
T: 01837 54555
E: isc.bestpractice@btconnect.com
W: www.isc-bestpracticeconsultancy.co.uk

Ischebeck Titan
John Dean House, Wellington Rd,
Burton upon Trent DE14 2TG
T: 01283 515677
F: 01283 516126
E: sales@ischebeck-titan.co.uk
W: www.ischebeck-titan.co.uk

IS-Rayfast Ltd
Unit 2, Westmead, Swindon SN5 7SY
T: 01793 616700
F: 01793 644304
E: sales@israyfast.com
W: www.israyfast.com

ISS Labour
Suite 5/6, Acorn Place, Alfreton Rd,
Derby DE21 4AS
T: 01332 542800
F: 01332 542829
E: info@isslabour.co.uk
W: www.isslabour.co.uk

ITIC
90 Fenchurch St, London EC3M 4ST
T: 020 7338 0150
F: 020 7338 0151
E: itic@thomasmiller.com
W: www.itic-insure.com

itmsoil Group Ltd
Bell Lane, Uckfield,
E Sussex TN22 1QL
T: 01825 765044
F: 01825 744398
E: sales@itmsoil.com
W: www.itmsoil.com

ITSO Ltd
Luminar House, Deltic Ave,
Milton Keynes MK13 8LW
T: 01908 255455
F: 01908 255450
E: info@itso.org.uk
W: www.itso.org.uk

ITS United Kingdom
Suite 312,
Tower Bridge Business Centre,
46-48 East Smithfield,
London E1W 1AW
T: 020 7709 3003
F: 020 7709 3007
E: mailbox@its-uk.org.uk
W: www.its-uk.org.uk

ITT Water & Wastewater UK Ltd
Colwick,
Nottingham NG4 2AN
T: 0115 940 0111
F: 0115 940 0444
W: www.itwww.co.uk

ITW Plexus
Unit 3, Shipton Way,
Express Business Park,
Northampton Rd,
Rushden,
Northants NN10 6GL
T: 01933 354550
F: 01933 354555
E: sales@itwppe.eu
W: www.staput.co.uk

J.A.B Services (UK)
September Cottage,
Haven Rd,
Rudgwick,
Horsham RH12 3JH
T: 01403 822326
M: 07786 636495
E: baggsja@hotmail.com

Jacobs Consultancy UK Ltd
See Lee Fisher

Jacobs UK Ltd
1180 Eskdale Rd,
Winnersh,
Wokingham RG41 5TU
T: 0118 946 7000
F: 0118 946 7001
W: www.jacobs.com

Jafco Tools Ltd
Access House,
Great Western St,
Wednesbury,
West Midlands WS10 7LE
T: 0121 556 7700
F: 0121 556 7788
E: info@jafcotools.com
W: www.jafcotools.com

JBA Management Consultants
see j boyle associates ltd

JCB
World Headquarters,
Rocester,
Staffs ST14 5JP
T: 01889 590312
F: 01889 593455
W: www.jcb.co.uk

Jefferson Sheard Architects
Fulcrum, 2 Sidney St,
Sheffield S1 4RH
T: 0114 276 1651
F: 0114 279 9191
W: www.jeffersonsheard.com

Jestico + Whiles
1 Cobourg St,
London NW1 2HP
T: 020 7380 0382
E: jw@jesticowhiles.com
W: www.jesticwhiles.com

Jewers Doors td
Stratton Business Park,
Biggleswade,
Beds SG18 8QB
T: 01767 317090
F: 01767 312305
E: mjewers@jewersdoors.co.uk
W: www.jewersdoors.co.uk

Jim Hailstone Ltd
Far End, Old Haslemere Rd,
Haslemere, Surrey GU27 2NN
T: 01428 641691
M: 07860 478197
E: jimhailstoneltd@gmail.com
W: www.icrg.co.uk

JMJ Laboratories
See Synergy Health Plc

JMP Consultants Ltd
8th Floor, 3 Harbour Exchange Sq,
London E14 9GE
T: 020 7536 8040
F: 020 7005 0462
E: docklands@jmp.co.uk
W: www.jmp.co.uk

Jobson James - Specialist Rail Supply Chain Insurance
4 Park Place, St James,
London SW1A 1LP
T: 020 7898 9100
E: rail@jobson-james.co.uk
W: www.jobson-james.co.uk

John Fishwick & Sons
Golden Hill Lane, Leyland,
Lancs PR25 3LE
T: 01772 421207
F: 01772 622407
E: enquiries@fishwicks.co.uk
W: www.fishwicks.co.uk

John Prodger Recruitment
The Courtyard, Alban Park,
Hatfield Rd, St Albans,
Herts AL4 0LA
T: 01727 841101
F: 01727 838272
E: jobs@jprecruit.com
W: www.jprecruit.com

Johnson Rail
Orchard Ind Est, Toddington,
Glos GL54 5EB
T: 01242 621362
F: 01242 621554
E: stephen.phillips@johnson-security.co.uk

Joint Line Railtours
15 The Greenway, Ickenham,
Uxbridge, Middx UB10 8LS
M: 07905 023322
E: contact@jointlinerailtours.co.uk
W: www.jointlinerailtours.co.uk

Jonathan Lee Recruitment
3 Sylvan Court,
Southfield Business Park,
Basildon,
Essex SS15 6TU
T: 01268 455520
F: 01268 455521
E: southfields@jonlee.co.uk
W: www.jonlee.co.uk

Jones Garrard Move Ltd
7 Beaker Close,
Smeeton Westerby,
Leics LE8 0RT
M: 07802 380 252
E: michael-rodber@jonesgarrardmove.com
W: www.jonesgarrardmove.com

Jotun Paints (Europe) Ltd
Stather Rd, Flixborough,
Scunthorpe,
N. Lincs DN15 8RR
T: 01724 400000
F: 01724 400100
E: decpaints@jotun.co.uk
W: www.jotun.com/eu.com

Journeycall Ltd
Laurencekirk Business Park,
Laurencekirk AB30 1AJ
T: 01561 376070
F: 01561 377983
M: 07545 696236
E: enquiries@journeycall.com
W: www.journeycall.com

JourneyPlan
12 Abbey Park Place, Dunfermline,
Scotland KY12 7PD
T: 01383 731048
F: 01383 731788
W: www.journeyplan.co.uk

JSD Research & Development Ltd
Old Carriage Works,
Holgate Park Drive,
York YO24 4EH
T: 01904 623500
E: info@jsdrail.com
W: www.jsdrail.com

Judge 3d
34 New St, St Neots,
Cambs PE19 1AJ
T: 01480 211080
F: 05601 152019
W: www.judge3dltd.com

Kaba (UK) Ltd
Lower Moor Way,
Tiverton,
Devon EX16 6SS
T: 01884 256464
F: 01884 234415
E: info@kaba.co.uk
W: www.kaba.co.uk

Kapsch Group
AM Europlatz 2, 1120 Vienna,
Austria
T: 0043 508110
F: 0043 50811 9999
W: www.kapsch.net/uk

Karcher Vehicle Wash
Karcher UK Ltd, Karcher House,
Beaumont Rd, Banbury OX16 1TB
T: 01295 752172
F: 01295 752040
W: www.karchervehiclewash.co.uk

Kavia Moulded Products Ltd
Rochdale Rd, Walsden, Todmorden,
West Yorks OL14 6UD
T: 01706 816696
F: 01706 813822
E: enquiries@kavia.info
W: www.kavia.info

Kaymac Marine & Civil Engineering Ltd
Osprey Business Park, Byng St,
Landore, Swansea SA1 2NR
T: 01792 301818
F: 01792 645698
E: claire.williamson@kaymacltd.co.uk
W: www.kaymacmarine.co.uk

Kelly Integrated Transport Services Ltd
unit 21, Kynock Rd, Eley Ind. Est,
Edmonton, London N18 3BD
T: 020 8884 6605
F: 020 8884 6633
E: kitsenquiries@kelly.co.uk
W: www.kelly.co.uk

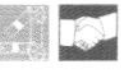

Keltbray Aspire Rail Ltd
Unit 4a/5b,
Crewe Hall Enterprise Park,
Weston Lane, Crewe CW1 6UA
T: 01270 254176
F: 01270 253267
W: www.keltbray.com

Keltbray
St Andrews House, Portsmouth Rd,
Esher, Surrey KT10 9TA
T: 020 7643 1000
F: 020 7643 1001
E: enquiries@keltbray.com
W: www.keltbray.com

Kelvatek Ltd
Bermuda Innovation Centre,
Bermuda Park, Nuneaton CV10 7SD
T: 02476 320100
F: 02476 641172
E: mail@kelman.co.uk
W: www.kelman.co.uk

Kendall Poole Consulting
Pinewood Business Park TS2,
Coleshill Rd, Marston Green,
Solihull B37 7HG
T: 0121 779 0934
E: scm@kendallpoole.com
W: www.kendallpoole.com

Kennedy Solutions
1 Bromley Lane, Chislehurst,
Kent BR7 6LH
T: 020 8468 1016
F: 01689 855261
E: martin@kennedy-solutions.com
W: www.kennedy-solutions.com

Kent Modular Electronics Ltd (KME)
621 Maidstone Rd, Rochester,
Kent ME1 3QJ
T: 01634 835407
F: 01634 830619
E: sales@kme.co.uk
W: www.kme.co.uk

Kent PHK Ltd
Hermitage Way,
Mansfield,
Notts NG18 5ES
T: 01623 421202
F: 01623 421302
E: enquiries@kentphk.co.uk

Kent Stainless (Wexford) Ltd
Ardcavan, Wexford,
Ireland
T: 0800 376 8377
F: 00353 53914 1802
E: info@kentstainless.com
W: www.kentstainless.com

Keolis (UK) Ltd
City Executive Centre,
344-354 Gray's Inn Rd,
London WC1X 8BP
T: 020 7092 8240
E: communication@keolis.com
W: www.keolis.com

KeTech Ltd
Glaisdale Drive East,
Bilborough,
Nottingham NG8 4GU
T: 0115 900 5600
F: 0115 900 5601
E: info@ketech.com
W: www.ketech.com

Keyline Builders Merchants
National Rail Office, Unit 1,
Electra Business Park, 160 Bidder St,
London E16 4ES
T: 020 7473 5288
F: 020 7473 5171
E: rail@keyline.co.uk
W: www.keyline.co.uk

Kiel Seating UK Ltd
Regents Pavilion,
4 Summerhouse Road,
Moulton Park,
Northampton NN3 6BJ
T: 01604 641148
F: 01604 641149
E: p.scott@kiel-seating.co.uk
W: www.kiel-sitze.de

Kier Rail
Tempsford Hall, Sandy,
Beds SG19 2BD
T: 01767 640111
F: 01767 641710
E: info@kier.co.uk
W: www.kier.co.uk

Kilborn Consulting Ltd
Kilborn House, 1 St Johns St,
Wellingborough,
Northants NN8 4LG
T: 01933 279909
F: 01933 276629
E: pmcsharry@kilborn.co.uk
W: www.kilborn.co.uk

Kilfrost Ltd
4th Floor, Time Central,
32 Gallowgate,
Newcastle upon Tyne NE1 4SN
T: 01434 323182
F: 0191 230 0426
E: alex.stephens@kilfrost.com
W: www.kilfrost.com

Kilnbridge Construction Services Ltd
Mc Dermott House,
Cody Rd.
Business Park,
South Crescent,
London E16 4TL
T: 020 7511 1888
F: 020 7511 1114
E: sales@kilnbridge.com
W: www.kilnbridge.com

Kimberley-Clark Professional
1 Tower View,
Kings Hill,
West Malling,
Kent ME19 4HA
T: 01732 594000
F: 01732 594060
E: marta.longhurst@kcc.com
W: www.kcprofessional.com/uk

Kingfisher Railtours
Felmersham, Mills Rd,
Osmington Mills,
Weymouth,
Dorset DT3 6HE
T: 0845 053 3462
E: roger@kingfisher-prods.demon.co.uk
W: www.railwayvideo.com

Kingfisher Resources Management Ltd
First Floor, Azrec Centre, Aztec West,
Almondsbury, Bristol BS323 4TD
T: 01454 612799
M: 07590 297705
E: mike@kingfisherlimited.com
W: www.kingfisherlimited.com

King Rail
King Trailers Ltd, Riverside,
Market Harborough,
Leics LE16 7PX
T: 01858 467361
F: 01858 467161
E: info@kingtrailers.co.uk
W: www.kingtrailers.co.uk

Kingston Engineering Co (Hull) Ltd
Pennington St, Hull HU8 7LD
T: 01438 325676
F: 01438 216438
E: sales@kingston-engineering.co.uk
W: www.kingston-engineering.co.uk

Klaxon Signals Ltd
Wrigley St,
Oldham OL4 1HW
T: 0161 287 5555
F: 0161 287 5511
E: sales@klaxonsignals.com
W: www.klaxonsignals.com

Klueber Lubrication GB Ltd
Hough Mills, Bradford Rd,
Northrowam,
Halifax HX3 7BN
T: 01422 205115
F: 01422 207365
E: sales@uk.klueber.com
W: www.kluber.com

KM&T Ltd
The Techno Centre,
Coventry University
Technology Park,
Puma Way,
Coventry CV1 2TT
T: 02476 236275
E: info@kmandt.com
W: www.kmandt.com

KMC International
7 Old Park Lane,
London W1K 1QR
T: 020 7317 4600
F: 020 7317 4620
W: www.kmcinternational.com

KME
See Kent Modular

Knights Rail Services Ltd (KRS)
The Bakery, 23 Church St,
Coggeshall, Essex CO6 1TX
T: 01376 561194
F: 01376 563992
E: bruce@knightsrail.fsnet.co.uk
W: www.rail-services.net

Knorr Bremse Rail Systems (UK) Ltd
Westinghouse Way,
Hampton Park East,
Melksham,
Wilts SN12 6TL
T: 01225 898700
F: 01225 898705
E: ian.palmer@knorr-bremse.com
W: www.knorr-bremse.co.uk

Kone UK
Global House, Station Place,
Chertsey,
Surrey KT16 9HW
T: 0870 770 1122
F: 0870 770 1144
E: sales.marketinguk@kone.com
W: www.kone.com

Korec Group
34-44, Mersey View,
Brighton le Sands,
Liverpool L22 6QB
T: 0845 603 1214
F: 0151 931 5559
E: info@korecgroup.com
W: www.korecgroup.com

Kroy (Europe) Ltd
Unit 2, 14 Commercial Rd,
Reading,
Berks RG2 0QJ
T: 0118 986 5200
F: 0118 986 5205
E: sales@kroyeurope.com
W: www.kroyeurope.com

KV Mobile Systems Division
See Parker - KV

Kwik Step Ltd
Unit 5, Albion Dockside,
Hanover Place, Bristol BS1 6UT
T: 0117 929 1400
F: 0117 929 1404
E: info@kwik-step.com
W: www.kwik-step.com

Laboursite Group Ltd (Rail)
See Wyse Rail

Lafarge Aggregates (UK) Ltd
Granite House, PO Box 7388,
Watermead Business Park, Syston,
Leicester LE7 1WA
T: 0870 336 8250
F: 0870 336 8602
W: www.lafarge.co.uk

Laing O'Rourke Infrastructure
Bridge Place, Anchor Blvd.,
Admirals Park,
Crossways,
Dartford,
Kent DA2 6SN
T: 01322 296200
F: 01322 296262
E: info@laingorourke.com
W: www.laingorourke.com

Laing Rail
Western House,
14 Rickfords Hill,
Aylesbury,
Bucks HP20 2RX
T: 01296 332108
F: 01296 332126
W: www.laingrail.co.uk

Lakesmere Ltd
The Ring Tower Centre,
Moorside Rd, Winnall,
Winchester,
Hants SO23 7RZ
T: 01962 826500
E: enquiries@lakesmere.com
W: www.lakesmere.com

Lancsville Rail Engineers
The Corner House,
Joiners Lane,
Wetwang,
Driffield YO25 9YN
T: 01377 236700
F: 01377 236701

Lanes Group Plc - Lanes For Drains
17 Parkside Lane,
Parkside Ind. Est,
Leeds LS11 5TD
T: 0800 526488
F: 0161 788 2206
E: sales@lanesfordrains.co.uk
W: www.lanesfordrains.co.uk

Lankelma Limited
Cold Harbour Barn,
Cold Harbour Lane, Iden,
East Sussex TN31 7UT
T: 01797 280050
F: 01797 280195
E: info@lankelma.co.uk
W: www.lankelma.com

Lantern Engineering Ltd
Hamilton Rd, Maltby,
Rotherham S66 7NE
T: 01709 813636
F: 01709 817130
W: www.lantern.co.uk

Laser Rail
Fitology House, Smedley St. East,
Matlock, Derbys DE4 3GH
T: 01629 760750
F: 01629 760751
E: info@laser-rail.co.uk
W: www.laser-rail.co.uk

Lattix Solutions
Unit 5, Clarendon Drive,
The Parkway, Tipton,
West Midlands DY4 0QA
T: 0121 506 4770
F: 0121 506 4771
E: i.thomas@signfix.co.uk
W: www.signfix.co.uk

Leda Recruitment
see mcginley support services

Leewood Projects
38 Deacon Rd,
Kingston upon Thames,
Surrey KT2 6LU
T: 020 8541 0715
F: 020 8546 4260
E: david.cockle@leewoodprojects.co.uk
W: www.leewoodprojects.co.uk

Legioblock (A Jansen B.V.)
Kanaaldojk Zuid 24,
5691 NL SON
T: 0845 689 0036
F: 0845 689 0035
M: 07725 853677
E: sales@legioblock.com
W: www.legioblock.com

Legion
22-26 Albert Embankment, Vauxhall,
London SE1 7TJ
T: 020 7793 0200
F: 020 7793 8948
E: info@legion.com
W: www.legion.com

Legrand Electric Ltd
Great King St. North,
Birmingham B19 2LF
T: 0121 515 0522
E: legrand.sales@legrand.co.uk
W: www.legrand.co.uk

Leica Geosystems Ltd
Davy Avenue, Knowlhill,
Milton Keynes MK5 8LB
T: 01908 256500
F: 01908 256509
E: uk.sales@leica-geosystems.com
W: www.leica-geosystems.co.uk

Leigh Fisher
65 Chandos Place,
London WC2 4HG
T: 020 7420 1770
E: david.bradshaw@leighfisher.com
W: www.leighfisher.com

Leighs Paints
Tower Works,
Kestor St,
Bolton,
Lancs BL2 2AL
T: 01204 521771
F: 01204 382115
E: enquiries@leighspaints.com
W: www.leighspaints.com

L.E.K Consulting
40 Grosvener Place,
London SW1X 7JL
T: 020 7389 7200
F: 020 7389 7440
E: surfacetransport@lek.com
W: www.lek.com

Lemon Consulting
See AMCL

Lesmac (Fasteners) Ltd
73 Dykehead St,
Queenslie Ind. Est,
Queenslie,
Glasgow KA7 4SN
T: 0141 774 0004
F: 0141 774 2229
E: sales@lesmac.co.uk
W: www.lesmac.co.uk

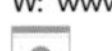

Level 3 Communications
7th Floor, 10 Fleet Place,
London EC4M 7RB
T: 0845 000 1000
F: 202 7954 2385
E: europe@level3.com
W: www.level3.com

Lexicraft Ltd
Unit 32,
Woodside Business Park,
Birkenhead, Wirral CH41 1EL
T: 0151 647 9281
F: 0151 666 1079
E: sales@lexicraft.co.uk
W: www.lexicraft.co.uk

Ley Hill Solutions
Beech House, 9 Cheyne Walk,
Chesham, Bucks HP5 1AY
T: 01494 772327
F: 0870 169 5984
E: graham.hull@leyhill.com
W: www.leyhill.com

Leyland & Birmingham Rubber Ltd
Unit 1, Bentley Ave,
Middleton,
Manchester M24 2GP
T: 0161 655 0300
F: 0161 655 0301
E: info@leylandandbirminghamrubber.com
W: www.leylandandbirminghamrubber.com

LH Group Services
Graycar Business Park,
Barton-under-Needwood,
Burton upon Trent
DE13 8EN
T: 01283 722600
F: 01283 722622
E: lh@lh-group.co.uk
W: www.lh-group.co.uk

LH Safety Footwear
Greenbridge,
Rawtenstall,
Rossendale,
Lancs BB4 7NX
T: 01706 235100
F: 01706 235150
E: enquiries@lhsafety.co.uk
W: www.lhsafety.co.uk

Liebherr- Great Britain Ltd
Normandy Lane,
Stratton Business Park,
Biggleswade,
Beds SG18 8QP
T: 01767 602100
F: 01767 602110
E: info.lgb@liebherr.com
W: www.liebherr.com

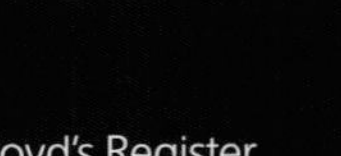

Liebherr Transportation Systems UK
Liebherr Sunderland Works Ltd,
Ayres Quay,
Deptford Terrace,
Sunderland SR4 6DD
T: 0191 515 4930
F: 0191 515 4936
E: alan.lepatourel@liebherr.com
W: www.liebherr.com

Light Rail Transit Association (LRTA)
138 Radnor Ave,
Welling,
Kent DA16 2BY
T: 01179 517785
E: office@lrta.org
W: www.lrta.org

Linbrooke Services Ltd
Sheffield 35a Business Park,
Churchill Way,
Chapeltown,
Sheffield S35 2PY
T: 0844 800 0983
F: 0844 800 0984
W: www.linbrooke.co.uk

Lindapter International
Lindsay House,
Brackenbeck Rd,
Bradford BD7 2NF
T: 01274 521444
F: 01274 521130
E: enquiries@lindapter.com
W: www.lindapter.com

Link Associates International
Trent House,
RTC Business Park,
London Rd,
Derby DE24 8UP
T: 01332 222299
F: 01332 222298
E: info@linkassociates.com
W: www.linkassociates.com

Link-up
See Achilles

Lionverge Civils Ltd
Unit 5, Ransome Rd,
Far Cotton,
Northampton NN4 8AA
T: 01604 677227
F: 01604 677218
E: enquiries@lionverge.co.uk
W: www.lionverge.co.uk

Lloyds Register Rail Ltd
Edward Lloyd House,
8 Pinnacle Way,
Pride Park,
Derby DE24 8ZS
T: 01332 268727
F: 01332 268799
E: martin.hayhoe@lr.org
W: www.lr.org/transportation

Lloyds TSB General Leasing (No 8) Ltd
c/o Rail Capital,
Lloyds TSB Corporate Markets,
33 Old Broad St,
London EC2N 1HW
W: www.lloydsbankcorporatemarkets.com/railfinance

Llumar Anti-Grafitti Coating
See CP Films

LML Products Ltd
13 Portemarsh Rd, Calne,
Wilts SN11 9BN
T: 01249 814271
F: 01249 812182
E: sales@lmlproducts.co.uk
W: www.lmlproducts.co.uk

LNWR Co Ltd
PO Box 111,
Crewe,
Cheshire CW1 2FB
T: 01270 251467
F: 01270 251468
E: m.knowles@lnwr.com
W: www.lnwr.com

LogiKal Ltd
Fleet House,
8-12 New Bridge St,
Blackfriars,
London EC4V 6AL
T: 020 7936 4403
E: admin@logikal.co.uk
W: www.logikal.co.uk

Logic Engagements Ltd
45-47 High St,
Cobham,
Surrey KT11 3DP
T: 01932 869869
F: 01932 864455
E: info@logicrec.com
W: www.logicrec.com

London Midland
PO Box 4323,
Birmingham B3 4JB
T: 0121 634 2040
F: 0121 654 1234
E: comments@londonmidland.com
W: www.londonmidland.com

London Overground Rail Operations Ltd (LOROL)
Customer Services Centre,
Overground House,
125 Finchley Rd,
London NW3 6HY
T: 0845 601 4867
E: overgroundinfo@tfl.gov.uk
W: www.lorol.co.uk

London Rail
See Transport for London

London TravelWatch
Dexter House,
Royal Mint Court,
London EC3N 4QN
T: 020 3176 2999
F: 020 3176 5991
E: janet.cooke@londontravelwatch.org.uk
W: www.londontravelwatch.org.uk

London Underground Customer Service Centre,
55 Broadway,
London SW1W 0BD
T: 0845 330 9880
W: www.tfl.gov.uk/tube

Look CCTV
Unit 4, Wyrefields,
Poulton le Fylde,
Lancs FY6 8JX
T: 01253 891222
F: 01253 891221
E: enquiries@lookcctv.com
W: www.lookcctv.com

Lordgate Engineering
London Rd, St Ives, Cambs PE27 5EZ
T: 01480 300111
F: 01480 494880
E: paulbright@lordgate.com
W: www.lordgate.com

Lorne Stewart Plc
Stewart House, Orford Park,
Greenfold Way, Leigh,
Lancs WN7 3XJ
T: 01942 683333
M: 07919 001767
E: andy.vickers@lornestewart.co.uk
W: www.lornestewart.co.uk

LPA Group
Todor Works, Debden Way,
Saffron Walden, Essex CB11 4AN
T: 01799 512800
F: 01799 512828
E: enquiries@lpa-niphan.com
W: www.lpa-group.com

Lucchini UK Ltd
Wheel Forge Way, Ashburton Park,
Trafford Park, Manchester M17 1EH
T: 0161 886 0342
F: 0161 872 2895
E: salesuk@lucchinirs.co.uk
W: www.lucchinirs.co.uk

Lundy Projects Ltd
195 Chestergate, Stockport,
Cheshire SK3 0BQ
T: 0161 476 2996
F: 0161 476 3760
E: mail@lundy-projects.co.uk
W: www.lundy-projects.co.uk

Luxury Train Club
Benwell House, Preston,
Chippenham SN15 4DX
T: 01249 890176
E: info@luxurytrainclub.com
W: www.luxurytrainclub.com

Maber Architects
85 Tottenham Court Rd,
London W1T 4TQ
T: 020 3402 2065
F: 020 7268 3100
E: info@maber.co.uk
W: www.maber.co.uk

Mace Group
153 Moorgate, London EC2M 6XB
T: 020 3522 3000
E: info@macegroup.com
W: www.macegroup.com

Macemain + Amstad Ltd
Boyle Rd, Willowbrook Ind. Est.,
Corby, Northants NN17 5XU
T: 01536 401331
F: 01536 401298
E: sales@macemainamstad.com
W: www.macemainamstad.com

Mack Brooks Exhibitions Ltd
Romelands House, Romelands Hill,
St Albans AL3 4ET
T: 01727 814400
F: 01727 814401
E: infrarail@mackbrooks.co.uk
W: www.mackbrooks.co.uk

MacRail Systems Ltd
Units One & Two,
Morston Court, Aisecome Way,
Weston Super Mare BS22 8NG
T: 01934 319810
F: 01934 424139
E: info@macrail.co.uk
W: www.macrail.co.uk

Mac Roberts LLP
Capella, 60 York St,
Glasgow G2 8JX
T: 0141 303 1100
F: 0141 332 8886
E: lindsey.wright@macroberts.com
W: www.macroberts.com

Maddox Consulting Ltd
44 Wardour St,
London W1D 6QZ
T: 020 7292 8970
F: 020 7287 2905
E: info@maddoxconsulting.com
W: www.maddoxconsulting.com

Mainframe Communications Ltd
Network House, J
ourneymans Way,
Temple Farm Ind Est,
Southend on Sea,
Essex SS2 5TF
T: 01702 443800
F: 01702 443801
E: info@mainframecomms.co.uk
W: www.mainframecomms.co.uk

Mainline Resourcing Ltd
Suite 214, Business Design Centre,
52 Upper St, London N1 0QH
T: 0845 083 0245
F: 020 7288 6685
E: info@mainlineresourcing.com
W: www.mainlineresourcing.com

Malcolm Rail
Tillyflats, Laurieston Rd,
Grangemouth, Falkirk FK3 8XT
T: 01324 483681
F: 01324 665902
E: turnerd@whm.co.uk
W: www.malcolmgroup.co.uk

Mammoet (UK) Ltd
The Grange Business Centre,
Belasis Ave, Billingham,
Cleveland TS23 1LG
T: 0800 111 4449
E: saleseurope@mammoet.com
W: www.mammoet.com

MAN Diesel Ltd
1 Mirrlees Drive,
Hazel Grove,
Stockport SK7 5BP
T: 0161 483 1000
F: 0161 487 1438
E: primeserv-uk@mandiesel.com
W: www.mandieselturbo.com

M&M Rail Services Ltd
First Floor, Unit 7, Portland House,
1-7 Portland Place,
Doncaster DN1 3DF
T: 01302 349888
F: 01302 349899
W: www.mmrailservices.co.uk

Mane Rail
UCB House, 3
St George St,
Watford WD18 0UH
T: 01923 470720
E: rail@mane.co.uk
W: www.mane.co.uk

Mansell Recruitment Group
Mansell House,
Priestley Way,
Crawley,
West Sussex RH10 9RU
T: 01293 404050
F: 01293 404122
E: neil@mansell.co.uk
W: www.mansell.co.uk

Maple Resourcing
Regus House,
1 Liverpool St,
London EC2M 7QD
T: 020 7048 0775
F: 0845 052 9357
W: www.mapleresourcing.com

Macquarie Group
Ropemaker Place,
28 Ropemaker St,
London EC2Y 9HD
T: 020 3037 2000
W: www.macquarie.com

Marcroft Engineering Services
Whieldon Rd,
Stoke-on-Trent ST4 4HP
T: 01782 844075
F: 01782 843578
W: www.marcroft.co.uk

Maritime and Rail
E-Business Centre,
Consett Business Park,
Villa Real,
Consett DH8 6BP
T: 01207 693616
F: 01207 693917
W: www.maritimeandrail.com

Marl International
Marl Business Park,
Ulverston,
Cumbria LA12 9BN
T: 01229 582430
F: 01229 585155
E: sales@marl.co.uk
W: www.marlrail.com

Marsh Bellofram Europe Ltd
9 Castle Park,
Queens Drive,
Nottingham NG2 1AH
T: 0115 993 3300
F: 0115 993 3301
E: bellofram@aol.com
W: www.marshbellofram.eu

Martek Power Ltd
Glebe Farm
Technical Campus Knapwell,
Cambridge CB23 4GG
T: 01954 267726
F: 01954 267626
E: sales@martekpower.co.uk
W: www.martekpower.co.uk

Martin Higginson Transport Research & Consultancy
5 The Avenue,
Clifton,
York YO30 6AS
T: 01904 636704
M: 07980 874126
E: mhrc@waitrose.com
W: www.martinhigginson.co.uk

Martineau
see sgh martineau llp

Masabi
56 Ayres St, London SE1 1EU
T: 020 7089 8860
E: mobileticketing@masabi.com
W: www.masabi.com

Matisa (UK) Ltd
PO Box 202,
Scunthorpe DN15 6XR
T: 01724 877000
F: 01724 877001
E: melissa.carne@matisa.co.uk
W: www.matisa.ch

Matchtech Group
1450 Park Way, Solent Business Park,
Whiteley, Fareham, Hants PO15 7AF
T: 01489 898989
F: 01489 898290
W: www.matchtech.com

Max Integrated Systems Ltd
Strathclyde Business Centre,
120 Carstairs St, Glasgow G40 4JD
T: 0141 551 0921
F: 0141 556 0335
W: www.maxgroup.co.uk

Maxim Power Tools (Scotland) Ltd
40 Couper St, Glasgow G4 0DL
T: 0141 552 5591
F: 0141 552 5064
E: akilpatrick@maximpower.co.uk
W: www.maximpower.co.uk

Maxmax Ltd
Beech Grove, Wootton, Eccleshall,
Staffs ST21 6HU
T: 01785 859106
E: sales@maxmaxltd.com
W: www.maxmaxltd.com

May Gurney Ltd
Rail Services, 312 Tadcaster Rd,
York YO24 1GS
T: 01904 770150
E: marketing@maygurney.co.uk
W: www.maygurney.co.uk
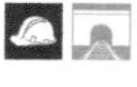

FP McCann
Brascote Lane, Cadeby, Nuneaton,
Warks CV13 0BE
T: 01455 290780
F: 01455 292189
E: scarson@fpmccann.co.uk
W: www.fpmccann.co.uk

Mc Culloch Rail
Craigiemains, Main St,
Ballantrae KA26 0NB
T: 01465 831350
F: 01465 831350
E: enquiries@mccullochrail.com
W: www.mccullochrail.com

MC Electronics
61, Grimsdyke Rd, Hatch End,
Middx HA5 4PP
T: 020 8428 2027
F: 020 8428 2027
E: info@mcelectronics.co.uk
W: www.mcelectronics.co.uk

McGee Group Ltd
340-342 Athlon Rd, Wembley,
Middx HA0 1BX
T: 020 8998 1001
F: 020 8997 7689
E: mail@mcgee.co.uk
W: www.mcgee.co.uk

McGeoch LED Technology
Unit 5, Daltongate Business Centre,
Daltongate, Ulverston,
Cumbria LA12 7AJ
T: 01229 580180
E: debbie.albion@mcgeoch.co.uk
W: www.mcgeochled.co.uk

McGinley Support Services
Ground Floor,
Edward Hyde Building,
38 Clarendon Rd, Watford,
Herts WD17 1JW
T: 0845 543 5953
F: 0845 543 5956
E: info@mcginley.co.uk
W: www.mcginley.co.uk

McKenzie Martin Partnership Ltd
126 Above Bar,
Southampton SO14 7DW
T: 02380 216940
E: info@mmpartnership.co.uk
W: www.mmpartnership.co.uk

MCL (Martin Childs Ltd)
Wimbledon Ave, Brandon,
Suffolk IP27 0NZ
T: 01842 812882
F: 01842 812002
W: www.martinchilds.com

McLellan & Partners
Sheer House, West Byfleet,
Surrey KT14 6NL
T: 01932 343271
F: 01932 348037
E: hq@mclellan.co.uk
W: www.mclellan.co.uk

McML Systems UK Ltd
3rd Floor, 34 Clarendon Rd,
Watford WD17 1JJ
T: 01923 630871
F: 01923 226122
W: www.mcmlsystems.com

McNealy Brown Limited - Steelwork
Prentis Quay, Mill Way,
Sittingbourne,
Kent ME10 2QD
T: 01795 470592
F: 01795 471238
E: info@mcnealybrown.co.uk
W: www.mcnealybrown.co.uk

Mc Nicholas Rail
1st Floor, Consort House,
Waterdale,
Doncaster DN1 3HR
T: 01302 380551
F: 01302 380591
E: mark.bugg@mcnicholas.co.uk
W: www.mcnicholas.co.uk

MCT Brattberg Ltd
Commerce St,
Carrs Ind. Est,
Haslingden,
Lancs BB4 5JT
T: 01706 244890
F: 01706 244891
E: info@mctbrattberg.co.uk
W: www.brattberg.com

MDA Rail Ltd
Millbank House,
Northway, Runcorn,
Cheshire WA7 2SX
T: 01928 751000
F: 01928 751555
E: enquiries-runcorn@mdarail.com
W: www.mdarail.com

MDL Laser Measurement Systems
Acer House,
Hackness Rd,
Northminster Business Park,
York YO26 6QR
T: 01904 791139
F: 01904 791532
E: privers@mdl.co.uk
W: www.laserace.com

MDM Transportation
Walkmill Lane,
Bridgetown,
Cannock, Staffs

MDS Transmodal Ltd
5-6 Hunters Walk,
Canal St,
Chester CH1 4EB
T: 01244 348301
F: 01244 348471
W: www.mdst.co.uk

Mechan Ltd
Davy Industrial Park,
Prince of Wales Rd,
Sheffield S9 4EX
T: 0114 257 0563
F: 0114 245 1124
E: richard.carr@mechan.co.uk
W: www.mechan.co.uk

Mechan Technology Ltd
see zonegreen

MEDC Ltd
Colliery Rd, Pinxton,
Nottingham NG16 6FF
T: 01773 864100
F: 01773 582800
W: www.medc.com

Medicals Direct
Buckingham House East,
The Broadway, Stanmore HA7 4EB
T: 020 8416 1401
F: 0871 900 2861
E: sales@medicalsdirect.com
W: www.medicalsdirect.com

Medscreen
Harbour Quay, 100 Prestons Rd,
London E14 9PH
T: 020 7712 8000
F: 020 7712 8001
E: sales@medscreen.com
W: www.medscreen.com

Melford Electronics Ltd
Cressex Business Park, Blenheim Rd,
High Wycombe HP12 3RS
T: 01494 638069
F: 01494 463358
E: info@melford-elec.co.uk
W: www.melford-elec.co.uk

Mendip Rail Ltd
Merehead, East Cranmore,
Shepton Mallet, Somerset BA4 4RA
T: 01749 881202
F: 01749 880141
E: karen.taylor@mendip-rail.co.uk
W: www.fosteryeoman.co.uk

Mennekes Electric Ltd
Unit 4, Crayfields Ind. Park,
Main Rd, St Pauls Cray, Orpington,
Kent BR5 3HP
T: 01689 833522
F: 01689 833378
E: sales@mennekes.co.uk
W: www.mennekes.co.uk

Merc Engineering UK Ltd
Lower Clough Hill, Pendle St,
Barrowford, Lancs BB9 8PH
T: 01282 694290
F: 01282 613390
E: sales@merceng.co.uk
W: www.merceng.co.uk

Mercia Charters
PO Box 1926,
Coventry CV3 6ZL
T: 07535 759344
E: team@merciacharters.co.uk
W: www.merciacharters.co.uk

Merebrook Consulting Ltd
Suite 2B, Bridgefoot,
Belper,
Derbys DE56 2UA
T: 01773 829988
F: 01773 829393
E: consulting@merebrook.co.uk
W: www.merebrook.co.uk

Merseyrail
Rail House, Lord Nelson St,
Liverpool L1 1JF
T: 0151 702 2534
F: 0151 702 3074
E: comment@merseyrail.org
W: www.merseyrail.org

Meteo Group UK Ltd
292 Vauxhall Bridge Rd,
London SW1V 1AE
T: 020 7963 7534
F: 020 7963 7599
E: jeremy.fidlin@meteogroup.com
W: www.meteogroup.com

Met Systems Ltd
Wool House,
74 Back Church Lane,
London E1 1AB
T: 020 3246 1000
F: 020 7712 2146
E: info@metsystems.co.uk
W: www.metsystems.co.uk

Mettex Electronic Co Ltd
Beaumont Close, Banbury,
Oxon OX16 1TG
T: 01295 250826
F: 01295 268643
E: sales@mettex.com
W: www.mettex.com

Metham Aviation Design ltd (MADCCTV Ltd)
Unit 5, Station Approach,
Four Marks, Alton,
Hants GU34 5HN
T: 01420 565618
F: 01420 565628
E: stuart@madcctv.com
W: www.madcctv.com

Metrolink (Manchester)
Serco Metrolink, Metrolink House,
Queens Rd, Manchester M8 0RY
T: 0161 205 8665
W: www.metrolink.co.uk

Metronet
see transport for london

MF Hydraulics
The Brookworks, 174 Bromyard Rd,
St Johns, Worcester WR2 5EE
T: 01905 748569
F: 01905 420700
E: les@mfhydraulics.co.uk
W: www.mfhydraulics.co.uk
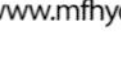

MGB Electrical Ltd
see ilecsys

MGB Signalling Ltd
MGB House, Unit D, Eagle Rd,
Langage Business Park, Plympton,
Plymouth PL7 5JY
T: 0845 070 2490
F: 0845 070 2495
E: enquiries@mgbl.co.uk
W: www.mgbl.co.uk

Michael Evans & Associates Ltd
34 Station Rd, Draycott,
Derbys DE72 3QB
T: 01332 871840
F: 01332 871841
E: mike@mevans.co.uk
W: www.mevans.co.uk

Micro-Epsilon UK Ltd
Dorset House, West Derby Rd,
Liverpool L6 4BR
T: 0151 260 9800
F: 0151 261 2480
E: info@micro-epsilon.co.uk
W: www.micro-epsilon.co.uk

Micro-Mesh Filtration
60 Basford Rd, Old Basford,
Nottingham NG6 0JL
T: 01159 786348
F: 01159 422688
E: enquiries@micro-mesh.co.uk
W: www.micro-mesh.co.uk

Micromotive (A1 Results Ltd)
38 Coney Green Business Centre,
Wingfield View, Clay Cross,
Derbys S45 9JW
T: 01246 252360
F: 01246 252361
E: a1micromotive@btopenworld.com
W: www.a1micromotive.co.uk

Middle Peak Railways Ltd
PO Box 71, High Peak,
Derbys. SK23 7WL
T: 0870 881 6743
F: 0870 991 7350
E: info@middlepeak.co.uk
W: www.middlepeak.co.uk

Midland Metro
Travel Midland Metro,
Metro Centre,
Potters Lane, Wednesbury,
West Midlands WS10 0AR
T: 0121 502 2006
F: 0121 556 6299
W: www.travelmetro.co.uk

Mike Worby Survey Consultancy
37 Ramblers Way,
Welwyn Garden City, Herts AL7 2JU
T: 01707 333677
F: 01707 333677
M: 07767 456196
E: survey@mw-sc.co.uk
W: www.mw-sc.co.uk

Millar Bryce Ltd
5 Logie Mill, Beaverbank Office Park,
Logie Green Rd,
Edinburgh EH7 4HH
T: 0131 556 1313
F: 0131 557 5960
E: marketing@millar-bryce.com
W: www.millar-bryce.com

Millcroft Services Plc
Salutation House, 1 Salutation Rd,
Greenwich, London SE10 0AT
T: 020 8305 1988
F: 020 8305 1986
E: sales@millcroft.co.uk
W: www.millcroft.co.uk
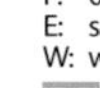

Millenium Site Services Ltd
Units 10/11, Riverside Park,
East Service Rd, Spondon,
Derby DE21 7RW
T: 01332 820003
F: 01332 660081
E: millenium.site@btconnect.com
W: www.milleniumsiteservices.co.uk

Mirror Technology Ltd
Redwood House, Orchard Ind Est,
Toddington, Glos GL54 5EB
T: 01242 621534
F: 01242 621529
E: malcolm@mirrortechnology.co.uk
W: www.mirrortechnology.co.uk

Mita (UK) Ltd
Manor Ind. Est., Bagillt,
Flint CH6 5UY
T: 01352 792300
F: 01352 792314
W: www.mita.co.uk

Mitchell Bridges Ltd
London Rd,
Kingsworthy,
Winchester,
Hants SO23 7QN
T: 01962 885040
F: 01962 885040
E: chris@mitchellbridges.com
W: www.temporarybridges.com

MLM Rail Consulting Engineers Ltd
North Lodge,
25 London Rd,
Ipswich,
Suffolk IP1 2HF
T: 01473 231100
F: 01473 231515
E: lee.bowker@mlm.uk.com
W: www.mlm.uk.com

The Mobile Catering Group
The Monkey House, Kersoe,
Pershore,
Worcs WR10 3JD
T: 01386 710123
F: 01386 710123
M: 07850 915959
E: fred@cateringcontracts.com
W: www.careingcontracts.com

Mono Design
4 St Andrews House,
Vernon Gate,
Derby DE1 1UJ
T: 01332 361616
E: lynne@monodesign.co.uk
W: www.monodesign.co.uk

Moonbuggy Ltd
Solway Ind. Est, Maryport,
Cumbria CA15 8NF
T: 01900 815831
F: 01900 815553
E: r.smith@moonbuggy.com
W: www.moonbuggy.com

Moore Concrete Products Ltd
Caherty House,
41 Woodside Rd,
Ballymena,
Co Antrim NI BT42 4QH
T: 028 2565 2566
F: 028 2565 8480
E: info@moore-concrete.com
W: www.moore-concrete.com

Morgan Advanced Materials
Upper Fforest Way,
Swansea Enterprise Park,
Swansea SA6 8PP
T: 01792 763052
F: 01792 763167
E: meclsales@morganplc.com
W: www.morganamt.com

Morgan Hunt
5th Floor,
16 Old Bailey,
London EC4M 7EG
T: 020 7419 8968
F: 020 7419 8999
E: rail@morganhunt.com
W: www.morganhunt.com

Morgan Marine Ltd
Llandybie, Ammanford,
Carms SA18 3GY
T: 01269 850437
F: 01269 850656
E: sales@morgan-marine.com
W: www.morgan-marine.com

Morgan Sindall (infrastructure) Plc
Unit 9, Home Farm Ind. Est,
Hundson Rd,
Stanstead Abbotts, Ware,
Herts SG12 8LA
T: 01920 871047
F: 01920 871828
E: enquiries@morgansindall.com
W: www.morgansindall.com

Morris Material Handling
PO Box 7, North Rd,
Loughborough,
Leics LE11 1RL
T: 01509 643200
F: 01509 610666
E: info@morriscranes.co.uk
W: www.morriscranes.co.uk

Mors Smitt
Vrieslantlaan 6,
3526 AA Utrecht,
Netherlands
T: 0031 30 288 1311
F: 0031 30 289 8816
E: sales@nieaf-smitt.nl
W: www.morssmitt.com

Mors Smitt UK Ltd
Doulton Rd,
Cradley Heath,
West Midlands B64 5QB
T: 01384 567755
F: 01384 567710
E: info@morssmitt.co.uk
W: www.morssmitt.com

Morson International
Stableford Hall, Monton,
Eccles,
Manchester M30 8AP
T: 0161 707 1516
F: 0161 788 8372
E: rail@morson.com
W: www.morson.com

Morson Projects Ltd
Adamson House,
Centenary Way, Salford,
Manchester M50 1RD
T: 0161 707 1516
F: 0161 786 2360
E: andy.hassall@morson-projects.co.uk
W: www.morsonprojects.co.uk

Motorail Logistics
The Control Tower,
Long Marston Storage Site,
Long Marston,
Stratford upon Avon,
Warks CV37 8QR
T: 01789 721995
F: 01789 721396
E: ruth.dunmore@motorail.co.uk
W: www.motorail.co.uk

Mott MacDonald Group
Mott Macdonald House,
8-10 Sydenham Rd,
Croydon CR0 2EE
T: 020 8774 2000
F: 020 8681 5706
E: railways@mottmac.com
W: www.mottmac.com

Mouchel
4 Matthew Parker Street,
London SW1H 9NP
T: 020 7227 6800
F: 020 7227 6801
E: consultingsales@mouchel.com
W: www.mouchel.com

Movares
Mireille Ros,
Leidseveer 10,
3511 SB Utrecht,
Netherlands
T: 0031 30265 3101
F: 0031 30265 3111
E: info@movares.nl
W: www.movares.com

Moveright International Ltd
Dunton Park,
Dunton Lane,
Wishaw,
Sutton Coldfield B76 9QA
T: 01675 475590
F: 01675 475591
E: andrew@moverightinternational.com
W: www.moverightinternational.com

Moxa Europe GmbH
Einsteinstrasse 7,
85716 Unterschleissheim,
Germany
T: 0049 893700 3940
F: 0049 893700 3999
M: 0049 172 281 3615
E: silke.boysen-korya@moxa.com
W: www.moxa.com

MPEC Technology Ltd
Wyvern House,
Railway Terrace,
Derby DE1 2RU
T: 01332 363979
F: 08701 363958
E: andrew.whawell@mpec.co.uk
W: www.mpec.co.uk

MPI Ltd
International House,
Tamworth Rd,
Hertford SG13 7DQ
T: 01992 501111
F: 01992 535570
E: stuartg@mpi.ltd.uk
W: www.mpi.ltd.uk

MRO Software Now part of IBM UK Ltd
PO Box 41,
North Harbour,
Portsmouth, PO6 3AU
T: 0870 542 6426
E: maximo@uk.ibm.com
W: www.maximo.com

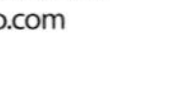

MRX Technologies Ltd
22 Royal Scot Rd,
Pride Park,
Derby DE24 8AJ
T: 01332 226282
F: 01332 381421
E: bww@mrxtech.co.uk
W: www.mrxtech.com

MTR Corporation
Finland House,
56 Haymarket,
London SW1Y 4RN
T: 020 7766 3500
F: 020 7839 6217
E: europe@mtr.com.hk
W: www.mtr.com.hk

MTR Training Ltd
see hss training

MTU UK Ltd
Unit 29,
The Birches Ind. Est,
East Grinstead,
West Sussex RH19 1XZ
T: 01342 335450
F: 01342 335475
E: firstname.lastname@mtu-online.com
W: www.mtu-online.com

Multicell
Swannington Rd, Broughton Astley,
Leicester LE9 6TU
T: 01455 283443
F: 01455 284250
E: help@multicell.co.uk
W: www.multicell.co.uk

Multipulse
Units 1-3,
Goldsworth Park Trading Est,
Kestrel Way, Woking,
Surrey GU21 3BA
T: 01483 713600
F: 01483 729851
E: trevor.collins@multipulse.com
W: www.multipulse.com

J Murphy & Sons Ltd
Hiview House,
81 Highgate Rd,
London NW5 1TN
T: 020 7692 9540
F: 020 7692 9539
E: info@murphygroup.co.uk
W: www.murphygroup.co.uk

Murphy Surveys
Head Office UK,
9 Devonshire Square,
London EC2M 4YF
T: 020 3178 6644
F: 020 3178 6642
E: london@murphysurveys.co.uk
W: www.murphysurveys.co.uk

MVA Consultancy
Seventh Floor,
15 Old Bailey,
London EC4M 7EF
T: 020 7342 7315
E: info@mvaconsultancy.com
W: www.mvaconsultancy.com

MWH Treatment Ltd
Biwater Place, Gregge St, Heywood,
Lancs OL10 2DX
T: 01706 626258
F: 01706 626294
E: info@mwhglobal.com
W: www.mwhglobal.com

Nacco (UK) Ltd
Office 3, The Dairy, Crewe Hall Farm,
Old Park Rd, Crewe,
Cheshire CW1 5UE
T: 01270 254100
F: 0872 115 0919
E: sales@naccorail.co.uk
W: www.naccorail.com

National Car Parks Ltd (NCP)
6th Floor, Centre Tower,
Croydon CR0 1LP
T: 0845 050 7080
E: derek.hulyer@ncp.co.uk
W: www.ncp.co.uk

National Express East Anglia
see greater anglia

National Express Group Plc
75, Davies St, London W1K 5HT
T: 020 7529 2000
F: 020 7529 2100
E: info@natex.co.uk
W: www.nationalexpressgroup.com

National Rail Enquiries
T: 08457 484950
W: www.nationalrail.co.uk

National Railway Museum
Leeman Rd, York YO26 4XJ
T: 0844 815 3139
E: nrm@nrm.org.uk
W: www.nrm.org.uk

The Nationwide Accreditation Bureau Ltd
The Olympic Office Centre,
8 Fulton Rd, Wembley HA9 0NU
T: 08458 902902
F: 08458 903903
E: enquiries@thenab.co.uk
W: www.thenab.co.uk

Nationwide Healthcare Connect
see healthcare connections

Nazeing Glass Works Ltd
Nazeing New Rd, Broxbourne,
Herts EN10 6SU
T: 01992 464485
F: 01992 450966
E: sales@nazeing-glass.co.uk
W: www.nazeing-glass.com

NCH (UK) Ltd - Chemsearch
Landchard House, Victoria St,
West Bromwich B70 8ER
T: 0121 524 7300
F: 0121 500 5386
W: www.chemsearch.co.uk

NDT Services Ltd
see intertek

Neale Consulting Engineers Ltd
Highfield, Pilcot Hill, Dogmersfield,
Fleet, Hants RG27 8SX
T: 01252 629199
F: 01252 815625
E: ncel@tribology.co.uk
W: www.tribology.co.uk

Neary Rail
6 Coal Pit Lane,
Atherton,
Manchester M46 0RY
T: 0845 217 7150
F: 0845 217 7160
E: alex.riley@neary.co.uk
W: www.neary.co.uk

NedRailways
see abellio

Nedtrain BV
Kantorencentrum Katereine 9,
Stationshal 17, 3511 ED Utrecht
T: 0031 30 300 4929
F: 0031 30 300 4647
W: www.nedtrain.nl

Nelsons Solicitors
Sterne House,
Lodge Lane,
Derby DE1 3WD
T: 01332 372372
E: enquiries@nelsonslaw.co.uk
W: www.nelsonslaw.co.uk

Nelson Stud Welding UK
47/49 Edison Rd,
Rabans Lane Ind. Est,
Aylesbury HP19 8TE
T: 01296 433500
F: 01296 487930
E: enquiries@nelson-europe.co.uk
W: www.nelson-europe.co.uk

Nemesis Rail Ltd
Burton Rail Depot,
Derby Rd,
Burton upon Trent DE14 1RS
T: 01283 531562
E: enquiries@nemesisrail.com
W: www.nemesisrail.com

Nenta Traintours
Railtour House, 10 Buxton Rd,
North Walsham,
Norfolk NR28 0ED
T: 01692 406152
F: 01692 406152
E: ray.davies@nentatraintours.co.uk
W: www.nentatraintours.co.uk

NES Track
Station House,
Stamford New Rd,
Altrincham,
Cheshire WA14 1EP
T: 0161 942 4016
F: 0161 942 7969
E: nestrack.manchester@nes.co.uk
W: www.nestrack.co.uk

Network Construction Services Ltd
Ercall House,
Pearson Rd,
Central Park,
Telford.
Shropshire TF2 9TX
T: 01952 210243
F: 01952 290168
E: sales@ncsjob.co.uk
W: www.ncsjob.co.uk

Network Rail Consulting Ltd
Enterprise House,
167-169 Westbourne Terrace,
London W2 6JX
T: 020 3356 0454
E: contactnrc@networkrail.co.uk
W: www.networkrail consulting.co.uk

Network Rail Infrastructure Ltd
Kings Place,
90 York Way,
London N1 9AG
T: 020 3356 9595
W: www.networkrail.co.uk

Neway Training Solutions Ltd
Kelvin House,
RTC Business Park,
London Rd,
Derby DE24 8UP
T: 01332 360033
F: 01332 366367
E: artp@neway-training.com
W: www.neway-training.com

Newbury Data Recording Ltd
T: 0870 224 8110
F: 0870 224 8177
E: ndsales@newburydata.co.uk
W: www.newburydata.co.uk

Newey & Eyre
Eagle Court 2,
Hatchford Brook,
Hatchford, Sheldon,
Birmingham B26 3RZ
T: 0121 366 1000
F: 0121 366 1029
E: marc.roberts@rexel.co.uk
W: www.neweysonline.co.uk

NewRail, The Centre for Railway Research
Stephenson Building,
Newcastle University,
Claremont Rd,
Newcastle upon Tyne NE1 7RU
T: 0191 222 5821
E: newrail@ncl.ac.uk
W: www.newrail.org

Nexans
Nexans House,
Chesney Wold,
Bleak Hall,
Milton Keynes MK6 1LF
T: 01908 250840
F: 01908 250841
E: iandi.sales@nexans.com
W: www.nexans.com

Nextiraone (UK) Ltd
Aldershawe Hall,
Claypit Lane,
Wall,
Lichfield WS14 0AQ
T: 01543 414751
F: 01543 250159
E: enquiries@nextiraone.co.uk
W: www.nextiraone.co.uk

Nexus (Tyne & Wear Metro)
Nexus House,
33 St James Blvd,
Newcastle upon Tyne NE1 4AX
T: 0191 203 3333
F: 0191 203 3180
E: contactus@twmetro.co.uk
W: www.tyneandwearmetro.co.uk

Nexus Alpha Low Power Systems Ltd
7 Prescott Place,
Clapham,
London SW4 6BS
T: 020 7622 6816
F: 020 7622 6817
E: commercialdept@lps.nexusalpha.com
W: www.lps.nexusalpha.com

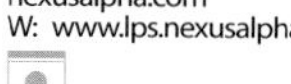
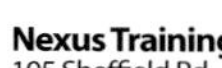

Nexus Training
105 Sheffield Rd,
Godley,
Hyde,
Cheshire SK14 2PLT
T: 0161 339 2190
E: info@nexustraining.org.uk
W: www.nexustraining.org.uk

NG Bailey
14 Mercury Park,
Mercury Way,
Manchester M41 7LY
T: 0161 866 2040
E: generalenquiries@ngbailey.co.uk
W: www.ngbailey.co.uk

Nichols Group Ltd
53 Davies St,
London W1K 5JH
T: 020 7292 7000
F: 020 7292 5200
E: operations@nichols.uk.com
W: www.nicholsgroup.co.uk

Nigel Nixon Consulting
Suite 1, AD Business Centre,
Hithercroft Rd,
Wallingford,
Oxon OX10 9EZ
T: 01491 824030
F: 01491 824078
E: nigel@nigelnixon.com
W: www.nigelnixon.com

Nightsearcher Ltd
Unit 4, Applied House,
Fitzherbert Spur,
Farlington,
Portsmouth PO6 1TT
T: 023 9238 9774
F: 023 9238 9788
E: carrie.f@nightsearcher.co.uk
W: www.nightsearcher.co.uk

Nitech Ltd
4-6 Highfield Business Park,
St Leonards on Sea TN38 9UB
T: 01424 852788
F: 01424 851008
E: sales@nitech.co.uk
W: www.nitech.co.uk

NMB Minebea UK Ltd
Doddington Rd,
Lincoln LN6 3RA
T: 01522 500933
F: 01522 500975
W: www.nmb-minebea.co.uk

NNN Ltd (Northcroft Group Ltd)
One Horseguards Ave,
London SW1A 2HU
T: 020 7839 7858
F: 020 7930 2594
E: surv@northcroft.co.uk
W: www.northcroft.com

No1 Scaffolding Service
Swinbourne Rd,
Burnt Mills Ind.Est.,
Basildon,
Essex SS13 1EF
T: 01268 724793
F: 01268 725606
E: enquiries@no1scaffolders.co.uk
W: www.no1scaffolders.co.uk

Nomad Rail
First Floor, Baltic Chambers,
3 Broad Chere,
Newcastle NE1 3DQ
T: 020 7096 6966
F: 0191 221 1339
E: enquiries@nomadrail.com
W: www.nomadrail.com

Nomix Enviro Ltd - A division of Frontier Agriculture Ltd
The Grain Silos, Weyhill Rd,
Andover,
Hants SP10 3NT
T: 01264 388050
F: 01264 337642
E: nomixenviro@frontierag.co.uk
W: www.nomix.co.uk

Nord-Lock Ltd
Room 9, Main Building,
Aspire Business Centre,
Ordnance Rd, Tidworth,
Wilts SP9 7QD
T: 01980 847129
F: 01980 847674
E: enquiries@nord-lock.co.uk
W: www.nord-lock.com

Norgren Ltd
PO Box 22, Eastern Ave, Lichfield,
Staffs WS13 6SB
T: 01543 265000
F: 01543 265827
E: rail@norgren.com
W: www.norgren.com/rail

Norman Butcher & Jones (NBJ)
52 Lime St, London EC3M 7AF
T: 020 7337 4060
F: 020 7337 4061
E: jberry@normanbutcherjonesltd.co.uk
W: www.normanbutcherjones ltd.co.uk

North East Railtours
T: 0191 252 3774
W: www.srps.org.uk

Northern Ireland Railways
see translink

Northern Rail Ltd
Northern House, 9 Rougier St,
York YO1 6HZ
T: 0870 000 5151
E: firstname.lastname@northernrail.org
W: www.northernrail.org

North Star Consultancy Ltd
78 York St, London W1H 1DP
T: 020 7692 0936
F: 020 7692 0937
E: enquiries@northstar consultancy.com
W: www.northstarconsultancy.com

Northwood Railway Eng. Ltd
9 Scot Grove, Pinner, Middx HA5 4RT
T: 020 8428 9890
E: davidnbradley@btopenworld.com

Norton & Associates
32a, High St,
Pinner, Middx HA5 5PW
T: 020 8869 9237
F: 07005 964635
E: mail@nortonweb.co.uk
W: www.nortonweb.co.uk

Norton Rose Fulbright LLP
3 More London, Riverside,
London SE1 2AQ
T: 020 7283 6000
F: 020 7283 6500
E: tim.marsden@nortonrose fulbright.com
W: www.nortonrose.com

Norwest Holst Construction
see vinci

Nottingham Trams Ltd
NET Depot, Wilkinson St,
Nottingham NG7 7NW
T: 0115 942 7777
E: info@thetram.net
W: www.thetram.net

Novacroft
Cirrus Park, Lower Farm Rd,
Moulton Park,
Northampton NN3 6UR
T: 0845 330 0601
F: 0845 330 0745
E: projects@novacroft.com
W: www.novacroft.com

Novah Ltd
Unit 3, Portside Business Park,
Portside North,
Ellesmere Port CH65 2HQ
T: 0151 357 1799
F: 0151 357 2811
E: sales@novah.co.uk
W: www.novah.co.uk

Novus Rail Ltd
Solaris Centre, New South Prom,
Blackpool FY4 1RW
T: 01253 478027
F: 01253 478037
E: mmcm@novusrail.com
W: www.novusrail.com

NTM Sales & Marketing Ltd
PO Box 2, Summerbridge,
Harrogate HG3 4XN
T: 01423 781010
F: 01423 781279
E: info@xl-lubricants.com
W: www.xl-lubricants.com

Nu Star Material Handling
Unit C, Ednaston Business Centre,
Ednaston, Derby DE6 3AE
T: 0870 443 5646
F: 0870 443 5647
E: matt@nu-starmhl.com
W: www.nu-starmhl.com

Nusteel Structures
Lympne, Hythe, Kent CT21 4LR
T: 01303 268112
F: 01303 266098
E: general@nusteelstructures.com
W: www.nusteelstructures.com

Nuttall Finchpalm
see bam nuttall

NVR Fleet UK
see hitachi capital vehicle hire

Oce UK Ltd
Oce House,
Chatham Way,
Brentwood,
Essex CM14 4DZ
T: 0870 600 5544
F: 0870 600 1113
W: www.oce.com

Odgers Ray & Berndtson
11 Hanover Square,
London W1S 1JJ
T: 020 7529 1111
F: 020 7529 1000
E: info@rayberndtson.co.uk
W: www.odgers.com

Office of Rail Regulation (ORR)
One Kemble St,
London WC2B 4AN
T: 020 7282 2000
F: 020 7282 2040
E: contact.cct@orr.gsi.gov.uk
W: www.rail-reg.gov.uk

Ogier Electronics Ltd
Unit 13, Sandridge Park,
Porters Wood,
St Albans,
Herts AL3 6PH
T: 01727 845547
F: 01727 852186
E: jacqui.robbins@ogierelectronics.com
W: www.ogierelectronics.com

Oil Analysis Services Ltd
Unit 6/7, Blue Chalet Ind. Park,
London Rd, West Kingsdown,
Kent TN15 6BQ
T: 01474 854450
F: 01474 854408
E: ihbrown@oas-online.co.uk
W: www.oas-online.co.uk

Oleo International
Grovelands,
Longford Rd,
Exhall,
Coventry CV7 9ND
T: 02476 645555
F: 02476 645900
E: roy.hunt@oleo.co.uk
W: www.oleo.co.uk

Omega Red Group Ltd
Dabell Ave,
Blenheim Ind.Est.,
Bulwell,
Nottingham NG6 8WA
T: 0115 877 6666
F: 0115 876 7766
E: enquiries@omegaredgroup.com
W: www.omegaredgroup.com

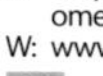

Omnicom Engineering Ltd
292 Tadcaster Rd,
York YO24 1ET
T: 01904 778100
F: 01904 778200
E: sales@omnicomengineering.co.uk
W: www.omnicom engineering.co.uk

Onboard Retail Solutions
see iridium onboard

O'Neill Transport Consultancy
87, Neville Rd,
Darlington,
Co.Durham DL3 8NQ
T: 01325 482193
E: rita.oneill@talk21.com
W: www.icrg.co.uk

One-On Ltd
7 Home farm Courtyard,
Meriden Rd,
Berkswell,
West Midlands CV7 7SH
T: 0845 505 1955
F: 0845 505 1977
E: info@one-on.co.uk
W: www.one-on.co.uk

On Track Design Solutions Ltd
1st Floor Suite, 11 Pride Point Drive,
Pride Park, Derby DE24 8BX
T: 01332 204450
F: 01332 204458
E: brianchadwick@ontrackdesign.co.uk
W: www.ontrackdesign.co.uk

On Track Flooring Ltd
Unit E18, Laws Lane,
Stanton by Dale, Derbys DE7 4RT
T: 01159 321691
E: t.carter@ontrackflooring.co.uk

Onyxrail Ltd
Scarborough House,
35 Auckland Rd,
Birmingham B11 1RH
T: 0121 771 4219
E: enquiry@onyxrail.co.uk
W: www.onyxrail.co.uk

Open Access Rail (The Train Chartering Company Ltd)
Benwell House, Preston,
Wilts SN15 4DX
T: 01249 890176
E: info@openaccessrail.com
W: www.openaccessrail.com

Open Technology Ltd
1 Woodlands Courrt,
Albert Drive,
Burgess Hill, W Sussex RH15 9TN
T: 0845 680 4004
F: 0845 680 4005
E: info@opentechnology.com
W: www.opentechnology.com

Optilan Communication Systems
Sibree Rd, Stonebridge Ind. Est,
Coventry CV3 4FD
T: 01926 864999
F: 01926 851818
E: sales@optilan.com
W: www.optilan.com

Optimized Systems & Solutions Ltd
SIN D-7, PO Box 31,
Derby DE24 8BJ
T: 01332 771700
F: 01332 770921
W: www.o-sys.com

Optimum Consultancy Ltd
Spencer House, Mill Green Rd,
Haywards Heath,
West Sussex RH16 1XQ
T: 020 3694 4100
F: 01444 448071
E: enquiries@optimum.uk.com
W: www.optimum.uk.com

Orchard Consulting
see optimum

Oracle Recruitment
see exell group

Ordnance Survey
Romsey Rd,
Southampton SO16 4GU
T: 02380 305030
F: 02380 792615
E: customerservice@ordnancesurvey.co.uk
W: www.ordnancesurvey.co.uk

Orient Express
T: 020 7921 4028
F: 020 7805 5908
E: oesales.uk@orient-express.com
W: www.orient-express.com

Orion Electrotech
4 Danehill,
Lower Earley,
Reading RG6 4UT
T: 0118 923 9239
F: 0118 975 3332
W: www.orionelectrotech.com

Orion Rail Services Ltd
29-31 Lister Road,
Hillington Park,
Glasgow G52 4BH
T: 0141 892 6666
F: 0141 892 6662
E: sales@orioneng.com
W: www.orioneng.com

Osborne Rail
Fonteyn House,
47-49 London Rd,
Reigate,
Surrey RH2 2PY
T: 01737 378200
F: 01737 378295
W: www.osborne.co.uk

OSL Rail
Unit 1.3,
Alexander House,
19 Fleming Way,
Swindon SN1 2NG
T: 01793 600793
F: 08701 236249
E: enquiries@osl-rail.co.uk
W: www.osl-rail.co.uk

OTN Systems
E: info@otnsystems.com
W: www.otnsystems.com

Owen Williams
see amey

Oxford Hydrotechnics Ltd
Baynards Green,
Bicester,
Oxon OX27 7SR
T: 01869 346001
F: 01869 345455
E: info@h2ox.net
W: www.h2ox.net
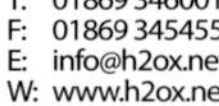

Panasonic Electric Works UK Ltd
Sunrise Parkway,
Linford Wood,
Milton Keynes
MK14 6LF
T: 01908 231555
F: 01908 231599
E: info-uk@eu.pewg.panasonic.com
W: www.panasonic-electricworks.co.uk

Pandrol UK Ltd
Gateford Rd,
Worksop,
Notts S81 7AX
T: 01909 476101
F: 01909 500004
E: info@pandrol.com
W: www.pandrol.com

Panolin
Ripon Way,
Harrogate,
N Yorks HG1 2AU
T: 01423 522911
F: 01423 530043
E: admin@cardev.com
W: www.cardev.com

Pantrak Transportation Ltd
G&S Building, 5, Sholto Cresc.,
Righead Ind. Est., Bellshill,
Lanarkshire ML4 3LX
T: 01698 840465
F: 01698 749672
E: gavinroser@pantrak.com
W: www.pantrak.com

Parallel Project Training
Davidson House, Forbury Sq,
Reading RG1 3EU
T: 0845 519 2305
F: 0118 900 0501
W: www.parallelprojecttraining.com

Parallel Studios
22 Balmoral Ave, Bedford MK40 2PT
F: 01234 217200
M: 07872 307692
E: rick@parallelstudios.co.uk
W: www.parellelstudios.co.uk

Parkeon Ltd
10 Willis Way, Fleets Ind Est, Poole,
Dorset BH15 3SS
T: 01202 339494
F: 01202 667293
E: sales_uk@parkeon.com
W: www.parkeon.com

Park Signalling Ltd
Houldsworth Mill Business Centre,
Houldsworth St, Reddish,
Stockport SK5 6DA
T: 0161 975 6161
F: 0161 975 6160
E: info@park-signalling.co.uk
W: www.park-signalling.co.uk

Parker Hannifin (UK) Ltd
Brunel Way, Thetford,
Norfolk IP24 1HP
T: 01842 763299
F: 01842 756300
E: filtrationinfo@parker.com
W: www.parker.com

Parker KV Division
Presley Way, Crownhill,
Milton Keynes MK8 0HB
T: 01908 561515
F: 01908 561227
E: saleskv@parker.com
W: www.parker.com

Parry People Movers Ltd
Overend Rd, Cradley Heath,
West Midlands B64 7DD
T: 01384 569553
F: 01384 637753
E: info@parrypeoplemovers.com
W: www.parrypeoplemovers.com

Parsons Brinckerhoff
6 Devonshire Square,
London EC2M 4YE
T: 020 7337 1700
F: 020 7337 1701
E: railandtransit@pbworld.com
W: www.pbworld.co.uk

Parsons Transportation Group
Regis House,
45 King William Street,
London EC4R 9AN
T: 020 3102 6915
F: 020 3102 6906
E: enquiries.pgil@parsons.com
W: www.parsons.com

Partsmaster Ltd (NCH Europe)
Landchard House,
Victoria St,
West Bromwich B70 8ER
T: 0121 525 8939
F: 0121 524 7379
E: victoria.summerfield@nch.com
W: www.partsmaster.com

Passcomm Ltd
Unit 24, Tatton Court,
Kingsland Garage,
Warrington WA1 4RR
T: 01925 821333
F: 01925 821321
E: info@passcomm.co.uk
W: www.passcomm.co.uk

Passenger Focus
Fleetbank House,
2-6 Salisbury Square,
London EC4Y 8JX
T: 0300 123 0860
F: 020 7630 7355
E: info@passengerfocus.org.uk
W: www.passengerfocus.org.uk

Passenger Transport Networks
49, Stonegate,
York YO1 8AW
T: 01904 611187
E: ptn@btconnect.com
W: www.passengertransportnetworks.co.uk

Pathfinder Services (UK) Ltd
Pathfinder House,
2 Cross Farm Rd,
Draycott,
Somerset BS27 3SE
T: 0845 017 1247
F: 0117 9811352
E: james@pathfinderservicesuk.com
W: www.pathfinderservicesuk.com

Pathfinder Systems UK PTY Ltd
Unit 6,
Bighams Park Farm,
Waterend,
Hemel Hempstead HP1 3BN
T: 07711 189366
F: 020 7328 8818
E: cel@pathfindersystems.com.au
W: www.pathfindersystems.com.au

Pathfinder Tours
Stag House, Gydynap Lane,
Inchbrook, Woodchester,
Glos GL5 5EZ
T: 01453 835414/834477
F: 01453 834053
E: office@pathfindertours.co.uk
W: www.pathfindertours.co.uk

Paul Fabrications Ltd
Unit 10a,
Sills Rd,
Willow Farm Business Park,
Castle Donington DE74 2US
T: 01332 818000
F: 01332 818089
E: sales@paulfabs.co.uk
W: www.paulfabs.co.uk

Paul John Plant
Telford Way,
Stephenson Ind. Est,
Coalville,
Leics LE67 3HE
T: 01530 513400
F: 01530 513446
E: coalvilleplant@pauljohngroup.com
W: www.pauljohngroup.com

PB – Consult GmbH
Am Plaerrer 12,
90429 Nuremburg,
Germany
T: 0049 911 322390
F: 0049 911 3223910
E: info@pbconsult.de
W: www.pbconsult.eu

PB Design & Development
Unit 9/10,
Hither Green Ind. Est.,
Clevedon,
Bristol BS21 6ZT
T: 01275 874411
E: sales@pbdesign.co.uk
W: www.pbdesign.co.uk

PBL Training
53 Guildford St,
Bagshot,
Surrey GU19 5NG
T: 01276 477499
F: 01276 562726
E: mike@pbl-training.co.uk
W: www.pbl-training.com

PCC.eu
Units 51/52,
Llantarnam Ind. Park,
Cwmbran, NP44 3AW
T: 01633 214565
F: 01633 840884
E: info@occ.eu.com
W: www.pcc.eu.com

PD Devices Ltd
Old Station Yard,
South Brent, Devon TQ10 9AL
T: 01364 649248
F: 01364 649250
E: marketing@pddevices.co.uk
W: www.pddevices.co.uk

Peacock Salt Ltd
North Harbour, Ayr KA8 8AE
T: 01292 292000
F: 01292 292001
E: info@peacocksalt.co.uk
W: www.peacocksalt.co.uk

Pearsons Engineering Services Ltd
PO Box 7512, Heanor,
Derbys DE75 7AP
T: 01773 763508
F: 01773 763508
E: nathan@pearsonsengineeringservices.co.uk
W: www.pearsonsengineeringservices.co.uk

A S Peck Engineering
116 Whitby Rd, Ruislip,
Middx HA4 9DR
T: 01895 621398
F: 01895 613761
E: markjones@aspeckeng.co.uk
W: www.aspeckeng.co.uk

Peeping Ltd
see tracsis

Pegasus Transconsult Ltd
17 North Court, Hassocks,
West Sussex BN6 8JS
T: 01273 845 583
E: sales@pegasustransconsult.com
W: www.pegasustransconsult.com

Peek Traffic Ltd
Hazlewood House, Limetree Way,
Chineham Business Park,
Basingstoke RG24 8WZ
T: 01256 891800
E: sales@peek.co.uk
W: www.peekglobal.com

PEI Genesis UK Ltd
George Curl Way,
Southampton SO18 2RZ
T: 02380 621260
F: 0844 871 6070
E: peiuk@peigenesis.com
W: www.peigenesis.com

Peli Products (UK) Ltd
Peli House, Peakdale Rd,
Brookfield,
Glossop,
Derbys SK13 6LQ
T: 01457 869999
F: 01457 569966
E: sales@peliproducts.co.uk
W: www.peliproducts.co.uk

Pell Frischmann
5 Manchester Square,
London W1A 1AU
T: 020 7486 3661
F: 020 7487 4153
E: pflondon@pellfrischmann.com
W: www.pellfrischmann.com

Pelma Services and Autobuild Ltd
Chestnut Tree Cottage,
One Pin Lane,
Farnham Common,
Bucks SL2 3QY
T: 01753 648484
M: 07778 651876
E: pelma@btconnect.com
W: www.autobuilduk.co.uk

Pennant Consulting Ltd
1 Sopwith Cres.,
Wickford Business Park,
Wickford, Essex SS11 8YU
T: 01268 493495
E: enquiries@pennant-recruit.com
W: www.pennant-consult.com

Pennant Information Services Ltd
Parkway House,
Palatine Rd,
Northenden,
Manchester M22 4DB
T: 0161 947 6940
F: 0161 947 6959
E: john.churchman@pennantplc.co.uk
W: www.pennantplc.co.uk

Pennant International Group Plc
Pennant Court,
Staverton Technology Park,
Cheltenham GL51 6TL
T: 01452 714914
F: 01452 714920
E: sales@pennantplc.co.uk
W: www.pennantplc.co.uk

People 1st
Second Floor,
Armstrong House,
38 Market Square,
Uxbridge UB8 1LH
T: 01895 817000
F: 01895 817035
E: info@people1st.co.uk
W: www.people1st.co.uk

Perco Engineering Services Ltd
The Old Nurseries,
Nottingham Rd,
Radcliffe on Trent,
Nottingham NG12 2DU
T: 0115 933 5000
F: 0115 933 4692
W: www.perco.co.uk

Permali Gloucester Ltd
Permali Park,
Bristol Rd,
Gloucester GL1 5TT
T: 01452 528282
F: 01452 507409
E: fraser.rankin@permali.co.uk
W: www.permali.co.uk

Permanent Way Institution
4 Coombe Rd,
Folkestone CT19 4EG
T: 01303 274534
M: 07768 105691
E: secretary@permanentwayinstitution.com
W: www.permanentwayinstitution.com

Permaquip Ltd
Brierley Industrial Park, Stanton Hill,
Sutton-in-Ashfield NG17 3JZ
T: 01623 513349
F: 01623 517742
E: sales@permaquip.co.uk
W: www.permaquip.co.uk

Perpetuum Ltd
Epsilon House,
Southampton Science Park,
Southampton SO16 7NS
T: 02380 765888
F: 02380 765889
E: info@perpetuum.com
W: www.perpetuum.com/rail

Petards Joyce-Loebl Ltd
390, Pricesway North,
Team Valley Est., Gateshead,
Tyne & Wear NE11 0TU
T: 0191 423 3608
F: 0191 423 3604
E: sales@petards.com
W: www.petards.com

Peter Brett Associates
Caversham Bridge House,
Waterman Place,
Reading RG1 8DN
T: 0118 950 0761
F: 0118 959 7498
E: reading@pba.co.uk
W: www.pba.co.uk

Peter Davidson Consultancy
Brownlow House, Ravens Lane,
Berkhamsted, Herts HP4 2DX
T: 01442 891665
F: 01442 879776
E: mail@peter-davidson.com
W: www.peter-davidson.com

Peter Staveley Consulting
247 Davidson Rd,
Croydon CR0 6DQ
T: 07973 168742
E: peter@peterstaveley.co.uk
W: www.peterstaveley.co.uk

Pfisterer
Unit 9, Ellesmere Business Park,
off Swingbridge Rd, Grantham,
Lincs NG31 7XT
T: 01476 578657
F: 01476 568631
E: beverley.stokes@pfisterer.com
W: www.pfisterer.com

Pfleiderer
see railone

PFS Ltd
Unit 1, Parker House Est., Manor Rd,
West Thurrock, Essex RM20 4EH
T: 01708 252960
F: 01708 864140
E: trevor.mason@pfsfueltec.com
W: www.pfsfueltec.com

Phi Group Ltd
Harcourt House, Royal Crescent,
Cheltenham, Glos GL50 3DA
T: 0870 333 4126
F: 0870 333 4127
E: marketing@phigroup.co.uk
W: www.phigroup.co.uk

Phoenix Contact Ltd
Halesfield 13, Telford,
Shropshire TF7 4PG
T: 0845 881 2222
F: 0845 881 2211
E: info@phoenixcontact.co.uk
W: www.phoenixcontact.co.uk
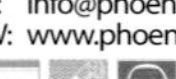

Phoenix Systems UK Ltd
Unit 48, Standard Way,
Fareham Ind. Est.,
Fareham,
Hants PO16 8XQ
T: 0845 658 6111
F: 0845 658 6222
E: sales@phoenixsystemsuk.com
W: www.phoenixsystemsuk.com
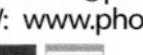

PHS Besafe incorporating Hiviz Laundries Ltd
Western Ind. Est.,
Caerphilly CF83 1XH
T: 02920 851000
F: 02920 863288
E: enquiries@phs.co.uk
W: www.phs.co.uk/hiviz

Pilkington Glass Ltd
Prescot Rd, St Helens,
Merseyside WA10 3TT
T: 01744 28882
F: 01744 692660
W: www.pilkington.com

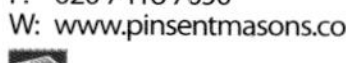

Pinsent Masons
City Point, One Ropemaker St,
London EC2Y 9AH
T: 020 7418 7000
F: 020 7418 7050
W: www.pinsentmasons.com

Pipeline Drillers Ltd
10 Kirkford, Stewarton,
Kilmarnock KA3 5HZ
T: 01560 482021
F: 01560 484809
E: info@pipelinedrillers.co.uk

Pipex PX
Pipex House, 1 Belliver Way,
Roborough, Plymouth,
Devon PL6 7BP
T: 01752 581200
F: 01752 581209
E: sales@pipexpx.com
W: www.pipexpx.com
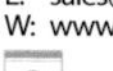

Pirtek (UK) Ltd
35 Acton Park Estate,
The Vale,
Acton,
London W3 7QE
T: 020 8749 8444
F: 020 8749 8333
E: info@pirtek.co.uk
W: www.pirtekuk.com

Pitchmastic PmB Ltd
Panama House,
184 Attercliffe Rd,
Sheffield S4 7WZ
T: 0114 270 0100
F: 0114 276 8782
E: info@pitchmasticpmb.co.uk
W: www.pitchmasticpmb.co.uk

Planet Platforms
Brunel Close, Century Park,
Wakefield 41 Ind. Est,
Wakefield WF2 0XG
T: 0800 085 4161
F: 01924 267090
E: info@planetplatforms.co.uk
W: www.planetplatforms.co.uk

Plan Me Project Management
PO Box 281,
Malvern WR14 9EP
T: 07906 439055
F: 0800 471 5332
E: info@planme.com
W: www.planme.com

Plasser Machinery, Parts & Services Ltd
Manor Rd,
West Ealing,
London W13 0PP
T: 020 8998 4781
F: 020 8997 8206
E: info@plasser.co.uk
W: www.plasser.co.uk

Platipus Anchors Ltd
Unit Q, Philanthropic Rd,
Kingsfield Business Centre,
Redhill,
Surrey RH1 4DP
T: 01737 762300
F: 01737 773395
E: info@platipus-anchors.com
W: www.platipus-anchors.com

Plettac Security UK Ltd
Unit 39,
Sir Frank Whittle Business Centre,
Great Central Way, Rugby CV1 3XH
T: 0844 800 1725
F: 01788 544549
E: info@plettac.co.uk
W: www.plettac.co.uk

Plowman Craven Ltd
141 Lower Luton Rd, Harpenden,
Herts AL5 5EQ
T: 01582 765566
F: 01582 765370
E: post@plowmancraven.co.uk
W: www.plowmancraven.co.uk

PMA UK Ltd (Thomas & Betts Ltd)
Unit 4, Imperial Court,
Magellan Close, Walworth Ind. Est.,
Andover, Hants SP10 5NT
T: 01264 333527
F: 01264 333643
E: sales@pma-uk.com
W: www.pma-uk.com

PMProfessional Learning
see aikona

PM Safety Consultants Ltd
Suite D, 3rd Floor, Saturn Facilities,
101 Lockhurst Lane,
Coventry CV6 5SF
T: 02476 665770
F: 02476 582401
E: info@pmsafety.com
W: www.pmsafety.com

Pod-Track Ltd
Unit 8 Fleetway Business Park,
14-16 Wadsworth Rd, Perivale,
Middx UB6 7LD
T: 020 8998 0010
E: info@pod-track.com
W: www.pod-track.com
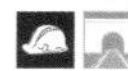

Polyamp AB
Box 229, Atvidaberg, 597 25 Sweden
T: 0046 120 85410
F: 0046 120 85405
E: info@polyamp.se
W: www.polyamp.com

Polyflor Ltd
Transport Flooring Division,
PO Box 3, Radcliffe New Rd,
Whitefield, Manchester M45 7NR
T: 0161 767 1111
F: 0161 767 2515
E: transport@polyflor.com
W: www.polyflor.com

Polydeck Ltd
Unit 14, Burnett Ind Est, Cox's Green,
Wrington, Bristol BS40 5QS
T: 01934 863678
F: 01934 863683
E: sales@gripfast.co.uk
W: www.gripfast.co.uk

Polypipe
Charnwood Business Park, North Rd,
Loughborough, Leics LE11 1LE
T: 01509 615100
F: 01509 610215
E: emma.thompson@polypipe.com
W: www.polypipe.com

Polysafe Level Crossings
King St. Ind. Est., Langtoft,
Peterborough PE6 9NF
T: 01778 560555
F: 01778 560773
E: sales@polysafe.co.uk
W: www.polysafe.co.uk

Portaramp UK Ltd
Units 3&4, Dolphin Business Park,
Thetford, Norfolk IP24 2RY
T: 01953 681799
F: 01953 688153
E: sales@portaramp.co.uk
W: www.portaramp.co.uk

Portec Rail Group
Stamford Street, Sheffield S9 2TL
T: 0114 256 2225
F: 0114 261 7826
E: uk.sales@portecrail.co.uk
W: www.portecrail.com

Porterbrook Leasing Company Ltd
Ivatt House, 7 The Point,
Pinnacle Way, Pride Park,
Derby DE24 8ZS
T: 01332 285050
F: 01332 285051
E: enquiries@porterbrook.co.uk
W: www.porterbrook.co.uk

Portwest Clothing Ltd
Commercial Rd, Goldthorpe Ind. Est.,
Goldthorpe, S.Yorks S63 9BL
T: 01709 894575
F: 01709 880830
E: info@portwest.com
W: www.portwest.com

Postfield Systems
53, Ullswater Cres.,
Coulsdon,
Surrey CR5 2HR
T: 020 8655 6080
F: 020 8655 6082
E: sales@postfield.co.uk
W: www.postfield.co.uk

Potensis Ltd
7th Floor, Froomsgate House,
Rupert St, Bristol BS1 2QJ
T: 0117 910 7999
F: 0117 927 2722
E: office@potensis.com
W: www.potensis.com

Potter Logistics Ltd
Melmerby Ind. Est,
Green Lane, Melmerby, Ripon,
North Yorks HG4 5HP
T: 01353 646703
E: sales@potterlogistics.co.uk
W: www.potterlogistics.co.uk

Power 4 from Fox & Cooper
see stuart group

Powerbox Group
4/5 Knights Court,
Magellan Close,
Walworth Ind. Est,
Andover,
Hants SP10 5NT
T: 01264 337800
E: warren.venn@powerboxgroup.co.uk
W: www.powerbox.info

Power Electronics (PE Systems Ltd)
Victoria St, Leigh,
Lancs WN7 5SE
T: 01942 260330
F: 01942 261835
E: sales@pe-systems.co.uk
W: www.power-electronics.co.uk

Power Jacks Ltd
Balmacassie Commercial Park,
Ellon,
Aberdeenshire AB41 8BX
T: 01358 285100
F: 01358 724105
E: sales@powerjacks.com
W: www.powerjacks.com

Powernetics International Ltd
Jason Works, Clarence St,
Loughborough,
Leics LE11 1DX
T: 01509 214153
F: 01509 262460
E: sales@powernetics.co.uk
W: www.powernetics.co.uk

Powertron Convertors Ltd
see martek power

Praxis
see altran praxis

Praybourne Ltd
Unit 11 Dunlop Road,
Hunt End Ind. Est,
Redditch B97 5XP
T: 0870 242 0004
F: 01527 543 752
E: enquiries@praybourne.co.uk
W: www.praybourne.co.uk

PRB Consulting
167 London Rd,
Hailsham,
E.Sussex BN27 3AN
T: 0845 557 6814
W: www.prbconsulting.co.uk

PRC Rail Consulting
10 Park Lane,
Sutton Bonington,
Loughborough LE12 5NH
T: 01509 670679
F: 01509 670679
E: piers.connor@railway-technical.com
W: www.railway-technical.com

Preformed Markings Ltd
Unit 6, Oyster Park,
109 Chertsey Rd,
Byfleet KT14 7AX
T: 01932 359270
F: 01932 340936
E: info@preformedmarkings.co.uk
W: www.preformedmarkings.co.uk

Premier Calibration Ltd
Unit 3K/L, Lake Enterprise Park,
Sandall Stores Rd, Kirk Sandall,
Doncaster DN3 1QR
T: 01302 888448
F: 01302 881197
E: enquiries.premcal@btconnect.com
W: www.premier-calibration.co.uk

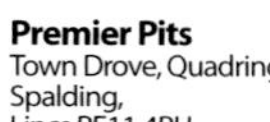

Premier Pits
Town Drove, Quadring,
Spalding,
Lincs PE11 4PU
T: 01775 821222
F: 01775 820914
E: info@premierpits.com
W: www.premierpits.com

Premier Stampings
Station St,
Cradley Heath,
West Midlands B64 6AJ
T: 01384 353100
F: 01384 353101
E: ashleyh@premierstampings.co.uk
W: www.premierstampings.co.uk

Premier Train Catering
see creative rail dining

PremTech Solutions Ltd
9 Saffron Meadow,
Harrogate,
North Yorks HG3 2NU
M: 07778 981641
E: david@premtech.net
W: www.premtech.net

Preserved Traction Technical Services
3 No4 Pembroke Rd,
London N15 4NW
M: 07561 472654
E: markb754@aol.com
W: www.preservedtractiontechservice.com

Preston Trampower Ltd
48 Watling St Rd,
Fulwood,
Preston PR2 8BP
T: 01772 713900
F: 0151 521 5509
M: 07831 337356
E: lincoln.shields@trampower.co.uk
W: www.prestontrampower.co.uk

Price Tool Sales Ltd
see birchwood price tools

PricewaterhouseCoopers LLP
1 Embankment Place,
London WC2N 6NN
T: 020 7583 5000
F: 020 7822 4652
E: julian.smith@uk.pwc.com
W: www.pwcglobal.com

Primarius UK Ltd
12b, Earlstrees Rd, Earlstrees Ind Est,
Corby, Northants NN17 4AZ
T: 01536 263691
E: sales@primariusuk.com
W: www.primariusuk.com

Priority Vehicle Hire Ltd
Unit 4, Quaking Farm Buildings,
Bestmans Lane, Kempsey, Worcester
T: 01905 821843/07939 038875
F: 01227 770035

Progress Rail Services
see caterpillar

Prolec Ltd
25 Benson Rd, Nuffield Ind. Est.,
Poole, Dorset BH17 0GB
T: 01202 681190
F: 01202 677909
E: info@prolec.co.uk
W: www.prolec.co.uk

Prostaff Rail Recruitment
172, Buckingham Ave, Slough,
Bucks SL1 4RD
T: 01753 575888
W: www.prostaff.com

Protec Fire Detection Plc
Protec House, Churchill Way, Nelson,
Lancs BB9 6RT
T: 01282 717171
F: 01282 717273
E: sales@protec.co.uk
W: www.protec.co.uk

Proteq
96, High St, Epworth,
Doncaster DN9 1JJ
T: 01427 872572
E: info@proteq.co.uk
W: www.proteq.co.uk

PRV Engineering
Pegasus House, Polo Grounds,
New Inn, Pontypool,
Gwent NP4 0TW
T: 01495 769697
F: 01495 769776
E: enquiries@prv-engineering.co.uk
W: www.prv-engineering.co.uk

Prysmian Cables & Systems
Chickenhall Lane, Bishopstoke,
Hants SO50 6YU
T: 023 8029 5029
F: 023 8060 8769
E: marketing.telecom@prysmian.com
W: www.prysmian.co.uk

Prysm Rail
see archer signs
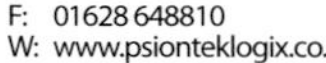

Psion Teklogix
Unit Q,
Bourne End Business Centre,
Cores End Rd,
Bourne End,
Bucks SL8 5AS
T: 01628 648800
F: 01628 648810
W: www.psionteklogix.co.uk

PSV Glass
16 Hill Bottom Rd,
Sands Ind Est,
High Wycombe,
Bucks HP12 4HJ
T: 01494 533131\0845 600 9801
F: 01494 462675
E: rail@psvglass.co.uk
W: www.psvglass.com

Ptarmigan Transport Solutions Ltd
see trainpeople.co.uk

PTH Group Ltd
see bhsf

PTM Design Ltd
Unit B2,
Sovereign Park Ind Est,
Lathkill St,
Market Harborough LE16 9EG
T: 01858 463777
F: 01858 463777
E: ptmdesign@aol.com
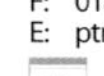

PTP Associates
The Lodge,
21 Harcourt Rd.,
Dorney Reach,
Berks SL6 0DT
T: 01628 776059
E: ces@ptpassociates.co.uk
W: www.ptpassociates.co.uk

P T Rail & Civils Ltd
57A Dock Rd,
London E16 1AG
T: 020 7511 0811
F: 0560 345 8060
W: www.ptrail.co.uk

Pullman Rail
Train Maintenance Depot,
Leckwith Rd,
Cardiff CF11 8HP
T: 02920 368850
F: 02920 368874
E: sales@pullmanrail.co.uk
W: www.pullmanrail.co.uk

Pulsarail
see praybourne ltd
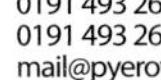

Pyeroy Group
Kirkstone House,
St Omers Rd,
Western Riverside Route,
Gateshead,
Tyne & Wear NE11 9EZ
T: 0191 493 2600
F: 0191 493 2601
E: mail@pyeroy.co.uk
W: www.pyeroy.co.uk

Pym & Wildsmith (Metal Finishers) Ltd
Bramshall Ind. Est,
Bramshall, Uttoxeter,
Staffs ST14 8TD
T: 01889 565653
F: 01889 567064
E: enquiries@pymandwildsmith.co.uk
W: www.pymandwildsmith.co.uk

QA-Aikona Ltd
Rath House,
55-65 Uxbridge Rd,
Slough SL1 1SG
T: 0845 757 3888
E: info@qa.com
W: www.qa.com

QC Data Ltd
Park House, 14 Kirtley Drive,
Castle Marina,
Nottingham NG7 1LD
T: 0115 941 5806
F: 0115 947 2901
E: rjohnson@qcdata.com
W: www.qcdata.com

QHI Rail
1 Allied Business Centre,
Coldharbour Lane, Harpenden,
Herts AL5 4UT
T: 01582 461123
F: 01582 461117
E: info@qhigroup.com
W: www.qhirail.com

QinetiQ
Cody Technoogy Park, Building A7,
Room 2008, Iveley Road,
Farnborough, Hants GU14 0LX
T: 01252 394 786
F: 01252 397 298
E: jldavies1@qinetiq.com
W: www.qinetiq.com

The QSS Group Ltd
2 St Georges House, Vernon Gate,
Derby DE1 1UQ
T: 01332 221400
F: 01332 221401
E: enquiries@theqssgroup.co.uk
W: www.theqssgroup.co.uk

Q'Straint
Unit 72-76,
John Wilson Business Park,
Whitstable, Kent CT5 3QT
T: 01227 773035
F: 01227 770035
E: info@qstraint.co.uk
W: www.qstraint.com

QTS Plant
QTS Group, Rench Farm,
Drumclog, Strathaven,
S. Lanarks ML10 6QJ
T: 01357 440222
F: 01357 440364
E: enquiries@qtsgroup.com
W: www.qtsgroup.com

Qualitrain Ltd
Bridge House, 12 Mansfield Rd,
Tibshelf, Derbys DE55 5NF
F: 01773 590671
M: 07906 990399
E: richard.bates@qualitrain.co.uk
W: www.qualitrain.co.uk

Qualter Hall & Co Ltd
PO Box 8, Johnson St,
Barnsley S75 2BY
T: 01226 205761
F: 01226 286269
E: admin@qualterhall.co.uk
W: www.qualterhall.co.uk

Quasar Associates
8 Flitcroft St, London WC2H 8DJ
T: 020 7010 7700
F: 020 7010 7701
E: jonathan@quasarassociates.co.uk
W: www.quasarassociates.co.uk

Quattro Plant Ltd
Greenway Court, Canning Rd,
Stratford, London E15 3ND
T: 020 8519 6165
F: 020 8503 0505
E: sales@quattroplant.co.uk
W: www.quattroplant.co.uk

Quest Diagnostics
Unit B1, Parkway West,
Cranford Lane,
Heston,
Middx TW5 9QA
T: 020 8377 3378
F: 020 8377 3350
E: uksales@questdiagnostics.com
W: www.questdiagnostics.com

Quickbuild (UK) Ltd
Imperial House, 1 Factory Rd,
Silvertown, London E16 2EL
T: 020 7473 2712
F: 020 7476 2713
E: davidbrowne@hiremasters.co.uk
W: www.hiremasters.co.uk/www.quickbuild.uk.com

Quickway Buildings
Hardys Yard, London Rd, Riverhead,
Sevenoaks, Kent TN13 2DN
T: 01304 612284
F: 01304 620012
E: sales@quickway-wingham.co.uk
W: www.quickway-wingham.co.uk

QW Rail Leasing
12 Plumtree Court,
London EC4A 4HT

R&I Consulting
29 Marylebone Rd,
London NW1 5JK
T: 020 3598 2479
M: 07515 615045
E: info@raics.co.uk
W: www.raics.co.uk

Ra'alloy Ramps Ltd
Unit B8 Hortonwood 10,
Telford,
Shropshire TF1 7ES
T: 01952 677877
F: 01952 677883
E: enquiries@raalloy.co.uk
W: www.raalloyramps.co.uk

Radio-Tech Ltd
U1/U2, The London Road Campus,
London Road, Harlow,
Essex CM17 9NA
T: 01279 635 849
F: 01279 442 261
E: sales@radio-tech.co.uk
W: www.radio-tech.co.uk

RAICS
see r&i consulting

Rail-Ability Ltd
Tilcon Ave, Baswich,
Stafford ST18 0YJ
T: 01785 214747
F: 01785 214717
E: skelly@railability.co.uk
W: www.railability.co.uk

Rail Accident Investigation Branch
Cullen House,
Berkshire Copse Rd,
Aldershot,
Hants GU11 2HH
T: 01932 440000
E: enquiries@raib.gov.uk
W: www.raib.gov.uk

Rail Accident Investigation Branch
The Wharf, Stores Rd,
Derby DE21 4BA
T: 01332 253300
F: 01332 253301
E: enquiries@raib.gov.uk
W: www.raib.gov.uk

Rail Alliance
The Control Tower,
Long Marston Storage,
Campden Rd, Long Marston,
Stratford upon Avon,
Warks CV37 8QR
T: 01789 720026
E: info@railalliance.co.uk
W: www.railalliance.co.uk

Rail & Road Protec GmbH
Norderhofenden 12-13,
Flensburg 24937, Germany
T: 01628 635497
F: 00461 500 33820
M: 07747 460509
E: balvinder.chana@r2protec.com
W: www.r2protec.com

Rail Audit & Assurance Services (RAAS)
54 Highfield Rd, Cheadle Hulme,
Stockport SK8 6EP
T: 0161 486 1237
M: 07940 887437
E: stockport@raas.co.uk
W: www.raas.co.uk

Rail-Blue Charters
32 Sydney Rd, Haywards Heath,
West Sussex RH16 1QA
T: 01444 450011
F: 01444 450011
E: ingrid.sluis@rail-bluecharters.co.uk
W: www.rail-bluecharters.co.uk

Railcare Ltd
see knorr bremse rail services (uk) ltd

Rail Door Solutions Ltd
Blackhill Drive, Wolverton Mill,
Milton Keynes MK12 5TS
T: 01908 224140
F: 01908 224149
E: info@raildoorsolutions.co.uk
W: www.raildoorsolutions.co.uk

Raileasy
10 Station Parade, High St,
Wanstead, London E11 1QF
T: 0906 202 0002
E: admin@raileasy.co.uk
W: www.raileasy.co.uk

Railex Aluminium Ltd
12/26 Dry Drayton Ind. Est,
Dry Drayton, Cambridge CB3 8AT
T: 0845 612 9555
F: 01954 210352
E: tony@humanhi.com
W: www.railex.net

Rail Freight Group
7 Bury Place, London WC1 2LA
T: 020 3116 0007
F: 020 3116 0008
E: phillippa@rfg.org.uk
W: www.rfg.org.uk

Railfuture
29 Granby Hill, Bristol BS8 4LT
M: 07759 557389
E: media@railfuture.org.uk
W: www.railfuture.org.uk

Rail Gourmet Group
Mac Millan House,
Paddington Station, London W2 1FT
T: 020 7313 0720
F: 020 7922 6596
E: jfleet@railgourmetuk.com
W: www.railgourmet.com

Rail Images & Rail Images Video
5 Sandhurst Crescent, Leigh on Sea,
Essex SS9 4AL
T: 01702 525059
F: 01702 525059
E: info@railimages.co.uk
W: www.railimages.co.uk

Rail Industry Contractors Association Ltd (RICA)
Gin Gan House, Thropton,
Morpeth,
Northumberland NE65 7LT
T: 01669 620569
E: enquiries@rica.uk.com
W: www.rica.uk.com

Rail Industry First Aid Association (RIFAA)
Room 103,
Denison House South,
Hexthorpe Road,
Doncaster DN4 0BF
T: 01302 329 729
F: 01302 320 590
E: bookings@rifaa.com
W: www.rifaa.com

Rail Insights Ltd
Highlands,
St Andrews Rd,
Henley-on-Thames RG9 1PG
T: 01491 414218
E: info'railinsights.com
W: www.railinsights.com

Rail Manche Finance EEIG
Times House,
Bravingtons Walk,
Regent Quarter,
London N1 9AW
T: 020 7042 9961
F: 020 7833 3896
E: david.hiscock@rmf.co.uk
W: www.rmf.co.uk

Rail Measurement Ltd
The Mount, High St, Toft,
Cambridge CB23 2RL
T: 01223 264327
F: 01223 263273
M: 07803 290252
E: enquiries@railmeasurement.com
W: www.railmeasurement.com

RAIL.ONE GmbH
Ingolstaedter Strasse 51,
92318 Neumarkt,
Germany
T: 0049 9181 8952-0
F: 0049 9181 8952-5001
E: info@railone.com
W: www.railone.com

Rail Operations Competence Solutions Ltd
40 Weston Lane,
Shavington,
Crewe,
Cheshire CW2 5AN
M: 07796 548651
E: info@rail-operations-competence-solutions.co.uk
W: www.rail-operations-competence-solutions.co.uk

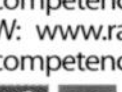

Rail Op UK Ltd
13 The Links Ind. Est, Raynham Rd,
Bishops Stortford,
Herts CM23 5NZ
T: 0845 450 5332
E: info@railop.co.uk
W: www.railop.co.uk

Rail Operations Developments Ltd
Electra House, Electra Way,
Crewe Business Park,
Crewe CW1 6GL
T: 01270 588500
F: 01270 588500
E: enquiries@rodl.co.uk
W: www.railoperationsdevelopment.co.uk

Rail Order
Unit 3,
Sherwood Networking Centre,
Sherwood Energy Village,
Ollerton,
Notts NG22 9FD
T: 01623 862431
F: 01623 861881
E: sales@rail-order.co.uk
W: www.rail-order.co.uk

Rail Personnel Ltd
Level 26, Office Tower,
Convention Plaza, 1 Harbour Rd,
Wanchai, Hong Kong
T: 00 852 2753 5636
F: 00 852 2305 4512
E: info@railpersonnel.com
W: www.railpersonnel.com

Rail Photo Library
F: 0116 259 2068
E: studio@railphotolibrary.com
W: www.railphotolibrary.com

Rail Positive Relations
The Bothy, 18 Holloway Rd,Duffield,
Derbys DE56 4FE
T: 020 7617 7018
M: 07973 950923
E: rupert@railpr.com
W: www.railpr.com

Rail Professional Development
Cranes House, 5 Paycocke Rd,
Basildon, Essex SS14 3DP
T: 01268 822842
F: 01268 822841
E: info@rpd.co.uk
W: www.rpd.co.uk

Rail Research UK Association (RRUK-A)
Block 2, Angel Square, 1
Torrens St,
London EC1V 1NY
T: 02380 598454
F: 02380 677519
E: secretariat@rruka.org.uk
W: www.rruka.org.uk

Rail Restorations North East Ltd
8A Hackworth Industrial Park,
Shildon DL4 1HF
T: 01388 777138
M: 07971 100092
E: enquiries@rail-restorations-north-east.co.uk
W: www.rail-restorations-north-east.co.uk

RailRoute Ltd
The Business and Innovation Centre,
Enterprise Park East,
Sunderland SR5 2TA
T: 0191 516 6354
M: 0776 586 0998
E: michael.beaney@railroute.co.uk
W: www.railroute.co.uk

Rail Safety and Standards Board (RSSB)
Block 2, Angel Square,
1 Torrens St,
London EC1V 1NY
T: 020 3142 5300
E: enquirydesk@rssb.co.uk
W: www.rssb.co.uk

Rail Safety Solutions
Unit 27, Royal Scot Rd,
Pride Park,
Derby DE24 8AJ
T: 01332 989593
F: 020 3142 5301
E: info@railsafetysolutions.com
W: www.railsafetysolutions.com

Railscape Ltd
15 Totman Cresc,
Brook Rd Ind Est,
Rayleigh,
Essex SS6 7UY
T: 01268 777795
F: 01268 777762
E: info@railscape.com
W: www.railscape.com

Rail Tech Group (Railway & Signalling Engineering) Ltd
91 Dales Rd, Ipswich IP1 4JR
T: 01473 242330
F: 01473 242379
W: www.railtech.co.uk

Rail Technology Ltd
Mill End Lane, Alrewas,
Staffs DE13 7BY
T: 01283 790012
M: 07715 374635
E: bg@track-man.co.uk
W: www.railtechnologyltd.com

Railtex/Infrarail - Mack Brooks Exhibitions Ltd
Romelands House, Romelands Hill, St Albans AL3 4ET
T: 01727 814400
F: 01727 814401
E: railtex@mackbrooks.co.uk
W: www.mackbrooks.co.uk

Railtourer Ltd
42 Kingston Rd, Willerby, Hull HU10 6BH
T: 01482 659082
W: www.railtourer.co.uk

Rail Training International Ltd
North Suite, Parsonage Offices, Church Lane, Canterbury, Kent CT4 7AD
T: 01227 769096
F: 01227 479435
E: rtiuk@rti.co.uk
W: www.rti.co.uk

Rail Vision
2 Cygnus Court, Beverley Rd, Pegasus Business Park, East Midlands Airport, Castle Donnington, Leics DE74 2UZ
T: 01509 672211
E: enquiries@rail-vision.com
W: www.rail-vision.com

Rail Waiting Structures
Dyffryn Business Park, Llantwit Major Rd, Llandow, Vale of Glamorgan
T: 01446 795444
F: 01446 793344
E: lisa.brown@shelters.co.uk
W: www.shelters.co.uk

Railway Approvals Ltd
Derwent House, rtc Business Park, London Rd, Derby DE24 8UP
T: 01332 483800
F: 01332 483800
E: info@railwayapprovals.co.uk
W: www.railwayapprovals.co.uk

Railway Civil Engineers Association
One Great George St, Westminster, London SW1P 3AA
T: 020 7665 2233
F: 020 7799 1325
W: www.rcea.co.uk

The Railway Consultancy Ltd
1st Floor, South Tower, Crystal Palace Station, London SE19 2AZ
T: 020 8676 0395
F: 020 8778 7439
M: 07802 623548
E: info@railwayconsultancy.com
W: www.railwayconsultancy.com

Railway Convalescent Home (RCH)
Bridge House, 2 Church St, Dawlish, Devon EX7 9AU
T: 01626 863303
F: 01626 866676
E: sueg@rch.org.uk
W: www.rch.org.uk

Railway Drainage Ltd
The Steadings, Maisemore Court, Maisemore, Glos GL2 8EY
T: 01452 422666
W: www.rdlonline.co.uk

Railway Employees & Public Transport Association
see repta

Railway Engineering Associates Ltd
68 Boden St, Glasgow G40 3PX
T: 0141 554 3868
F: 0141 556 5091
E: postmaster@rea.uk.com
W: www.rea.uk.com

The Railway Engineering Company Ltd
Manvers House, Kingston Rd, Bradford-on-Avon, Wilts BA15 1AB
T: 01225 860140
F: 01225 867698
E: info@therailenq.co.uk
W: www.therailenq.co.uk

Railway Finance Ltd
Barrow Rd, Wincobank, Sheffield S9 1JZ
T: 01223 891300
F: 01223 891302
E: nick.preston@railwayfinance.co.uk
W: www.railwayfinance.co.uk

Railway Industry Association
22 Headfort Place, London SW1X 7RY
T: 020 7201 0777
F: 020 7235 5777
E: ria@riagb.org.uk
W: www.riagb.org.uk

Railway Management Services
Kingfisher House, Suite 27, 21-23 Elmfield Rd, Bromley, Kent BR1 1LT
T: 020 8315 6767
F: 020 8315 6766
E: peter.coysten@railwayms.com
W: www.railwayms.com

The Railway Mission
Rugby Railway Station, Rugby CV21 3LA
T: 0845 269 1881
M: 07841 985768
E: office@railwaychaplain.net
W: www.railwaymission.org

Railways Pension Scheme
2nd Floor, Camomile Court, 23 Camomile St, London EC3A 7LL
T: 0800 234 3434
E: csu@rpmi.co.uk
W: www.railwayspensions.co.uk

Railway Projects Ltd
Lisbon House, 5-7 St Marys Gate, Derby DE1 3JA
T: 01332 349255
F: 01332 349261
E: enquiries@railwayprojects.co.uk
W: www.railwayprojects.co.uk

Railway Study Association (RSA)
PO Box 375, Burgess Hill, West Sussex RH15 5BX
T: 01444 246379
E: info@railwaystudyassociation.org
W: www.railwaystudyassociation.org

Railway Support Services
Montpellier House, Montpellier Drive, Cheltenham GL50 1TY
T: 0870 803 4651
F: 0870 803 4652
E: info@railwaysupportservices.co.uk
W: www.railwaysupportservices.co.uk

Railway Systems Engineering & Integration Group
Birmingham Centre for Railway Reasearch & Education College of Engineering Sciences, University of Birmingham, Edgbaston, Birmingham B15 2TT
T: 0121 414 4342
F: 0121 414 4291
E: j.grey@bham.ac.uk
W: www.eng.bham.ac.uk/civil/study/postgrad/railway.shtml

Railway Touring Company
14a Tuesday Market Place, Kings Lynn, Norfolk PE30 1JN
T: 01553 661500
F: 01553 661800
E: enquiries@railwaytouring.co.uk
W: www.railwaytouring.co.uk

Railway Vehicle Engineering Ltd (RVEL)
RTC Business Park, London Rd, Derby DE24 8UP
T: 01332 293035
F: 01332 331210
E: enquiries@rvel.co.uk
W: www.rvel.co.uk

Railweight
Foundry Lane, Smethwick, Birmingham B66 2LP
T: 0121 568 1708
F: 0121 697 5655
E: sales@railweight.co.uk
W: www.averyweightronix.com/railweight

Ramboll UK Ltd
Carlton House, Ringwood Rd, Woodlands, Southampton SO40 7HT
T: 02380 817500
F: 02380 817600
E: tim.holmes@ramboll.co.uk
W: www.ramboll.co.uk

Rampart Carriage & Wagon Services Ltd
Brunel Gate, RTC Business Park, London Rd, Derby DE24 8UP
T: 01332 263261
F: 01332 263181
E: admin@rampartderby.co.uk
W: www.rampartderby.co.uk

Ramtech Electronics Ltd
Abbeyfield House, Abbeyfield Rd, Nottingham NG7 2SZ
T: 0115 988 7090
F: 0115 970 5415
E: matt.sadler@ramtech.co.uk
W: www.ramtech.co.uk

R&B Switchgear Services Ltd
F: 01706 364564
E: ian.penswick@rb-power.co.uk
W: www.rbswitch.co.uk

Ranstad CPE
Forum 4, Parkway, Solent Business Park, Whiteley, Fareham PO15 7AD
T: 01489 560000
F: 01489 560001
E: info@ranstadcpe.com
W: www.ranstadcpe.com

Ransome Engineering Services Ltd
Clopton Commercial Park, Clopton, Woodbridge, Suffolk IP13 6QT
T: 01473 737731
F: 01473 737398
E: info@ransomeengineering.co.uk
W: www.ransomeengineering.co.uk

Raspberry Software Ltd
9 Deben Mill Business Centre, Old Maltings Approach, Melton, Woodbridge, Suffolk IP12 1BL
T: 01394 387386
F: 01394 387386
E: info@raspberrysoftware.com
W: www.raspberrysoftware.com

Ratcliff Palfinger
Bessemer Rd, Welwyn Garden City, Herts AL7 1ET
T: 01707 325571
F: 01707 327752
E: info@ratcliffpalfinger.co.uk
W: www.ratcliffpalfinger.com

Rayleigh Instruments
Raytel House, Brook Rd, Rayleigh, Essex SS6 7XH
T: 01268 749300
F: 01268 749309
E: sales@rayleigh.co.uk
W: www.rayleigh.co.uk

REACT Beyond Cleaning
Stanhope Rd, Swadlincote, Derbys DE11 9BE
T: 08707 510422
F: 08707 510417
E: info@ractbeyondcleaning.co.uk
W: www.reactbeyondcleaning.co.uk

React Engineering Ltd
Fleswick Court, Westlakes Science & Tech. Park, Moor Row, Whitehaven, Cumbria CA24 3HZ
T: 01946 590511
F: 01946 591044
E: mail@react-engineering.co.uk
W: www.react-engineering.co.uk

Readypower
Readypower House, Molly Millars Bridge, Wokingham, Berks RG41 2WY
T: 01189 774901
F: 01189 774902
E: info@readypower.co.uk
W: www.readypower.co.uk

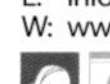

Real Time Consultants Plc
118-120, Warwick St, Royal Leamington Spa, Warks CV32 4QY
T: 01926 313133
F: 01926 422165
E: contract@rtc.co.uk
W: www.rtc.co.uk

Record Electrical Associates Ltd
Unit C1, Longford Trading Est., Thomas St., Stretford, Manchester M32 0JT
T: 0161 864 3583
F: 0161 864 3603
E: alanj@reauk.com
W: www.record-electrical.co.uk

Recruitrail (Recruit Engineers)
Bank Chambers, 36 Mount Pleasant Rd, Tunbridge Wells, Kent TN1 1RA
T: 01909 540825
F: 0870 443 0453
W: www.recruitrail.com

Redman Fisher Engineering Ltd
Birmingham New Rd, Tipton, West Midlands DY4 9AQ
T: 01902 880880
F: 01902 880446
E: sales@redmanfisher.co.uk
W: www.redmanfisher.co.uk

Reg Harman Consultancy Services Ltd
2 Valley Close, Hertford SG13 8BD
T: 01992 415248
E: reg.harman@ntlworld.com

Rehau Ltd
Hill Court, Walford, Ross-on-Wye, Herefordshire HR9 5QN
T: 01989 762655
F: 01989 762601
E: anthonia.ifeany-okoro@rehau.com
W: www.rehau.co.uk

Reid Lifting Ltd
Unit 1, Severnlink, Newhouse Farm Ind. Est, Chepstow, Monmouthshire NP16 6UN
T: 01291 620796
F: 01291 626490
E: enquiries@reidlifting.com
W: www.reidlifting.com

Reinforced Earth Company
Innovation House, Euston Way, Town Centre, Telford TF3 4LT
T: 01952 201901
F: 01952 211523
E: info@reinforcedearth.co.uk
W: www.reinforcedearth.co.uk

Relec Electronics Ltd
Animal House, Justin Bus. Park, Sandford Lane, Wareham, Dorset BH20 4DY
T: 01929 555700
F: 01929 555701
E: sales@relec.co.uk
W: www.relec.co.uk

Renaissance Trains Ltd
4 Spinneyfield, Ellington, Cambs PE28 0AT
T: 07977 917148
E: peter.wilkinson@renaissancetrains.com
W: www.renaissancetrains.com

Renown Training
Brookside House, Brookside Business Park, Cold Meece, Staffs ST15 0RZ
T: 01785 764476
F: 01785 760896
E: enquiries@renownrailway.co.uk
W: www.renownrailway.co.uk

Replin Fabrics
March St Mills, Peebles EH45 8ER
T: 01721 724311
F: 01721 721893
E: enquiries@replin-fabrics.co.uk
W: www.replin-fabrics.co.uk

REPTA (Railway Employees and Public Transport Association)
24 Foxglove Drive, Biggleswade, Beds SG18 8SP
T: 01767 317683
F: 01767 317683
E: 24foxglove@tiscali.co.uk
W: www.repta.co.uk

Resourcing Solutions
Vector House, 5 Ruscombe Park, Ruscombe, Berks RG10 9JW
T: 0118 932 0100
F: 0118 932 1818
E: info@resourcing-solutions.com
W: www.resourcing-solutions.com

RE: Systems
Systems House, Deepdale Business Park, Bakewell, Derbys DE45 1FZ
T: 01629 815902
F: 01629 813349
E: steve.england@re-systems.co.uk
W: www.re-systems.co.uk

Rethinking Transport
E: jon@rethinkingtransport.com
W: www.rethinkingtransport.com

Retro Railtours Ltd
2 Brookfield Grove, Ashton-under-Lyne, Lancashire OL6 6TL
T: 0161 330 9055
E: info@retrorailtours.co.uk
W: www.retrorailtours.co.uk

Revitaglaze
Unit 9, Park Industrial Estate, Frogmore, St Albans Herts AL2 2DR
T: 0843 289 3901
F: 01372 200881
E: marketing@revitaglaze.com
W: www.revitaglaze.com

Rexquote Ltd
Broadgauge Business Park, Bishops Lydeard, Taunton,Somerset TA4 3RU
T: 01823 433398
F: 01823 433378
E: sales@rexquote.co.uk
W: www.rexquote.co.uk

RGB Integrated Services Ltd
Unit 3007, Access House, Nestle Ave, Hayes, Middlesex UB3 4UZ
T: 020 8573 9882
F: 020 8711 3916
E: info@rgb-services.com
W: www.rgb-services.com

RGS Rail
6 Clarendon St, Nottingham NG1 5HQ
T: 0115 959 9687
M: 07973 676323
E: enquiries@rgsexecutive.co.uk
W: www.rgsexecutive.co.uk

RIB Software (UK) Ltd
12 Floor, The Broadgate Tower, 20 Primrose St, London EC2A 2EW
T: 020 7596 2747
F: 020 7596 2701
W: www.rib-software.co.uk

Ricardo UK
Midlands Technical Centre, Southam Rd, Radford Semele, Leamington Spa, Warks CV31 1FQ
T: 01926 477171
F: 01926 319352
E: jim.buchanan@ricardo.com
W: www.ricardo.com

Riello UPS Ltd
Unit 68, Clywedog Rd North, Wrexham Ind. Est., Wrexham LL13 9XN
T: 01978 729297
F: 01978 729290
E: marketing@riello-ups.co.uk
W: www.riello-ups.co.uk

Riley & Son (E) Ltd
Baron St, Bury, Lancs BL9 0TY
T: 0161 764 2892
F: 0161 763 5191
E: ian.riley@btconnect.com

Ring Automotive
Gelderd Rd, Leeds LS12 6NA
T: 0113 213 2000
F: 0113 231 0266
E: autosales@ringautomotive.co.uk
W: www.ringautomotive.co.uk

RIQC Ltd
2 St Georges House,Vernon Gate, Derby DE1 1UQ
T: 01332 221421
F: 01332 221401
E: enquiries@riqc.co.uk
W: www.riqc.co.uk

RISC Ltd – Railway & Industrial Safety Consultants Ltd
Harlyn House, 3 Doveridge Rd, Stapenhill, Burton Upon Trent DE15 9GB
T: 0844 840 9420
F: 0871 247 2961
M: 07941 212568
E: enquiries@railwaysafety.co.uk
W: www.railwaysafety.co.uk

Risk Solutions
Dallam Court, Dallam Lane, Warrington WA2 7LT
T: 01925 413984
E: enquiries@risksol.co.uk
W: www.risksol.co.uk

Risktec Solutions
wilderspool Park, Greenalls Ave, Warrington WA4 6HL
T: 01925 611200
F: 01925 611232
E: enquiries@risktec.co.uk
W: www.risktec.co.uk

Ritelite Systems Ltd
Meadow Park, Bourne Rd, Essendine, Stamford, Lincs PE9 4LT
T: 01780 765600
F: 01780 765700
E: sales@ritelite.co.uk
W: www.ritelite.co.uk

Rittal Ltd
Braithwell Way, Hellaby Ind Est, Hellaby, Rotherham S66 8QY
T: 01709 704000
F: 01709 701217
E: information@rittal.co.uk
W: www.rittal.co.uk

Riviera Trains
116, Ladbroke Grove, London W10 5NE
T: 020 7727 4036
F: 020 7727 2083
E: enquiries@riviera-trains.co.uk
W: www.riviera-trains.co.uk

RJ Power Ltd
Unit 1, Gaugemaster Ind. Est, Gaugemaster Way, Ford, West Sussex BN18 0RX
T: 01903 868535
F: 01903 885932
E: info@rjpower.biz
W: www.rjpower.biz

RMS Locotec locomotive Hire
British American Railway Services, Stanhope Station, Stanhope, Bishop Auckland DL13 2YS
T: 01388 526203
E: documentcontroller@britamrail.com
W: www.rmslocotec.com

RMT
National Union of Rail, Maritime & Transport Workers, Unity House, 39 Chalton St, London NW1 1JD
T: 020 7387 4771
F: 020 7387 4123
E: info@rmt.org.uk
W: www.rmt.org.uk

Robel Bahnbaumaschmen GmbH
Industriestrasse 31, D 83395, Freilassing, Germany
T: 0049 8654 6090
F: 0049 8654 609100
E: info@robel.info
W: www.robel.info

Robert West Consulting
Delta House, 175-177 Borough High St, London SE1 1HR
T: 020 7939 9916
F: 020 7939 9909
E: london@robertwest.co.uk
W: www.robertwest.co.uk

Rock Mechanics Technology Ltd
Bretby Business Park, Ashby Rd, Stanhope Bretby, Burton on Trent DE15 0QP
T: 01283 522201
F: 01283 522279
E: rmt@rmtltd.com
W: www.rmtltd.com

ROCOL Acme Panels
Rocol House, Wakefield Rd, Swillington, Leeds LS26 8BS
T: 0113 232 2800
F: 0113 232 2850
E: customer-service.safety@rocol.com
W: www.rocol.com

ROCOL Site Safety Systems
ROCOL Site Safety Systems
T: 0113 232 2800
F: 0113 232 2850
E: enquiries@rocol.com
W: www.rocol.com

Roechling Engineering Plastics (UK) Ltd
Waterwells Business Park, Waterwells Drive, Quedgeley, Glos GL2 2AA
T: 01452 727905
F: 01452 728056
E: david.ward@roechling-plastics.co.uk
W: www.roechling-plastics.co.uk

Roevin Engineering
4th Floor, Clydesdale Bank House, 33 Lower Regent St, Piccadilly, London WC1Y 4NB
T: 0845 643 0486
F: 0870 759 8443
E: rail@roevin.co.uk
W: www.roevin.co.uk

Rollalong Ltd
Woolsbridge Ind. Park, Three Legged Cross, Wimborne, Dorset BH21 6SF
T: 01202 824541
F: 01202 826525
E: enquiries@rollalong.co.uk
W: www.rollalong.co.uk

Romac Technical Services Ltd
Clements House, Mount Ave, Mount Farm, Bletchley, Milton Keynes MK1 1LS
T: 01908 375845
F: 01908 270524
E: tom.appleton@romac.co.uk
W: www.romac.co.uk

Romag
Leadgate Ind. Est., Leadgate, Consett, Co Durham DH8 7RS
T: 01207 500000
F: 01207 591979
E: tiffany.sott@romag.co.uk
W: www.romag.co.uk

Romic House
A1/M1 Business Centre, Kettering, Northants NN16 8TD
T: 01536 414244
F: 01536 414245
E: sales@romic.co.uk
W: www.romic.co.uk

Ronfell Ltd
Challenge House, Pagefield industrial Est., Miry Lane, Wigan WN6 7LA
T: 01942 492200
F: 01942 492233
E: sales@ronfell.com
W: www.ronfell.com

Rose Hill P&OD Ltd
1a Queen St, Rushden, Northants NN10 0AA
F: 01933 663846
M: 07771 612321
E: info@rose-hill.co.uk
W: www.rose-hill.co.uk

Rosehill Rail
Spring Bank Mills, Watson Mill Lane, Sowerby Bridge HX6 3BW
T: 01422 839456
F: 01422 316952
E: peter.anderson@rosehillrail.com
W: www.rosehillrail.com

Rosenqvist Rail AB
Box 334, 82427 Hudiksvall, Sweden
T: 0046 650 16505
F: 0046 650 16501
E: info@rosenqvist-group.se
W: www.rosenqvistrail.se

Rotabroach Ltd
Imperial Works, Sheffield Rd, Tinsley, Sheffield S9 2YL
T: 0114 221 2510
F: 0114 221 2563
E: sales@rotabroach.co.uk
W: www.rotabroach.co.uk

Roughton Group
A2, Omega Park, Electron Way, Chandlers Ford, Hants SO53 4SE
T: 023 8027 8600
F: 023 8027 8601
E: hq@roughton.com
W: www.roughton.com

Rowe Hankins Ltd
Power House, Parker St, Bury BL9 0RJ
T: 0161 765 3000
F: 0161 705 2900
E: sales@rowehankins.com
W: www.rowehankins.com

Roxtec Ltd
Unit C1, Waterfold Business Park, Bury, Lancs BL9 7BQ
T: 0161 761 5280
F: 0161 763 6065
E: russell.holmes@uk.roxtec.com
W: www.roxtec.com

Royal British Legion Industries (RBLI)
Royal British Legion Village, Hall Rd, Aylesford, Kent ME20 7NL
T: 01622 795900
F: 01622 795978
E: sales.office@rbli.co.uk
W: www.rbli.co.uk/manufacturing/services/19/

Royal Haskoning Ltd
Rightwell House, Bretton, Peterborough PE3 8DW
T: 01733 334455
F: 01733 262243
E: info@peterborough.royalhaskoning.com
W: www.royalhaskoning.com

RPS Planning and Development
RPS Planning and Development
T: 01636 605700
F: 01636 610696
E: alan.skipper@rpsgroup.com
W: www.rpsgroup.com

RS Components Ltd
Birchington Rd, Corby, Northants NN17 9RS
T: 0845 602 5226
W: www.rswww.com/purchasing

RSK STATS Health & Safety Ltd
Spring Lodge, 172 Chester Rd, Helsby, Cheshire WA6 0AR
T: 01928 726006
F: 01928 725633
W: www.rsk.com

RSK STATS Ltd
18 Frogmore Rd, Hemel Hempstead, Herts HP3 9RT
T: 01442 437500
F: 01442 437550
E: info@stats.co.uk
W: www.stats.co.uk

RTC Group
The Derby Conference Centre, London Rd, Derby DE24 8UX
T: 01332 861336
F: 0870 890 0034
E: info@rtcgroupplc.co.uk
W: www.rtcgroupplc.co.uk

RTI UK
35 Old Queen St,
London SW1H 9JD
T: 020 7340 0900
F: 020 7233 3411
E: rtiuk@rti.co.uk
W: www.rti.co.uk

RTS Infrastructure Services Ltd
The Rail Depot,
Bridge Rd,
Holbeck,
Leeds LS11 9UG
T: 01132 344899
E: info@rtsinfrastructure.com
W: www.rtsinfrastructure.com

RTS Solutions Ltd
Atlantic House,
Imperial Way,
Reading RG2 0TD
T: 0118 903 6045
F: 0118 903 6100
E: stuart@rts-solutions.net
W: www.rts-solutions.net

Rugged Com Inc. (UK)
InfoLab21,
Knowledge Business Centre,
Lancaster University,
Lancaster LA1 4WA
T: 01524 510434
F: 01524 510433
E: ianpoulett@ruggedcom.com
W: www.ruggedcom.com

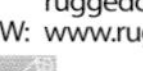

Rullion Engineering Personnel
2nd Floor, Unit 5,
Bath Court,
Islington Row,
Edgbaston,
Birmingham B15 1NE
T: 0121 622 7720
F: 0121 622 7721
E: james.millward@rullion.co.uk
W: www.rullion.co.uk/rep

RWD Technologies UK Ltd
Furzeground Way,
First Floor,
Stockley Park,
Uxbridge UB11 1AJ
T: 020 8569 2787
F: 020 8756 3625
W: www.rwd.com

Rydon Signs
Unit 3, Peek House,
Pinhoe Trading Est,
Exeter,
Devon EX4 8JN
T: 01392 466653
F: 01392 466671
E: sales@rydonsigns.com
W: www.rydonsigns.com

Sabre Rail Services Ltd
Grindon Way,
Heighington Lane Business Park,
Newton Aycliffe,
Co Durham DL5 6SH
T: 01325 300505
F: 01325 300485
E: sales@sabre-rail.co.uk
W: www.sabre-rail.co.uk

Safeaid LLP
Signal House, 16,
Arnside Rd,
Waterlooville,
Hants PO7 7UP
T: 02392 254442
F: 02392 257444
E: sales@safeaidsupplies.com
W: www.safeaidsupplies.com

Safeglass (Europe) Ltd
Nasmyth Building,
Nasmyth Ave,
East Kilbride G75 0QR
T: 01355 272828
F: 01355 272788
E: sales@safeglass.co.uk
W: www.safeglass.co.uk

Safeguard Pest Control Ltd
6 Churchill Bus. Park,
The Flyers Way, Westerham,
Kent TN16 1BT
T: 0800 195 7766
F: 01959 565888
E: info@safeguardpestcontrol.co.uk
W: www.safeguardpestcontrol.co.uk

Safeline Training Ltd
69-71, Haltwhistle Rd,
South Woodham Ferrers,
Essex CM3 5ZA
T: 01245 425617
F: 01245 426042
E: info@safelinetraining.co.uk
W: www.safelinetraining.co.uk

Safestyle Security Services
Exe. Suite 1,
Cardiff International Arena,
Mary Ann St, Cardiff CF10 2FQ
T: 02920 221711
F: 02920 234592
E: office@safestylesecurity.co.uk
W: www.safestylesecurity.co.uk

Safetech Environmental Care
4 Upton St, Hull HU8 7DA
T: 01482 224165
F: 01482 214522
E: info@safetechenv.com
W: www.safetechenv.com

Safetell Ltd
Unit 46, Fawkes Ave,
Dartford Trade Park,
Dartford DA1 1JQ
T: 01322 223233
F: 01322 277751
E: sales@safetell.co.uk
W: www.safetell.co.uk

Safetrack Baavhammar AB
1 Moleberga, S-245 93 Staffanstorp,
Sweden
T: 0046 4044 5300
F: 0046 4044 5553
E: sales@safetrack.se
W: www.safetrack.se

Safetykleen UK Ltd
Profile West, 950 Great West Rd,
Brentford, Middx TW8 9ES
T: 01909 519300
E: skuk@sk-europe.com
W: www.safetykleen.co.uk

SAFT Ltd
1st Floor, Unit 5, Astra Centre,
Edinburgh Way, Harlow CM20 2BN
T: 01279 772550
F: 01279 420909
E: sarah.carter@saftbatteries.com
W: www.saftbatteries.com

SAFT Power Systems Ltd
see aeg

Saint Gobain Abrasives Ltd
Doxey Rd, Stafford ST16 1EA
T: 01785 279550
F: 01785 213487
E: sonia.uppal@saint-gobain.com
W: www.saint-gobain.com

St Leonards Railway Engineering Ltd
Bridgeway, St Leonards on Sea,
E Sussex TN38 8AP
T: 01233 617001

St Pancras International Station Chaplaincy
Network Rail Station Reception,
St Pancras Station, Euston Rd,
London N1C 4QP
T: 020 7485 2472
F: 020 7843 7715
M: 07896 934881
E: jonathan.barker@networkrail.co.uk
W: www.stpancras.com

Saltburn Railtours
16 Bristol Ave,
Saltburn TS12 1BW
T: 01287 626572
E: r.dallara@btinternet.com
W: www.saltburnrailtours.co.uk

Samsung Electronics Hainan Fibreoptics
c/o Go Tel Communications Ltd,
4 Hicks Close, Wroughton,
Swindon SN4 9AY
T: 01793 813600
F: 01793 529380
E: robindash@gtcom.co.uk
W: www.samsungfiberoptics.com

Santon Switchgear Ltd
Unit 9, Waterside Court,
Newport NP20 5NT
T: 01633 854111
F: 01633 854999
E: sales@santonswitchgear.co.uk
W: www.santonswitchgear.com

Sartoria Corporatewear
Gosforth Rd, Derby DE24 8HU
T: 01332 342616
F: 01332 226940
W: www.sartorialtd.co.uk.co.uk

Savigny Oddie Ltd
Wallows Ind. Est, Wallows Rd,
Brierley Hill, West Midlands DY5 1QA
T: 01384 481598
F: 01384 482383
E: keith@oddiefasteners.com
W: www.savigny-oddie.co.uk

SBC Rail Ltd
Littlewell Lane,
Stanton by Dale,
Ilkeston,
Derbys DE7 4QW
T: 0115 944 1448
F: 0115 944 1466
E: sbc@stanton-bonna.co.uk
W: www.stanton-bonna.co.uk

SB Rail (Swietelsky Babcock)
Kintail House, 3 Lister Way,
Hamilton International Park,
Blantyre G72 0FT
T: 01698 203005
F: 01698 203006
E: shona.jamieson@babcock.co.uk
W: www.babcock.co.uk/rail

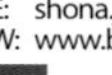

Schaeffler (UK) Ltd
Forge Lane, Minworth,
Sutton Coldfield,
West Midlands B76 1AP
T: 0121 313 5870
F: 0121 313 0080
E: info.uk@schaeffler.com
W: www.schaeffler.co.uk

Schaltbau Machine Electrics
335/336, Springvale Industrial Estate,
Woodside Way,
Cwmbran NP44 5BR
T: 01633 877555
F: 01633 873366
E: sales@schaltbau-me.com
W: www.schaltbau-me.com

Scheidt & Bachmann (UK) Ltd
7 Silverglade Business Park,
Leatherhead Rd,
Chessington,
Surrey KT9 2QL
T: 01372 230400
F: 01372 722053
E: info@scheidt-bachmann.de
W: www.scheidt-bachmann.de

Schenck Process UK
Carolina Court, Lakeside,
Doncaster DN4 5RA
T: 01302 321313
F: 01302 554400
E: enquiries@schenckprocess.co.uk
W: www.schenckprocess.co.uk

Schneider Electric Ltd
Stafford Park 5, Telford,
Shropshire TF3 3BL
T: 01952 209226
F: 01952 292238
W: www.schneider-electric.co.uk

Schofield Lothian Ltd
Temple Chambers,
3-7 Temple Ave,
London EC4Y 0DT
T: 020 7842 0920
F: 020 7842 0921
E: enquiries@schofieldlothian.com
W: www.schofieldlothian.com

Schroff UK Ltd
Maylands Ave,
Hemel Hempstead,
Herts HP2 7DE
T: 01442 240471
F: 01442 213508
E: schroff.uk@pentair.com
W: www.schroff.co.uk

Schweerbau GmbH & Co KG
UK Branch Office,
20 Beattyville Gardens,
Ilford IG6 1JN
F: 020 7681 3971
M: 07725 888933
E: verheijen@schweerbau.de
W: www.schweerbau.de

Schweizer Electronic AG
Industriestrasse 3,
CH-6260 Reiden,
Switzerland
T: 0041 6274 90707
F: 0041 6274 90700
E: info@schweizer-electronic.ch
W: www.schweizer-electronic.ch

Schwihag AG
Lebernstrasse 3, PO Box 152, CH-8274 Tagerwilen, Switzerland
T: 0041 71 666 8800
F: 0041 71 666 8801
E: info@schwihag.com
W: www.schwihag.com

Scientifics
ESG House,
Bretby Business Park, Ashby Rd,
Burton upon Trent DE15 0YZ
T: 0845 603 2112
F: 01283 554401
E: sales@esg.co.uk
W: www.esg.co.uk

Scisys
Methuen Park,
Chippenham,
Wilts SN14 0GB
T: 01249 466466
F: 01249 466666
E: marketing@scisys.co.uk
W: www.scisys.co.uk

Scotrail
see first scotrail

Scott Bader
Wollaston, Wellingborough,
Northants NN29 7RL
T: 01933 663100
E: composites@scottbader.com
W: www.scottbader.com

Scott Brownrigg – Design Research Unit
77 Endell St,
London WC2H 9DZ
T: 020 7240 7766
F: 020 7240 2454
E: enquiries@scottbrownrigg.com
W: www.scottbrownrigg.com

Scott White & Hookings
Fountain House, 26 St Johns St,
Bedford MK42 0AQ
T: 01234 213111
F: 01234 213333
E: bed@swh.co.uk
W: www.swh.co.uk

Scott Wilson Railways
see urs

Scotweld Employment Services
see sw global resourcing

Screwfast Foundations Ltd
7-14 Smallford Works,
Smallford Way,
St. Albans,
Herts AL4 0SA
T: 01727 821282
F: 01727 828098
E: info@screwfast.com
W: www.screwfast.com

SCT Europe Ltd
see wabtec

SEA (Group) Ltd
SEA House,
PO Box 800,
Bristol BS16 1SU
T: 01373 852000
F: 01373 831133
E: info@sea.co.uk
W: www.sea.co.uk

Seaton Rail Ltd
Bridlington Business Centre,
Enterprise Way,
Bridlington YO16 4SF
T: 01262 608313
F: 01262 604493
E: info@seaton-rail.com
W: www.seaton-rail.com

Secheron SA
Rue de pre-Bouvier 25,
Zimeysa 1217 Meyrin, Geneva,
Switzerland
T: 0041 22 739 4111
F: 0041 22 739 4811
E: info@secheron.com
W: www.secheron.com

Sefac UK Ltd
Unit C211, Barton Rd, Water Eaton,
Bletchley MK2 3HU
T: 01908 821274
F: 01908 821275
E: info@sefac-lift.co.uk
W: www.sefac-lift.co.uk

Select Cables Ltd
Painter Close, Anchorage Park,
Portsmouth
T: 02392 652552
F: 02392 652277
E: sales@selectcables.com
W: www.selectcables.com

Selectequip Ltd
Unit 7, Britannia Way,
Britannia Enterprise Park, Lichfield,
Staffs WS14 9UY
T: 01543 416641
F: 01543 416083
E: sales@selectequip.co.uk
W: www.selectequip.co.uk

Selex ES Ltd
8-10 Great George St,
London SW1P 3AE
F: 0207 340 6199
M: 07500 813468
E: amanda.lachlan@selex-es.com
W: www.selex-es.com

Semikron Ltd
John Tate Rd,
Foxholes Business Park,
Hertford SG13 7NW
T: 01992 584677
F: 01992 503847
E: sales.skuk@semikron.com
W: www.semikron.com

Semmco Ltd
9 Kestrel Way,
Goldsworth Park Trading Est,
Woking,
Surrey GU21 3BA
T: 01483 757200
F: 01483 740795
E: sales@semmco.com
W: www.semmco.co.uk

Semperit Industrial Products
25 Cottesbrooke Park, Heartlands,
Daventry, Northants NN11 8YL
T: 01327 313144
F: 01327 313149
E: ian.rowlinson@semperit.co.uk
W: www.semperit.at

Senator Security Services Ltd
1 The Thorn Tree,
Elmhurst Business Park, Lichfield,
Staffs WS13 8EX
T: 01543 411811
F: 01543 411611
E: senatorgroup@senatorsecurity.co.uk
W: www.senatorsecurity.co.uk

Serco Integrated Transport
Serco House,
16 Bartley Wood Bus. Park,
Bartley Way, Hook,
Hants RG27 9XB
T: 01256 745900
F: 01256 744111
E: generalenquiries@serco.com
W: www.serco.com/markets/transport

Serco Rail Technical Services
Derwent House,
RTC Business Park, London Rd,
Derby DE24 8UP
T: 01332 262672
F: 01332 264965
E: richard.hobson@serco.com
W: www.serco.com/srts

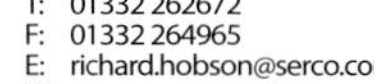

Sersa (UK) Ltd
Sersa House, Auster Rd,
Clifton Moor, York YO30 4XA
T: 01904 479968
F: 01904 479970
E: sersa.uk@sersa-group.com
W: www.sersa-group.com

S.E.T. Ltd
Atlas Works, Litchurch Lane,
Derby DE24 8AQ
T: 01332 346035
F: 01332 346494
E: sales@set.gb.com
W: www.set.gb.com

Severn Lamb
Tything Rd,
Alcester B49 6ET
T: 01789 400140
F: 01789 400240
E: sales@severn-lamb.com
W: www.severn-lamb.com

The Severn Partnership Ltd
The Maltings,
59 Lythwood Rd,
Bayston Hill,
Shrewsbury SY3 0NA
T: 01743 874135
F: 01743 874716
E: mark.combes@severn-partnership.co.uk
W: www.severnpartnership.co.uk

Severn Valley Railway
The Railway Station,
Bewdley,
Worcs DY12 1BG
T: 01299 403816
F: 01299 400839
E: mktg@svr.co.uk
W: www.svr.co.uk

SGA (Stuart Gray Associates)
88 Spring Hill, Arley,
Warks CV7 8FE
T: 01676 541402
E: info@stuartgrayassociates.co.uk
W: www.stuartgrayassociates.co.uk

SGH Martineau LLP
No.1 Colmore,
Birmingham B4 6AA
T: 0800 763 1000
F: 0800 763 1001
W: www.sghmartineau.com

SGS Correl Rail Ltd
Gee House, Holborn Hill,
Birmingham B7 5PA
T: 0121 326 3672
F: 0121 328 5343
E: gary.winstanley@sgs.com
W: www.sgs.com

SGS Engineering (UK) Ltd
Cranmer Rd, West Meadows Ind. Est,
Derby DE21 6JL
T: 01332 298126/ 01332 366552
F: 01332 366232
E: sales@sgs-engineering.com
W: www.sgs-engineering.com

SGS UK Ltd
Inward Way,
Rossmore Business Park,
Ellesmere Port CH65 3EN
T: 0151 350 6666
F: 0151 350 6600
W: www.sgs.com

Shay Murtagh Precast Ltd
Raharney, Mullingar, Co Westmeath,
Republic of Ireland
T: 0844 202 0263
E: sales@shaymurtagh.co.uk
W: www.shaymurtagh.co.uk

Sheerspeed Shelters Ltd
Unit 3, Diamond House,
Reme Drive, Heath Park, Honiton,
Devon EX14 1SE
T: 01404 46006
F: 01404 45520
E: sales@sheerspeed.com
W: www.sheerspeed.com

Shere Ltd
see atos origin

Sheridan Maine
Regus House, George Curl Way,
Southampton SO18 2RZ
T: 0871 218 0573
F: 0871 218 0173
E: southampton@sheridanmaine.com
W: www.sheridanmaine.com

Shield Batteries
277 Stansted Rd,
Bishops Stortford,
Herts CM23 2BT
T: 01279 652067
F: 01279 758041
M: 07900 403716
E: paul.bowles@shieldbatteries.co.uk
W: www.shieldbatteries.co.uk

S H Lighting
Salcombe Rd,
Meadow Lane Ind. Est,
Alfreton,
Derbys DE55 7RG
T: 01773 522390
F: 01773 520693
E: sales@shlighting.co.uk
W: www.shlighting.co.uk

Shorterm Rail
The Barn, Philpots Close,
Yiewsley,
Middx UB7 7RY
T: 01895 427900
E: info@shortermgroup.co.uk
W: www.shorterm.co.uk

Shotcrete Services Ltd
Old Station Yard, Hawkhurst Rd,
Cranbrook,
Kent TN17 2SR
T: 01580 714747
E: stuart.manning@shotcrete.co.uk
W: www.shotcrete.co.uk

SICK (UK) Ltd
39 Hedley Rd,
St Albans AL1 5DN
T: 01727 831121
E: info@sick.co.uk
W: www.sick.co.uk

Siegrist-Orel Ltd
Pysons Rd Ind. Est., Broadstairs,
Kent CT10 2LQ
T: 01843 865241
F: 01843 867180
E: info@siegrist-orel.co.uk
W: www.siegrist-orel.co.uk

Siemens Rail Systems
2 Queen Annes Gate Buildings,
Dartmouth Street,
London SW1H 9BP
T: 020 7227 0722
F: 020 7227 4435
E: info.railsystems.gb@siemens.com
W: www.siemens.co.uk/rail

Siemens Rail Automation
PO Box 79, Pew Hill,
Chippenham SN15 1JD
T: 01249 441441
E: info.railautomation.gb@siemens.com
W: www.siemens.co.uk/rail

SigAssure UK Ltd
Unit 16,
Sherwood Network Centre,
Sherwood Energy Village,
Ollerton,
Notts NG22 9FP
T: 01623 836128
E: enquiries@sig-ukgroup.com
W: www.sig-ukgroup.com

Sig Cyclone
Unit 16,
Gerald House,
Sherwood Network Centre,
Sherwood Energy Village,
Newton Hill, Ollerton,
Notts NG22 9FD
T: 07833 433404
E: liane.launders@sigcyclone.co.uk
W: www.sig-ukgroup.com

Sigma Coachair Group UK Ltd
Unit 1, Queens Drive,
Newhall,
Swadlincote,
Derbys DE11 0EG
T: 01283 559140
F: 01283 225253
W: www.sigmacoachair.com

Signal House Ltd
Cherrycourt Way, Stanbridge Rd,
Leighton Buzzard,
Beds LU7 8UH
T: 01525 377477
F: 01525 850999
E: sales@signalhouse.co.uk
W: www.signalhousegroup.co.uk

Signalling Solutions Ltd
Bridgefoot House, Watling St,
Radlett, Herts WD7 7HT
T: 01923 635000
E: info@signallingsolutions.com
W: www.signallingsolutions.com

Signature Aromas Ltd
Signature House,
65-67 Gospel End St,
Sedgley,
West Midlands DY3 3LR
T: 01902 678822
F: 01902 672888
E: enquiries@signaturearomas.co.uk
W: www.signaturearomas.co.uk

Signet Solutions
Kelvin House,
RTC Business Park,
London Rd,
Derby DE24 8UP
T: 01332 343585
F: 01332 367132
E: enquiries@signet-solutions.com
W: www.signet-solutions.com

Sill Lighting UK
3 Thame Park Bus. Centre,
Wenman Rd, Thame,
Oxon OX9 3XA
T: 01844 260006
E: sales@sill-uk.com
W: www.sill-uk.com

Silver Atena
Cedar House,
Riverside Business Park,
Swindon Rd,
Malmesbury,
Wilts SN16 9RS
T: 01666 580000
F: 01666 580001
E: info@silver-atena.com
W: www.silver-atena.com

Silver Software
see silver atena

Silver Track Training
Fleet House, Pye Close,
Haydock,
St Helens WA11 9JT
T: 01942 728196
E: angela@silvertracktraining.co.uk
W: www.silvertracktraining.co.uk

Simmons & Simmons
City Point, One Ropemaker St,
London EC2Y 9SS
T: 020 7628 2020
F: 020 7628 2070
E: juliet.reingold@simmons-simmons.com
W: www.simmons-simmons.com
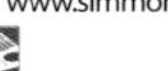

Simona UK
Telford Drive,
Brookmead Ind. Park,
Stafford ST16 3ST
T: 01785 222444
F: 01785 222080
E: mail@simona-uk.com
W: www.simona.de

SIMS
Fourth Floor,
Roman Wall House,
1-2 Crutched Friars,
London EC3N 2HT
T: 020 7481 9798
F: 020 7481 9657
E: inbox@sims-uk.com
W: www.simsrail.co.uk

Simulation Systems Ltd
Unit 12, Market Ind.Est,
Yatton,
Bristol BS49 4RF
T: 01934 838803
F: 01934 876202
W: www.simulation-systems.co.uk

Sinclair Knight Merz
Victoria House,
Southampton Row,
London WC1B 4EA
T: 020 7759 2600
F: 020 7759 2601
E: enquiries@globalskm.com
W: www.skmconsulting.com

Site Vision Surveys
19 Warwick St,
Rugby,
Warks CV21 3DH
T: 01788 575036
F: 01788 576208
W: www.svsltd.net

Skanska UK
Maple Cross House,
Denham Way, Maple Cross,
Rickmansworth,
Herts WD3 9SW
T: 01923 423100
F: 01923 423111
W: www.cementation foundations.skandka.co.uk

HJ Skelton & Co Ltd
9 The Broadway,
Thatcham,
Berks RG19 3JA
T: 01635 865256
F: 01635 865710
E: email@hjskelton.com
W: www.hjskelton.co.uk

SKF UK Ltd
Railway Sales Unit, Sundon Park Rd,
Luton LU3 3BL
T: 01582 496490
F: 01582 496327
E: stewart.mclellan@skf.com
W: www.skf.com

SKM Colin Buchanan
The Metro Buiding, 33 Trafford Rd,
Salford Quays, Manchester M5 3NN
T: 0161 873 8500
F: 0161 873 8501
E: enquiries@globalskm.com
W: www.skmcolinbuchanan.com

Skymasts Antennas
Unit 2, Clayfield Close,
Moulton Park Ind. Est,
Northampton NN3 6QF
T: 01604 494132
F: 01604 494133
E: info@skymasts.com
W: www.skymasts.com

Slender Winter Partnership
The Old School, London Rd,
Westerham, Kent TN11 1DN
T: 01959 564777
F: 01959 562802
E: swp@swpltd.co.uk
W: www.swpltd.co.uk

SMC Light & Power
Belchmire Lane, Spalding,
Lincs PE11 4HG
T: 01775 840020
F: 01775 843063
E: info@smclightandpower.com
W: www.smclightandpower.com

S M Consult Ltd
3 High St,
Stanford in the Vale,
Faringdon,
Oxon SN7 8LH
T: 01367 710152
F: 01367 710152
E: info@smcsolar.co.uk
W: www.smconsult.co.uk

SMC Pneumatics Ltd
Vincent Ave,
Crownhill,
Milton Keynes MK8 0AN
T: 0845 121 5122
F: 01908 555064
E: sales@smcpneumatics.co.uk
W: www.smcpneumatics.co.uk

SMI Conferences
SMI Group Ltd, Unit 122,
Great Guildford Business Square,
30 Great Guildford St,
London SE1 0HS
T: 020 7827 6000
F: 020 7827 6001
E: info@smi-online.com
W: www.smi-online.co.uk

Smith Cooper
Wilmot House,
St Helen's House, King St,
Derby DE1 3EE
T: 01332 332021
F: 01332 290439
E: janet.morgan@smithcooper.co.uk
W: www.smithcooper.co.uk

Smith Bros & Webb Ltd
Britannia House,
Arden Forest Ind.Est,
Alcester,
Warks B49 6EX
T: 01789 400096
F: 01789 400231
E: sales@sbw-wash.com
W: www.sbw-wash.com

SML Resourcing
Unit 3.07, New Loom House,
101 Back Church Lane,
London E1 1LU
T: 020 7423 4390
F: 020 7702 1097
E: jobs@sml-resourcing.com
W: www.sml-resourcing.com

SMP Electronics
Unit 6, Border Farm, Station Rd,
Chobham, Surrey GU24 8AS
T: 01276 855166
F: 01276 855115
E: sales@smpelectronics.com
W: www.smpelectronics.com

Snap-On Rail Solutions
Distribution Centre, Telford Way,
Kettering, Northants NN16 8SN
T: 01536 413904
F: 01536 413874
E: rail@snapon.com
W: www.snapon.com/industrialuk

Society of Operations Engineers (SOE)
22 Greencoat Place,
London SW1P 1PR
T: 020 7630 1111
F: 020 7630 6677
E: soe@soe.org.uk
W: www.soe.org.uk

Socomec UPS (UK)
Units 7-9A, Lakeside Business Park,
Broadway Lane, South Cerney,
Cirencester, Glos GL7 5XL
T: 01285 863300
F: 01285 862304
E: rail.ups.uk@socomec.com
W: www.socomec.co.uk/ups

Softech Global Ltd
Softech House, London Rd,
Albourne,
West Sussex BN6 9BN
T: 01273 833844
F: 01273 833044
E: rail@softechglobal.com
W: www.softechglobal.com

SOLID Applications Ltd
Old Market Place, Market St,
Oldbury B69 4DH
T: 0121 544 1400
E: anton.plackowski@saplm.co.uk
W: www.saplm.co.uk/rail

Solo Fabrications
Landor St, Saltley,
Birmingham B8 1AE
T: 0121 327 3378
F: 0121 327 3757
W: www.solofabs.com

Solution Rail
22 Somers Way, Bushey,
Herts WD23 4HR
F: 0871 989 5700
M: 07717 712272
E: enquiries@solutionrail.co.uk
W: www.solutionrail.co.uk

Solvay Speciality Polymers
Baronet Rd,
Warrington WA4 6HA
T: 01925 943546
F: 01925 943548
E: shayel.ahmed@solvay.com
W: www.solvayplastics.com

Somers Totalkare
15 Forge Trading Est., Mucklow Hill,
Halesowen B62 8TR
T: 0121 585 2700
F: 0121 501 1458
E: sales@somerstotalkare.co.uk
W: www.somerstotalkare.co.uk

Sonic Rail Service Ltd (SRS)
Unit 15, Springfield Ind. Est,
Springfield Rd, Burnham-on-Crouch, Essex CM0 8UA
T: 01621 784688
F: 01621 786594
E: stewart.robinson@sonicrail.co.uk
W: www.sonicrail.co.uk

Sonic Windows Ltd
Unit 14/15, Beeching Park Ind.Est.,
Wainwright Rd,
Bexhill on Sea,
E Sussex TN39 3UR
T: 01424 223864
F: 01424 215859
E: enquiries@sonicwindows.co.uk
W: www.sonicwindows.co.uk

Sortimo International Ltd
Old Sarum Park, Salisbury,
Wilts SP4 6EB
T: 01722 411585
F: 01722 320831
E: vanrack1@sortimo.co.uk
W: www.sortimo.co.uk

Sotera Risk Solutions Ltd
22 Glanville Rd,
Bromley BR2 9LW
F: 01737 551203
M: 07946 638 424
E: chris.chapman@sotera.co.uk
W: www.sotera.co.uk

Southco Manufacturing Ltd
Touch Point,
Wainwright Rd,
Warndon,
Worcs WR4 9FA
T: 01905 346722
F: 01905 346723
E: info@southco.com
W: www.southco.com

Southeastern
Friars Bridge Court, 41-45 Blackfriars Rd,
London SE1 8PG
T: 020 7620 5000
W: www.southeasternrailway.co.uk

Southern/Gatwick Express
Go-Ahead House,
26-28 Addiscombe Rd,
Croydon CR9 5GA
T: 020 8929 8600
F: 020 8929 8687
E: communications@southernrailway.com
W: www.southernrailway.com / www.gatwickexpress.com

M H Southern & Co Ltd
Church Bank Sawmills, Jarrow,
Tyne & Wear NE32 3EB
T: 0191 489 8231
F: 0191 428 0146
E: timber@mhsouthern.co.uk
W: www.mhsouthern.co.uk

Southern Electric Contracting
55 Vastern Rd,
Reading RG1 8BU
T: 0118 958 0100
F: 0118 953 4755
E: marketing@sec.eu.com
W: www.sec.eu.com

South West Trains
Stagecoach Group,
10 Dunkeld Rd,
Perth PH1 5TW
T: 01738 442111
F: 01738 643648
E: mail@stagecoachgroup.com
W: www.stagecoachgroup.com

South Yorkshire Passenger Trasport Executive
11 Broad St West,
Sheffield S1 2BQ
T: 0114 276 7575
F: 0114 275 9908
E: comments@sypte.co.uk
W: www.sypte.co.uk

Sovereign Planned Services On Line Ltd
Unit 3d, Forge Way,
Brown Lees Ind Est,
Biddulph,
Stoke on Trent ST8 7DN
T: 01782 510600
F: 01782 510700
E: sales@sovonline.co.uk
W: www.sovonline.co.uk

Spartan Safety Ltd
Unit 3, Waltham Park Way,
Walthamstow, London E17 5DU
T: 020 8527 5888
F: 020 8527 5999
E: ryan@spartansafety.co.uk
W: www.spartansafety.co.uk

Specialist Engineering Services Ltd (SES)
SES House, Harworth Park,
Doncaster DN11 8DB
T: 01302 756800
E: info@ses-holdings.com
W: www.ses-holdings.com

Specialist Plant Associates
Airfield Rd, Hinwick,
Wellingborough,
Northants NN29 7JG
T: 01234 781882
F: 01234 781992
E: info@specialistplant.co.uk
W: www.specialistplant.co.uk

Spectro
Palace Gate, Odiham RG29 1NP
T: 01256 704000
F: 01256 704006
E: enquiries@spectro-oil.com
W: www.spectro-oil.com

Spectrum Freight Ltd
PO Box 105, Chesterfield,
Derbys S41 9XY
T: 01246 456677
F: 01246 456688
E: sales@spectrumfreight.co.uk
W: www.spectrumfreight.co.uk

Spectrum Technologies
Western Avenue,
Bridgend,
Mid Glamorgan CF31 3RT
T: 01656 655437
F: 01656 655920
E: ehardy@spectrumtech.com
W: www.spectrumtech.com

Speedy Hire Plc
Chase House, 16 The Parks,
Newton le Willows,
Merseyside WA12 0JQ
T: 01942 720000
F: 01942 720077
E: admin@speedyhire.co.uk
W: www.speedyhire.co.uk

Spence Ltd
Parcel Deck, Barnby St,
Euston Station, London NW1 2RS
T: 020 7387 1268
F: 020 7380 1255
E: info@spenceltd.co.uk
W: www.spenceltd.co.uk

Speno International SA
26 Parc Chateau-Banquet POB 16,
1211 Geneva 21,
Switzerland
T: 0041 22906 4600
F: 0041 22906 4601
E: info@speno.ch
W: www.speno.ch

C Spencer
Mill Lane,
Barrow upon Humber DN19 7DB
T: 01469 532266
F: 01469 532233
E: mailbox@cspencerltd.co.uk
W: www.cspencerltd.co.uk

Sperry Rail International Ltd
Trent House, RTC Business Park,
London Rd, Derby DE24 8UP
T: 01332 262565
F: 01332 262541
W: www.sperryrail.com

Spescom Software Ltd
Woolbrook House,
Crabtree Office Village, Eversley Way,
Thorpe, Surrey TW20 8RY
T: 0870 890 8000
F: 0870 890 9000
W: www.spescomsoftware.com

Spitfire Tours
PO Box 824, Taunton TA1 9ET
T: 0870 879 3675
E: info@spitfirerailtours.co.uk
W: www.spitfirerailtours.co.uk

SPL Powerlines UK Ltd
Unit 3A, Hagmill Cres,
East Shawhead Enterprise Park,
Coatbridge, Lanarkshire ML5 4NS
T: 01236 424666
F: 01236 426444
W: www.powerlines-group.com

Spring Personnel
1 Canal Arm, Festival Park,
Stoke on Trent ST1 5UR
T: 01782 221500
F: 01782 221600
E: personnel@spring.com
W: www.spring.com

SPX Rail Systems
Unit 7, Thames Gateway Park,
Choats Rd, Dagenham,
Essex RM9 6RH
T: 020 8526 7100
F: 020 8526 7151
E: brian.cannon@spx.com
W: www.spx.com

SRPS Railtours
3 South Cathkin Farm Cottages,
Glasgow G73 5RG
T: 01698 263814/457777
E: railtours@srps.org.uk
W: www.srps.org.uk

SRS Rail Systems Ltd
3, Riverside Way,
Gateway Business Park, Bolsover,
Chesterfield S44 6GA
T: 01246 241312
F: 01246 825076
E: info@srsrailuk.co.uk
W: www.srsrailuk.com

SSDM
see aura graphics

SSP
169, Euston Rd, London NW1 2AE
T: 020 7543 3300
F: 020 7543 3389
W: www.foodtravelexpert.com

Stadler Pankow GmbH
Lessingstrasse 102,
D-13158 Berlin,
Germany
T: 0049 309191 1616
F: 0049 309191 2150
E: stadler.pankow@stadlerrail.de
W: www.stadlerrail.com

Stagecoach Supertram
Nunnery Depot,
Woodbourn Rd, Sheffield S9 3LS
T: 0114 275 9888
F: 0114 279 8120
E: enquiries@supertram.com
W: www.supertram.com

Stagecoach Group
10 Dunkeld Rd, Perth PH1 5TW
T: 01738 442111
F: 01738 643648
E: info@stagecoachgroup.com
W: www.stagecoachgroup.com

Stahlwille Tools Ltd
Unit 2D, Albany Park Ind. Est,
Frimley Rd, Camberley,
Surrey GU16 7PD
T: 01276 24080
F: 01276 24696
E: scottsheldon@stahlwille.co.uk
W: www.stahlwille.co.uk

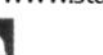

Stanley Tools
Sheffield Business Park,
Sheffield City Airport, Europa Link,
Sheffield S3 9PD
T: 0114 244 8883
F: 0114 273 9038

Stannah Lifts
Anton Mill, Andover,
Hants SP10 2NX
T: 01264 339090
E: liftsales@stannah.co.uk
W: www.stannahlifts.co.uk

Stansted Express
Enterprise House, Stansted Airport,
Essex CM20 1QW
E: eleni.jordan@nationalexpress.com
W: www.stanstedexpress.com

Stanton Bonna Concrete Ltd
Littlewell Lane, Stanton by Dale,
Ilkeston, Derbys DE7 4QW
T: 0115 944 1448
F: 0115 944 1466
E: sbc@stanton-bonna.co.uk
W: www.stanton-bonna.co.uk

Star Fasteners (UK) Ltd
Unit 3, Gallows Ind. Est, Furnace Rd,
Ilkeston, Derbys DE7 5EP
T: 0115 932 4939
F: 0115 944 1278
E: sales@starfasteners.co.uk
W: www.starfasteners.co.uk

Statesman Rail Ltd
PO Box 83, St Erth, Hayle,
Cornwall TR27 9AD
T: 0845 310 2458
F: 0115 944 1278
W: www.statesmanrail.com

STATS
see rsk stats

Stauff Ltd
500 Carlisle St East, Sheffield S4 8BS
T: 01142 518518
F: 01141 518519
E: sales@stauff.co.uk
W: www.stauff.co.uk

Staytite Ltd
Staytite House, Coronation Rd,
Cressex Bus.Park, High Wycombe,
Bucks HP12 3RP
T: 01494 462322
F: 01494 464747
E: fasteners@staytite.com
W: www.staytite.com

Steatite Ltd
Ravensbank Business Park,
Acanthus Rd,
Redditch,
Worcs B98 9EX
T: 01527 512400
F: 01527 512419
E: sales@steatite.co.uk
W: www.steatite.co.uk

Steam Dreams
PO Box 169,
Albury,
Guildford,
Surrey GU5 9YS
T: 01483 209888
F: 01483 209889
E: info@steamdreams.co.uk
W: www.steamdreams.com

Stego UK Ltd
Unit 12,
First Quarter Bus. Park,
Blenheim Rd,
Epsom,
Surrey KT19 9QN
T: 01372 747250
F: 01372 729854
E: info@stego.co.uk
W: www.stego.co.uk

Steelteam Construction (UK) Ltd
46 Goods Station Rd,
Tunbridge Wells,
Kent TN1 2DD
T: 01892 533677
F: 01892 511535
E: sales@steelteamconstruction.co.uk
W: www.steelteamconstruction.co.uk

Steelway Rail
Queensgate Works,
Bilston Rd,
Wolverhampton,
West Midlands
WV2 2NJ
T: 01902 451733
F: 01902 452256
E: sales@steelway.co.uk
W: www.steelway.co.uk

Steer Davies Gleave
28-32 Upper Ground,
London SE1 9PD
T: 020 7910 5000
F: 020 7910 5001
E: sdginfo@sdgworld.net
W: www.steerdaviesgleave.com

Stent
Pavilion C2, Ashwood Park,
Ashwood Way, Basingstoke,
Hants RG23 8BG
T: 01256 366000
F: 01256 366001
E: neil.beresford@stent.co.uk
W: www.stent.co.uk

Stephenson Harwood LLP
1 Finsbury Circus,
London EC2M 7SH
T: 020 7329 4422
F: 020 7003 8521
E: graeme.mclellan@shlegal.com
W: www.shlegal.com

Stewart Signs Rail
Trafalgar Close,
Chandlers Ford Ind. Est,
Eastleigh, Hants SO53 4BW
T: 023 8025 4781
F: 023 8025 5620
E: sales@stewartsigns.com
W: www.stewartsigns.com

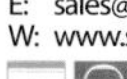

Stirling Maynard
Construction Consultants,
Stirling House, Rightwell,
Bretton, Peterborough PE3 8DJ
T: 01733 262319
F: 01733 331527
E: enquiries@stirlingmaynard.com
W: www.stirlingmaynard.com

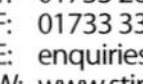

Stobart Rail
Solway Business Centre,
Carlisle,
Cumbria CA6 4BY
T: 01228 882300
F: 01228 882301
E: grant.mcnab@stobartrail.com
W: www.stobartrail.co.uk

Stock Redler Ltd
Redler House, Dudbridge, Stroud,
Glos GL3 3EY
T: 01423 819461
F: 0049 6151 321043
E: r.illsley@schenckprocess.com
W: www.schenckprocess.com

Stocksigns Ltd/ Burnham Signs
43,Ormside Way,
Holmethorpe Ind Est, Redhill,
Surrey RH1 2LG
T: 01737 764764
F: 01737 763763
E: jgodden@stocksigns.co.uk
W: www.stocksigns.co.uk

Stockton Engineering Management Ltd
1 Warwick Row, London SW1E 5ER
T: 020 7808 7808
F: 020 7117 5253
E: info@stocktonlondon.com
W: www.stocktonlondon.com

Stored Energy Technology
see s.e.t.

Story Rail
Burgh Rd Ind Est, Carlisle CA2 7NA
T: 01228 640880
F: 01228 640881
E: info@storygroup.co.uk
W: www.storygroup.co.uk

STRAIL (UK) Ltd
Room 2, First Floor, 3 Tannery House,
Tannery Lane, Send, Woking,
Surrey GU23 7EF
T: 01483 222090
F: 01483 222095
E: richard@srsrailuk.co.uk
W: www.strail.com

Strainstall UK Ltd
9-10, Mariners Way, Cowes,
IOW PO31 8PD
T: 01983 203600
F: 01983 201335
E: enquiries@strainstall.com
W: www.strainstall.co.uk

Strataform
see technocover

Strategic Team Group Ltd
Head Office,
Strategic Business Centre,
Blue Ridge Park,
Thunderhead Ridge,
Glasshoughton, Castleford,
West Yorks WF10 4UA
T: 01977 555550
E: contact@strategicteamgroup.com
W: www.strategicteamgroup.com

Strathclyde Partnership for Transport
Consort House, 12 West George St,
Glasgow G2 1HN
T: 0141 332 6811
E: enquiry@spt.co.uk
W: www.spt.co.uk

Street Crane Co. Ltd
Chapel-en-le-Frith, High Peak,
Derbys SK23 0PH
T: 01298 812456
E: sales@streetcrane.co.uk
W: www.streetcrane.co.uk

STS Signals
see mors smitt

Stuart Group
Lancaster Approach,
North Killingholme, Immingham,
NE Lincs DN40 3TZ
T: 0870 4141 400
F: 0870 4141 440
E: enquiries@stuartgroup.info
W: www.stuartgroup.info

Stuart Maher Ltd (SML)
Unit 3.07, New Loom House,
101 Back Church Lane,
London SE1 1LU
T: 020 7423 4390
F: 07092 810 920
E: nick.stuart@stuart-maher.co.uk
W: www.stuart-maher.co.uk

Sulzer Dowding & Mills
Camp Hill, Bordesley,
Birmingham B12 0JJ
T: 0121 766 6333
F: 0121 766 7247
E: engineering.birmingham@sulzer.com
W: www.sulzer.com

Superform Aluminium
Cosgrove Close, Worcester WR3 8UA
T: 01905 874300
F: 01905 874301
E: sales@superform-aluminium.com
W: www.superforming.com

Superjet London
Unit 5, Kennet Rd, Dartford,
Kent DA1 4QN
T: 01322 554595
F: 01322 557773
E: chris@superjet.co.uk
W: www.jetchem.com

Supersine Duramark
see ssdm

Survey Systems Ltd
Willow Bank House, Old Road,
Handforth,
Wilmslow SK9 3AZ
T: 01625 533444
F: 01625 526815
E: enquiries@survsys.co.uk
W: www.survsys.co.uk/rail

Survey Inspection Systems Ltd (SIS)
Green Lane Ind. Est,
Enterprise House,
Meadowfield Ave,
Spennymoor, Co Durham DL16 6JF
T: 01388 810308
F: 01388 819260
E: sales@survey-inspection.com
W: www.survey-inspection.com

Sweetnam & Bradley Ltd
Industrial Est,
Gloucester Rd,
Malmesbury,
Wilts SN16 0DY
T: 01666 823491
F: 01666 826010
E: sales@sweetnam-bradley.com
W: www.sweetnam-bradley.com

Swietelsky Babcock
see sb rail

Swietelsky International UK & Ireland
7 Clairmont Gardens,
Glasgow G3 7LW
T: 0141 353 1915
W: www.swietelsky.com

SW Global Resourcing
270 Peters Hill Rd, Glasgow G21 4AY
T: 0141 557 6133
F: 0141 557 6143
E: admin@sw-gr.com
W: www.scotweld.com

Sydac Ltd
Derwent Business Centre,
Clarke St,
Derby DE1 2BU
T: 01332 299600
F: 01332 299624
E: paul.williamson@sydac.co.uk
W: www.sydac.co.uk
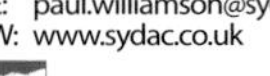

Sylmasta Ltd
Unit 1, Dales Yard,
Lewes Rd,
Scaynes Hill,
W Sussex RH17 7PG
T: 01444 831459
F: 01444 831971
W: www.sylmasta.co.uk

Synectic Systems Group Ltd
32 Alexandra Way,
Tewkesbury,
Glos GL20 8NB
T: 01684 295807
F: 01684 850011
E: sales@synx.com
W: www.synecticsystems.com

Synergy Health Plc
Gavenny Court,
Brecon Rd,
Abergavenny,
Monmouthshire NP7 7RX
T: 01873 856688
F: 01873 585982
E: enquiries@synergyhealthplc.com
W: www.synergyhealthplc.com

Syntax Recruitment
1 College Place,
Derby DE1 3DY
T: 01332 287720
F: 01332 296128
E: caroline.evans@syntaxconsulting.com
W: www.syntaxnet.com

Systecon (UK) Ltd
PO Box 4612, Weymouth,
Dorset DT4 9YY
T: 0871 641 2202
F: 01305 768480
E: phil.sturgess@systecon.co.uk
W: www.systecon.co.uk

System Store Solutions Ltd
Ham Lane, Lenham, Maidstone,
Kent ME17 2LH
T: 01622 859522
F: 01622 858746
E: sales@systemstoresolutions.com
W: www.system-store.com

Systra UK
Fourth Floor, Dukes Court, Duke St,
Woking, Surrey GU21 5BH
T: 01483 742941
F: 01483 755207
E: jonions@systra.com
W: www.systra.com

TAC Europe
Matrix House, Basing View,
Basingstoke, Hants
T: 08700 600822
F: 01256 356371
E: enquiries@taceurope.com
W: www.taceurope.com

Talascend Ltd
First Floor, Broadway Chambers,
Hammersmith Broadway,
London W6 7PW
T: 020 8600 1600
F: 020 8741 2001
E: info@talascend.com
W: www.talascend.com

T & RS Engineering Ltd
Woodfield Business Centre,
Balby Carr Bank, Doncaster DN4 8DE
T: 01302 515390
M: 07939 470111
E: mail@trsengineering.co.uk
W: www.trsengineering.co.uk

Tanfield Engineering Systems
Tanfield Lea Ind. Est. North,
Stanley, Co Durham DH9 9NX
T: 01207 521111
F: 01207 523318
E: enquiries@tanfieldgroup.co.uk
W: www.tanfieldgroup.co.uk

Tarmac Precast Concrete
Tallington, Stamford,
Lincs PE9 4RL
T: 01778 381000
E: enquiries@tarmac.co.uk
W: www.tarmac.co.uk/precast

The TAS Partnership Ltd.
Guildhall House, 59-61,
Guildhall St, Preston PR1 3NU
T: 01772 204998
E: info@taspartnership.co.uk
W: www.tas.uk.net

Tasty Plant Sales
Chipstead Farm, Amersham Rd,
Chalfont St Giles, Bucks HP8 4RT
T: 0845 677 4444
E: info@tastyplant.co.uk
W: www.tastyplant.co.uk

Tata Steel Projects
Meridian House, The Crescent,
York YO24 1AW
T: 01904 454600
F: 01904 454601
E: tatasteelprojects@tatasteel.com
W: www.tatasteeleurope.com

Tata Steel Rail
Rail Service Centre, PO Box 1,
Brigg Rd, Scunthorpe DN16 1BP
T: 01724 403398
E: rail@tatasteel.com
W: www.tatasteeleurope.com

Tate Rail Ltd
Station House, Station Hill,
Cookham,
Berks SL6 9BP
T: 0844 381 9956
F: 0844 381 9957
E: info@taterail.com
W: www.taterail.com

Taylor Precision Plastics / Commercial Vehicle Rollers Ltd
Mile Oak Ind. Est,
Maesbury Rd, Oswestry,
Shropshire SY10 8GA
T: 01691 679516
F: 01691 670538
E: sales@cvrollers.co.uk
W: www.cvrollers.co.uk

Taylor Woodrow
Astral House,
Imperial Way,
Watford WD24 4WW
T: 01923 233433
F: 01923 800085
M: 07919 228399
E: david.booker@taylorwoodrow.com
W: www.taylorwoodrow.com

Taziker Industrial Ltd t/a TI Protective Coatings
Unit 6, Lodge Bank, Crown Lane,
Horwich, Bolton BL6 5HY
T: 01204 468080
F: 01204 695188
E: sales@ti-uk.com
W: www.ti-uk.com

TBM Consulting Group
Unit 8, H2O Business Complex,
Sherwood Business Park, Annesley,
Nottingham NG15 0HT
T: 01623 758298
F: 01623 755941
E: nfletcher@tbmcg.com
W: www.tbmcg.com

TDK-Lambda UK
Kingsley Ave, Ilfracombe,
Devon EX34 8ES
T: 01271 856600
F: 01271 856741
E: powersolutions@emea.tdk-lambda.com
W: www.emea.tdk-lambda.com

TEAL Consulting Ltd
Deangate, Tuesley Lane, Godalming,
Surrey GU7 1SG
T: 01483 420550
F: 01483 420550
E: info@tealconsulting.co.uk
W: www.tealconsulting.co.uk

Team Surveys Ltd
Team House,
St Austell Bay Business Park,
Par Moor Rd, St Austell PL25 3RF
T: 01726 816069
F: 01726 814611
E: email@teamsurveys.com
W: www.teamsurveys.co.uk

Tecalemit Garage Equipment Co Ltd
Eagle Rd, Langage Business Park,
Plymouth PL7 5JY
T: 01752 219111
F: 01752 219128
E: sales@tecalemit.co.uk
W: www.tecalemit.co.uk

Tecforce
Litchurch Lane, Derby DE24 8AA
T: 01332 268000
F: 01332 268030
E: sales@tecforce.co.uk
W: www.tecforce.co.uk

Technical Cranes Ltd
Holmes Lock Works, Steel St,
Holmes, Rotherham S61 1DF
T: 01709 561861
F: 01709 556516
E: info@technicalcranes.co.uk
W: www.technicalcranes.co.uk

Technical Resin Bonders
See TRB Lightweight Structures Ltd

Technocover
See Technorail

Technology Project Services Ltd
1 Warwick Row, London SW1E 5LR
T: 020 7963 1234
F: 020 7963 1299
E: mail@tps.co.uk
W: www.tps.co.uk

Technology Resourcing Ltd
The Technology Centre,
Surrey Research Park,
Guildford GU2 7YG
T: 01483 302211
F: 01483 301222
E: railways@tech-res.co.uk
W: www.railwayengineeringjobs.co.uk

TechnoRail (Technocover)
Henfaes Lane, Welshpool,
Powys SY21 7BE T:
01938 555511
F: 01938 555527
E: admin@technocover.co.uk
W: www.technocover.co.uk

Tecnopali UK ltd
Unit 3, Headway Rd, Wobaston Rd,
Wolverhampton WV10 6PZ
T: 01902 788588
F: 01902 788589
E: sales@tecnopali.co.uk
W: www.tecnopali.co.uk

TEK Personnel Consultants Ltd
Norwich Union House, Irongate,
Derby DE1 3GA
T: 01332 360055
F: 01332 363345
E: derby@tekpersonnel.co.uk
W: www.tekpersonnel.co.uk

Telent – Rail
Point 3, Haywood Rd,
Warwick CV34 5AH
T: 01926 693569
F: 01926 693023
E: services@telent.com
W: www.telent.com

Telerail Ltd
Royal Scot Suite,
Carnforth Station Heritage Centre,
Warton Rd, Carnforth,
Lancs LA5 9TR
T: 01524 735774
F: 01524 736386
E: steve@telerail.co.uk
W: www.telerail.co.uk

Televic Rail
Leo Bakaertlaan 1,
B-8870 Izegem,
Belgium
T: 0032 5130 3045
E: rail@televic.com
W: www.televic-rail.com

Temple Group Ltd
Tempus Wharf,
33A Bermondsey Wall West,
London SE16 4TQ
T: 020 7394 3700
F: 020 7394 7871
E: enquiries@templegroup.co.uk
W: www.templegroup.co.uk

Ten 47 Ltd
Unit 2B, Frances Ind. Park,
Wemyss Rd, Dysart,
Kirkcaldy KY1 2XZ
T: 01592 655725
F: 01592 651079
E: admin@ten47.com
W: www.ten47.com

TenBroeke Company Ltd
Dorset House, Refent Park,
Kingston Rd, Leatherhead,
Surrey KT22 7PL
T: 01372 824722
F: 01372 824332
E: paul.tweedale@tenbroekco.com
W: www.tenbroekco.com

Tenmat Ltd (Railko Ltd)
Ashburton Road West, Trafford Park,
Manchester M70 1RU
T: 0161 872 2181
F: 0161 872 7596
E: info@tenmat.com
W: www.tenmst.com

Tensar International
Cunningham Court,
Shadsworth Business Park,
Shadsworth,
Blackburn BB1 2QX
T: 01254 262431
F: 01254 266868
E: info@tensar-international.com
W: www.tensar.co.uk

Tension Control Bolts
Whitchurch Business Park,
Shakespeare Way,
Whitchurch,
Shropshire SY13 1LJ
T: 01948 667700
F: 01948 667744
E: info@tcbolts.co.uk
W: www.tcbolts.co.uk

Terram Ltd
Mamhilad Park Estate, Pontypool,
Gwent NP4 0YR
T: 01495 757722
F: 01495 762383
E: info@terram.co.uk
W: www.terram.com

Terrawise Construction Ltd
104 The Court Yard,
Radway Green Business Centre,
Radway Green,
Crewe CW2 5PR
T: 01270 879011
F: 01270 875079
E: info@terrawise.co.uk
W: www.terrawise.co.uk

TES 2000 Ltd
TES House, Heath Industrial Park,
Grange Way,
Colchester CO2 8GU
T: 01206 799111
F: 01206 227910
E: info@tes2000.co.uk
W: www.tes2000.co.uk

Testo Ltd
Newman Lane, Alton,
Hants GU34 2QJ
T: 01420 544433
W: www.testo.co.uk

Tevo Ltd
Maddison house, Thomas Rd,
Wooburn Green Ind Est, Thomas Rd,
Wooburn Green,
Bucks HP10 0PE
T: 01628 528034
E: sales@tevo.eu.com
W: www.tevo.eu.com

Tew Engineering Ltd
Crocus St,
Nottingham NG2 3DR
T: 0115 935 4354
F: 0115 935 4355
E: sales@tew.co.uk
W: www.tew.co.uk

Thales Ground Transportation Systems
4 Thomas More Square,
Thomas More St,
London E1W 1YW
T: 020 3300 6000
F: 020 3300 6994
E: uk.enquiries@thalesgroup.com
W: www.thalesgroup.com/transportation

Thales Uk Thermal Economics Ltd
Thermal House,
8 Cardiff Rd,
Luton, Beds LU1 1PP
T: 01582 450814
F: 01582 429305
W: www.thermal-economics.co.uk

Thermit Welding (GB) Ltd
87 Ferry Lane, Rainham,
Essex RM13 9YH
T: 01708 522626
F: 01708 553806
E: rsj@thermitwelding.co.uk
W: www.thermitwelding.co.uk

Thomas & Betts Ltd
see pma

T J Thomson & Sons Ltd
Millfield Works, Grangefield Rd,
Stockton on Tees TS18 4AE
T: 01642 672551
F: 01642 672556
E: postbox@tjthomson.co.uk
W: www.tjthomson.co.uk

Thomson Rail Equipment Ltd
Valley Rd, Cinderford,
Glos GL14 2NZ
T: 01594 826611
F: 01594 825560
E: sales@thomsonrail.com
W: www.thomsonrail.com

Thurlow Countryside Management Ltd
2 Charterhouse Trading Est,
Sturmer Rd, Haverhill,
Suffolk CB9 7UU
T: 01440 760170
F: 01440 760171
E: info@t-c-m.co.uk
W: www.t-c-m.co.uk

Thurrock Engineering Supplies Ltd
Unit 1, Tes House, Motherwell Way,
West Thurrock,
Essex RM20 3XD
T: 01708 861178
F: 01708 861158
E: info@thurrockengineering.com
W: www.thurrockengineering.com

Thursfield Smith Consultancy
25 Grange Rd,
Shrewsbury SY3 9DG
T: 01743 246407
E: david@thursfieldsmith.co.uk
W: www.thursfieldsmith.co.uk

Thyssenkrupp GFT Gleistechnik GmbH
Altendorfstrasse 120,
45143 Essen,
Germany
T: 0049 201 188 3710
F: 0049 201 188 3714
E: gleistechnik@thyssenkrupp.com
W: www.tkgftgleistechnik.de

TICS Ltd
Oxford House,
Sixth Avenue,
Robin Hood Airport,
Doncaster DN9 3GG
T: 01302 623074
F: 01302 623075
E: andrewmackenzie@tics-ltd.co.uk
W: www.tics-ltd.co.uk

Tidyco Ltd
Unit 2, Pentagon Island,
Nottingham Rd,
Derby DE21 6BW
T: 01332 851300
F: 01332 290369
E: enquiries@tidyco.co.uk
W: www.tidyco.co.uk

tie Ltd (Transport Initiatives Edinburgh)
Citypoint,
65 Haymarket Terrace,
Edinburgh EH12 5HD
T: 0131 622 8300
F: 0131 622 8301
E: comms@tie.ltd.uk
W: www.tie.ltd.uk

Tiflex Ltd
Tiflex House, Liskeard,
Cornwall PL14 4NB
T: 01579 320808
F: 01579 320802
E: sales@tiflex.co.uk
W: www.tiflex.co.uk

Time 24 Ltd
19 Victoria Gardens,
Burgess Hill,
West Sussex RH15 9NB
T: 01444 257655
F: 01444 259000
E: sales@time24.co.uk
W: www.time24.co.uk

Timeplan Ltd
12 The Pines, Broad St,
Guildford, Surrey GU3 3BH
T: 01483 462340
F: 01483 462349
E: dave@timeplansolutions.com
W: www.timeplansolutions.com

TI Protective Coatings
see taziker industrial ltd

TMD Friction UK Ltd
PO Box 18 Hunsworth Lane,
Cleckheaton, West Yorks BD19 3UJ
T: 01274 854000
F: 01274 854001
E: info@tmdfriction.com
W: www.tmdfriction.com

TMP Worldwide
Chancery House,
Chancery Lane,
London WC2A 1QS
T: 020 7406 5075
W: www.tmpw.co.uk

Tony Gee and Partners LLP
Hardy House, 140 High St, Esher,
Surrey KT10 9QJ
T: 01372 461600
F: 01372 461601
E: enquiries@tonygee.com
W: www.tonygee.com

TopDeck Parking
Springvale Business &
Industrial Park,
Bilston,
Wolverhampton WV14 0QL
T: 01902 499400
F: 01902 494080
E: info@topdeckparking.co.uk
W: www.topdeckparking.co.uk

Topdrill
1 Seagrave Court, Walton Park,
Milton Keynes MK7 7HA
T: 01908 666606
E: info@topdrill.co.uk
W: www.topdrill.co.uk

Toray Textiles Europe Ltd
Crown Farm Way, Forest Town,
Mansfield,
Notts NG19 0FT
T: 01623 415050
F: 01623 415070
E: sales@ttel.co.uk
W: www.ttel.co.uk

Torrent Trackside Ltd
Network House, Europa Way,
Britannia Enterprise Park, Lichfield,
Staffs WS14 9TZ
T: 01543 421900
F: 01543 421931
E: richard.donald@torrent.co.uk
W: www.torrent.co.uk

Total Access Training
Unit 5, Raleigh Hall Ind. Est,
Eccleshall, Staffs ST21 6JL
T: 01785 850333
E: sales@totalaccess.co.uk
W: www.totalaccess.co.uk

Total Rail Solutions
Unit 1, Hazeley Enterprise Park,
Twyford, Winchester SO21 1QA
T: 01962 711642
F: 01962 717330
E: info@totalrailsolutions.co.uk
W: www.totalrailsolutions.org

Total UK Ltd
Pottery Lane, Ferrybridge,
West Yorks WF11 8JY
T: 01977 636100
E: tom.hyde@total.co.uk
W: www.lubricants.total.com

Totectors (UK) Ltd
9 Pondwood Close,
Moulton Park Ind. Estate,
Northampton NN3 6RT
T: 0870 600 5055
F: 0870 600 5056
E: sales@totectors.net
W: www.totectors.net

Touchstone Renard Ltd
123 Pall Mall, London SW1Y 5EA
T: 020 7101 0788
M: 07768 366744
E: paustin@touchstonerenard.com
W: www.touchstonerenard.com

Tower Surveys Ltd
Vivian House, Vivian Lane,
Nottingham NG5 1AF
T: 0115 960 1212
F: 0115 962 1200
E: beverley.chiang@opusjoynespike.co.uk
W: www.towersurveys.co.uk

TPA Portable Roadways Ltd
Dukeries Mill, Claylands Ave,
Worksop, Notts S81 7DJ
T: 0870 240 2381
F: 0870 240 2382
E: enquiries@tpa-ltd.co.uk
W: www.tpa-ltd.co.uk

TPK Consulting Ltd (RPS Group)
Centurion Court, 85, Milton Park,
Abingdon, Oxon OX14 4RY
T: 01235 438151
F: 01235 438188
E: rpsab@rpsgroup.com
W: www.rpsplc.co.uk

TQ Catalis
Garden Court, Lockington Hall,
Main St, Lockington, Derby DE74 2SJ
T: 0845 880 8108
E: hotline@catalis.co.uk
W: www.catalis.com

TRAC Engineering Ltd
Dovecote Rd, Eurocentral,
North Lanarkshire ML1 4GP
T: 01698 831111
F: 01698 832222
E: engineering@trac.com
W: www.tracengineering.com

Tracklink UK Ltd
Unit 5, Miltons Yard, Petworth Rd,
Witley, Surrey GU8 5LH
T: 01428 685124
F: 01428 687788
W: www.tklink.co.uk

Track Maintenance Equipment Ltd
Witham Wood, Marley Lane,
Haslemere, Surrey GU27 3PZ
T: 01428 651114
F: 01428 644727
E: info@tmeltd.co.uk
W: www.tmeltd.co.uk

Track Safe Telecom (TST)
See Centregreat

Tracksure Ltd
8 Woburn St, Ampthill,
Beds MK45 2HP
T: 01525 840557
F: 01525 403918
E: sales@tracksure.co.uk
W: www.tracksure.co.uk

Trackwork Ltd
PO Box 139, Kirk Sandall Lane,
Kirk Sandall Ind. Est,
Doncaster DN31WX
T: 01302 888666
F: 01302 888777
E: sales@trackwork.co.uk
W: www.trackwork.co.uk

Tracsis Plc
Unit 6, The Point, Pinnacle Way,
Pride Park, Derby DE24 8ZS
T: 01332 226860
F: 01332 226862
E: info@tracsis.com
W: www.tracsis.com

Tractel UK Ltd
Old Lane, Halfway,
Sheffield S20 3GA
T: 0114 248 2266
F: 0114 247 3350
E: tracteluk.info@tractel.com
W: www.tractel.com

TracTruc Bi-modal
See TruckTrain

Traffic Management Services Ltd
PO Box 10, Retford, Notts DN22 7EE
T: 01777 705053
F: 01777 709878
E: info@traffic.org.uk
W: www.traffic.org.uk

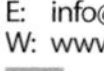

Train'd Up
Elmbank Mill,
Menstrie Business Centre, Menstrie,
Clackmannanshire FK11 7BU
T: 0845 602 9665
F: 0870 850 3397
E: enquiries@traindup.org
W: www.traindup.org

Train FX Ltd
15 Melbourne Business Court,
Millennium Way, Pride Park,
Derby DE24 8LZ
T: 01332 366175
F: 01332 298761
E: enquiries@trainfx.com
W: www.trainfx.com

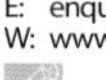

The Train Chartering Company Ltd
Benwell House, Preston,
Wilts SN15 4DX
T: 01249 890176
E: info@trainchartering.com
W: www.trainchartering.com

The Trainline
Trainline Holdings Ltd,
498 Gorgie Rd, Edinburgh EH11 3AF
T: 08704 111111
W: www.thetrainline.com

Trainpeople.co.uk Ltd
Arran House, Arran Rd,
Perth PH1 3DZ
T: 01738 446110
F: 01738 622055
E: info@trainpeople.co.uk
W: www.trainpeople.co.uk

Trakside Systems Ltd
See High Voltage Maintenance Services Ltd

Tramlink (Croydon)
See Transport for London

TRAM Power Ltd
99 Stanley Rd, Bootle,
Merseyside L20 7DA
T: 0151 547 1425
F: 0151 521 5509
M: 07976 949618
E: lewis.lesley@trampower.co.uk
W: www.trampower.co.uk

Tranect Ltd
Unit 4, Carraway Rd, Gilmoss Ind. Est,
Liverpool L11 0EE
T: 0151 548 7040
F: 0151 546 6066
E: sales@tranect.co.uk
W: www.tranect.co.uk

Transaction Systems Ltd
See Transys

Transcal Ltd
Firth Rd, Houstoun Ind. Est,
Livingston, West Lothian EH54 5DJ
T: 01506 440111
F: 01506 442333
E: info@transcal.co.uk
W: www.transcal.co.uk

Transdev Plc
401 King St, London W6 9NJ
T: 020 8600 5650
F: 020 8600 5651
E: information@transdevplc.co.uk
W: www.transdevplc.co.uk

Transec UK Ltd (Bowden Bros Ltd)
Brickworks House, Spook Hill,
North Holmwood, Dorking,
Surrey RH5 4HR
T: 01306 743355
F: 01306 876768
E: ian.bowden@bowden-bros.com
W: www.bowden-bros.com

Translec Ltd
Saddleworth Business Centre,
Huddersfield Rd, Delph,
Oldham OL3 5DF
T: 01457 878888
F: 01457 878887
E: mail@translec.co.uk
W: www.translec.co.uk

Translink NI Railways
Central Station, East Bridge St,
Belfast BT1 3PB
T: 02890 666630
F: 02890 899452
E: feedback@translink.co.uk
W: www.translink.co.uk

Transmitton
See Siemens

Trans Pennine Express (TPE)
See First Trans Pennine

Transport 2000
See Campaign for Better Transport

Transport & Travel Research Ltd (TTR)
Minster House,
Minster Pool Walk,
Lichfield, Staffs
T: 01543 416416
F: 01543 416681
E: enquiries@ttr-ltd.com
W: www.ttr-ltd.com

Transport Benevolent Fund
22 Lovat Lane,
London EC3R 8EB
T: 0300 333 2000 (ETD 00 38571)
F: 0870 831 2882
E: help@tbf.org.uk
W: www.tbf.org.uk

Transport for London
55 Broadway,
London SW1H 0BD
T: 020 7222 5600
E: enquire@tfl.gov.uk
W: www.tfl.gov.uk/rail

Transport iNet
SEIC,
Holywell Business Park,
Loughborough University LE11 3TU
T: 01509 635270
F: 01509 635231
E: a.m.wilkinson@lboro.ac.uk
W: www.eminnovation.org.uk/transport

Transport Interchange Consultants Ltd
1 Lochaline St, London W6 9ST
T: 020 8563 0555
F: 020 8563 0555
E: mw@ticonsultants.co.uk
W: www.ticonsultants.co.uk

Transportation Planning International
International Design Hub,
Colmore Plaza,
20 Colmore Circus,
Birmingham B4 6AT
T: 0121 2125102
E: info@tpi-world.com
W: www.tpi-world.com

Transport Scotland
Buchanan House,
58 Port Dundas Rd,
Glasgow G4 0HF
T: 0141 272 7100
E: info@transportscotland.gsi.gov.uk
W: www.transportscotland.gov.uk

Transsol Ltd
32 Buxton Rd West,
Disley,
Cheshire SK12 2LY
F: 0870 052 5838
M: 07775 893620
E: enquiries@transsol.net
W: www.transsol.net

Transys Projects Ltd
see vossloh kiepe

Trapeze Group Rail Ltd
Middleham House,
6 St Mary's Court, Blossom St,
York YO24 1AH
T: 01904 639091
F: 01904 639092
E: sales.railuk@trapezegroup.com
W: www.trapezegroup.com

Travel Info. Systems
Suite 1, Grand Union House,
20 Kentish Town Rd,
London NW1 9NX
T: 020 7428 1288
F: 020 7267 2745
E: enquiries@travelinfosystems.com
W: www.travelinfosystems.com

Traxsydes Training
Room 11, E.L.O.C, 80-86 St Mary Rd,
Walthamstow, London E17 9RE
T: 020 8223 1257
F: 020 8223 1258
E: bookings@traxsydes.co.uk
W: www.traxsydes.co.uk

TRB Lightweight Structures Ltd
12 Clifton Rd, Huntingdon,
Cambs PE29 7EN
T: 01480 447400
F: 01480 414992
E: sales@trbls.com
W: www.trbls.com

TRE Ltd
See The Railway Engineering Company

Treadmaster Flooring
See Tiflex

Trelleborg Industrial AVS
1 Hoods Close, Leicester LE4 2BN
T: 0116 267 0300
F: 0116 267 0310
E: rail@trelleborg.com
W: www.trelleborg.com/industrialavs

Tremco Illbruck Limited
Coupland Rd, Hindley Green,
Wigan WN2 4HT
T: 01942 251400
F: 01942 251410
E: uk.info@tremco-illbruck.com
W: www.tremco-illbruck.com

Trent Instruments Ltd
Unit 39, Nottingham South and
Wilford Ind. Est, Ruddington Lane,
Nottingham NG11 7EP
T: 0115 969 6188
F: 0115 945 5696
E: phillip@trentinstruments.co.uk
W: www.trentinstruments.co.uk

Triforce Security Solutions Ltd
Westmead House, Westmead,
Farnborough, Hants GU14 7LP
T: 01252 373496
E: enquiries@triforcesecurity.co.uk
W: www.triforcesecurity.co.uk

Trimble UK
Trimble House,
Meridian Office Park,
Osborn Way, Hook,
Hants RG27 9HX
T: 01256 760150
F: 01256 760148
W: www.trimble.com

Tritech Rail/Tritech Rail Training
See AECOM

TRL
Crowthorne House,
Nine Mile Ride,
Wokingham,
Berks RG40 3GA
T: 01344 773131
F: 01344 770356
E: rail@trl.co.uk
W: www.trl.co.uk

Trojan Services Ltd
PO Box 675, Chichester,
West Sussex PO19 9LG
T: 0845 074 0407
F: 01243 783654
E: info@trojan-services.com
W: www.trojan-services.com

Trolex Ltd
Newby Rd,
Hazel Grove,
Stockport SK7 5DY
T: 0161 483 1435
F: 0161 483 5556
E: sales@trolex.com
W: www.trolex.com

TRS Staffing Solutions
8th Floor, York House,
Kingsway,
London WC2B 6UJ
T: 020 7419 5800
F: 020 7419 5801
E: info-uk@trsstaffing.com
W: www.trsstaffing.com

Truck Train Developments Ltd (and TracTruc Bi-Modal)
4 Elfin Grove, Bognor Regis,
W.Sussex PO21 2RX
T: 01243 869118
E: pmtrucktrain@tiscali.co.uk

Truflame Welding
Truflame House,
56 Newhall Rd,
Sheffield S9 2QL
T: 0114 243 3020
F: 0114 243 5297
E: sales@truflame.co.uk
W: www.truflame.co.uk

tsa Advet ltd
CAB-i-NET House,
7 Ellerbeck Court,
Stokesley Business Park,
Middlesbrough TS9 5PT
T: 01642 714471
F: 01642 714451
E: andrew.frank@tsaadvet.co.uk
W: www.tsaadvet.co.uk

TSSA (Transport Salaried Staff's Association)
Walkden House, 10 Melton St,
London NW1 2EJ
T: 020 7387 2101
F: 020 7383 0656
E: enquiries@tssa.org.uk
W: www.tssa.org.uk

TTCI UK
13 Fitzroy St, London, W1T 4BQ
T: 020 7755 4080
F: 020 7755 4203
E: michele_johnson@aar.com
W: www.ttc.aar.com

TT Electronics plc
Clive House, 12-18 Queens Rd,
Weybridge, Surrey KT13 9XB
T: 01932 825300
F: 01932 836450
E: info@ttelectronics.com
W: www.ttelectronics.com

TTG Transportation Technology (Europe) Ltd
The iD Centre, Lathkill House,
rtc Business Park, London Rd,
Derby DE24 8UP
T: 01332 258867
F: 01332 258823
M: 07767 002298
E: enquiries@ttgeurope.com
W: www.ttgtransportationtechnology.com

TTR
See Transport & Travel Research

Tubelines
15 Westferry Circus, Canary Wharf,
London E14 4HD
T: 0845 660 5466
E: enquiries@tubelines.com
W: www.tubelines.com

Tuchschmid Constructa AG
Langdorfstrasse 26, CH-8501,
Frauenfeld, Switzerland
T: 0041 52 728 8111
F: 0041 52 728 8100
E: w.luessi@tuchschmid.ch
W: www.intermodallogistics.co.uk

Tufcoat
Fox House, 8-10 Whimple St,
Plymouth PL1 2DH
T: 01752 227333
F: 0871 264 5801
E: info@tufcoat.co.uk
W: www.tufcoat.co.uk

Tufnol Composites Ltd
Wellhead Lane, Perry Barr,
Birmingham B42 2TB
T: 0121 356 9351
F: 0121 331 4235
E: sales@tufnol.co.uk
W: www.tufnol.com

Turbex Ltd
Unit 1, Riverwey Ind. Park,
Newman Lane, Alton,
Hants GU34 2QL
T: 01420 544909
F: 01420 542264
E: sales@turbex.co.uk
W: www.turbex.co.uk

Turbo Power Systems Ltd
1 Queens Park, Queensway North,
Team Valley Trading Est, Gateshead,
Tyne & Wear NE11 0NX
T: 0191 482 9200
F: 0191 482 9201
E: sales@turbopowersystems.com
W: www.turbopowersystems.com

Turkington Precast
James Park, Mahon Rd, Portadown,
Co. Armagh, N.Ireland BT62 3EH
T: 028 38 332807
F: 028 38 361770
E: gary@turkington-precast.com
W: www.turkington-precast.com

Turner & Townsend
Low Hall, Calverley Lane,
Horsforth,
Leeds LS18 4GH
T: 0113 258 4400
F: 0113 258 2911
E: lee@turntown.com
W: www.turnerandtownsend.com

Turner Diesel Ltd
Unit 1A, Dyce Ind. Park,
Dyce,
Aberdeen AB21 7EZ
T: 01224 214200
F: 01224 723927
E: diesel.sales@turner.co.uk
W: www.turner-diesel.co.uk

TSL Turton Ltd
Burton Rd,
Sheffield S3 8DA
T: 0114 270 1577
F: 0114 275 6947
E: sales@tslturton.com
W: www.tslturton.com

tusp Ltd
Barrow Hill,
Maidstone Rd,
Ashford,
Kent TN24 8TY
T: 01233 640257
E: enquiries@tusp.co.uk
W: www.tusp.co.uk

TUV Product Service Ltd
Octagon House, Concorde Way,
Segensworth, North Fareham,
Hants PO15 5RL
T: 01489 558100
F: 01489 558101
E: info@tuvps.co.uk
W: www.tuvps.co.uk

TUV-SUD Rail GmbH
Ridlerstrasse 65, D-80339,
Munich,
Germany
T: 0049 89519 03537
F: 0049 89519 02933
W: www.tuv-sued.com

TXM Plant Ltd
TXM Plant House,
Harbour Rd Trading Est, Portishead,
Bristol BS20 7AT
T: 01275 399400
F: 01275 399500
E: info@txmplant.co.uk
W: www.txmplant.co.uk

TXM Projects Ltd
1 St Peters Court,
Church Lane,
Bickenhill B92 0DN
M: 07814 422589
E: simon.pitt@txmprojects.co.uk
W: www.txmprojects.co.uk

TXM Recruit Ltd
Blackhill Drive, Wolverton Mill,
Milton Keynes,
Bucks MK12 5TS
T: 0845 2263454
F: 0845 2262453
E: info@txmrecruit.co.uk

Tyne & Wear Metro
See Nexus

Tyrone Fabrication Ltd (TFL)
Goland Rd, Ballygawley,
Co Tyrone BT70 2LA
T: 028 8556 7200
F: 028 8556 7089
E: sales@tfl.eu.com
W: www.tfl.eu.com

UK Accreditation Service (UKAS)
21-47 High St, Feltham,
Middx TW13 4UN
T: 020 8917 8400
E: info@ukas.com
W: info@ukas.com

UKDN Waterflow
12-16 David Rd,
Poyle Trading Est,
Colnbrook SL3 0DG
T: 01753 810999
F: 01753 681442
E: sales@waterflow.co.uk
W: www.waterflow.co.uk

UK Power Networks Services
237 Southwark Bridge Rd,
London SE1 6NP
T: 0207 397 7695
E: rail@ukpowernetworks.co.uk
W: www.ukpowernetworks.co.uk/rail

UK Railtours
T: 01438 715050
E: john@ukrailtours.com
W: www.ukrailtours.com

UKRS Projects Ltd
see bowen projects ltd

UK Trade & Investment - Investment Services
1 Victoria St,
London SW1H 0ET
T: 0845 539 0419/020 7333 5442
E: enquiries@ukti-invest.com
W: www.ukti.gov.uk

UK Ultraspeed
Warksburn House,
Wark,
Hexham,
Northumberland NE48 3LS
T: 020 7861 2497
F: 020 7861 2497
E: ncameron@bell-pottinger.co.uk
W: www.500kmh.com

Ultra Electronics-Electrics
Kingsditch Lane,
Cheltenham,
Glos GL51 9PG
T: 01242 221166
F: 01242 221167
E: info@ultra-electrics.com
W: www.ultra-electrics.com

Ultra Electronics PMES Ltd
Towers Business Park,
Wheelhouse Rd,
Rugeley,
Staffs WS15 1UZ
T: 01889 503300
F: 01889 572929
E: enquiries@ultra-pmes.com
W: www.ultra-pmes.com

Underground Pipeline Services Ltd
see integrated water services ltd

Unic Cranes Europe
see ggr group ltd

UNIFE
Avenue Louise 221,
B-1050 Brussels,
Belgium
T: 0032 2642 2328
F: 0032 2626 1261
E: judit.sandor@unife.org
W: www.unife.org

Unilokomotive Ltd
Dunmore Rd, Tuam,
Co. Galway,
Ireland
T: 00353 93 52150
F: 00353 93 52227
E: omcconn@unilok.ie
W: www.unilok.ie

Unipart Dorman
see dorman

Unipart Rail (T&RS) Ltd
Jupiter Building, First Point,
Balby Carr Bank, Doncaster DN4 5JQ
T: 01302 731400
F: 01302 731401
E: trsenquiries@unipartrail.com
W: www.unipartrail.com

Unipart Rail (infrastructure)
Gresty Rd, Crewe CW2 6EH
T: 01270 847600
F: 01270 847601
E: enquiries@unipartrail.com
W: www.unipartrail.com

Unipart Rail (infrastructure)
Leeman Rd, York YO26 4ZD
T: 01904 544020
F: 01904 544021
E: enquiries@unipartrail.com
W: www.unipartrail.com

Unite - The Union
General Secretary, 35 King St,
Covent Garden, London WC2E 8JG
T: 020 7420 8900
F: 020 7420 8998
W: www.unitetheunion.com

United Kingdom Society for Trenchless Technology
38 Holly Walk, Leamington Spa,
Warks CV32 4LY
T: 01926 330935
E: admin@ukstt.org.uk
W: www.ukstt.org.uk

Universal Heat Transfer Ltd
Well Spring Close, Carlyon Rd,
Atherstone, Warks CV9 1QZ
T: 01827 722171
F: 01827 722174
E: sales@uhtltd.com
W: www.universalheattransfer.co.uk

The Universal Improvement Company
17 Knowl Ave, Belper,
Derbys DE56 2TL
T: 01773 826659
F: 01773 826659
E: info@theuic.com
W: www.theuic.com

Universal Railway Equipment Ltd
Princess Royal Buildings,
Whitecroft Rd, Bream,
Lydney,
Glos GL15 6LY
T: 01594 560555
E: unirail@btconnect.com
W: www.peeway.co.uk

University of Derby - Faculty of Arts, Design & Technology
Markeaton St,
Derby DE22 3AW
T: 01332 593216
E: adtenquiry@derby.ac.uk
W: www.derby.ac.uk

Up & Cuming Consultancy Ltd (UCCL)
74 Chenies Mews,
London WC1E 6HU
T: 020 7388 2232
F: 020 7388 3730
E: info@uccl.net
W: www.uccl.net

Urban Hygiene Ltd
Sky Business Park,
Robin Hood Airport,
Doncaster DN9 3GA
T: 01302 623193
E: enquiries@urbanhygiene.com
W: www.urbanhygiene.co.uk

Urbis Lighting Ltd
see urbis schreder ltd

Urbis Schreder Ltd
Sapphire House, Lime Tree Way,
Hampshire International
Business Park, Chineham,
Basingstoke RG24 8GG
T: 01256 354446
F: 01256 841314
E: sales@urbis-schreder.com
W: www.urbis-schreder.com

Uretek UK Ltd
Unit 6, Peel Rd,
Skelmersdale,
Lancs WN8 9PT
T: 01695 50525
F: 01695 555212
E: sales@uretek.co.uk
W: www.uretek.co.uk

URS
Scott House,
Alencon Link,
Basingstoke,
Hants RG21 7PP
T: 01256 310200
F: 01256 310201
E: rail.marketing@scottwilson.com
W: www.urscorp.eu

URS Corporation Ltd
6-8 Greencoat Place,
London SW1P 1PL
T: 0115 907 7086
F: 0115 907 7001
E: railways@scottwilson.com
W: www.urscorp.eu

Albashaw Ltd (t/a Vacuum Reflex Ltd)
Unit 2, Gamma Terrace,
West Rd,
Ransomes Euro Park,
Ipswich IP3 9SX
E: info@vacuum-reflex.com
W: www.vacuum-reflex.com

VAE UK Ltd
Sir Harry Lauder Rd,
Portobello,
Edinburgh EH15 1DJ
T: 0131 550 2297
F: 0131 550 2660
E: jim.gemmell@vae.co.uk
W: www.voestalpine.com/vae

Vaisala Ltd
351, Bristol Rd,
Birmingham B5 7SW
T: 0121 683 1200
F: 0121 683 1299
E: liz.green@vaisala.com
W: www.vaisala.com

Van der Vlist UK Ltd
Burma Drive,
Kingston upon Hull HU9 5SD
T: 01482 210100
F: 01482 216222
E: info@vandervlist.co.uk
W: www.vandervlist.co.uk

Van Elle
Kirkby Lane, Pinxton,
Notts NG16 6JA
T: 01773 580580
F: 01773 862100
E: mark.williams@van-elle.co.uk
W: www.van-elle.co.uk

Variable Message Signs Ltd (VMS)
Unit 1,
Monkton Business Park North,
Mill Lane,
Hebburn,
Tyne & Wear NE31 2JZ
T: 0191 423 7070
F: 0191 423 7071
E: aisaacs@vmslimited.co.uk
W: www.vmslimited.co.uk

Vector Management Ltd
Strathclyde House,
Green Man Lane,
London Heathrow Airport,
Feltham,
Middx TW14 0NZ
T: 020 8844 0444
F: 020 8844 0666
E: ju-liang.trigg@vecman.com
W: www.vecman.com

Vectra Group Ltd
see arcadis

Verint Systems
241 Brooklands Rd,
Weybridge,
Surrey KT13 0RH
T: 01932 839500
F: 01932 839501
E: marketing.emea@verint.com
W: www.verint.com

Veritec Sonomatic Ltd
Ashton House,
The Village,
Birchwood Bus.Park,
Warrington WA3 6FZ
T: 01925 414000
F: 01925 655595
E: jl@vsonomatic.com
W: www.veritecltd.co.uk

Vertex Systems
see amcl

Veryards Opus
see opus international

Video 125 Ltd
Glade House,
High St,
Sunninghill,
Berks SL5 9NP
T: 01344 299551
E: sales@video125.co.uk
W: www.video125.co.uk

Vi Distribution
Unit 7,
Springvale Business Centre,
Millbuck Way,
Sandbach, CW11 3HY
T: 01270 750520
F: 01270 750521
E: sales@vidistribution.co.uk
W: www.vidistribution.co.uk

SA Viewcom (now Axion Technologies)
Lokesvej 7-9,
3400 Hilleroed,
Denmark
T: 0045 721 93500
F: 0045 721 93501
E: info@axiontech.dk
W: www.axiontech.dk

VINCI Construction UK Ltd
Astral House,
Imperial Way,
Watford WD24 4WW
see taylor woodrow

Vinci Park Services UK Ltd
Oak House, Reeds Cres,
Watford,
Herts WD24 4QP
T: 01908 223500
F: 01923 231914
E: info@vincipark.co.uk
W: www.vincipark.co.uk

Vintage Trains Ltd
670 Warwick Rd,
Tyseley,
Birmingham B11 2HL
T: 0121 708 4960
F: 0121 708 4963
E: vintagetrains@btconnect.com
W: www.vintagetrains.co.uk

Virgin Trains (West Coast)
North Wing Offices,
Euston Station,
London NW1 2HS
T: 0845 000 8000
E: firstname.lastname@virgintrains.co.uk
W: www.virgin.com/trains

Vision Infrastructure Services Ltd
Unit 7,
Durham Lane,
West Moor Park,
Doncaster DN1 3FE
T: 01302 831730
F: 01302 832671
E: ian@visioninfrastructure services.com
W: www.visioninfrastructure services.com

Vistorm Ltd
see hp information security

Visul Systems
Kingston House,
3 Walton Rd,
Pattinson North,
Washington, Tyne & Wear NE38 8QA
T: 0191 402 1960
F: 0191 402 1906
E: ross.carty@usluk.com
W: www.visulsystems.com

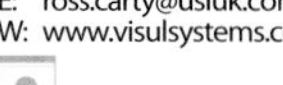

Vita Safety Ltd
1 Gillingham Rd,
Eccles,
Manchester M30 8NA
T: 0161 789 1400
F: 0161 280 2528
E: ian.hutchings@vitasafety.com
W: www.vitasafety.com

Vital Rail
The Mill,
South Hall St,
Ordsall Lane,
Manchester M5 4TP
T: 0161 836 7000
F: 0161 836 7001
E: info@vital-rail.com
W: www.vital-rail.com

Vitec
3 Cae Gwrydd,
Greenmeadow Springs Bus. Park,
Cardiff CF15 7AB
T: 02920 620232
F: 02920 624837
E: cardiff@viteconsult.com
W: www.vitecwebberlenihan.com

Vix Technology
ACIS House,
168 Cowley Rd,
Cambridge CB4 0DL
T: 01223 728700
F: 01223 506311
E: uk.marketing@vixtechnology.com
W: www.vixtechnology.com

VMS
see variable message systems

Voestalpine UK Ltd
Voestalpine House,
Albion Place,
Hammersmith,
London W6 0QT
T: 020 8600 5800
E: catherine.crisp@voestalpine.com
W: www.voestalpine.com

Vogelsang Ltd
Crewe Gates Ind. Est,
Crewe,
Cheshire CW1 6YY
T: 01270 216600
F: 01270 216699
E: sales@vogelsang.co.uk
W: www.vogelsang.co.uk

Voith Turbo GmbH & Co.KG
Alexanderstrasse 2,
89522 Heidenheim,
Germany
T: 0044 7321 37 4069
F: 0044 7321 37 7616
E: rail.uk@voith.com
W: www.voith.com

Voith Turbo Ltd
Unit 49, Metropolitan Park,
Bristol Rd, Greenford,
Middx UB6 8UP
T: 020 8436 1051
F: 020 8578 4489
E: roger.everest@voith.com
W: www.uk.voithturbo.com

Volker Rail
Carolina Court, Lakeside,
Doncaster DN4 5RA
T: 01302 791100
F: 01302 791200
E: marketing@volkerrail.co.uk
W: www.volkerrail.co.uk

Volker Fitzpatrick Ltd
Hertford Rd, Hoddesden,
Herts EN11 9BX
T: 01992 305000
F: 01992 305001
E: volkerfitzpatrickrail
@volkerfitzpatrick.co.uk
W: www.volkerfitzpatrick.co.uk

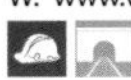

Volo TV & Media Ltd
Departure Side Offices, Platform 1,
Paddington Station, Praed St,
London W2 1FT
T: 020 7193 0997
F: 020 7402 2498
E: findoutmore@volo.tv
W: www.volo.tv

Vortok International
Innovation House,
3 Western Wood Way,
Langage Science Park,
Plymouth PL7 5BG
T: 01752 349200
F: 01752 338855
E: gfermie@vortok.co.uk
W: www.vortok.co.uk

Vossloh Cogifer UK Ltd
80a Scotter Rd, Scunthorpe,
North Lincs DN15 8EF
T: 01724 862131
F: 01724 295243
E: info@vcuk-vossloh.com
W: www.vossloh-cogifer.com

Vossloh Fastening Systems GmbH
Am Schimmersfeld 7a,
D-40880 Ratingen, Germany
T: 0049 2102 49090
F: 0049 2102 49094
W: www.vossloh-fastening-systems.de

Vossloh AG
Vosslohstrasse 4, 58791 Werdohl,
Germany
T: 0049 2392 520
F: 0049 2392 520
W: www.vossloh.com

Vossloh Kiepe
2 Priestley Wharf,
Birmingham Science Park, Holt St,
Aston, Birmingham B7 4BN
T: 0121 359 7777
F: 0121 359 1811
E: enquiries@vkb.vossloh.com
W: www.vossloh-kiepe.co.uk

VTG Rail UK Ltd
Sir Stanley Clarke House,
7 Ridgeway,
Quinton Business Park,
Birmingham B32 1AF
T: 0121 421 9180
F: 0121 421 9192
E: sales@vtg.com
W: www.vtg-rail.co.uk

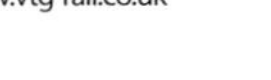

VTS Track Technology Ltd
see vossloh cogifer (uk) ltd

Vulcascot Cable Protectors Ltd
Unit 12, Norman-D-Gate,
Bedford Rd, Northampton NN1 5NT
T: 0800 035 2842
F: 01604 632344
E: sales@vulcascotcable
protectors.co.uk
W: www.vulcascotcable
protectors.com

Wabtec Rail Ltd
PO Box 400,
Doncaster Works,
Hexthorpe Rd,
Doncaster DN1 1SL
T: 01302 340700
F: 01302 790058
E: wabtecrail@wabtec.com
W: www.wabtecgroup.com

Wacker Neuson (GB) Ltd
Lea Rd, Waltham Cross,
Herts EN9 1AW
T: 01992 707228
F: 01992 707201
E: chris.pearce@
eu.wackergroup.com
W: www.wackerneuson.com

W A Developments Ltd
see stobart rail

Wagony Swidnica S.A.
UL. Strzelinska 35,
58-100 Swidnica,
Poland
T: 0048 74 856 2000
F: 0048 853 0323
E: secretariat@gbrx.com
W: www.gbrx.com

A N Wallis & Co Ltd
Greasley St, Bulwell,
Nottingham NG6 8NG
T: 0115 927 1721
F: 0115 875 6630
M: 07710 144800
E: mark.rimmington@
an-wallis.com
W: www.an-wallis.com

Washroom Joinery Ltd
The Loughton Seedbed Centre,
Langston Rd,
Loughton,
Essex IG10 3TQ
F: 08700 111860
M: 0700 492 7476
E: info@washroomjoinery.co.uk
W: www.washroomjpinery.co.uk

Washtec UK Ltd
Unit 14A, Oak ind. Park,
Great Dunmow,
Essex CM9 1XN
T: 01371 878800
F: 01371 878810
W: www.washtec-uk.com

Waterflow
see ukdn waterflow

Waterman Transport & Development Ltd
Pickfords Wharf,
Clink St,
London SE1 9DG
T: 020 7928 7888
F: 020 7902 0992
E: paul.worrall@
watermangroup.com
W: www.waterman-group.co.uk

Waverley Rail Project
see borders railway

Wavesight Ltd
Talon House,
Presley Way,
Crownhill,
Milton Keynes MK8 0ES
T: 01908 265223
F: 01908 265143
E: sales@wavesight.com
W: www.wavesight.com

Webasto AG
Kraillinger Strasse 5,
82131 Stockdorf,
Germany
T: 0049 89 857 948 444
F: 0049 89 899 217 433
E: tac3@webasto.com
W: www.rail.webasto.com

AP Webb Plant Hire Ltd
Common Rd,
Stafford ST16 3DQ
T: 01785 241335
F: 01785 255178
E: mail@apwebbplanthire.co.uk
W: www.apwebbplanthire.co.uk

Webro Cable & Connectors Ltd
Vision House,
Meadow Brooks Business Park,
Meadow Lane, Long Eaton,
Notts NG10 2GD
T: 0115 972 4483
F: 0115 946 1230
E: info@webro.com
W: www.webro.com

WEC Group Ltd
Spring Vale House,
Spring Vale Rd,
Darwen,
Lancs BB3 2ES
T: 01254 773718
F: 01254 771109
E: stevecooke@wecl.co.uk
W: www.welding-eng.com

Weedfree
Holly Tree Farm,
Park Lane,
Balne,
Goole DN14 0EP
T: 01405 860022
F: 01405 862283
E: sales@weedfree.net
W: www.weedfree.net

Weidmuller Ltd
Klippon House,
Centurion Court Office Park,
Meridian East,
Meridian Business Park,
Leicester LE19 1TP
T: 0116 282 3470
F: 0116 289 3582
E: marketing@weidmuller.co.uk
W: www.weidmuller.co.uk

Weightmans
High Holborn House, 52-
54 High Holborn, London WC1V 6RL
T: 020 7822 1900
F: 020 7822 1901
E: sarah.seddon@
weightmans.com
W: www.weightmans.com

Weighwell Ltd
23 Orgreave Place,
Sheffield S13 9LU
T: 0114 269 9955
F: 0114 269 9256
E: rwood@weighwell.co.uk
W: www.weighwell.co.uk

Weld-A-Rail Ltd
Lockwood Close, Top Valley,
Nottingham NG5 9JM
T: 0115 926 8797
F: 0115 926 4818
E: admin@weldarail.co.uk
W: www.weldarail.co.uk

The Welding Institute
see institute of rail welding

Welfare Cabins UK (WCUK)
see garic

A J Wells & Sons Vitreous Enamellers
Bishop's Way, Newport,
IOW PO30 5WS
T: 01983 537766
F: 01983 537788
E: enamel@ajwells.co.uk
W: www.ajwells.com

West Coast Railway Co.
Jesson Way, Carnforth,
Lancs LA5 9UR
T: 01524 732100
F: 01524 735518
E: info@wcrc.co.uk
W: www.wcrc.co.uk

Westcode Semiconductors
Langley Park Way,
Langley Park,
Chippenham,
Wilts SN15 1GE
T: 01249 444524
F: 01249 659448
E: customer.services@
westcode.com
W: www.westcode.com

Westermo Data Communications Ltd
Talisman Business Centre,
Duncan Rd, Park Gate,
Southampton SO31 7GA
T: 01489 580585
F: 01489 580586
E: sales@westermo.co.uk
W: www.westermo.com

Westinghouse Rail Systems
see invensys rail

West Midlands PTE
see centro

Westinghouse Platform Screen Doors
Knorr-Bremse Rail Systems (UK) Ltd,
Westinghouse Way,
Hampton Park East, Melksham,
Wilts SN12 6TL
T: 01225 898700
F: 01225 898705
E: wpsd.enquiries@knorr-bremse.com
W: www.platformscreendoors.com

Westley Engineering Ltd
120 Pritchett St, Aston,
Birmingham B6 4EH T:
0121 333 1925
F: 0121 333 1926
E: g.dunne@westleyengineering.co.uk
W: www.westleyengineering.co.uk

Westquay Trading Co. Ltd
3F, Lyncastle Way, Appleton Thorn,
Warrington, WA4 4ST
T: 01925 265333
F: 01925 211700
E: enquiries@westquaytrading.co.uk
W: www.westquaytrading.co.uk

Westshield Ltd
Waldron House, Drury Lane,
Chadderton,
Oldham OL9 8LU
T: 0161 682 6222
F: 0161 682 6333
E: mail@westshield.co.uk
W: www.westshield.co.uk

Weston Williamson
43, Tanner St,
London SE1 3PL
T: 020 7403 2665
F: 020 7403 2667
E: chris@westonwilliamson.com
W: www.westonwilliamson.com

West Yorkshire PTE (Metro)
Wellington House, 40-
50 Wellington St,
Leeds LS1 2DE
F: 0113 251 7272
W: www.wypte.gov.uk

Wettons
Wetton House,
278-280 St James's Rd,
London SE1 5JX
T: 020 7237 2007
F: 020 7252 3277
E: mark.hammerton@
wettons.co.uk
W: www.wettons.co.uk

Wheelsets UK
Unit 46, Denby Way,
Hellaby Ind. Est,
Rotherham S66 8NZ
T: 01302 322266
F: 01302 322299
E: martin@wheelsets.co.uk
W: www.wheelsets.co.uk

White & Case LLP
5 Old Broad St,
London EC2N 1DW
T: 020 7532 2310
F: 020 7532 1001
E: twinsor@whitecase.com
W: www.whitecase.com

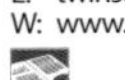

Whiteley Electronics Ltd
see gemma lighting

White Young Green
see amey

Wicek Sosna Architects
Unit 15, 21 Plumbers Row,
London E1 1EQ
T: 020 7655 4430
E: office@sosnaarchitects.co.uk
W: www.sosnaarchitects.co.uk

Wilcomatic Ltd
Unit 5, Commerce Park,
19 Commerce Way,
Croydon CR0 4YL
T: 020 8649 5760
F: 020 8680 9791
E: sales@wilcomatic.co.uk
W: www.wilcomatic.co.uk

Wilkinson Star Ltd
Shield Drive, Wardsley Ind Est,
Manchester M28 2WD
T: 0161 793 8127
F: 0161 727 8538
E: steve.ross@wilkinsonstar.com
W: www.wilkinsonstar.com

WillB Brand Consultants
Studio 17,
Royal Victoria Patriotic Building,
John Archer Way, London SW18 3SX
T: 020 7112 8911
M: 07815 056026
E: will@willbaxter.com
W: www.willbaxter.com

William Bain Fencing Ltd
Lochin Works, 7 Limekilns Rd,
Blairlinn Ind. Est,
Cumbernauld G67 2RN
T: 01236 457333
F: 01236 451166
E: sales@lochrin-bain.co.uk
W: www.lochrin-bain.co.uk

William Cook Rail
Cross Green,
Leeds LS9 0SG
T: 0113 249 6363
F: 0113 249 1376
E: castproducts@
william-cook.co.uk
W: www.william-cook.co.uk

Williamette Valley Company – WVCO Railroad Division
1075 Arrowsmith St, Eugene,
OR 97402 USA
T: 001 541 484 9621
F: 001 541 284 2096
E: sales@wilvaco.com
W: www.wvcorailroad.com

Williams Hybrid Power
Grove, Wantage, Oxon OX12 0DQ
T: 01235 777777
W: www.williamshybridpower.com

T & R Williamson Ltd
36 Stonebridgegate, Ripon,
N Yorks HG4 1TP
T: 01765 607711
F: 01765 607908
E: info@trwilliamson.co.uk
W: www.trwilliamson.co.uk

Willie Baker Leadership & Development Ltd
Aggborough Farm, College Rd,
Kidderminster,
Worcs DY10 1LU
M: 07789 943043
E: willie@williebaker.co.uk
W: www.williebaker.co.uk

Winckworth Sherwood
Minerva House,
5 Montague Close,
London SE1 9BB
T: 020 7593 5000
F: 0207 593 5099
E: info@wslaw.co.uk
W: www.wslaw.co.uk

Windhoff Bahn und Anlagentechnik GmbH
Hovestrasse 10,
D-48431 Rheine,
Germany
T: 0049 5971 580
F: 0049 5971 58209
E: aw@windhoff.de
W: www.windhoff.de

Wind River UK Ltd
Oakwood House,
Grove Business Park,
White Waltham,
Maidenhead,
Berks SL6 3HY
T: 01793 831831
F: 01793 831808
E: sue.woolley@windriver.com
W: www.windriver.com

DW Windsor UK
Pindar Rd, Hoddesden,
Herts EN11 0DX
T: 01992 474600
F: 01992 474601
E: info@dwwindsor.co,.uk
W: www.dwwindsor.co.uk

Winn & Coales (Denso) Ltd
Denso House, Chapel Rd,
London SE27 0TR
T: 020 8670 7511
F: 020 8761 2456
E: mail@denso.net
W: www.denso.net

Winstanley & Co Ltd
Racecourse Rd, Pershore,
Worcs WR10 2DF
T: 01386 552278
F: 01386 556531
E: info@winstanleyco.co.uk
W: www.winstanleyco.com

Winsted Ltd
Units 7/8, Lovett Rd,
Hampton Lovett Ind Est, Droitwich,
Worcs WR9 0QG
T: 01905 770276
F: 01905 779791
E: info@winsted.co.uk
W: www.winsted.com

Wintersgill
110 Bolsover St,
London W1W 5NU
T: 020 7580 4499
F: 020 7436 8191
E: info@wintersgill.net
W: www.wintersgill.net

WM Plant Hire Ltd
Manor Farm Lane, Bridgnorth,
Shropshire WV16 5HG
T: 01452 722200
F: 01452 769666
E: info@wmplanthire.com
W: www.wmplanthire.com

Woking Homes
Oriental Rd, Woking,
Surrey GU22 7BE
T: 01483 763558
F: 01483 721048
W: www.uknursinghomes.org/wokinghomes

Wood & Douglas Ltd
Lattice House, Baughurst,
Tadley,
Hants RG26 5LP
T: 0118 981 1444
F: 0118 981 1567
E: sales@woodanddouglas.co.uk
W: www.woodanddouglas.co.uk

Wood & Wood Signs
Heron Rd,
Sowton Estate,
Exeter EX2 7LX
T: 01392 444501
F: 01392 252358
E: info@wwsigns.co.uk
W: www.wwsigns.co.uk

HV Wooding Ltd
Range Rd, Hythe,
Kent CT21 6HG
T: 01303 264471
F: 01303 262408
E: sales@hvwooding.co.uk
W: www.hvwooding.co.uk

Woodstone Ltd
68 Houghton Rd,
St Ives,
Huntingdon PE27 6RL
T: 01480 469402
F: 01480 380280
E: mail@gripdeck.co.uk
W: www.gripdeck.co.uk

Woodward Diesel Systems
Lancaster Centre,
Meteor Business Park,
Cheltenham Rd East,
Gloucester GL2 9QL
T: 01452 859940
F: 01452 855758
W: www.woodward.com/gloucester

Workthing
Beaumont House,
Kensington Village,
Avonmore Rd,
London W14 8TS
T: 0870 898 0022
F: 0870 898 0033
E: info@workthing.com
W: www.workthing.com

Works infrastructure Ltd
Mallard House, 75 The Mount,
York YO24 1AX
T: 01904 672233
F: 01904 672244
E: enquiries@worksinfrastructure.co.uk
W: www.worksinfrastructure.co.uk

Wor-Rail
Guild House, Sandy Lane, Wildmoor,
Bromsgrove, Worcs B61 0QU
T: 0121 460 1113
F: 0121 460 1116
E: sales@wor-rail.co.uk
W: www.wor-rail.co.uk

Wrekin Circuits Ltd
29/30 Hortonwood 33, Telford,
Shropshire TF1 7EX
T: 01952 670011
F: 01952 606565
E: sales@wrekin-circuits.co.uk
W: www.wrekin-circuits.co.uk

WSP UK
Mountbatten House, Basing View,
Basingstoke, Hants RG21 4HJ
T: 01256 318802
F: 01256 318700
W: www.wspgroup.com

WTB Geotechnics
Earl Russell Way, Lawrence Hill,
Bristol BS5 0WT
T: 0845 600 5505
F: 0845 609 2525
E: geotechnics@wtbgroup.com
W: www.geotechnics-uk.com

WVCO Railroad Division of The Williamette Valley Company
1075 Arrowsmith St,
PO Box 2280,
Eugene, OR 97402, USA
T: 001 541 484 9621
F: 001 541 284 2096
E: sales@wvcorailroad.com
W: www.wvcorailroad.com

WWP Consultants
5-15 Cromer St,
London WC1H 8LS
T: 020 7833 5767
F: 020 7833 5766
W: www.wwp-london.co.uk

Wynnwith Rail
Wynnwith House,
Church St,
Woking,
Surrey GU21 6DJ
T: 01483 748206
E: rail@wynnwith.com
W: www.wynnwith.com

Wyse Rail Ltd
Cressex Business Park,
Lancaster Rd,
Bucks HP12 3QP
T: 0870 145 0552
F: 01494 560929
E: wyserail@wysegroup.co.uk
W: www.wysegroup.com

WyvernRail Plc
Wirksworth Station,
Station Rd, Wirksworth,
Derbys DE4 4FB
T: 01629 821828
E: wirksworth_station@wyvernrail.co.uk
W: www.mytesttrack.com

Xervon Palmers Ltd
331 Charles St, Glasgow G21 2QA
T: 0141 553 4040
F: 0141 552 6463
E: info@xervonpalmers.com
W: www.xervonpalmers.com

XiTRACK Ltd
see dow hyperlast

Xl Lubricants Ltd
see ntm sales & marketing ltd

Yardene Engineering 2000 Ltd
Daux Rd, Billingshurst,
West Sussex RH14 9SJ
T: 01403 783558
F: 01403 783104
E: sales@yardene.co.uk
W: www.yardene.co.uk

Yellow Rail Ltd
The iD Centre, Lathkill House,
rtc Business Park, London Rd,
Derby DE24 8UP
T: 01332 258865
F: 01332 258823
E: enquiries@yellowrail.org.uk
W: www.yellowrail.org.uk

YJL Infrastructure Ltd
39 Cornhill,
London EC3V 3ND
T: 020 7522 3220
F: 020 7522 3261
W: www.yjli.co.uk

York EMC Services Ltd
Market Square,
University of York,
Heslington,
York YO10 5DD
T: 01904 324440
F: 01904 324434
E: enquiry@yorkemc.co.uk
W: www.yorkemc.co.uk

Yorkshire Rail Academy
National Railway Museum,
Leeman Rd, York YO26 4XJ
T: 01904 770780
E: reception@yra.ac.uk
W: www.yorkcollege.ac.uk

ZF UK Laser Ltd
9 Avacado Court,
Commerce Way,
Trafford Park, Manchester M17 1HW
T: 0161 871 7050
F: 0161 312 5063
E: info@zf-uk.com
W: www.zf-uk.com

Zarges (UK) Ltd
Holdom Ave,
Saxon Park Ind. Est,
Bletchley,
Milton Keynes MK1 1QU
T: 01908 641118
F: 01908 648176
E: sales@zargesuk.co.uk
W: www.zargesuk.co.uk

Zetica
Units 15/16,
Hanborough Business Park,
Long Hanborough,
Oxon OX29 8LH
T: 01993 886682
F: 01993 886683
E: rail@zetica.com
W: www.zeticarail.com

ZF Services UK
Abbeyfield Rd,
Lenton,
Nottingham NG7 2SX
T: 0844 257 0333
F: 0115 986 9261
E: mark.doughty@zf.com
W: www.zf.com/uk

Zigma Ground Solutions
Unit 11,
M11 Business Link,
Parsonage Lane,
Stansted,
Essex CM24 8TY
F: 0845 643734
M: 07514 025121
E: amandacc@zigmagroundsolutions.com
W: www.zigmagroundsolutions.com

Zircon Software Ltd
Bellefield House, Hilperton Rd,
Trowbridge, Wilts BA14 8AS
T: 01225 764444
F: 01225 753087
E: info@zirconsoftware.co.uk
W: www.zirconsoftware.co.uk

Zollner UK Ltd
Clayton Business Ctr, Midland Rd,
Leeds LS10 2RJ
T: 0113 270 3008
E: frank.peters@zollner-uk.co.uk
W: www.zollner-uk.co.uk

Zonegreen
Sir John Brown Building,
Davy Ind. Park, Prince of Wales Rd,
Sheffield S9 4EX
T: 0114 230 0822
F: 0871 872 0349
E: info@zonegreen.co.uk
W: www.zonegreen.co.uk

ZTR Control Systems
8050 Country Rd, 101 East,
Shakopee, Minneapolis,
Minnesota 55379, USA
T: 001 952 233 4340
F: 001 952 233 4375
E: railinfo@ztr.com
W: www.ztr.com

Zuken
1500 Aztec West, Almondsbury,
Bristol BS32 4RF
T: 01454 207800
E: dionne.hayman@zuken.com
W: www.zuken.com

Zwicky Track Tools
see arbil

ADDENDUM

Train Door Solutions
Unit 3, Garamonde Drive, Wymbush,
Milton Keynes MK8 8DF
T: 01908 265652
F: 01908 565666
W: www.traindoor.com

Fainsa UK
Mulberry Cottage, Rickerscote Hall
Lane, Stafford ST17 4HY
T: 01785 228009
M: 07786 869220
E: mark.carter@fainsa.co.uk
W: www.fainsa.com

ADVERTISERS INDEX